In Partnership with

KNOWLEDGE INDIA
Publication

1e 2025

A Comprehensive Study of

SCIENCE & TECHNOLOGY

For UPSC and State PSC Examinations

AF633191

VISHAL MISHRA
SATYAM JAIN

S. CHAND
PUBLISHING

S Chand And Company Limited
(ISO 9001 Certified Company)

S Chand And Company Limited
(ISO 9001 Certified Company)
Head Office: D-92, Sector – 02, Noida 201301, U.P. (India), Ph. 91-120-4682700
Registered Office: A-27, 2nd Floor, Mohan Co-operative Industrial Estate, New Delhi – 110 044
Phone: 011-49731800
www.**schandpublishing.com**; e-mail: **info@schandpublishing.com**

Marketing Offices:

Chennai	:	Ph: 044-2363 2120, chennai@schandpublishing.com
Guwahati	:	Ph: 0361-4066 369, guwahati@schandpublishing.com
Hyderabad	:	Ph: 040-4018 6018, hyderabad@schandpublishing.com
Jalandhar	:	Ph: 0181-4645 630, jalandhar@schandpublishing.com
Kolkata	:	Ph: 033-2335 7458 kolkata@schandpublishing.com
Lucknow	:	Ph: 0522-400 3633, lucknow@schandpublishing.com
Mumbai	:	Ph: 022-2500 0297, mumbai@schandpublishing.com
Patna	:	Ph: 0612-226 0011, patna@schandpublishing.com

First Edition 2025

ISBN : 978-93-6958-755-1 **Product Code:** H1SCT47SCIN10ENAA25O

PRINTED IN INDIA

By Vikas Publishing House Private Limited, Plot 20/4, Site-IV, Industrial Area Sahibabad, Ghaziabad – 201 010 and Published by S Chand And Company Limited, A-27, 2nd Floor, Mohan Co-operative Industrial Estate, New Delhi – 110 044

Index

India's Contribution in Science and Technology (i-v)

Unit-1

- **Energy, Fuels and Emerging Technology in Transportation (1-23)**
  - Renewable Energy (3-5)
  - Advantages of Renewable Energy Resources (5)
  - Concerns and Challenges (6)
  - Biofuels (7)
  - Generations of Biofuels (7)
  - Biofuel Conversion Processes (8-9)
  - Important of Biofuels (9-10)
  - Significance of Biofuels (10-12)
  - Green Hydrogen (12-14)
  - Green Ammonia (14-15)
  - Emerging Technologies in Transport (15-16)
  - Electric Vehicles (17-19)
  - Hyperloop (19-21)
  - Urban Air Mobility (UAM) - Heli Taxis (21-23)
  - PYQ (23)

Unit-2

- **Modern Electronics and Semiconductors (24-35)**
  - Development of Modern Electronics: From Vacuum Tubes to Integrated Circuits (25-27)
  - Emerging Technologies (28-29)
  - Semiconductors 29-31
  - Applications of Semiconductors (31-33)
  - Indian Semiconductor Mission (ISM) (33-35)
  - PYQ (35)

Unit -3

- **Nutrition, Diseases and Vaccination (36-85)**
  - Nutrients (36-39)
  - Diseases (40-42)
  - Communicable Diseases (42-54)
  - Non-Communicable Diseases (54-70)
  - Antimicrobial Resistance (AMR) (71-72)
  - Immunity (72-74)
  - Vaccines (74-78)
  - Vaccination in India (78-80)
  - Universal Immunization Program (80)
  - Mission Indradhanush (MI) (80-81)
  - One Health Approach (81- 83)
  - Global Centre for Traditional Medicine (83-84)
  - PYQ (84-85)

Unit -4

- **Biotechnology (86-132)**
  - Introduction to Biotechnology (88)
  - Types of Biotechnology (88-89)
  - Introduction to Basics : Cells (89)
  - Structural Organisation of a Cell (89-90)
  - Basics Of Genetics (90-94)
  - Principles Of Biotechnology (94)
  - Gene Therapy (94-97)
  - Genome Editing (97)
  - Crispr Case: Revolution In Genetic Engineering (97-99)
  - Recombinant Dna Technology (99-100)
  - Steps In Recombinant Dna Technique (100-103)
  - Genetic Modification (GM) (103-105)
  - Challenges Of GM Crops (105-109)
  - Transgenic/Genetically Modified Organisms (GMOS) (110-111)
  - Stem Cells (111-114)
  - Cloning (114-116)
  - Assisted Reproductive Technology (117-118)
  - Biosensors (118-120)
  - Bioinformatics (120-121)
  - Applications Of Biotechnology (122- 125)
  - Environmental Biotechnology (126- 129)
  - Important Terminology (129-130)
  - PYQ (130-132)

Unit 5

- **Information and Communications Technology (133-169)**
  - Evolution Of Computers (133-134)
  - Internet : An Introduction (135)
  - Computer Network (135-138)
  - Near Field Communication (138-139)
  - Radio Frequency Identification (RFID) Technology (139)
  - Wi-Fi Technology (139-140)
  - Lifi Technology (140-141)
  - Satellite Based Internet Connectivity (141)
  - D2m Technology (141-142)
  - Serverless Computing (142)
  - Content Delivery Network (CDN) (142-143)
  - Important Terminologies Associated With Internet (143- 144)
  - Generations Of Internet (144-146)
  - Generations Of Cellular Technology (146-147)
  - 5G Technology (147-149)
  - Challenges Associated With The Adoption Of 5G/6G In India (149)
  - Applications Of Internet (149-150)
  - Supercomputers (150-151)
  - Quantum Technology (151-153)
  - Quantum Computing (153-155)
  - Important Terminology telated to Quantum Computing (155-157)
  - Semantic Communication: A Paradigm Shift In ICT (157)
  - Big Data (158-159)
  - Virtual Private Networks (VPN) (159-160)
  - Encryption (160)
  - Computer Viruses And Cyber Threats (160-163)
  - Cybercrimes (163-164)
  - Dark Net (164-165)
  - Cyberspace And Cyber Attacks (165)
  - Critical Infrastructure (165-166)
  - Government Initiatives (166)
  - PYQ (167-169)

Unit- 6

- **Industrial Revolution 4.0, Artificial Intelligence And Related Technologies (170-205)**
  - Industry 4.0 (170)
  - Industrial Revolution 4.0 (171-175)
  - Biometric (175-179)
  - Blockchain Technology And Cryptocurrency (179-182)
  - Applications Of Blockchain Technology (182-184)
  - Cryptocurrency (184-185)
  - WEB 3.0 (185- 186)
  - Challenges of IoT (186)
  - Metaverse (186-187)
  - Artificial Intelligence (187-189)
  - Applications Of Artificial Intelligence (189-192)
  - Chatbot (192-194)
  - OpenAI (194-196)
  - Deepfake (196-199)
  - NEURALINK (199-200)
  - Disruptive And Futuristic Technologies (200)
  - Deep Tech (200-201)
  - Smart Cities (201-203)
  - PYQ (203-205)

Unit- 7

- **Robotics (206-222)**
  - Robotics (206-207)
  - Types Of Robots (207-209)
  - Other Types of Robots (209)
  - Applications of Robotics (209-215)
  - Unmanned Aerial Vehicles/Drones (215-221)
  - Challenges And Limitations Of Drones (222)
  - PYQ (222)

Unit- 8

- **Nano-Technology (223-236)**
  - Nano-technology (223-224)
  - Special Properties Of Nanomaterials (224)
  - Types of Nanomaterials (Based On Dimensional) (224-226)
  - Carbon Nanomaterials (226)
  - Types of Nanmaterials (Based On Composition) (226-227)
  - Types of Nano-technology (227)
  - Applications of Nano-technology (228-232)

- Emerging Applications of Nano-technology (232-233)
- Quantum Dots (233-234)
- Challenges of Nano-technology (234-23)
- India And Nano-Technology (235)
- PYQ (236)

Unit - 9

⊡ **Defence Technology (237-254)**

- Missile Technology (237-239)
- Integrated Missile Development Programme (239-243)
- Fractional Orbital Bombardment System (FOBS) (243)
- Missile Defence System (243-245)
- Warships (245-246)
- Submarines (246- 249)
- Air Defence (249-252)
- Radar Technology (252-254)
- PYQ (254)

Unit-10

⊡ **Nuclear Science (255-275)**

- Nuclear Energy (255- 256)
- Nuclear Power Reactors (256-257)
- Types Of Nuclear Reactors (257- 259)
- Atomic Energy In India (259)
- India's Nuclear Programme (259-262)
- India's 3-Stage Nuclear Programme (262-263)
- India Nuclear/Atomic Power Plant (263-270)
- Bhabha Atomic Research Centre (270-272)
- India's Nuclear Doctrine (272-273)
- Challenges To India's Nuclear Programme (273)
- Measures To Address The Challenges (273- 274)
- Nuclear Proliferation : Issues And Challenges (274)
- Strategic Concerns For India Regarding Nuclear Energy (274-275)
- PYQ (275)

Unit-11

⊡ **Space Technology (276-330)**

- Space Science (277-278)
- Stellar Formation (Star Formation) (278-281)
- World Space Agencies: At A Glance (281-284)
- Orbits (284)
- Classification of Orbits (285)
- Space Missions in Low Earth Orbit (LEO) (285-287)
- Satellite Systems In Medium Earth Orbit (287)
- GPS : Navstar (Navigation System Using Timing And Ranging) (287-288)
- NAVIC (Navigation Indian Constellation) (288- 290)
- Launch Vehicles (290)
- Types Of Engines (290-292)
- Propellants (292-293)
- Indian Launch Vehicles (293-296)
- Satellites (296-297)
- Indian National Satellite System (Insat) And Geosynchronous Satellite System (GSAT) (297)
- Gagan Satellite (297)
- India's Space Programme And Isro (297-306)
- Technology Obstacles In Space Missions(306)
- Indian Space Architecture (306 -307)
- Organisational Structure (307- 311)
- Emergence Of Private Space Sector, India (311- 313)
- Space Sector Reforms (314-315)
- Significance Of Space Missions (315-317)
- Space Tourism (318)
- Nasa's Space Missions (318 -319)
- James Webb Space Telescope (319- 320)
- Parker Space Probe (321)
- Space Science Related Concepts (321- 323)
- Gravitational Waves (323-324)
- Gravitational Lensing (324)
- Solar Flares (325)
- Space Debris (325- 327)
- Space Sustainability (327- 328)
- PYQ (328-330)

Unit 12

⊡ **Ministries And Departments : Indian Science Technology & Innovation (331-349)**

Unit 13

⊡ **Miscellaneousunit (350-360)**

India's Contribution in Science and Technology

Ancient Era

- *India developed the decimal place value system, which was later adopted worldwide.Aryabhata and Brahmagupta formally introduced the concept of zero (0) as a number.*
- *India pioneered cotton textile manufacturing as early as 5000 BCE. Indigo dyeing techniques were mastered in ancient India.*
- *Delhi Iron Pillar (375–415 CE) built in the Gupta period depicts rust-resistant iron composition. The zinc extraction process was developed by Indian scientists centuries before Europeans.*
- *India developed the first zinc extraction and distillation techniques, long before Europe.*
- *Indian Wootz steel was famous for its high-carbon content, later used to make Damascus swords.*
- *Ajanta & Ellora Caves were carved from single rock formations. Brihadeeswara Temple (1000 CE) used advanced engineering without binding materials*
- *Indians built large seafaring ships and used monsoon winds for navigation. The Sanskrit term "Nav" (ship) is the root of "Navy" and "Navigation."*

Ancient Indian Scientists

Lagadha (c. 1400 BCE)

- Wrote the Vedanga Jyotisha, one of the oldest astronomical texts in India.

Kanada (6th Century BCE)

- Founder of Vaisheshika school of philosophy that deals with Atomic theory (notions of Anu and Paramanu).

Aryabhata (476 CE)

- Developed Aryabhatiya, introducing concepts of zero, trigonometry, and π (Pi ≈ 3.1416).
- Defined sine and cosine functions in trigonometry.
- Proposed that the Earth rotates on its axis and that planetary orbits are elliptical.
- Suggested that the moon shines due to reflected sunlight.
- Explained the cause of solar and lunar eclipses.

Brahmagupta (598 CE – 668 CE)

- First to define zero as a number and Developed rules for arithmetic operations
- Authored Brahmasphutasiddhanta, covering algebra, geometry, and planetary motion.
- Worked on quadratic equations and the concept of gravity.

Varahamihira (505 CE – 587 CE)

- Contributed to astronomy and astrology.
- Predicted water presence on Mars.

Sushruta (600 BCE)

- Known as the Father of Surgery.
- Authored Sushruta Samhita, detailing surgical techniques, including plastic surgery and cataract surgery.
- Performed over 300 surgical procedures using 120+ surgical instruments.

Charaka (2nd Century BCE)

- Known as the Father of Indian Medicine.
- Authored the Charaka Samhita, a foundational text of Ayurveda.
- Introduced concepts of digestion, metabolism, immunity, and over 1,500 medicinal plants.
- Classified diseases and treatments, laying the foundation of modern pharmacology.

Baudhayana (c. 800 BCE)

- Stated the Pythagorean theorem in his work Sulbasutras centuries before Pythagoras.

Medieval Era

- *Emperor Akbar's court chronicler, Abul Fazl in Ain-i-Akbari (16th century CE) documented scientific practices in agriculture, irrigation, and metallurgy. It describes water-lifting devices, Persian wheels, and improved cannon-making techniques.*
- *Advanced irrigation systems like stepwells, tanks, and canals flourished under medieval Indian rulers. Sultanate and Mughal engineers built Baolis (stepwells), aqueducts, and artificial lakes to improve water storage and supply.*
- *Medieval India was known for its advanced shipbuilding techniques. The Zamorin's naval fleet in Kerala used ships made from teak wood, resistant to decay. The Mughals and Marathas developed warships with multiple cannon decks.*

Medieval Indian Scientists

Bhaskara II (1114 – 1185 CE)

- **Authored Siddhanta Shiromani and Lilavati covering algebra, arithmetic, trigonometry, and calculus.**
- **Introduced the concept of Differential Calculus.**
  - **Lilavati (Arithmetic):** Covered number theory, zero, algebraic equations, and permutations.
  - **Bijaganita (Algebra):** Introduced methods for solving quadratic and cubic equations.
  - **Goladhyaya (Astronomy):** Estimated planetary motions and eclipses with remarkable accuracy.
- **Differential Calculus:** Concepts resembling calculus were introduced 500 years before Newton and Leibniz.

Madhava of Sangamagrama (1340–1425 CE)

- A pioneer of mathematical analysis and precursor of calculus.
- Introduced infinite series expansion for trigonometric functions (sine, cosine, and tangent).
- Developed Madhava's Pi series, approximating π with remarkable precision.
- His work laid the foundation for calculus, influencing later European mathematicians.

Nagarjuna (10th century CE)

- Renowned Ayurvedic scholar and alchemist.
- Developed Rasashastra (Alchemy) to prepare medicines using minerals and metals.
- Authored Rasaratnakara, focusing on mercury-based medicine.
- Advanced the understanding of surgery and herbal medicine.

Nilakantha Somayaji (1444 – 1544 CE)

- Improved planetary models of the solar system.
- Worked on mathematical astronomy.

Sharangadhara (13th century CE)

- Wrote Sharangadhara Samhita, an important Ayurvedic text.
- Focused on pulse diagnosis, pharmacology, and herbal medicines.

Modern Era

- *Smiling Buddha (1974) India's first successful nuclear test succeeded by Pokhran-II (1998) made India a nuclear power.*
- *Bhabha Atomic Research Centre (BARC) & Nuclear Reactors developed indigenous nuclear reactors for electricity generation. India is among the top nations using thorium-based nuclear energy.*
- *India became the world's IT hub, with companies like Infosys, TCS, Wipro, and HCL. Digital India Initiative (2015-Present) was launched to promote e-governance, digital banking (UPI), and online education. India's Unified Payments Interface (UPI) is one of the world's most advanced digital payment systems. India launched 5G services in 2022, aiming for 6G by 2030. Advancements in AI, robotics, and quantum computing are boosting India's tech industry.*
- *Covaxin (Bharat Biotech) & Covishield (Serum Institute of India) were developed and exported to over 100 countries.*
- *Green Revolution & GM Crops strengthened India's self sufficiency in food production. India is developing genetically modified (GM) crops like BT Cotton for improved yield.*
- *India has sequenced human genomes for better disease prediction and treatment.*
- *Indigenously developed Agni & Prithvi Missiles give India a credible nuclear deterrent. BrahMos – a joint Indo-Russian project is the world's fastest supersonic cruise missile. INS Vikrant (2022) is India's Indigenous Aircraft Carrier.*
- *India is Fourth-largest in wind power and third-largest in solar energy globally.International Solar Alliance (ISA), launched by India, promotes solar energy adoption worldwide. ISRO's Climate Observation Satellites RISAT & INSAT series satellites monitor cyclones, monsoons, and climate change.*
- *India is investing ₹6,000 crores in National Quantum Mission (NQM) developing AI-based tools for healthcare, agriculture, and automation.*
- ***India's Space Missions as Chandrayaan Missions (2008, 2019, 2023) marked notable feats. Chandrayaan-1 (2008): Discovered water molecules on the Moon. Chandrayaan-2 (2019): Conducted detailed lunar mapping. Chandrayaan-3 (2023):** Achieved a soft landing on the Moon's south pole, making India the first country to do so. Mangalyaan (2013) made India the first country to reach Mars in its first attempt*
- *Aditya L1 (2023) is India's first space-based solar observatory to study the Sun's corona and solar winds. Gaganyaan (scheduled for 2025) is India's Human Space Mission to low-Earth orbit.*

Modern Indian Scientists

Jagadish Chandra Bose (1858 – 1937)

- Pioneered work in radio waves and microwaves.
- Demonstrated that plants have life and respond to stimuli.

Srinivasa Ramanujan (1887–1920)

- Contributed to number theory, infinite series, and modular functions.
- Developed Ramanujan Prime, Ramanujan Theta Function, and solved mathematical paradoxes.

Prafulla Chandra Ray (1861 – 1944)

- Known as the Father of Indian Chemistry,. Laying foundations of Pharmacy sector in India in backdrop of Non Cooperation Movement.
- Discovered the compound mercurous nitrite.

Meghnad Saha (1893–1956)

- Developed the Saha Ionization Equation, explaining stellar spectra.
- Contributed to nuclear physics and Cosmology.

Satyendra Nath Bose (1894 – 1974)

- Developed Bose-Einstein Statistics (In collaboration with Albert Einstein), leading to the concept of Bose-Einstein Condensate.
- Laid the foundation for quantum mechanics and Bose-Einstein condensate.

C.V. Raman (1888 – 1970)

- Discovered the Raman Effect (Scattering of light).
- Made pioneering studies in acoustics and optics, contributing to understanding the blue color of the sea.

- National Science Day is celebrated in India on 28th February every year to commemorate the discovery of the Raman Effect by Sir C.V. Raman (on 28th February 1928), for which he was awarded the Nobel Prize in Physics in 1930.

Meghnad Saha (1893 – 1956)

- Developed the Saha Ionization Equation, crucial in astrophysics.

Homi J. Bhabha (1909 – 1966)

- Father of India's Nuclear Program.
- Established Tata Institute of Fundamental Research (TIFR)
- Pioneered India's nuclear energy program, leading to Bhabha Atomic Research Centre (BARC).

Vikram Sarabhai (1919 – 1971)

- Father of Indian Space Program
- Established Indian Space Research Organisation (ISRO).
- Laid the foundation for India's missile and space technology.
- Led the development of Aryabhata, India's first satellite (1975).

A.P.J. Abdul Kalam (1931 – 2015)

- Known as the Missile Man of India, he led the development of Agni and Prithvi missiles under the Integrated Guided Missile Development Program (IGMDP).

- Led ISRO's SLV-III project, launching Rohini satellite (1980).
- Played a crucial role in India's 1998 Pokhran-II nuclear tests and Contributed significantly to India's space and satellite programs while working at ISRO.
- Served as the 11th President of India (2002–2007), promoting education, science, and innovation.
- Inspired millions with his vision of a self-reliant India in technology and authored books like Wings of Fire.

Har Gobind Khorana (1922 – 2011)

- Deciphered the genetic code and its role in protein synthesis.
- Synthesized the first artificial gene.
- Won the Nobel Prize in Physiology/Medicine (1968).

M. S. Swaminathan (1925–2023)

- Father of Green Revolution in India

- Introduced high-yielding variety (HYV) seeds.
- Developed agricultural biotechnology to ensure food security.

Venkatraman Ramakrishnan (1952 -)

- Won the Nobel Prize in Chemistry (2009) for research on structure of ribosomes (essential for protein synthesis).

Raja Ramanna (1925–2004)

- Key figure in India's first successful nuclear test in 1974 at Pokhran (Op Smiling Buddha).
- Served as the Director of Bhabha Atomic Research Centre (BARC) and played a crucial role in nuclear weapons development. Contributed to nuclear energy research and defense applications in India.

G. N. Ramachandran (1922–2001)

- Discovered Ramachandran Plot, a fundamental concept in protein structure prediction.
- Made significant contributions to understanding collagen, an essential protein in the human body.
- His work laid the foundations for modern molecular biology and bioinformatics.

Nambi Narayanan (1941 -)

- Played a key role in developing cryogenic rocket technology for India's space program.
- Worked at ISRO and contributed to the VIKAS engine and developed the liquid propulsion system (used in PSLV and GSLV rockets).
- Honored with the Padma Bhushan for his contributions to India's space program.

K. Radhakrishnan (1949 -)

- Led ISRO during the successful Chandrayaan-1 (India's first moon mission) in 2008 and Mars Orbiter Mission (Mangalyaan) in 2014, making India the first country to reach Mars in its first attempt.
- Supervised several significant PSLV and GSLV missions, strengthening India's space capabilities.
- Strengthened India's space exploration capabilities.

Tessy Thomas (1963 -)

- First woman scientist to head a missile project in India, earning the title "Missile Woman of India".
- Key role in the development of the Agni-V missile, India's long-range intercontinental ballistic missile (ICBM).
- Served Director- General of Aeronautical Systems at DRDO.

Ritu Karidhal – Rocket Woman of India

- Led Chandrayaan-2 and Mangalyaan (Mars Orbiter Mission, MOM).

K. Sivan – ISRO Chairman (2018–2021)

- Led Chandrayaan-2, Gaganyaan, and PSLV missions.
- Gagandeep Kang – Leading virologist in vaccine research.
- Manindra Agrawal – Developed the AKS Primality Test in computational mathematics.
- Raghunath Mashelkar – Worked on polymer science and intellectual property rights.

UNIT 1

Energy, Fuels & Emerging Technologies in Transport

An Introduction to Energy and Fuels

- Since the **early phases of evolution**, humans have been **dependent** on some source of **external energy for - Generation of heat** (to keep themselves warm, protection from wild animals and cooking); Exploiting various available sources to **extract** a **form of energy** that could be used for **transportation** (rotational wheels to overcome friction for increased pace of mobility).
- **Discovery of Fire** and **Wheel** were the two most important **scientific events** in the **evolutionary history of Human race**. While the **former** was **incidentally generated** by **frictional force** of **stones** or **wild forest fires** and later **domesticated**, it paved way for a **settled civilisation** while the latter facilitated **human mobility driven by animals** and led to **increased connectivity** among various territories, and quest of humans for territorial expansion laying foundations of the prominent human civilizations.
- **Traditionally, humans** have been dependent on **wood** as the **most feasible form** of energy (both for generating fire and making wheels), that lasted for centuries. Even the early phase of **industrial revolution** was driven by **coal generated energy** in form of **steam engines** (railways for transportation) and industrial plants (for manufacturing).
- **Coal** is still used as a **fuel** in **thermal power plants** as of today making it the most significant conventional source of Energy. Though **rural communities** explored the usage of **organic waste** (biomass) as a **cooking fuel** (which is presently rejuvenated as a renewable form of energy for generating biogas).
- With **technological advancements, coal** was **substituted** by **crude oil** and it's **derivatives** (petroleum and diesel) at the later phases for **mobility** and **generation of electricity**. An **exponential growth of human population**, an **increased pace of human mobility** and **energy consumption** led to **increasing energy demands**, which had laid an **additional pressure** on **natural reserves/ fossils** (coal, petroleum etc), that had led to the quest of **alternative sources of energy generation** through a **more sustainable means.**
- Developments in all fronts had placed **additional burden** on the **energy sector**. With growing pace of **economic development, extraction of energy** through **conventional means** has led to a **drain of natural reserves** owing to our **traditional reliance** on **conventional sources of energy.**
- From **reliance on coal** in **thermal power plants** for **generation of electricity** to **nuclear energy**, from **horse driven chariots** to **petrol/ diesel driven vehicles** to **electric vehicles**, **technology** has played a vital role in exploring **alternate modes of energy generation** and **transportation** in a much **sustainable manner** (lesser pollutant emission and lesser drain on existing natural resources).
- **New and emerging energy technologies** refer to **innovative** and **advanced methods** of **generating, storing** and **utilizing energy** driven by Non Conventional Sources of Energy is gaining traction in the market. These technologies are typically focused on **addressing the challenges** of **traditional energy sources,** such as fossil fuels, by offering **cleaner, more efficient** and **sustainable alternatives.**

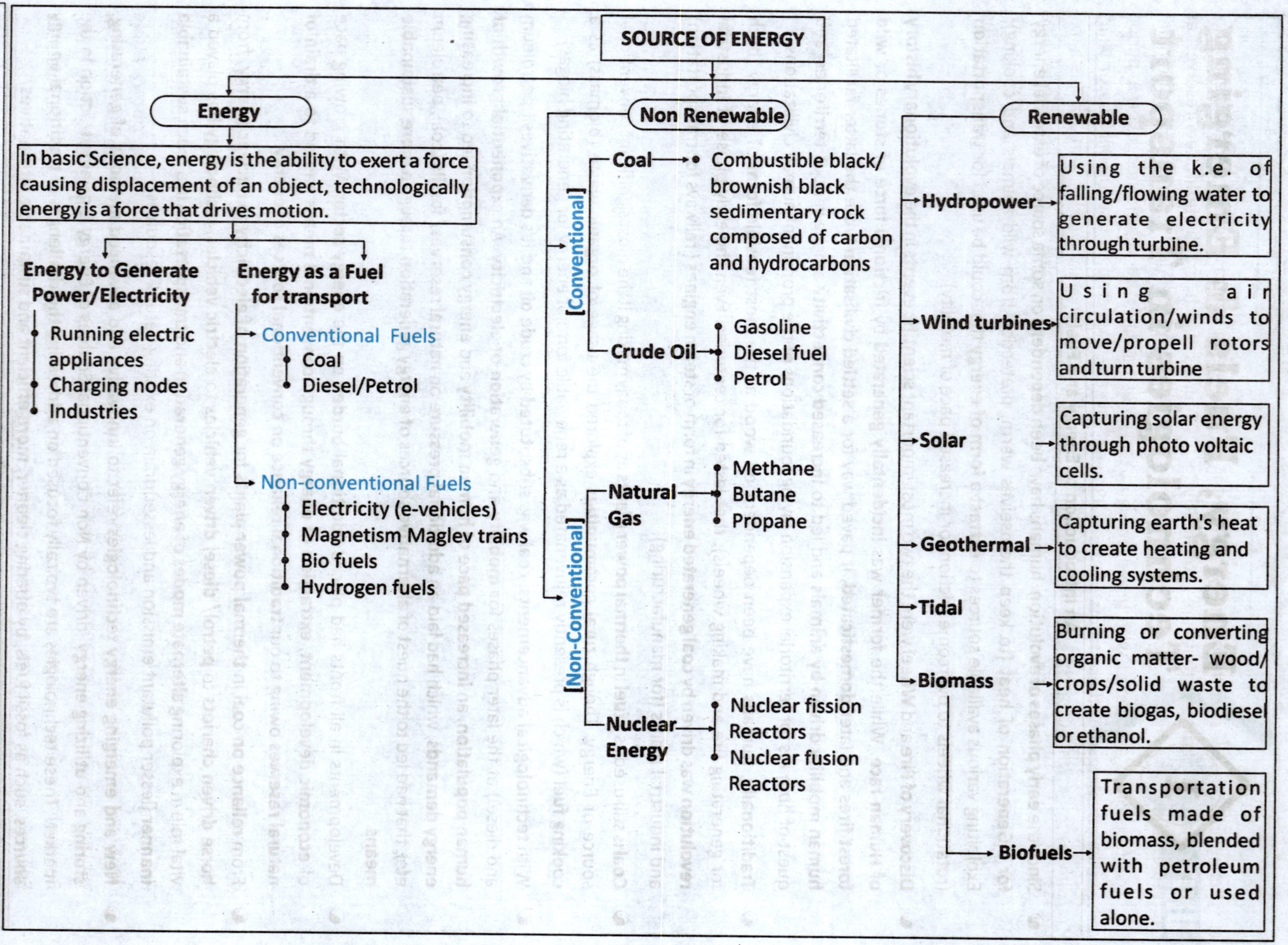
SOURCE OF ENERGY
Energy
In basic Science, energy is the ability to exert a force causing displacement of an object, technologically energy is a force that drives motion.
Energy to Generate Power/Electricity
Running electric appliances
Charging nodes
Industries
Energy as a Fuel for transport
Conventional Fuels
Coal
Diesel/Petrol
Non-conventional Fuels
Electricity (e-vehicles)
Magnetism Maglev trains
Bio fuels
Hydrogen fuels
Non Renewable
[Conventional]
Coal
Combustible black/ brownish black sedimentary rock composed of carbon and hydrocarbons
Crude Oil
Gasoline
Diesel fuel
Petrol
[Non-Conventional]
Natural Gas
Methane
Butane
Propane
Nuclear Energy
Nuclear fission Reactors
Nuclear fusion Reactors
Renewable
Hydropower
Using the k.e. of falling/flowing water to generate electricity through turbine.
Wind turbines
Using air circulation/winds to move/propell rotors and turn turbine
Solar
Capturing solar energy through photo voltaic cells.
Geothermal
Capturing earth's heat to create heating and cooling systems.
Tidal
Biomass
Burning or converting organic matter- wood/ crops/solid waste to create biogas, biodiesel or ethanol.
Biofuels
Transportation fuels made of biomass, blended with petroleum fuels or used alone.

Renewable Energy

- Renewable Energy is form of Energy derived from **natural sources** that are **constantly replenished.**
- They are often associated with **green energy** and **clean energy** but these terms can be used differently depending on the **type of renewable energy.**

> - **Renewable energy sources** are those that are **recyclable like Sunlight, Wind, Tides.**
> - **Clean energy** is form of Energy that **do not release pollutants** like carbon dioxide in process of generation. Clean Energy means Zero greenhouse Gas Emissions, but has the potential to release minimum amount of CO_2 pollutants during production. They are not necessarily renewable. The may adopt Carbon neutralising technologies as Carbon capture sequestatick.
> - **Green energy** is refers to the form of energy derived as Sunlight, Wind, Water, Geothermal which does't emits pollutants while generation. All Green Energy is clean Energy, but the reverse is not true that come from **natural sources.**

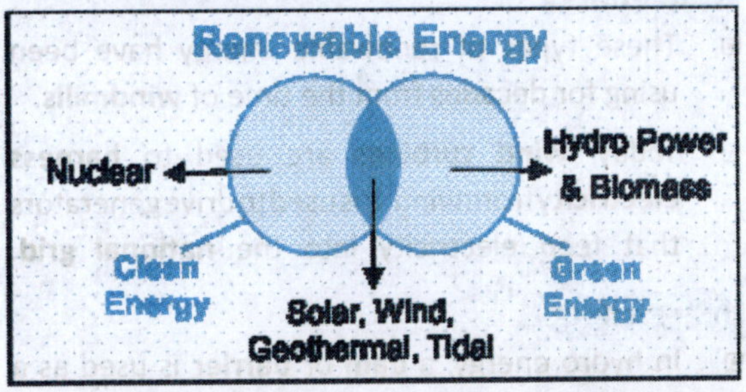

- So, not all energy available in such form is fully clean or green. For instance, **hydroelectric sources** like **dams** and **water reservoirs damage natural habitats,** may lead to **wide scale deforestation** and lead to loss of biodiversity yet they are referred to as **renewable energy.**
- Renewable energy sources are a continuous Energy source since they replenish over a period of time in contrast to non renewable Energy Sources which are finite/limited reserves as coal, oil, petroleum, Natural Gas or Uranium which cannot be replenished over a period of time expected to last for millions of years (if not for eternity). Taking **Sun**, for instance, they are a great alternative to non-renewable resources such as fossil fuels while many are also environmentally friendly and produce little or no CO_2.

Reasons for adopting Renewable sources of Energy

- Renewable energy is increasingly taking over the non-renewable energy resource as the **applications offer better advantages** over the conventional sources.
- **Tapping Renewable energy** requires **technology as development of photovoltaic cells and solar panels** for **tapping solar energy,** Constructing and **maintaining wind turbines** for **tapping wind energy** (though even that cannot be regarded favourable as it is found to harm and kill avian species), so it has been noticed that **Developed countries** (who underwent industrial revolution at early stages and boosted their economy through capitalism) and **with less population** (and consequently lesser energy demand) have started switching to renewable sources of energy.
- Another reason for adopting renewable sources of energy is to **reduce dependency on oil rich countries** (who have been historically manipulating the oil prices leading to global wars and have been accused to shelter and propel terrorist activities financed by the enormous profits earned by oil and petroleum reserves).

> **Germany** uses the **highest amount of renewable energy** with **12.74%** followed by the **UK** at **11.95%. Sweden** uses **10.96%, Spain 10.17%, Italy 8.8%, Brazil 7.35%, Japan 5.3%, Turkey 5.25%, Australia 4.75%** and **USA 4.32%.**

- The applications of renewable energy have the potential **to provide a ready supply of power without using conventional sources** like oil petroleum or coal. This **reduces the risk of importing fuels** and **lowers the risk of environmental risks/ threats** such as **fuel spills** and have **minimal emission issues.**
- Even though renewable energy is seen as yet to advance technology, **harnessing nature's power** has been used for **heating, transportation, lighting**, etc. for a long. The **sunlight** and **wind** keep shining and blowing, even if they depend on time and weather. The wind has powered boats to sail the seas and windmill to grind grain and pump water. **Wind energy** is also used for generating electricity, a clean way for that matter. Similarly Solar energy is mostly used and popular around the world, as it uses free natural source from the sun.
- **Geothermal energy** is also one of the common ways human energy needs are met. The energy is used to keep our homes warm and cool depending on the weather condition. It is also used to generating electric power.
- Applications of all types of renewable energy sources are to generate electricity, transportation, heating, etc.

Types of Renewable Energy Resources
- Solar Energy
- Wind Energy
- Hydro Energy
- Tidal Energy
- Geothermal Energy
- Biomass Energy

Solar energy

- Sunlight is one of the **freely available energy resources** on our planet. Solar energy has been in use by humans for thousands of years for **agriculture / cultivation of crops, growth of plants.**
- Researches have shown that the energy from the sun to earth in one hour is more than the total energy requirement for a whole year. The sun energy is used today to heat homes and our business places, to warm water, and to power devices.
- **Solar panels** are required to be installed for **Tapping Solar Energy.**
- **Solar** or **photovoltaic** (PV) **cell** is made from **silicon**, Cadmium telluride, Copper Indium, Gallium Selenide or Semiconductors materials that are capable of transforming the sunlight directly into electricity. They can be commercial mounted on rooftops or as community projects that power an entire neighborhood. Solar farms or plants can power thousands of homes.
- Solar cells work on the principal of photovoltaic effect where Sunlight absorbed by solar cell, phtovoltaic cells creates Electrical charges that move in response to an internal electrical field in the cell causing flow of electricity closely related to **Photoelectric effect**. (Emission of Electrons from a material that absorbed sunlight)
- **Photoelectric Effect** was discovered by Heinrich Rudolf Hertz in 1887, but explained by Albert Einstein in 1905 with hsi corpuscular theory of light (Photons) for which Einstein received Nobel in Physics. (1921).

Wind energy

- These types of renewable energy have been using for decades from the time of **windmills.**
- Today, **wind turbines** are used to **harness electricity** from wind. It is used to drive generators that feed electricity into the **national grid.**

Hydro energy

- In hydro energy, a **dam** or **barrier** is used as a **large water reservoir** to create a controlled flow of water that will **drive a turbine**. The turbine is what generates electricity.
- This renewable energy source can often be more reliable than solar or wind power (especially if it's tidal rather than river). The system allows electricity to be stored for use when demand reaches a peak.

Tidal energy

- Tidal energy is a type of hydro energy that uses twice-**daily tidal currents** to drive a **turbine generator.**
- Its flow is not constant like some other hydro energy it is highly predictable and can therefore compensate for the periods when the tide current is low.

Geothermal energy

- Geothermal energy is the **natural heat** below the **earth's surface** originating from lava it is used to heat and cool homes directly.
- It can also be used to generate electricity using a **hot spring.**
- The earth's core is hot at different levels due to the slow **decay** of radioactive particles in rocks at the center of the planet. The hot is brought to the earth's surface through a **drilled deep well surface** as a hydrothermal resource. It is then pumped through a turbine to generate electricity.

Biomass energy

- Biomass energy is the conversion of solid fuel made from **organic materials** into electricity. The system involves the **burning / decomposition of organic materials** to produce electricity.
- It is a cleaner and even more energy-efficient process nowadays. Converting **agricultural, industrial** and **domestic waste** into **solid, liquid** and **gas fuel**, biomass energy generates power at a much **lower economic** and **environmental cost.**

Advantages of Renewable Energy Resources

- **Sustainable source of Energy:** Unlike the mining of coal, oil, and natural gas which requires **extensive networks of heavy machinery, processing stations, pipelines** and **transportation, renewables convert natural resources directly** into electricity. While many fossil fuels are becoming harder and more expensive to source resulting in the **destruction of natural habitats** and **significant financial losses, renewable energy** never runs out.
- **Zero Carbon Emissions :** Perhaps the most significant benefit of renewable energy is that there are no **greenhouse gases** or other pollutants created during the process. Whereas **coal power plants** create around **2.2 pounds** of CO_2 for every kilowatt-hour of electricity – solar panels and wind turbines create none at all. Most renewable energy is green and clean energy hence environmentally sustainable.
- **Cleaner Source :** Burning fossil fuels to generate electricity does far more than warm the climate; it also contaminates the air we breathe and the water we drink. **Coal power stations,** for example, release high volumes of carbon dioxide (CO_2) and nitrous oxide (N_2O) directly into the atmosphere – two of the most potent greenhouse gasses. In addition, they also emit **mercury, lead, sulfur dioxide, particulates** and **dangerous metals** – which can cause a host of health problems ranging from breathing difficulties to premature death. **Fossil fuel electricity** can also **contaminate waterways,** both from **air pollution** that falls to the ground during rain, and **waste materials** created during the production process. On the other hand, renewable energy creates no pollution, waste, or contamination risks to air and water.
- **Economically feasible:** With the rapid growth of renewable energy over the last ten years, **solar** and **wind power** are now the **cheapest sources of electricity** in many parts of the world.
- **Boosts employment and job creation :** As new infrastructure needs to be created for the generation of renewable energy which is basically non conventional in nature. With an increasing focus on global warming and many governments setting ambitious carbon-reduction goals, one of the surprising renewable energy advantages is that it has quickly become a major source of **new job growth.**

Concerns and Challenges

- **High installation costs : Setting up solar panels** require a **large surface area** and consequently a large geographical area which remains a challenge owing to **population** and **spatial constraints**. While renewable energy systems need no fuel and can deliver substantial long-term savings, their **up-front costs** can still be prohibitive. On a larger scale, wind farms, solar parks, and hydropower stations require significant investment, land, and electrical infrastructure, resulting in some projects being delayed, altered, or even canceled.
- **Non uniform in nature** – Each source of Renewable energy requires a different topography and consequently a different infrastructure.

> - **Wind Mills** are suited for coastal areas where land and sea breezes are available.
> - **Solar panels** are suited for tropical regions with an continuous exposure to sunlight.
> - **Geothermal Energy** is feasible for regions with earth's opening like fissuring of magma.
> - Renewable eneries like **wind energy** and **solar energy** are **dependent on weather**, which it is highly **unstable.**
> - **Hydro electric generation** is possible in regions **lying in valleys** and **upper courses of river.**

- **High production** cost of power plants.
- Hydropower and biomass have **environmental impacts.**
- Efficiency of renewable energy systems also **depends on their location** and **surrounding environment.**

> - **Wind turbines** are only effective in **large, open areas** with **strong** and **consistent wind,** which limits their viability to specific regions.
> - While **solar panels** generate some electricity even on **cloudy days,** they are most productive in locations with **consistently bright** and **sunny climates** like the **tropical zones / Sunshine countries** but same is not the case with **Temperature zones** like European countries or say **Canada** and **Russia.**

- **Unreliable Energy Production:** Renewable energy systems rely on natural resources such as sunlight, wind, and water, and therefore, their electricity generation can be as unpredictable as the weather. Solar panels lose efficiency on cloudy days, wind turbines aren't effective in calm weather, and hydropower systems need consistent snow and rainfall to maintain reliable production. At the same time, when renewable systems produce too much energy, they risk overloading the grid and causing major problems for network operators.
- One of the advantages of non-renewable energy – such as the output from a coal power station – is a **consistent flow of energy** that can be ramped up and down. But the **intermittency of renewables,** combined with their **accelerating deployment,** requires many **expensive infrastructure** upgrades to maintain reliable supply – which are ultimately paid for by the end-users.
- **Renewables sources still have a Carbon Footprint to some extent:** While solar panels and wind turbines produce no carbon emissions as they make energy – their manufacturing, transport and installation still creates a carbon footprint. Renewable energy components are typically made in large factories that consume high amounts of electricity, in addition to the diesel and gasoline vehicles are needed for their transport and installation.
- **Energy Storage remains a Challenge :** Due to the intermittent nature of renewables, they need forms of energy storage to capture and release electricity in a consistent and controlled way. Utility-scale batteries have gained significant momentum in recent years, such as the world's largest system that recently came online in **California.**

> Despite falling costs, storage technology is still relatively expensive and there are some lingering questions regarding its reliability and lifespan.

Biofuels

Biofuels are fuels produced from **biomass-based renewable resources** such as **plants, animal by-products**, or **microorganisms.**

- **Peanut oil** was first used as a diesel fuel approximately a century ago.
- Currently, these fuels are usually **blended with petroleum fuels**, but in some circumstances, they may be used on their own.
- In order to function in an engine, a biofuel must be compatible with the performance requirements of existing engine technology, which as of today requires compatibility with conventional petroleum fuels.
- Any **hydrocarbon fuel** that is produced from an organic matter (living or once living material) in a short period of time (days, weeks, or even months) is considered a biofuel.
- Biofuels may be **solid, liquid** or **gaseous** in nature of State.

Types of Biofuels
Solid: Wood, dried plant material, and manure
Liquid: Bioethanol and Biodiesel
Gaseous: Biogas

Generations of Biofuels

- Biofuels research and development has led us to three different generations of biofuel. Each generation has a **unique feedstock** and its own **potential benefits** and **draw backs.**

First Generation Biofuels

- These are made from **food sources** such as **sugar, starch, vegetable oil,** or **animal fats** using **conventional technology.**

Example of First-generation biofuels : Bioalcohols, Biodiesel, Vegetable oil, Bioethers, Biogas.

- They are derived from **vegetable oil, starch,** or **sucrose.** Processing these elements to become a **transportation fuel** requires simple **biochemical treatments** for **vegetable oil** to **biodiesel** or **starch** and **sucrose to ethanol.**
- These processes have already been developed in the **food industry**, limiting the need for further research and development before producing transportation fuels.
- Those crops require **intensive agricultural input** (fertilizer), as opposed to less input for perennial grasses.
- Though the process of conversion is easy but use of food sources in the production of biofuels creates an imbalance in the food economy, leading to increased food prices and food insecurity.

Second Generation Biofuels

- These are produced from **non-food crops** or **portions of food crops** that are **not edible** and considered as **wastes**, e.g., **stems, husks, wood chips** and **fruit skins** due to diversion of food grains from consumption to fuel purpose.

Examples of Second Generation Fuels- Cellulose Ethanol, Biodiesel.

Thermochemical reactions or **biochemical conversion processes** are used for producing such fuels.

- They are expected to be derived from **cellulosic biomass sources** including **crop residues, perennial grasses** and **trees.** They may be grown on **marginal cropland** where row crop production is not profitable. By focusing on areas that are highly erodible or have marginal soil quality, this avoids competition with fertile ground that may be best used to grow food crops.
- Although these crops require **little initial input,** they do require additional treatment to break down cellulose for creating an end product such as a liquid fuel. **Transporting high quantities of biomass** can be a **logistical** and **financial challenge** for producers.

Third Generation Biofuel

- These are produced from **micro-organisms** like algae.

Examples of Third Generation Biofuels Butanol.

- **Micro-organisms** like **algae** can be grown using **land** and **water unsuitable** for food **production**, therefore **reducing the strain** on already depleted water sources.
- To create third generation biofuels biomass or **oil** is harvested from **algae**. Oil producing algae (so call Oilgae) does not require pretreatment, and grows quickly.
- However, controlling the environment for optimal growth is challenging, and expensive. Maintaining strict environmental control often requires expensive facilities and equipment.
- One disadvantage is that **fertilizers used** in the production of such crops lead to **environmental pollution.**

Fourth Generation Biofuels

- In the production of these fuels, crops that are **genetically engineered** to take in high amounts of carbon are grown and harvested as biomass.
- The crops are then converted into fuel using **second generation techniques.**
- The fuel is pre-combusted, and the carbon is captured. Then the carbon is geo-sequestered, meaning that the carbon is stored in depleted oil or gas fields or in unmineable coal seams.

> **Examples of Fourth Generation Biofuels :** Butanol, Microalgae & Algae Biofuels.
> Some of these fuels are considered **carbon negative** as their production pulls out carbon from the environment.

Biofuel Conversion Processes

Deconstruction

- Producing **advanced biofuels** (e.g., cellulosic ethanol and renewable hydrocarbon fuels) typically involves a **multistep process.**
- First, the tough rigid structure of the plant cell wall—which includes the **biological molecules cellulose, hemicellulose,** and **lignin bound tightly together**— is broken down. which is accomplished: **high temperature deconstruction** or **low temperature deconstruction.**

High-temperature Deconstruction

> **High-temperature deconstruction** makes use of extreme heat and pressure to break down solid biomass into liquid or gaseous intermediates.

Modes of High temperature Deconstruction
- Pyrolysis
- Gasification
- Hydrothermal Liquefaction

- During **pyrolysis**, **biomass** is **heated rapidly** at **high temperatures** (500°C–700°C) in an oxygen-free environment. The heat breaks down biomass into pyrolysis vapor, gas, and char. Once the char is removed, the vapors are cooled which get condensed into a liquid bio-crude oil.
- **Gasification** follows a slightly similar process; however, biomass is exposed to a **higher temperature range** (>700°C) with some **oxygen** present to produce **synthesis gas** (or syngas)—a mixture that consists mostly of carbon monoxide and hydrogen.
- When working with **wet feedstocks** like algae,. hydrothermal liquefaction is the preferred thermal process. It is uses water under moderate temperatures (200°C–350°C) and elevated pressures to convert biomass into liquid bio-crude oil.

Low-temperature deconstruction

- **Low-temperature deconstruction** typically makes use of biological catalysts called enzymes or chemicals to breakdown feedstocks into intermediates.
  - First, biomass undergoes a **pretreatment step** that opens up the physical structure of plant and algae cell walls, making sugar polymers like cellulose and hemicellulose more accessible.
  - These polymers are then **broken down enzymatically** or chemically into simple sugar building blocks during a process known as hydrolysis.
  - Following deconstruction, intermediates such as **crude bio-oils, syngas, sugars** and

other chemical building blocks must be **upgraded** to produce a finished product. This step can involve either biological or chemical processing.

- **Microorganisms**, such as **bacteria**, **yeast**, and **cyanobacteria**, can ferment sugar or gaseous intermediates into fuel **blendstocks** and **chemicals**.
- Alternatively, sugars and other intermediate streams, such as **bio-oil** and **syngas**, may be processed using a catalyst to remove any unwanted or reactive compounds in order to improve storage and handling properties.
- The finished products from upgrading may be **fuels** or **bioproducts** ready to sell into the commercial market or **stabilized intermediates** suitable for finishing in a petroleum refinery or chemical manufacturing plant.

Important of Biofuels

Ethanol

- **Ethanol** (CH_3CH_2OH) is a **renewable fuel** that can be made from various plant materials, collectively known as **biomass**.
- Ethanol is an **alcohol** used as a **blending agent** with **gasoline** to **increase octane** and **cut down carbon monoxide** and other **smog-causing emissions**.

> The most common blend of ethanol is **E10** (10% ethanol, 90% gasoline) and is approved for use in most conventional gasoline-powered vehicles up to **E15** (15% ethanol, 85% gasoline). Some vehicles, called **flexible fuel vehicles**, are designed to run on **E85** (a gasoline-ethanol blend containing 51%–83% ethanol.

- Most ethanol is made from **plant starches** and **sugars**—but scientists are continuing to develop technologies that would allow for the use of **cellulose** and **hemicellulose**, the **non-edible fibrous material** that constitutes the bulk of plant matter.

> The method for converting **biomass** into ethanol is called **fermentation**. During fermentation, **microorganisms** (e.g., bacteria and yeast) metabolize plant.

Bioethanol

- It is derived from **corn** and **sugarcane** using **fermentation process**.
- When mixed with **petrol**, **it improves combustion** performance and **lowers the emissions of carbon monoxide** and **sulphur oxide**.
- It is used as a blending agent with petrol to increase octane and reduce carbon monoxide and other harmful emissions.
- E10 (10% ethanol mix) is the most commonly used blend, alongside E-20. E100 is pure ethanol. Flexible fuel vehicles can run on up to 85% ethanol blends (E85).
- Bio-methanol: It is produced from syngas obtained from the gasification of renewable feedstocks like crop residues or wood waste.

Biodiesel

- Biodiesel is a liquid fuel produced from **renewable sources**, such as **new** and used **vegetable oils** and **animal fats** and is a cleaner-burning replacement for petroleum-based diesel fuel.

> Biodiesel is derived from **vegetable oils** like **soybean oil** or **palm oil, vegetable waste oils** and **animal fats** through a biochemical process called **Transesterification.**

- It produces very less or no amount of harmful gases as compared to diesel.
- **Biodiesel** is **nontoxic** and **biodegradable** and is produced by combining alcohol with **vegetable oil, animal fat**, or **recycled cooking grease.**
- Like petroleum-derived diesel, biodiesel is used to fuel **compression-ignition** (diesel) **engines.** Biodiesel can be blended with petroleum diesel in any percentage, including **B100** (pure biodiesel) and, the most common blend, **B20** (a blend containing 20% biodiesel and 80% petroleum diesel).

Biogas

- It is produced by **anaerobic decomposition of organic matter** like **sewage** from **animals** and **humans.**
- Biogas mainly comprises of **methane** and **carbon dioxide**, though it also contains small proportions of **hydrogen sulfide, hydrogen, carbon monoxide** and **siloxanes.**
- **Bio CNG:** A purified form of biogas, processed to that produces 95% of pure methane gas, using segregated biodegradable waste as the raw material. The process residue is a high-quality concentrated liquid fertilizer, and CO2 is measured and packed for food-grade CO2. It has a similar calorific value to (CNG and involves commercial refining to increase methane content.

> Biogas is commonly used for **heating, electricity** and for **automobiles.**

Biobutanol

- It is produced through the **fermentation of starch**. The energy content in butanol is the highest among the other gasoline alternatives. It can be added to diesel to reduce emissions.
- **Biojet fuel:** An aviation biofuel derived from biomass through conversion processes such as Fischer-Tropsch synthesis or synthesized paraffinic kerosene (SPK) hydrotreating. Major advantages : Reduced particulate emissions, carbon footprint and contrail formation with drop-in capability for existing aircraft fleets.

> Biobutanol serves as a solvent in textile industry and is also used as a base in perfumes.

Biohydrogen

- Biohydrogen, like biogas, can be produced using a number of processes such as **pyrolysis, gasification** or **biological fermentation.**

Renewable Hydrocarbons

- **Petroleum fuels**, such as **gasoline, diesel,** and **jet fuel**, contain a complex mixture of hydrocarbons (molecules of hydrogen and carbon), which are burned to produce energy.
- **Biochar:** A form of black carbon, produced by controlled pyrolysis of organic materials from forests and agricultural wastes. It is useful for carbon sequestration. Biochar has been traditionally used as a soil supplement in the Amazon basin thousands of years ago, where the regions of fertile soil known as Terra Pretan (dark earth), were created by the natives.

> Hydrocarbons can also be produced from **biomass** sources through a variety of **biological** and **thermochemical processes.**

- **Biomass-based renewable hydrocarbon fuels** are nearly identical to the petroleum-based fuels they are designed to replace—so they're compatible with today's **engines, pumps** and other **infrastructure.**

Significance of Biofuels

- A significant increase in biofuel production is needed to get on track with the **Net Zero Emissions by 2050** (NZE) **Scenario** and deliver the associated emission reductions.
- Biofuel production reaches over **10 EJ by 2030** in the **NZE Scenario**, requiring an average growth of around **11% per year**.
- Advanced feedstock usage must also expand: biofuels produced from waste and residues and nonfood energy crops meet over **40% of total biofuel** demand by **2030**, up from around a **9%** share in **2021.**

Advantages of Biofuels

- **Ease Availability:** Biofuels of different generations are produced from biomass / organic matter which is readily available in some form or the other.
- **Easy to Source :** Gasoline is refined from crude oil, which happens to be a non-renewable resource.
- **Environmentally Sustainable:** Biofuels don't produce any pollutant or greenhouse gases like carbon dioxide, nitrogen dioxide, sulphur dioxide, methane or ozone hence are on lines of net zero emission goals of India.

- **Efficiency :** Biofuel is made from renewable resources and is relatively less flammable than fossil diesel. Also, it has significantly better lubricating properties than its counterpart.
- **Cost Effective:** As such, the cost-benefit of using biofuel is much higher, making it a much more efficient option than fossil fuels. Currently, biofuels cost the same price in the market as Gasoline, although there's a likelihood that their increasing demand could induce the need for more efficient extraction methods, making them much cheaper in the future.
- **Biofuel generate enable high-value products or waste resources**: Ultimately reducing the cost of producing biopower.
- **Diversity in Source Material:** Whereas conventional energy sources oil is a limited resource that comes from specific materials, biofuels can be manufactured from a wide range of materials including crop waste, manure, and other byproducts.
- **Energy Security:** Biofuels can be produced locally, which decreases the nation's dependence upon foreign energy. By reducing dependence on foreign fuel sources, countries can protect the integrity of their energy resources and make them safe from outside influences.
- **Durability of Vehicles' Engine:** Biofuels are adaptable to current engine designs and perform very well in most conditions. It has higher cetane and better lubricating properties than fossil fuels. Even more, the engine's durability increases when biodiesel is used as a combustible fuel. With biofuel, there is also no need for engine conversion,
- **Economic Stimulation:** Because biofuels are produced locally, biofuel manufacturing plants can employ hundreds or thousands of workers, creating new jobs in rural areas. Biofuel production will also increase the demand for suitable biofuel crops, providing economic stimulation to the agriculture industry. With the fluctuating prices of crude oil switching to biofuels is an economic option.
- **Employment Generation:** Biofuel production increases the demand for suitable biofuel crops, boosting the agriculture industry. Fueling homes, businesses, and vehicles with it is less expensive than fossil fuels. More jobs will be created with a growing biofuel industry, keeps economy secure by creating opportunities.

Concerns and Challenges

- **High Cost of Production :** Even with all the benefits of biofuels, they are pretty expensive to produce in the current market. Currently, the interest and capital investment in biofuel production is fairly low but can match demand. Generally, biofuels are more expensive to produce than fossil fuels on a per-unit energy basis. This is due to the fact that biofuels are derived from renewable resources, such as crops and waste materials, which are more expensive to grow and process than fossil fuels.
- **Leads to Monoculture : Monoculture** refers to the practice of **producing the same crops year after year** rather than producing various crops through a farmer's fields over time. While this might be economically lucrative for farmers, growing the same crop yearly may deprive the soil of nutrients that are put back into the soil through crop rotation. Growing only one crop changes the environment regarding the food available to pests, and they are free to destroy an entire crop. Secondly, in due course of time, pests inevitably become **resistant to the chemicals**. The next problem comes with genetic engineering when we decide to modify the crop to resist the pest without the need for pesticides. It is still likely that at least a few pests aren't affected by the modification, and the problem remains.
- **Increased usage of Fertilizers :** Biofuels are produced from crops that need fertilizers to grow better. The downside of using fertilizers is that

they can harm the surrounding environment and cause water pollution. Fertilizers containing nitrogen and phosphorus and can be washed away from soil to nearby lakes, rivers, or ponds created soil and water pollution in the longer run.

- **Food Scarcity:** Biofuels are extracted from plants and crops that have high levels of sugar in them. However, most of these crops are also used as food crops. Even though plant waste can be used as raw material, the requirement for such food crops will still exist. It consumers agricultural space from other crops. Using **existing biofuel land** may not cause an **acute food shortage**; however, it pressurises the current crop growth.
- **Diversion of land and water sources:** Land used to grow biofuel feedstock has to be cleared of native vegetation, which leads to ecological damage. The damage is caused by destroying local habitats, animal dwellings, and micro-ecosystems, reducing the overall health of the region's natural resources.
- **Water Intensive : Large quantities of water** are required to irrigate the **biofuel crops**, which may strain local and regional water resources if not managed wisely. Mass quantities of water are used to produce corn-based ethanol to meet demand for biofuels.
- **Industrial Pollution** : The carbon footprint of biofuels is less than the traditional forms of fuel when burnt. However, the process by which they are produced makes up for that. Production is largely dependent on lots of water and oil.
- **Higher Cost in the Future:** Usage of Biofuels requires a high research. The cost of research and future installation means that the price of biofuels will see a significant spike.
- **Weather related challenges:** Biofuel is less suitable for use in low temperatures. That's because it's more likely to attract moisture than fossil diesel, which creates problems in cold weather. It also increases microbial growth in the engine that clogs the engine filters.

Green Hydrogen

Hydrogen is the most abundant element in the universe. But pure, or the elemental hydrogen, is very scarce. It almost always exists in compounds like with **oxygen** (O) to form **water** (H_2O).

- **Hydrogen** is a key industrial fuel that has a variety of applications including the **production of ammonia** (a key fertilizer), **steel**, **refineries** and **electricity**. However, all of the hydrogen manufactured now is the so-called **black** or **brown hydrogen** because they are produced from **coal**.
- When electric current is passed through **water**, it splits it into **elemental oxygen** and **hydrogen** through **electrolysis**. And if the **electricity** used for this process comes from a **renewable source** like **wind** or **solar** then the hydrogen thus produced is referred to as **green hydrogen**.

Types of Hydrogen (Based on Extraction Methods)

- There are several ways to produce Hydrogen on industrial scale (large-scale). These include **steam reforming of natural gas, oil reforming** or **coal gasification**. A small percentage is also produced using more **energy-intensive methods** such as the **electrolysis of water**. The hydrogen produced via these methods have been given various different names in order to distinguish them in terms of their **carbon footprints**.

Depending on the **nature of the method** of its **extraction**, **Hydrogen** is categorised into three categories : **Grey**, **Blue** and **Green.**

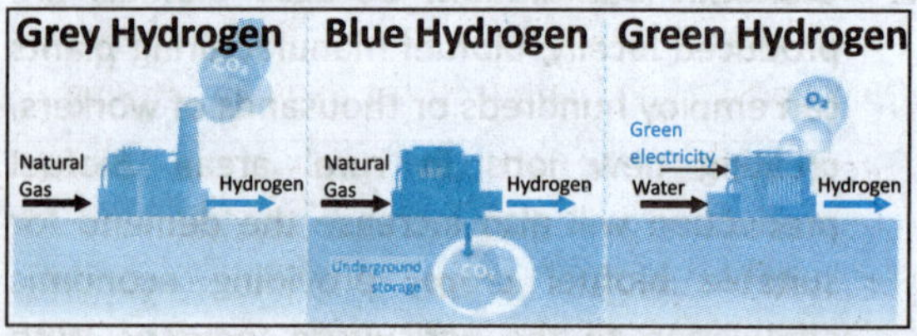

- **Grey Hydrogen :** It is traditionally produced from **methane** (CH_4), split with **steam** into **carbon-dioxide** (CO_2, Green House Gas) and hydrogen. Grey hydrogen is increasingly being produced from **coal**, with significantly higher CO_2 emissions per unit of hydrogen produced. It is produced at **industrial scale** today. It has **no energy transition value.**
- **Blue Hydrogen:** It is produced via natural gas or coal gasification combined with **carbon capture storage** (CCS) or **carbon capture use** (CCU) technologies to **reduce carbon emissions.**
- **Green Hydrogen:** It is produced using **electrolysis of water** with electricity generated by renewable energy. The carbon intensity ultimately depends on the **carbon neutrality** of the **source of electricity** (i.e., the more renewable energy there is in the electricity fuel mix, the greener the hydrogen produced).
- **Black and Brown Hydrogen :** Hydrogen manufactured through black coal or lignite (brown coal) and is most environmentally damaging. They also refer to any hydrogen made from fossil fuels through the process of Gasification.
- **Pink Hydrogen :** Hydrogen manufactured through electrolysis powered by nuclear energy. Nuclear-produced hydrogen can also be referred to as purple hydrogen or Red hydrogen.
- **Turquoise Hydrogen :** Hydrogen manufactured using methane pyrolysis to produce hydrogen and solid carbon.
- **Yellow Hydrogen :** Hydrogen manufactured through electrolysis using solar power.
- **White Hydrogen :** Naturally occurring, geological hydrogen found in underground deposits and manufactures through fracking.

Green hydrogen in particular is one of the cleanest sources of energy with close to **zero emission.** It can be used in **fuel cells** for cars or in **energy-guzzling industries** like **fertilizers** and **steel manufacturing.**

Advantages of Green Hydrogen

- Net Zero Pollutant Emission
- Energy Storage Solution
- Versatility
- Easy Availability of Water

Challenges

- High Operating Cost

Electrolysers are devices that use **electricity** to **split water** into **hydrogen** and **oxygen** and are expensive.

- High Energy Consumption
- Safety Concerns

National Green Hydrogen Mission

- It is a program under **Ministry of New and Renewable Energy** to **incentivise the commercial production of green hydrogen** and **make India a net exporter of the fuel.** The Mission will facilitate **demand creation, production, utilization** and **export of Green Hydrogen.**

On 4th **January 2023,** the Union Cabinet approved the **National Green Hydrogen Mission** with an outlay of Rs. 19,744 crore from **FY 2023-24** to **FY 2029-30.**

- **Components of National Green Hydrogen Mission:**
  - Facilitating demand creation through **exports** and **domestic utilization.**
  - **Strategic Interventions for Green Hydrogen Transition** (SIGHT) **programme,** which includes incentives for manufacturing of electrolysers and production of green hydrogen.

- **Pilot Projects** for **steel, mobility, shipping** etc.
- Development of **Green Hydrogen Hubs**.
- Support for **infrastructure development**.
- Establishing a robust framework of regulations and standards.
- Research & Development programme.
- Skill development programmes.
- Public awareness and outreach programmes.

Major Objectives of Green Hydrogen Mission:

- Making India a leading producer and supplier of Green Hydrogen in the world
- Creation of export opportunities for Green Hydrogen and its derivatives
- Reduction in dependence on imported fossil fuels and feedstock
- Development of indigenous manufacturing capabilities
- Attracting investment and business opportunities for the industry
- Creating opportunities for employment and economic development
- Supporting R&D projects

Mission outcomes projected by 2030 :

- India's Green Hydrogen production capacity is likely to reach **5 MMT per annum**, contributing to reduction in dependence on import of fossil fuels.
- Achievement of Mission targets is expected to reduce a cumulative Rs. 1 lakh crore worth of fossil fuel imports by 2030.
- Nearly **50 MMT per annum** of CO_2 emissions are expected to be averted through production and use of the targeted quantum of Green Hydrogen.
- Over **Rs. 8 lakh crore** in total investments.
- Creation of over **6 lakh jobs**.

Recently a **German energy** firm entered a pact with an Indian alternative fuel company to manufacture **hydrogen** and **methanol fuel cells** in India. They would manufacture a type of **hydrogen-based fuel cell**, which is a modular and emission free solution which would gradually replace diesel-based generators and could also be used in in a variety of other industrial applications.

Green Ammonia

Ammonia is a chemical mainly used in the manufacture of **nitrogenous fertilizers**, like **urea** and **ammonium nitrate**, but can be put to other uses too, such as to **run engines.**

- Green ammonia production is where the process of making ammonia is **100% renewable** and **carbon-free.**
- One way of making green ammonia is by using **hydrogen** from **water electrolysis** and **nitrogen** separated from the air. These are then fed into the **Haber process** (also known as Haber-Bosch), all powered by sustainable electricity.

In the Haber process, **hydrogen** and **nitrogen** are reacted together at **high temperatures** and pressures to produce ammonia NH_3.

- Green ammonia is intended to be used in the **production of carbon-neutral fertiliser products, decarbonising the food value chain,** and also has potential as a **future climate-neutral shipping fuel.**
- Green ammonia production makes use of renewable energy sources such as **hydro-electric, solar power** or **wind turbines.**

Applications of Green Ammonia

- **Energy storage:** Ammonia is easily stored in bulk as a liquid at modest pressures (10-15 bar) or refrigerated to -33°C. This makes it an ideal chemical store for renewable energy.
- **Zero-carbon fuel:** Ammonia can be burnt in an engine or used in a fuels cell to produce electricity. When used, ammonia's only by-products are water and nitrogen.
- The **maritime industry** is likely to be an early adopter, replacing the use of fuel oil in marine engines.
- Green ammonia is intended to be used in the production of **carbon-neutral fertilizer products,** decarbonizing the food value chain, and also has potential as a future climate-neutral shipping fuel.
- Green ammonia is crucial to tackle the **existential challenges** of producing enough food to feed a growing global population and generating CO_2-free energy.

Applications and Scope of Green Hydrogen Mission

Green Steel

Steel production is one of the potential sectors where **Green Hydrogen** can **replace fossil fuels.**

- **The National Steel Policy 2017** states that **Natural Gas** is a **greener alternative** to meeting India's goal of reducing the **carbon intensity** of GDP under the **Paris Climate Agreement.**
- The Mission will support efforts to enhance **low-carbon Steel production capacity.**

Transport

- Considering Hydrogen's advantages for heavy-duty, long-haul vehicles, certain routes are to be identified as **Hydrogen Highways.** The necessary **Green Hydrogen production projects,** distribution infrastructure and **refuelling stations** will be built along such highways, which will enable Hydrogen fuelled **inter-state buses** and commercial vehicles to ply on such routes.

Shipping

- Maritime transport and Ports have significant potential for decarbonisation through use of Green Hydrogen or its derivatives such as **Green Ammonia** and **Green Methanol** as fuel for propulsion and other operations.
- Prospects include development of **Green Hydrogen/Ammonia refuelling** hubs at Indian ports; development and operation of **Green Hydrogen/Ammonia fuelled vessels;** use of **Green Hydrogen/Ammonia to fuel zero-emission technologies for vehicles** and **terminal equipment at ports;** and **development of supply chains** and **capabilities** to support future export of Green Hydrogen/Ammonia from India.

Green Ammonia bunkers and refuelling facilities will be set up at least at one port by **2025.** Such facilities will be established at all major ports by **2035.**

Green Hydrogen Hubs

- Given the **technical** and **logistical challenges** inherent in transporting Hydrogen over long distances, a cluster-based production and utilisation model would enhance viability of Green Hydrogen projects in the initial years. This would, in turn, enable economies of scale and convergence of **key infrastructure requirements in geographically proximate areas.**

Emerging Technologies in Transport

Humanitarian challenges and advances in technology are leading a wave of transportation innovation across the globe. Issues as overcrowding and traffic congestion in metropolitans, vehicular pollution, global warming have led to various innovations in modes of transport to seek sustainable alternatives for transportation which causes lesser drain on fuels and lesser impact on the environment, within the legal ambits of individual and national security.

- Urban transportation worldwide faces the challenge of **traffic congestion. High population density** and **increased privately-owned vehicles** are the two major reasons behind traffic congestion in urban areas, especially during rush hours.
- The negative effects are **higher noise levels** and **harmful emissions,** and an increase in the so-called **door-to-door travel time.**
- In his **1977 book, Great Cities and Their Traffic, Michael Thomson** referred to some seven major interrelated problems of urban transport, as illustrated -
- Exploring beyond ground transportation modes is imperative to facilitate faster everyday commutes for passengers in urban areas and alleviate road congestion.

The Urban Transport Problem

- Traffic movement and congestion
- Accidents
- Peak-hour crowding on public transport
- Off-peak inadequacy of public transport
- Difficulties for pedestrians
- Environmental impact
- Parking difficulties

Emerging Modes of Transportation

Microbility

Dockless bike and scooter startups are hoping to make city travel more energy and space efficient.

Pros :	Cons:
• Limits fossil fuel emissions. • Reduces road congestion.	• Vehicle maintenane. • Vandalism.

Flying Taxis

20+ companies are in the race to get safe, cost-effective aerial rides between cities on the market, pending FAA approval.

Pros :	Cons:
• Reduces road congestion. • Increases travel speed.	• High costs. • Regulation challenges.

Delivery Drones

Flying robots will revolutionize the way we transport goods once they are able to receive type certification for mass commercial use.

Pros:	Cons :
• Curbs ratalities. • Ruduces road congestion.	• Higher risk of delivery defects. • Privacy risks. • Increases in delivery coasts.

Flying hotel pods

A Canadian company hopes to create self-sustaining hotels from drone technology that will allow guests to travel while sleeping.

Pros:	Cons:
• Increases travel speed.	• Technology advancements needed.

Driverless Cars

Imagine watching TV in the passenger seat while a robot system drives your car. This reality is just a few regulatory steps away.

Pros :	Cons:
• Curbs fatalities. • Reduces driver errors.	• Higher costs. • Increased road congestion. • State-to-state regulation challenges.

Maglev Trains

Six high-spedd magnetic trains are already running in Asia andthey are safer, faster and more eco-friendly than other transit methods.

Pros :	Cons:
• Increases travel speed • Curbs fatalities • Reduces fossil fuel emissions	• Expensive tracks • New infrastructure needed

Underground Tunnels

This futuristic vision aims to solve city infrastructrure issues by making road 3D through underground tunnels.

Pros:	Cons:
• Reduces road congestion.	• High coast.

Hyperloop

Passenger pods that can transport people and goods at speeds at 600 mph could be reality as early as 2021.

Pros :	Cons :
• Reduces road congestion. • Increases travel speed.	• High development costs. • Unproven system.

Smart Roads

Vehicles are not the only things getting smarter. Highways studded with sensors will alert commuters when a crash occurs nearby.

Pros:	Cons:
• Reduces road congestion. • Increases travel speed.	• High development costs. • Unproven system.

Electric Vehicles

Vehicles that run entirely or mostly on **electricity** are referred to as **electric vehicles.**

- Electric vehicles are particularly **environmentally friendly**. They consume **little to no fossil fuels,** have fewer moving components that need to be maintained, and have **minimal operating** expenses.
- The **Paris Agreement's global climate agenda** which aims to **cut carbon emissions** to **reduce global warming** is the driving force for the **demand for electric vehicles** (EVs).

India is the **fourth highest emitter** of **carbon dioxide globally** and at the **COP26**, pledged to reduce its carbon emissions to **net-zero** by **2070**. India has pledged to **reduce the intensity** of **GHG emissions** by **33%** to **35% below 2005 levels** by **2030**. The adoption of electric vehicles is consistent with India's pledge to lower carbon emissions and provide renewable energy sources of energy. India's advocacy of **five elements** for climate change – **Panchamrit** at the **COP26** in **Glasgow** is a commitment to the same.

- India aims to achieve **EV sales** accounting for **30% of private cars, 70% of commercial vehicles** and **80% of two** and **three-wheelers** by **2030**. For this reason, India is aggressively promoting the adoption of EVs in the country by offering various incentives at both **Central** and **State level**, to buyers and manufacturers.

Advantages of Electric Vehicles

- **Environmental Benefits**
- **Energy Diversity and Security**
- **Technological Advancements and Job Creation**
- **Long-Term Cost Savings**
- **Low cost of ownership**
- **Easier maintenance**
- **Favourable State EV policies**
- **Energy independence**
- **Improved performance**
- **Convenience**
- **Decongesting Cities**
- **Innovative** and **futuristic smart EVs**
- No congestion charge.
- Renewable electricity tariffs.
- Reduced noise pollution.

- **Shared Mobility :** It refers to the use of vehicles as a service rather than as a personal asset. This can reduce the number of vehicles on the road and the need for parking space.
- **Compact Design :** It refers to the use of smaller and lighter vehicles that can fit more easily in urban spaces.

Challenges of Electric Vehicles

- High Price
- High Initial Infrastructural Cost
- Consumer perception
- Limited / Inadequate Charging Infrastructure
- Limitation of Battery technology
- Range Anxiety
- Battery Technology and Supply Chain
- Limited domestic manufacturing capabilities
- Lack of awareness
- Lack of standardization
- Inadequate Power Grid infrastructure
- Limited Model Options

Government initiatives to promote Electric Vehicles

- **Faster Adoption and Manufacturing of Electric Vehicles (FAME) scheme II**, provides incentives for EV manufacturers and buyers. These incentives include subsidies, tax rebates, preferential financing and exemptions from road tax and registration fees.

- **National Electric Mobility Mission Plan** (NEMMP), launched in 2020 which aims to have atleast 30% vehicles to be electric by 2030. It has the target to achieve **6-7 million sales** of **hybrid** and electric vehicles year on year from **2020 onwards** by providing fiscal incentives.
- **National Mission on Transformative Mobility and Battery Storage**, seeks to create a **comprehensive ecosystem** for the **adoption of EVs** and **support the establishment** of **giga-scale battery manufacturing plants** in India.
- **Production Linked Incentive (PLI) scheme,** which provides **incentives** for the **manufacturing** of **electric vehicles** and **components.**
- **Vehicle Scrappage Policy**, provides incentives for the scrapping of old vehicles and the purchase of new electric vehicles.
- **Go Electric campaign** aims to create awareness on the benefits of EVs and EVz charging infrastructure.
- India is among a handful of countries that support the **global EV30@30 campaign,** which aims for at least **30% new vehicle** sales to be electric by **2030**.
- **Ministry of Power**, in its revised guidelines on **charging infrastructure** (MoP Guidelines), has prescribed that at **least one charging station** should be present in a grid of **3 km** and at every **25 kms** on both sides of the highways.
- **Ministry of Housing and Urban Affairs** has also amended the **Model Building Bye-laws, 2016** (MBBL) to mandate setting aside **20%** of the parking space for EV charging facilities in residential and commercial buildings.
- **Concessions on the GST:** The government levies a 5% GST on electric vehicles. On the other hand, it charges a GST of 28% on internal combustion automobiles.
- **Go Electric Campaign:** At the beginning of 2021, the government launched the Go Electric campaign to promote the use of electric vehicles and kitchen appliances and to ensure nation's energy security.
- India has set a very ambitious target to achieve **net zero** by **2070** at **UNFCC COP26**. To achieve this goal, EVs have a crucial role to play. While EVs themselves produce **zero tailpipe emissions**, the overall environmental impact of electric vehicles depends on the **source of the electricity** used to charge them.
- **Tax benefits:** The Government has announced plans to provide an additional income tax deduction of INR 1.5 Lakh on the interest paid on loans taken to purchase electric vehicles.
- **PLI:** The government has announced a Production Linked Incentive (PLI) scheme to boost domestic manufacturing and attract global companies to invest in the Indian market.
- **NTTM:** The Government also plans to set up a **National Technical Textiles Mission** (NTTM) to promote the use of technical textiles in various sectors, including the EV industry.
- **Manufacturing plants:** Setting up of battery manufacturing units in India to promote the use of electric vehicles.
- **Public transport:** The Government has also announced plans to promote the use of electric vehicles in the public transportation sector, by providing financial assistance to states for the purchase of electric buses.**Ex.** e-buses in Delhi.
- **Ensuring last-mile connectivity:** The government has also identified last-mile mobility as a key sector to drive the adoption of electric vehicles Ex., deployment of a fleet of over 5,000 vehicles in Chennai.
- **Promoting e-vehicles in government:** In an attempt to promote use of electric vehicles in the public sector, the government has plans to replace existing government vehicles with electric vehicles.
- **Phased Manufacturing Programme** (PMP): Indigenous manufacturing of electric vehicles,

- their assemblies/sub-assemblies, and parts/ sub-parts/inputs of the sub-assemblies to be promoted over time through a graded duty structure.
- **National Mission on Transformative Mobility and Storage:** Government aims to drive strategies for transformative mobility and Phased Manufacturing Programmes for electric vehicles, electric vehicle components and Batteries.

Emerging Battery Technologies

- **Lithium-ion battery technology** is causing a huge strain on global lithium reserves.
- Research on alternatives to lithium-ion battery technology is growing. With the demand for electric vehicles expected to grow at a **CAGR** of **49%**, one may expect **EV sales** to **cross 17million** by **2030.**
- Several Indian start-ups are engaged in emerging technology research and development to make ev battery more viable alternatives to **petrol, diesel** and **CNG.**
- A few of these include **battery intelligence software** to prolong **battery life, development of aluminium fuel cells** and **battery lifecycle** solutions which incorporates first life, **second life** and end of life extraction.

Maglev Trains/Bullet Trains

Maglev trains are the **high-speed trains** that use **magnetic levitation** from **powerful electromagnets** to **travel high speeds** with **less noise** and **vibration** than traditional trains. The driving movement for the maglev train is provided by the **magnetic field** that is created by **combining electrified coils** in the **guideway walls** and the **track**, which causes the **train to push forward.**

- It is a term generally used to describe a **high-speed train of speeds** above **250 kmph. Shinkansen high-speed trains** of **Japan** are colloquially called as bullet trains for their appearance and speed.

In **September 2017, Prime Minister Narendra Modi** and his **Japanese counterpart Shinzo Abe** laid the foundation stone of the **ambitious bullet train project** a **508 km long high-speed rail corridor**, connecting **Mumbai** with **Ahmedabad.**

Advantages of Bullet Trains

- An alternative mode of transport
- High-speed connectivity
- Economic growth
- Employment Opportunities
- Environment Friendly
- Time saving
- Urban expansion
- Migration Check
- Open new avenues

Concerns

- Cost Benefit Analysis
- **Objections have been raised by various departments** over the **economic viability** of the Shinkansen train, which could result in **losses** in the form of wasted **Floor Space Index** (FSI) and delayed loan repayment in the absence of proper frameworks.
- Safety Concerns
- High fares
- Land acquisition

Hyperloop

Hyperloop is an **ultra-high-speed ground transportation system** for **passenger** and **cargo** consisting of **sealed** and **partially evacuated tubes, connecting mobility hubs in large metropolitan areas** and **pressurized vehicles**, usually called **pods**, which can move at **very high speeds**, owing to **contactless levitation** and **propulsion systems** as well as to the **low aerodynamic drag.**

- The idea of using **low-pressure** or **vacuum tubes** as part of a transport system has a long heritage.

- The **Crystal Palace pneumatic railway** used **air pressure** to push a **wagon uphill** (and a vacuum to drag it back down) way back in **Victorian south London** in **1864**.
- Similar systems using **pneumatic tubes** to send mail and **packages** between buildings have been in use since the **late nineteenth century**, and can still be seen in **supermarkets** and **banks** to move money around today.
- One clear predecessor of the **Hyperloop** is the **vactrain concept** developed by **Robert Goddard** early in the **twentieth century**; Since then, many similar ideas have been proposed without much success.

However, it was entrepreneur **Elon Musk** who really reignited interest in the concept with his **Hyperloop Alpha paper** in **August 2013**, which set out how a modern system would work and how much it would cost.

- The basic idea of Hyperloop as envisioned by Musk is that the **passenger pods** or **capsules travel** through a **tube**, **either above** or **below ground**. To **reduce friction**, most but not all of the air is removed from the tubes by pumps.
- Hyperloop Technology consists of a **long vacuum tube**, and it has a **compartment like a capsule**, called pods. These pods run at **high speed** inside the vacuum tube. These tubes are **called loops**.

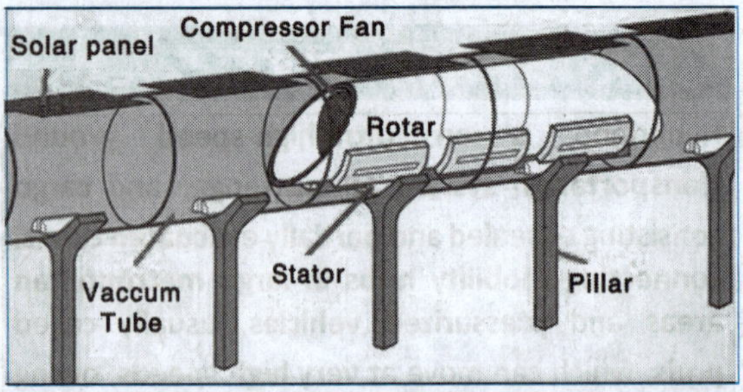

- It mainly uses two types of technology- **Magnetic levitation** and **Air pressure**. Because of this, there is **very less friction** between the **pods** and the **tube**. Due to this, its speed is so fast that it leaves the **maglev train** too far behind.
- Because in this technology transportation takes place in the loop itself, which means when passengers want to travel, they will travel through this loop. Hence this is named **hyperloop technology**.
- **Overcoming air resistance** is one of the biggest uses of energy in high speed travel. Airliners climb to high altitudes to travel through less dense air; in order to create a similar effect at ground level, Hyperloop encloses the capsules in a **reduced-pressure tube**, effectively allowing the trains to travel at airplane speeds while still on the ground.
- The Hyperloop capsules in Musk's model float above the tube's surface on a set of **28 air-bearing skis**, similar to the way that the puck floats just above the table on an air hockey game. One major difference is that it is the pod, not the track, that generates the air cushion in order to keep the tube as simple and cheap as possible. Other versions of Hyperloop use **magnetic levitation** rather than air skis to keep the passenger pods above the tracks.
- **Pods carrying passengers** travel through **tubes or tunnels** from which most of the air has been removed to reduce friction, allowing the pods to travel at up to **750 miles per hour**.
- Rather than using wheels like a train or car, the pods are designed to **float on air skis**, using the same basic idea as an air hockey table, or use **magnetic levitation** to **reduce friction**.

- Hyperloop technologies are in process to sign a **formal agreement** with Government of India for route which is been proposed between **Chennai** and **Bangalore**.
- Hyperloop tech signed an agreement with **Andhra Pradesh Government** to build India's first **Hyperloop project** connecting places of **Andhra Pradesh** that is **Amaravati to Vijayawada** in a 6-minute easy ride only.
- **Govt of Maharashtra** signed agreement with company in order to build hyperloop system between **Mumbai and Pune**.

- In **2020**, Government think-tank NITI Aayog has formed a high-level panel to explore the technological and commercial viability of the Virgin Hyperloop technology for ultrahigh speed travel in India. It aims to explore : technological, commercial, financial (viability) feasibility and (assess) safety standards and regulations to procure new technology.

Advantages of Hyperloop Technology

- Time Efficient
- A significant cost reduction in cost
- Climate-Neutral
- City Centre to City Centre
- Ultra-High Speeds
- Cost Effective

Concerns

- High speeds
- Collisions within the vacuum tubes
- Hyperloop pod damage
- Tunnel decompression
- Safety Concerns
- Absence of Regulatory Mechanism

Urban Air Mobility (UAM) - Heli Taxis

Heli Taxi/ Air Taxi is small or medium-sized commercial airplane that carries passengers, and often mail, to places not regularly served by scheduled airlines.

- One possible solution is the **extension** of **urban transportation system** with an **Urban Air Mobility** (UAM) concept, using fully **electric vertical takeoff and landing** (eVTOL) **vehicles** and **air taxi service** (ATS) for transporting passengers within the city.
- Air taxi services can offer **faster, reliable, flexible** and **energy-efficient, point-to-point transportation**, quieter than any modern helicopter.

- From **speeding** up the **response time** for **paramedics, police** and **first-responders** in **time-critical operations** to creating an avenue to help victims of **hurricanes, flood** and **fire** where land entries and exits are often cut off, this technology will help make a difference in many situations where every second wasted in traffic jams counts.

India's first helicopter shuttle service (HeliTaxi) was launched by **Thumby Aviation** in **Bengaluru**, in **2018**, between **Electronic City** and **Kempegowda International Airport** in **Bengaluru Karnataka** to provide last-mile connectivity.

- **India's first air taxi service** was launched from **Chandigarh**, operated by the **Air Taxi Aviation Company**, from **Chandigarh** for **Hisar** in **Haryana**, covering a 45-minute journey at a cost of Rs 1,755.
- As per reports in **2023**, **Kerala Tourism** is planning to introduce heli-tourism to attract premium tourists. Connecting Kochi with popular tourist destinations like **Thekkady, Munnar** and **Kumarakom**.

Advantages

- Alternative mode of transport
- Best suited for Fast travelling in urban areas where time is currency.
- Decongestion of Road
- Suitable for metropolis with huge daily commuters.
- Check on vehicular pollution and Reduced pollutant emissions.

Concerns and Challenges

- **High input** and **infrastructural costs.**
- **Limited operability** as the existing infrastructure mainly focuses on metropolitan cities.
- **High fares** and **affordability**
- **Noise Pollution** by the vehicles when they take off and land and while they are in flight especially during night hours.
- **Visual pollution** as a potential nuisance, which may hamper public acceptance of UAM and is, therefore, a risk to its widespread rollout.
- **Job losses** as some traditional jobs like taxis and cabs may become obsolete.
- **Environmental impact** of UAM may be almost zero on a local emissions level for battery electric vehicles, but the required electricity still has to be generated, and the vehicle components have to be manufactured, assembled, and eventually disposed of.
- **Privacy and security Concerns** as UAM aircraft like air taxis and drones may fly above or close to places of residence.
- Lack of trained personnels
- Lack of availability of aviation fuels.

GPS Based Toll System

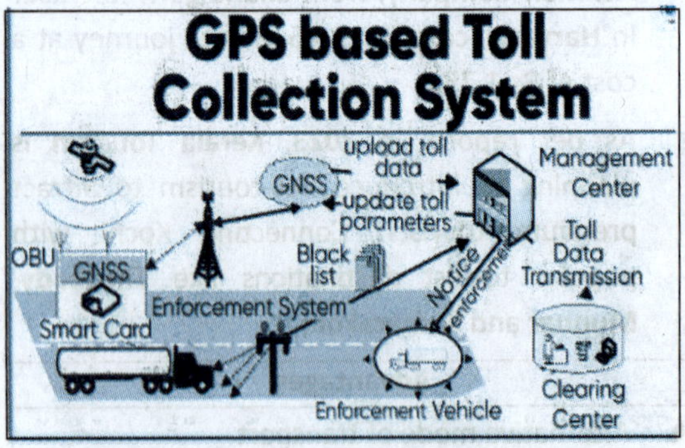

- India is set to revolutionise its highway toll collection system by introducing a GPS-based tolling mechanism starting May 1, 2025. This new system aims to replace the existing FASTag method, enhancing efficiency, reducing congestion, and ensuring more accurate toll charges for commuters. FASTag system implemented in 2016 uses RFID technology to enable electronic toll payments.
- However, issues including persistent lines at busy toll booths, system problems, and tag misuse have made a more sophisticated solution necessary. GPS-based toll collection system employs Global Navigation Satellite System (GNSS) technology to monitor vehicles and calculate toll fees based on the actual distance traveled on national highways.
- It ensures that drivers pay only for the distance they cover, promoting fairness and transparency in toll charges. Vehicles will be outfitted with On-Board Units (OBUs) that track their movements on roadways using GNSS technology. Based on the distance driven, the system will determine the toll as a car drives, after which the appropriate payment is automatically paid out of the driver's bank account or connected digital wallet.
- National Highways Authority of India (NHAI) will be responsible for rolling out the new toll collection system. In the initial phase, it will be implemented for commercial vehicles like trucks and buses, with private vehicles set to be included in later stages. This step-by-step rollout is designed to address any technical issues early on and ensure a seamless transition for all motorists.

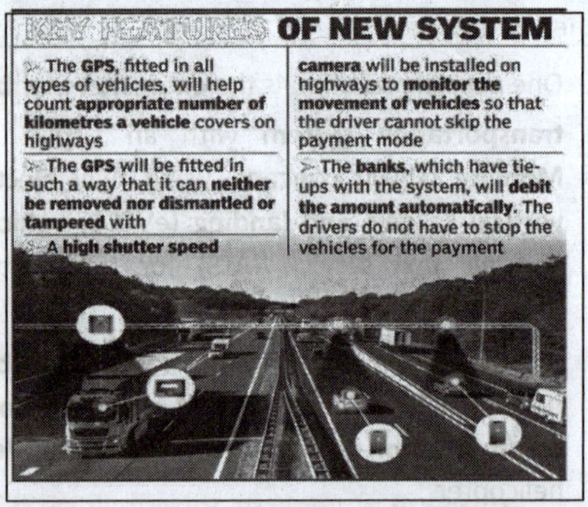

Advantages of GPS Based Toll System -

- **Distance-based charging:** Drivers are charged precisely for the distance they travel, ensuring equitable toll fees.
- **Reduced congestion:** Eliminating toll plazas minimizes traffic bottlenecks, leading to smoother highway travel.
- **Enhanced transparency:** Real-time tracking and automated deductions reduce the potential for human error and corruption.
- **Environmental impact:** Smoother traffic flow contributes to lower vehicle emissions, supporting environmental sustainability. Security Concerns : Indian Regional Navigation Satellite System (IRNSS), referred to as NavIC, is India's own satellite navigation system that the GNSS-based system will use to make sure data stays inside national borders. This strategy seeks to improve the accuracy of the tolling system while safeguarding the privacy of citizens.

PYQ (2013 – 2024)

Q. What is an FRP composite material? How are they manufactured? Discuss their application in the aviation and automobile industries.

(2013)

Q. To what factors can the recent dramatic fall in equipment costs and tariff of solar energy be attributed? What implications does the trend have for the thermal power producers and the related industry? (2015)

Q. Discuss several ways in which microorganisms can help in meeting the current fuel shortage.

(2023)

Q. The adoption of electric vehicles is rapidly growing worldwide. How do electric vehicles contribute to reducing carbon emissions and what are the key benefits they offer compared to traditional combustion engine vehicles?

(2023)

Q. Which one of the following is the exhaust pipe emission from Fuel Cell Electric Vehicles, powered by hydrogen? (UPSC Pre 2024)

(a) Hydrogen peroxide
(b) Hydronium
(c) Oxygen
(d) Water vapour

Q. Recently, the term "pumped-storage hydropower" is actually and appropriately discussed in the context of which one of the following? (2024)

(a) Irrigation of terraced crop fields
(b) Lift irrigation of cereal crops
(c) Long duration energy storage
(d) Rainwater harvesting system

Q What do you understand by run of the river hydroelectricity project? How is it different from any other hydroelectricity project?

(UPSC Mains 2013)

Q Give an account of the current status and the targets to be achieved pertaining to renewable energy sources in the country.

(UPSC Mains 2016)

Q Describe the benefits of deriving electric energy from sunlight in contrast to the conventional energy generation. What are the initiatives offered by our Government for this purpose?

(UPSC Mains 2020)

Q Each year a large amount of plant material, cellulose, is deposited on the surface of Planet Earth. What are the natural processes this cellulose undergoes before yielding carbon dioxide, water and other end products?

(UPSC Mains 2022)

Q What is the technology being employed for electronic toll collection on highways. What are its advantages and limitations? What are the proposed changes that will make this process seamless? Would this transition carry any potential hazard? (UPSC Mains 2024)

UNIT 2

MODERN ELECTRONICS AND SEMICONDUCTORS

- *Human civilization since it's early evolutionary phases has been dependent on **external sources of energy** for various **domestic needs**. Historically, **Energy** was **domesticated** in **form of fire** to **generate heat** and **light** for various **domestic usages. Electric current** is another form of energy that changed the course of human civilization.*
- *From hypothesis of **Anu/parmanu** in **Vaisheshik Darshan** by **Sage Kanad** to the **discovery of charged particles, electric current/ electricity** has witnessed various phases of **technological innovations**.*
- *In **600 BC**, a **Greek** named **Thales** discovered that **amber** when rubbed with **silk**, attracted feathers and other light object, called **static electricity, William Gilbert**, (a scientist and physician to Queen Elizabeth I) in **1600AD coined** the **term electricity**. He was the first to recognise that there was a connection between **magnetism** and **electricity**.*
- *In **1700s, machines** to **produce static electricity** were first introduced. **Francis Hauksbee** invented **neon light**. **Benjamin Franklin**, a famous U.S. politician in **1752** proved that **lightning** is a **form of electricity** by **flying a kite** with a **metal tip** into a **thunderstorm**.*
- ***Alessandro Volta** in **1800** created the very **first simple battery** using **pure silver** and **zinc discs**, placed between muslin dampened with a salt solution. During the same year, **Sir Humphry Davy** discovered electrolysis.*
- *In **1821, Michael Faraday** discovered that when a magnet is moved inside the coil of a copper wire, a tiny **electric current** flows through the **wire**, a discovery that led to the **invention of electric motors**. In the same year, **Thomas Johann Seebeck** discovered **thermo-electricity**.*
- *In **1830, Joseph Henry** discovered the principles of the dynamo (an electrical generator).*
- *In **1870, Thomas Edison** built a **DC** (direct current) **electric generator**. which later, he provided all of **New York's electricity**.*
- *In **1880's Nikola Tesla** developed an **AC** (alternating current) motor and a system of **AC power generation**. In **1896, Nikola Tesla's hydroelectric power generators** at Niagara Falls came into operation.*
- *In **1905, Albert Einstein** under his **Photoelectric Effect** (for which he won the Nobel Prize in Physics) demonstrated that **light energy** (Photon) could be used to **produce electricity**.*
- *Evolution of modern **electronic technology** has been based on the **fabrication of semiconductors** with the subsequent development of **integrated circuits**.*
- ***Semiconductors** are the building blocks of **high-tech, modern electrical systems** and will be the basis for more **advanced technological creations. Integrated circuits** have enabled **advanced computing, communication, transportation** and **medical diagnostics**, and also served as the foundation for **aerospace development**.*
- *Currently **USA, China** and **Taiwan** hold **monopolies** in the **semiconductor industry**. India is largely dependent on imports for it. However, the cabinet approved a comprehensive program of **$10 billion** to build India's stance as the **global hub** for **semiconductors** in the future. The program aims to support a sustainable semiconductor and display fab ecosystem in India.*

Development of Modern Electronics : From Vacuum Tubes to Integrated Circuits

Vacuum Tubes

- Vacuum tube also called **electron tube** or **valve** is an **electronic device** that controls the **flow of electrons** in a **vacuum**.

Vacuum Tubes work on the **principle of thermionic emission :** When a metal is heated, the thermal energy knocks some electrons loose.

- In **1904, English physicist John Ambrose Fleming** took advantage of this effect to create the **first vacuum tube** device, which he called an **Oscillation valve**. His invention, known as the valve, also referred to as a **vacuum tube** or **thermionic valve**, marked a significant advancement in **electrical engineering**.

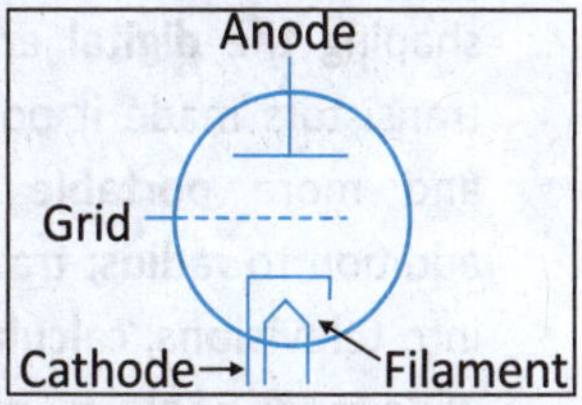

- Fleming's device consisted of **two electrodes**, a **cathode** and an **anode**, placed on either end of an **encapsulated glass tube**. When the cathode was heated, it gives off **electrons** via **thermionic emission**. Then, by applying a **positive voltage** to the **anode** (also called the plate), these electrons are attracted to the plate and can flow across the gap. By removing the air from the tube to create a vacuum, the electrons have a clear path from the cathode to the anode, and a current is created.
- This type of vacuum tube, consisting of only two electrodes, is called a **diode**. The term diode is still used today to refer to an electrical component that only allows an **electric current** to **flow in one direction**. **Diodes** are commonly used for **rectification**, that is, converting from an **Alternating Current** (AC) to a **Direct Current** (DC).
- In **1906, American inventor Lee de Forest** added a **third electrode** to the mix, creating the first **triode tube**. This third electrode, called the **control grid**, enabled the vacuum tube to be used not just as a **rectifier**, but as an **amplifier of electrical signals**. This innovation allowed for the **amplification of electrical signals**, making the **triode the first electronic amplifier**.
- The **triode's ability to amplify weak electrical signals** revolutionized the world of **telecommunications**, especially in the development of **radios** and **telephones**; opening up new horizons for **long-distance communication** and paved the way for modern **signal processing**.
- **Vacuum tubes** help **amplify electrical signals**, and when used in **computers** they provide **extremely fast switching speeds** with **short delays leading** to **faster computing performance overall**; making them particularly useful for certain applications such as high-frequency radio or **telecommunications technology** and **video circuitry** where speed is essential like **streaming**.
- Further enhancements of vacuum tubes placed an **additional grid** (called the screen grid) and yet another (called the suppressor grid) even closer to the **anode**, creating a type of vacuum tube called a **tetrode** and a **pentode**, respectively. These extra grids solve some stability problems and address other limitations with the triode design, but the function remains largely the same.
- Vacuum tubes were used in **television**, **radios**, **radar**, **electronic computers** and **amplifiers**.

During World War II, vacuum tubes played a vital role in military applications. Their robustness, reliability, and ability to handle high-power signals made them indispensable in various military technologies.

- Vacuum tubes were extensively used in **radar systems**, enabling the **detection** and **tracking** of enemy aircraft and vessels. They also formed an integral part of **code-breaking machines**, aiding in deciphering encrypted communications and gaining critical intelligence.

Electronic Numerical Integrator and Computer (ENIAC), built during the **1940s**, is often considered the **world's first general-purpose electronic digital computer**. It was a massive machine that relied heavily on **vacuum tubes** for its operation.

- **Limitation :** However owing to limitations of Vacuum tubes like their **bulky size, high voltage requirement** and **consumption of power, heat generation**, along with a **higher failure rate** led to the development of more efficient **Transistors.**
- **Significance :** Vacuum tubes are still used in high power **RF transmitters**, as they can **generate more power** than modern semiconductor equivalents. For this reason, Vacuum tubes are still found in **particle accelerators, MRI scanners, microwave ovens** and **guitar amplifiers.**

The subsequent invention of the transistor in **1947**, followed by the development of **integrated circuits** in the late **1950s** and early **1960s**, revolutionized the world of electronics, paving the way for the **digital revolution** and the rise of **modern computing** as we know it today.

Transistors

- Transistor is a three-terminal semiconductor device that amplifies the electronic signals such as radio and television signals.

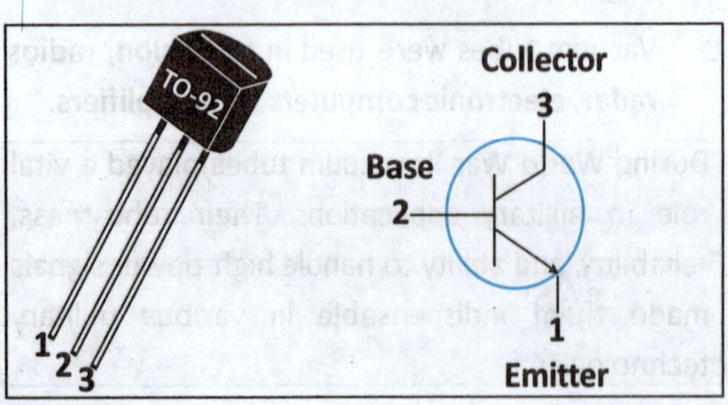

Transistor was successfully demonstrated on **December 23, 1947** at **Bell Laboratories, New Jersey** by **John Bardeen, William Shockley** and **Walter Brattain.**

- Their breakthrough was based on the concept of the **point-contact transistor**, which involved sandwiching a thin **semiconductor material,** typically **germanium** or **silicon**, between two **metal contacts.** By applying a **voltage** to the **metal contacts**, they found that the **flow of current through** the semiconductor layer could be **controlled**, effectively acting as an **amplifier** or **switch.**
- This fundamental discovery paved the way for the **miniaturization of electronic components, transforming** the **electronics industry** and shaping the **digital era.** The compact size of transistors made it possible to **create smaller** and more **portable electronic devices.** In addition to **radios, transistors** found their way into **televisions, calculators, telephones**, and a wide range of **electronic equipments.**
- The **transistor's reliability** made **electronic devices** more **durable** and **reduced maintenance costs**, further boosting their widespread adoption.
- Transistors are much more **durable**, much **smaller** and **require much less voltage** than tubes in order to function (transistors don't have a filament that needs heating). However Transistors came with their own limitations like less **tolerant of overloads** and **voltage spike** and **maintenance issues.**
- As the demand for smaller, faster, and more powerful electronic devices increased, researchers sought ways to pack more transistors into a **single chip,** leading to the development of the **Integrated Circuit** (IC).

Integrated Circuits (IC)

- In **1958, Jack Kilby**, working at **Texas Instruments** and **Robert Noyce,** co-founder of **Fairchild**

Semiconductor and later **Intel**, independently invented the IC. **Kilby's approach** involved **fabricating several transistors** and other components on a **single piece of germanium**, while **Noyce's** approach used **silicon**.

An **integrated circuit** (ICs) is an **electronic device** comprising **numerous functional elements** such as **transistors, resistors, condensers** etc. on a piece of **silicon semiconductor substrate**, and is sealed inside a package with multiple terminals.

- At present, **IC critical dimensions** (or smallest dimensions of IC elements) are in the order of **10 nanometers** (nm: 10^{-9}m), which is extremely small. The current IC is highly integrated and miniaturized, about **1/55000** of the size and **3 billionths of the area** of the transistor radio. Owing to their high integration, ICs with various functions embedded have dramatically enhanced the performance of electronics.
- In the **manufacturing of ICs**, many ICs are made on a **silicon wafer** and then cut (diced)

into numerous IC chips (dies). The IC chips are sealed inside packages because they are too small to be electrically bonded to a printed circuit board, and also because IC chips would get broken if left unprotected.

Depending on the number of components, ICs are classified as **LSI** (large-scale integration), **VLSI** (very large scale integration) and **ULSI** (ultra large scale integration).

- In 1967, **Texas Instruments** developed the **electronic desktop calculator** (the calculator) using IC. **IC integration** advanced even further, and the **large-scale integrated circuit** (LSI) was developed.
- The IC revolutionized electronics by enabling the **mass production of transistors** and other **electronic components** on a single chip; drastically **reduced the size** and **cost of**

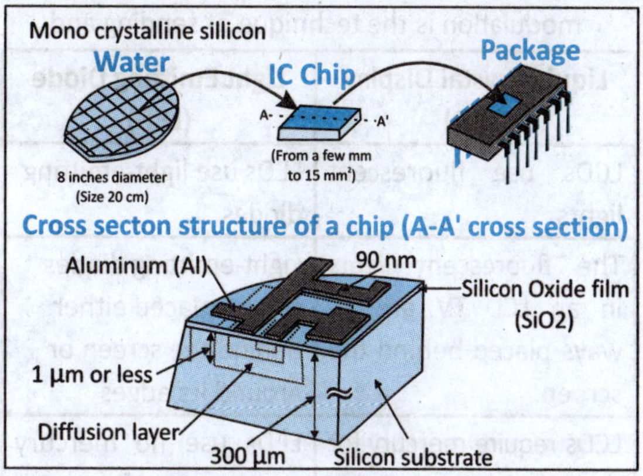

electronic devices, making them **accessible** to a broader audience.

- IC's impact was profound, leading to the creation of **microprocessors**, which are **complex integrated circuits** containing millions of transistors. The microprocessor revolutionized computing, giving rise to **personal computers** and other sophisticated **electronic devices.**
- One of the remarkable achievements of ICs was the development of 3D ICs, which involves **stacking multiple layers of transistors** and other components on top of each other, enabling more functionality in a smaller space leading to improved speed, reduced power consumption, and enhanced overall performance of electronic devices.

Significance : Integrated circuits are integral to nearly all modern electronic devices, powering everything from **smartphones** to **advanced medical equipment**, and continue to drive innovation across various industries.

Emerging Technologies

Liquid Crystal Display (LCD) :

- It is a type of flat-panel display technology that uses diodes, small cells and ionised gases for the production of images. LCD works on the principle of blocking light. It also works on the modulating property of light where light modulation is the technique of sending and

Liquid Crystal Display (LCD)	Light Emitting Diode (LED)
LCDs use fluorescent lights.	LEDs use light-emitting diodes
The fluorescent lights in an LCD TV are always placed behind the screen.	Light-emitting diodes can be placed either behind the screen or around its edges
LCDs require mercury for their products causing harm to the environment	LEDs use no mercury and are therefore environmentally friendly
LCD screen size comes in the range of 13-57 inches.	LED TVs can be up to 90 inches and they are much slimmer than LCD.
LCD TVs use the cold cathode fluorescent lamps (CCFL) for backlighting. The picture quality of LCD TV is noticeable in scenes with high contrast, as the dark portions of the picture may appear too bright or washed out.	LED TVs to use energy-efficient light-emitting diodes for backlighting and can provide a clearer, better picture, a thinner panel, and lesser heat dissipation than a customary LCD TV.
LCD TVs are the most efficient type of TVs are relatively cheaper, can save as much as 30-70% more electricity receiving the signal through the light.	LED TVs are slightly costlier than LCDs, but consume very little energy so there is almost a 50% reduction in power consumption.

- LCD technology is used in laptops, digital clocks, watches, digital cameras, watches, electronic games, electronic billboards, computer monitors, flat panel TVs and video projection systems.

There are three types of LCD TVs

- Flat-screen LCDs
- Front projection LCDs
- Rear projection LCDs

Light Emitting Diode (LED)

- They are usually found in smartphones, televisions, computer monitors and instrument panels and use a liquid crystal display panel to control where the light is displayed on your screen.
- LED Technology is used in Digital watches, Digital computers, Cell phones, Bulbs and tubes, Automotive heat lamps, Camera flashes, Calculators, Aviation lighting, Microprocessors, Burglar alarms systems, Traffic signals, Multiplexers

There are 3 types of LEDs based on their backlighting methods:

- Edge-LEDs
- Dynamic RGB LEDs
- Full-array LEDs

- LED/ Light Emitting Diode : A basic display technology using backlight to illuminate pixels.
- OLED/ Organic Light Emitting Diode : Each pixel emits its own light, resulting in deep blacks and high contrast
- QLED / Quantum Dot LED : Atype of LED display that uses quantum dots to enhance color accuracy and brightness, offering vibrant colors, particularly in bright environments

Neuromorphic Computing

- Neuromorphic computing is a cutting-edge area of research that draws inspiration from the **human brain's neural architecture.**

Significance : In neuromorphic ICs, the design emulates the structure and functionality of neurons and synapses, enabling more efficient image and speech recognition, among other tasks.

Silicon Photonics

- **Silicon photonics** is a groundbreaking technology that combines the **capabilities** of **silicon-based electronics** with the speed and bandwidth of **optical communication**. By **integrating optical components**, such as lasers and photodetectors, with electronic circuits on a **single chip, silicon photonics** revolutionizes data center **interconnects** and **autonomous vehicles**.

One of the key advantages of silicon photonics is its potential for high-speed data transfer over long distances with minimal signal loss. In autonomous vehicles, silicon photonics can enable advanced LiDAR systems, allowing for real-time, high-resolution 3D imaging to improve vehicle safety and navigation.

Quantum ICs

- Quantum ICs harness the principles of quantum mechanics to perform tasks that classical computers struggle with. These quantum integrated circuits use qubits - the basic units of quantum information, to process and store data in quantum states.

Significance : Quantum ICs offer extraordinary computational capabilities, especially in cryptography, drug discovery, and optimization problems. They can execute complex cryptographic algorithms with unparalleled security, making them promising for secure communications and data protection.

Semiconductors

- A semiconductor is a material that has **conductivity properties** between a **conductor**, which has the ability to **conduct electricity** and a **non-conductor** or an **insulator**, which doesn't allow electrical charges to flow through it.
- Under certain conditions, semiconductors have the **ability to act either as a conductor or an insulator.**
- Semiconductors can be **pure elements** such as the most commonly used **silicon** or **compounds** such as **gallium arsenide**.
- **Holes** and **electrons** are the **types of charge carriers** accountable for the **flow of current** in semiconductors.

Holes (valence electrons) are the **positively charged electric charge carrier**, whereas Electrons are the **negatively charged particles**. Both electrons and holes are **equal in magnitude** but **opposite in polarity**.

- In a semiconductor, the **mobility of electrons** is **higher** than that of the **holes**, mainly because of their different band structures and scattering mechanisms.
- **Electrons** travel in the **conduction band**, whereas **holes travel** in the **valence band**.
- The elevation of electrons from their **inner shells** to **higher shells** results in the **creation of holes** in **semiconductors**. Since the holes experience **stronger atomic force** by the nucleus than electrons, holes have lower mobility.
- **Valence Band :** The energy band involving the energy levels of **valence electrons**. It is the **highest occupied energy band**. When compared with insulators, the band gap in semiconductors is smaller. It allows the electrons in the valence band to jump into the conduction band on receiving any external energy.
- **Conduction Band :** It is the **lowest, unoccupied band** that includes the **energy levels** of **positive** (holes) or **negative** (free electrons) charge carriers. It has **conducting electrons** resulting in the **flow of current**. The conduction band possess a **high energy level** and is generally empty. The conduction band in semiconductors accepts the electrons from the valence band.

- **Fermi level :** Present between the **valence** and **conduction bands**. It is the **highest occupied molecular orbital** at **absolute zero**. The charge carriers in this state have their own quantum states and generally do not interact with each other. When the **temperature rises** above **absolute zero**, these charge carriers begin to occupy states above the **Fermi level**.
- Semiconductors can **conduct electricity** under **preferable conditions** or **circumstances** through **doping**. This unique property makes it an excellent material to conduct electricity in a controlled manner as required.
- Unlike conductors, the charge carriers in semiconductors arise only because of **external energy** (thermal agitation). It causes a certain number of valence electrons to cross the **energy gap** and jump into the **conduction band**, leaving an equal amount of **unoccupied energy states**, i.e., **holes**. The conduction due to electrons and holes is equally important.

Types of Semiconductors

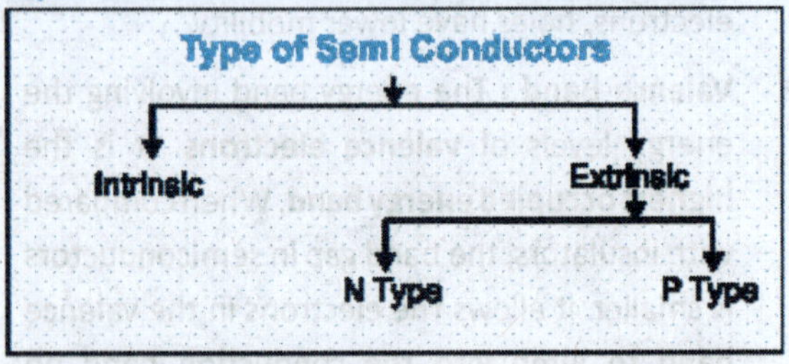

Intrinsic Semiconductors

- An intrinsic type of semiconductor material is made to be very pure chemically. It is made up of only a single type of element.

> **Germanium** (Ge) and **Silicon** (Si) are the most common types of **intrinsic semiconductor elements**, **four valence electrons** (tetravalent). They are bound to the atom by a covalent bond at absolute zero temperature.

Extrinsic Semiconductor

- The conductivity of semiconductors can be greatly improved by introducing a small number of suitable **replacement atoms** called **impurities**. The process of **adding impurity atoms** to the pure semiconductor is called **Doping**. Usually, only **1 atom** in $\mathbf{10^7}$ is replaced by a **dopant atom** in the **doped semiconductor**.
- **N-Type Semiconductor –** Conduction mainly due to **electrons**.
  - When a pure semiconductor (silicon or germanium) is doped by **pentavalent impurity** (P, As, Sb, Bi), then four electrons out of five valence electrons bond with the four electrons of **Ge** or **Si**.
  - The **fifth electron** of the dopant is set free. Thus, the impurity atom donates a **free electron** for **conduction** in the **lattice** and is called a donor.
  - Since the **number of free electrons** increases with the **addition of an impurity**, the negative charge carriers increase. Hence, it is called an **n-type semiconductor**.
- **P-Type Semiconductor -** Conduction mainly due to **holes**.
  - When a pure semiconductor is doped with a **trivalent impurity** (B, Al, In, Ga), then the **three valence electrons** of the impurity bond with three of the four valence electrons of the semiconductor.
  - This leaves an **absence of electron** (hole) in the impurity. These impurity atoms which are ready to **accept bonded electrons** are called **Acceptors**.
  - With an increase in the **number of impurities**, **holes** (the positive charge carriers) are increased. Hence, it is called a p-type semiconductor.

Important Facts about Semiconductors

- **Resistivity:** 10^{-5} to 10^{6} Ωm
- **Conductivity:** 10^{5} to 10^{-6} mho/m
- **Temperature coefficient of resistance:** Negative
- **Current flow:** Due to electrons and holes

- The **resistivity of semiconductors decreases** with **temperature** because the number of charge carriers increases rapidly with an increase in temperature.
- Semiconductors act like **insulators** at **zero Kelvin**. On increasing the temperature, they work as **conductors.**
- Due to their exceptional electrical properties, semiconductors can be modified by doping to make semiconductor devices suitable for energy conversion, switches and amplifiers.

Advantages of Semiconductors

- Lesser power losses.
- Smaller in size and possess less weight, hence highly portable.
- Resistivity is higher than conductors but lesser than insulators.
- Resistance of semiconductor materials decreases with an increase in temperature and vice-versa.
- Requires less input power.
- Semiconductor devices are shockproof.
- Have a longer lifespan.
- Noise-free while operating.

Uses and Applications of Semiconductors

Temperature sensors are made with semiconductor devices.

Used in **3D printing machines.**

Used in **microchips** and **self-driving cars.**

Used in **calculators, solar plates, computers** and other **electronic devices.**

- The most used semiconductor material is **silicon,** which is widely used in producing **integrated circuits** (ICs), also known as **microchips.** These chips contain **multiple transistors**, which act as **switches** that allow the flow of electricity to be controlled, enabling complex electronic functions.
- Other common semiconductor materials include **germanium**, **gallium arsenide** and **indium phosphide.** These materials have unique properties that make them suitable for specific applications, such as **high-speed communication systems** or **solar cells.**
- **Physical** and **chemical properties** of semiconductors make them capable of **designing technological wonders** like **microchips, transistors, LEDs, solar cells,** etc.
- The microprocessor used for controlling the operation of **space vehicles, trains, robots,** etc., which are made up of **transistors** and other controlling devices, which are manufactured by **semiconductor materials.**
- **Transistors** and **MOSFET** used as a switch in electrical circuits are manufactured using semiconductors.

The **MOSFET** (metal-oxide-semiconductor field-effect transistor) is the most common semiconductor device in the world. A huge amount of tiny MOSFETs are used in the **creation of microchips**. They are made up of a set of **electronic circuits** on a **small, flat piece of silicon,** with many transistors that can turn a current on or off.

- The two main types of **microchips** are the **logic chip** and the **memory chip. Logic chips process information** to help electronic devices complete their tasks. One of the most widely known and commonly used logic chips is the **CPU** or **central processing unit**.

- **Memory chips**, on the other hand, store information and come in two types – **NAND Flash**, and **working memory** chips known as **DRAM**.
- The main application of semiconductors is in the **creation of semiconductor devices** which are essential for a multitude of **electronic products.**
- Semiconductor devices **conduct electric currents** in the **solid state**, instead of as **free electrons** across a **vacuum**, and are the **successor to vacuum tubes** in almost all applications.
- **Microprocessors** are **ICs** that contain a **CPU**, memory, and other circuits and are the **brain** of many **electronic devices** such as **computers, smartphones** and **home appliances.**
- **Solar cells** convert **sunlight** into **electricity** and are made of semiconductor materials like **silicon.**
- **LED lights** are **semiconductor devices** that **emit light** when a current is applied and are used in **lighting applications.**

> **Microchips :** The semiconductor silicon serves as the base material for the microchip, also known as an **integrated circuit** or **monolithic integrated circuit**, a component used in almost every modern electronic device.

Emerging uses of Semiconductor Technology

- **Computing:** The semiconductor industry produces **microprocessors** and **memory chips,** which are the primary components in **computers, servers** and **data centers.** These devices are used in various industries, from **finance** and **healthcare** to **manufacturing** and **logistics.**
- **Communications:** Semiconductors are used to produce cell phones, satellite systems, and other communication devices. They are also used to create wireless communication systems, network equipment, and other hardware for data transmission.
- **Energy:** Semiconductors are used in the production of solar cells and other renewable energy systems. Power management applications also use semiconductors, including voltage regulators and power supplies.
- **Automotive:** Automotive electronics also use semiconductors, including engine control units, sensors, and safety systems. They are also used in electric vehicles and autonomous vehicles.
- **Healthcare:** Medical imaging, monitoring, and diagnostic equipment, as well as medical implants and devices, use semiconductors.
- **Consumer electronics:** Mobile phones, laptops, games consoles, microwaves and refrigerators all operate with the use of semiconductor components such as integrated chips, diodes and transistors.
- **Embedded systems:** Embedded systems are small computers that form part of a larger machine. They can control the device and allow user interaction. Embedded systems that we commonly use include central heating systems, digital watches, GPS systems, fitness trackers, televisions and engine management systems in vehicles.
- **Thermal conductivity:** Some semiconductors have high thermal conductivity, so can be used as a cooling agent in certain thermoelectric applications.
- **Lighting and LED displays:** Some semiconductors, usually those available in liquid or amorphous form as a thin-coated film, can produce light and are used in LEDs and OLEDs.
- **Solar cells:** Silicon is also the most commonly used semiconductor in the production of solar panel cells.
- **Temperature sensors** used in **air conditioners** are made with semiconductors.
- **Rice cookers cook rice** perfectly because semi-conductors control the temperature precisely.

- **CPUs** that operate personal computers are also made with semiconductors.
- **Digital consumer products** in everyday life such as mobile phones / smartphones, digital cameras, televisions, washing machines, refrigerators and use semiconductors.
- In addition to consumer electronics, semiconductors play a central role in the **operation of bank ATMs, trains, the internet, communications** and other parts of **social infrastructure**, such as the **medical network** used for the care of elderly, among other things.
- **Efficient logistics systems** help **save energy** and **promote the preservation** of the **global environment**. The number of car-mounted semiconductor devices has been increasing steadily. There are many types of **car-mounted semiconductors**. Particularly for future **ADAS** (Advanced Driver Assistance Systems), more semiconductors are expected to be used.
- The **rapid development of smartphones** along with computers and other electronics has forced a significant downscaling in the physical size of devices.

Graphene and related **two-dimensional** (2-D) **materials**, for example, have great potential to overcome the **limitations of silicon technology**.

The **integration of 2-D materials** with **silicon technology** in **computational systems** can reduce the **challenges of doping, contact resistance** and **dielectrics/encapsulation**. In the realm of **non computational applications**, these materials can be integrated into **future cameras, low-power optical data communications** and gas sensors and biosensors.

- **Compound semiconductors** can operate at **higher frequencies** and **higher temperatures** and also emit and **detect light** more efficiently. As such, they have **great potential value** for applications involving **power electronics, radio-frequency communications** such as **Wi-Fi**, and **photonics** such as **solar cells**.
- Progress in **Artificial Intelligence** (AI) is creating new demand for semiconductors and thus new industry growth and innovation.
- The development of **fifth-generation** (5G) **wireless cellular technology**, for example, portends new applications for semiconductors within the communications industry. Rapidly developing demands for **video game consoles** and **televisions** with **high-quality video streaming** will also create more demand for semiconductors.

Indian Semiconductor Market: Estimated approximately $38 billion in 2023, with projections indicating growth to $109 billion by 2030. India's semiconductor consumption market is expected to grow at a strong compound annual growth rate (CAGR) of 13% through to 2030.

Indian Semiconductor Mission (ISM)

- **India Semiconductor Mission (ISM) (2021):** A ₹76,000 crore incentive scheme aimed at:
  - Setting up semiconductor fabrication units (fabs) in India.
  - Encouraging global semiconductor firms to invest in India.
  - Developing design-linked incentive (DLI) schemes to support local start-ups.
  - Production-Linked Incentive (PLI) Scheme for Electronics Manufacturing
- A comprehensive program designed to develop a sustainable semiconductor and display ecosystem in India. It offers financial incentives and infrastructure support to encourage investments in semiconductor fabrication (fabs), display fabs, and related ventures.

Design Linked Incentive (DLI) Scheme -

- Under the DLI Scheme, the government provides financial incentives and design infrastructure support across various stages of semiconductor design development and deployment, including Integrated Circuits (ICs), Chipsets, System on Chips (SoCs), Systems, and IP Cores. The scheme aims to nurture at least 20 domestic companies involved in semiconductor design and facilitate the growth of the semiconductor design industry in India over a five-year period.

Modified Scheme for Setting Up Semiconductor Fabs in India -

- This scheme extends fiscal support of up to 50% of the project cost on a pari-passu basis to approved applicants establishing semiconductor fabrication units in India. The objective is to attract large-scale investments for setting up semiconductor wafer fabrication facilities, thereby strengthening the semiconductor manufacturing ecosystem in the country.

Production Linked Incentive (PLI) Scheme for Large Scale Electronics Manufacturing -

- To boost domestic manufacturing and attract investment in the electronics value chain, including semiconductor packaging, the PLI Scheme offers incentives ranging from 3% to 6% on incremental sales of goods manufactured in India. This scheme aims to enhance India's manufacturing capabilities and promote the production of electronic components and semiconductors.
- ISM has been setup as an **Independent Business Division** within **Digital India Corporation**, with the **administrative** and **financial powers** tasked with the responsibility of catalysing the **India Semiconductor ecosystem in manufacturing, packaging** and **design**.

Objectives of India Semiconductor Mission

- Formulate a **comprehensive long-term strategy** for developing **sustainable semiconductors** and **display manufacturing facilities** and **semiconductor design eco-system** in the country in consultation with the Government ministries / departments / agencies, industry, and academia.
- Facilitate the adoption of **secure microelectronics** and **developing trusted semiconductor supply chain**, including raw materials, specialty **chemicals, gases** and **manufacturing equipment.**
- Enable a multi-fold growth of **Indian semiconductor design industry** by providing requisite support in the form of **Electronic Design Automation** (EDA) **tools,** foundry services and other **suitable mechanisms** for early-stage startups.
- Promote and facilitate indigenous **Intellectual Property** (IP) generation.
- Encourage, enable and incentivize **Transfer of Technologies** (ToT).
- Establish suitable mechanisms to harness economies of scale in Indian semiconductor and display industry.
- Enable **cutting-edge research** in semiconductors and **display industry** including evolutionary and revolutionary technologies through grants, global collaborations and other mechanisms in academia / research institutions, industry, and through establishing **Centres of Excellence** (CoEs).
- Enable **collaborations and partnership programs** with **national** and **international agencies, industries** and **institutions** for **catalyzing collaborative research, commercialization** and **skill development.**

Semiconductor Indian Programme :

- Government has approved the Semicon India programme with a total outlay of Rs. 76,000 crore for the development of semiconductor and display manufacturing ecosystem in the country.

- The modified programme aims to provide **financial support** to companies investing in semiconductors, display manufacturing and design ecosystem to pave the way for India's growing presence in the global electronics value chains.

Following 4 schemes have been introduced under Semicon India programme :

- **Modified Scheme for setting up of Semiconductor Fabs in India :** For attracting **large investments** for setting up **semiconductor wafer fabrication facilities** in the country to strengthen the **electronics manufacturing** ecosystem and help establish a trusted value chain. The Scheme extends a fiscal support of 50% of the project cost on pari-passu basis for setting up of **Silicon CMOS** based **Semiconductor Fab** in **India.**
- **Modified Scheme for setting up of Compound Semiconductors / Silicon Photonics / Sensors Fab / Discrete Semiconductors Fab and Semiconductor Assembly, Testing, Marking and Packaging (ATMP) / OSAT facilities in India :** Under this, Government of India aims to extend a fiscal support of 50% of the Capital Expenditure on Pari-passu basis for setting up of Compound Semiconductors / Silicon Photonics (SiPh) / Sensors (including MEMS) Fab/ Discrete Semiconductor Fab and Semiconductor ATMP / OSAT facilities in India.
- **Modified Scheme for setting up of Display Fabs in India :** For attracting large investments for manufacturing **TFT LCD** or **AMOLED** based display panels in the country to strengthen the electronics manufacturing ecosystem. Scheme extends fiscal support of 50% of Project Cost on pari-passu basis for setting up of Display Fabs in India.
- **Semicon India Future Design:** Design Linked Incentive (DLI) Scheme - It offers financial incentives, design infrastructure support across various stages of development and deployment of semiconductor design for Integrated Circuits (ICs), Chipsets, System on Chips (SoCs), Systems & IP Cores and semiconductor linked design. The scheme provides Product Design Linked Incentive of up to 50% of the eligible expenditure subject to a ceiling of Rs. **15 Crore per** application and Deployment Linked Incentive of **6% to 4%** of net sales turnover over **5 years** subject to a ceiling of Rs. **30 Crore per** application.

Government of India has also approved modernisation of **Semi-Conductor Laboratory, Mohali** as a **brownfield Fab.**

PYQs (2013-24)

1. **What do you understand by Umpire decision review in cricket? Discuss its various components. Explain how silicon tape on the edge of a bat may fool the system?**

   (UPSC Mains 2013)

2. **Discuss in brief the importance of National Programme on Light Emitting Diodes (LEDs).**

   (UPSC Mains 2016)

3. **The Nobel Prize in Physics of 2014 was jointly awarded to Akasaki, Amano and Nakamura for the invention of Blue LEDs in 1990s. How has this invention impacted the everyday life of human beings?**

   (UPSC Mains 2021)

UNIT 3

NUTRITION, DISEASES AND VACCINATION

- ***Nutritional Sciences*** *is the study of* ***food, nutrients****, and other* ***food substances****, the* ***intake*** *and* ***biochemical processing*** *of* ***food substances****, their* ***relationship*** *to* ***health*** *and* ***disease****, and the application of this information to* ***policy*** *and* ***programs****.*
- ***Trophology*** *is the science of a combination of foods or nutrients to promote good health.*
- ***Poor nutritional status*** *is common and in its more extreme forms readily recognised as a* ***clinical disease****. Less severe forms give rise to* ***poor social functioning, low grade ill health*** *and* ***increased risk*** *of more severe* ***diseases****.*
- *Health is achieved through an* ***ongoing interaction*** *with the* ***environment*** *to access the* ***fundamental necessities*** *for life,* ***wholesome food, fresh air*** *and* ***clean water*** *and is more than simply the absence of disease.*
- ***Consuming food*** *enables the body's needs for* ***energy*** *and* ***nutrients*** *to be met. These needs vary with age and lifestyle, so there is variation in the amount and pattern of food that needs to be consumed.*
- **Let Food by the Medicine" Hippocrates (Father of Medicine)**
- *Considerable* ***processing****, or* ***metabolic exchange****, is required within the body to* ***modify food*** *as consumed to a pattern of nutrients which meets the needs of* ***individual cells*** *and* ***tissues*** *of the body.*
- *The nature and extent of this processing vary amongst individuals depending on factors including* ***genotype, past nutritional experience****,* ***lifestyle*** *and* ***current exposure*** *to a range of environmental stressors. The capacity for the regulation and.control of the metabolic exchange depends upon* ***previous dietary exposure, body composition*** *and* ***nutrient status, especially micronutrient status****.*
- ***Effective interventions*** *to enable health by* ***improving nutritional status*** *are often indirect and not specifically aimed at* ***improving food availability*** *or diet. For example, improvements in personal* ***hygiene, general sanitation, immunisation coverage*** *or* ***therapies*** *for* ***specific diseases*** *can have major impact by* ***reducing infective load****, thereby ensuring that* ***available nutrients*** *can be best used for* ***enabling normal development*** *and* ***function****.*
- ***Physical activity*** *is an important attribute of health. Physical* ***Activity*** *clearly confers* ***cardiovascular benefit*** *but also, by* ***increasing energy expenditure****, leads to* ***increased food intake*** *and hence* ***increased nutrient*** *intake if wholesome food is consumed. Indeed, activity can enable a diet of marginal nutrient density to become adequate because of increased consumption. Activity enables normal metabolic regulation and facilitates the appropriate partitioning and utilisation of nutrients within the body.*
- ***Nutrition*** *is a critical part of* ***health*** *and* ***development****. Better nutrition is related to improved* ***infant****,* ***child*** *and* ***maternal health, stronger immune systems, safer pregnancy*** *and* ***childbirth****, lower risk of non-communicable diseases (such as diabetes and cardiovascular disease) and* ***longevity****.*
- *Inadequate nutrition leads to* ***Malnutrition****, which in every form, presents significant threats to human health. Today the world faces a double burden of malnutrition that includes both* ***under nutrition*** *and* ***overweight****, especially in* ***low- and middle-income countries****. There are multiple forms of* ***malnutrition****, including under nutrition (wasting or stunting),* ***inadequate vitamins*** *or* ***minerals****,* ***overweight, obesity*** *and* ***resulting in diet-relatedor lifestyle related non-communicable diseases.***

Nutrients

- Nutrients are substances the body needs for energy as building materials and for control of body processes.

Classification of Nutrients

Based on Biochemical Properties

- **There are 6 major classes of nutrients based on biochemical properties:** Carbohydrates, proteins, lipids, water, vitamins, and minerals.

Fibre, which consists largely of **nondigestible carbohydrates**, is sometimes added as the 7th class of nutrients.

- Besides the biochemical classification of nutrients, they are also categorized as either **essential** or **non essential nutrients.**
- **Essential nutrients** cannot be synthesized by the human body, at least not in sufficient amounts for normal functioning, so these nutrients must be **obtained** from **food.**
- **Nonessential nutrients**, in contrast, can be **synthesized in the body** in sufficient quantities for **normal functioning**, although they are generally obtained from food as well. Except for dietary fiber, **all dietary carbohydrates** are considered **non essential.**
- Every other major class of nutrients contains **multiple essential compounds.**

There are **9 essential amino acids**, at least **2 essential fatty acids**, and many essential **vitamins** and **minerals. Water** and **fibre** are also regarded **essential nutrients.**

Based on Human Body Requirement

- **Nutrients on the basis of Human body requirement can be categorised into : Macronutrients and Micronutrients**
- **Macronutrients :** Macronutrients are nutrients that the body needs in relatively large amounts to maintain body's structure and systems.

Macro nutrients include carbohydrates, proteins, lipids and water.

- All macronutrients **except water** are used by the body for energy, although this is not their **sole physiological function.** The energy provided by macronutrients in food is measured in **kilocalories**, commonly called **Calories.**

1 Calorie is the **amount of energy** needed to raise **1 kilogram** of water by **1 degree Celsius.**

- **Micronutrients :** Micronutrients are nutrients the body needs in relatively small amounts. Micronutrients do not provide energy. Instead, they are necessary for the biochemical reactions of metabolism, among other vital functions.

Micor nutrients include **vitamins**, **minerals** and possibly **phytochemicals** as well.

- **Phytochemicals :** The naturally occurring, disease- and pest-fighting plant chemicals known as phytochemicals are commonly consumed in plant foods, particularly spices and fresh vegetables and fruits.

Besides resisting pest attacks on plants, many phytochemicals give plants their distinctive colors and characteristic flavors and aromas.

Diseases in lack of Nutrients/ Nutrition

Malnutrition

- Malnutrition is when a **person's diet** does not **provide enough nutrients** or the **right balance** for **optimal health.**

As per **World Health Organisation**, Malnutrition refers to **deficiencies, excesses** or **imbalances** in a person's intake of energy and/or nutrients.

- Symptoms often involve **weight loss, reduced appetite, tiredness** and **irritability.**
- As per **WHO, Malnutrition** covers **2 broad groups of conditions –**

Undernutrition : It is a type of malnutrition, that occurs when the body does not gets enough food and enough necessary nutrients.

Undernutrition includes **stunting** (low height for age), **wasting** (low weight for height), **underweight** (low weight for age) and **micronutrient deficiencies** or **insufficiencies** (a lack of important vitamins and minerals).

Malnutrition Conditions

- **Kwashiorkor :** Kwashiorkor is a severe form of **malnutrition** that mainly affects children. It's caused by **inadequate protein intake** and can result in a swollen belly, skin and hair changes, and a **weakened immune system.**
- Children with kwashiorkor might appear **bloated** due to **fluid accumulation** in their **abdomen.**
- **Marasmus :** Marasmus is another type of severe malnutrition, usually seen in **infants.** It arises from an **overall lack of calories, protein, and nutrients.**
- Children with marasmus often look extremely thin, with visible bones, sunken eyes, and a frail appearance. They may lack energy and have weakened muscles.

Overnutrition : It is another type of malnutrition, that occurs when a person takes in **more nutrients** than they need, resulting in an **accumulation of body fat** from the **excess nutrients**, leading to **overweight** or **obesity.**

Over nutrition may lead to **overweight, obesity** and **diet-related noncommunicable diseases** (such as heart disease, stroke, diabetes, and cancer). People who have **overweight** or **obesity** are at greater risk of **heart disease, high blood pressure, diabetes, cancer** and **high cholesterol.**

The Double Burden of Malnutrition

(**Source :** World Health Organization)

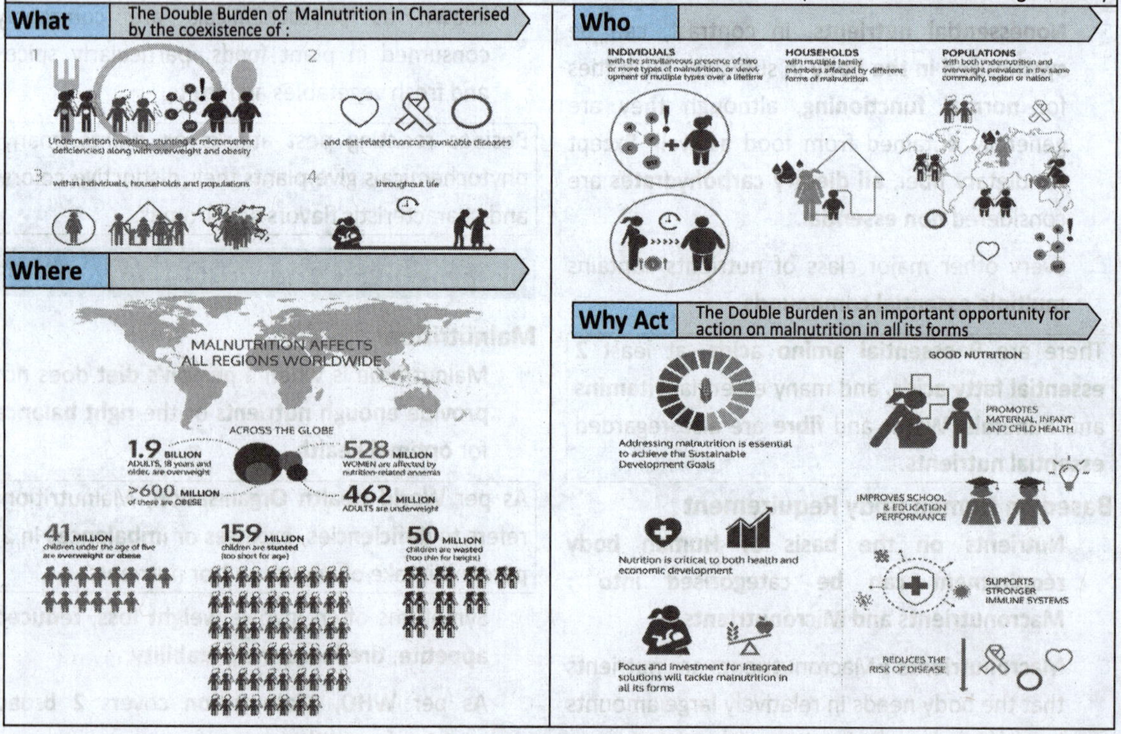

SDG's Goal 2.2 aims to end **Global Hunger** and all forms of **malnutrition** by **2030**. **Malnutrition** affected an estimated **45 million children under 5 world wide in 2022**. In **2022** approx **73 million children** received treatment for **Severe Acute Malnutrition** (SAM), **148 million** had stunted growth and **37 million** were overweight.

- In April 2016, the United Nations General Assembly adopted a resolution proclaiming the **UN Decade of Action on Nutrition** from **2016 to 2025**. The Decade aims to **catalyse policy commitments** that result in measurable action to address all forms of malnutrition.

Micronutrient Diseases		
Fat soluble Vitamins		
Vitamin	**Chemical Name**	**Deficiency Diseases**
A	Retinol, Retinal, Retinoic acid	Night-blindness and keratomalacia
D	Ergocalciferol (D2), Cholecalciferol (D3)	Rickets and Osteomalacia
E	Tocopherol	Mild hemolytic anemia in newborn infants
K	Phylloquinone (K1), Menaquinones (K2)	Bleeding diathesis
Water soluble Vitamins		
Vitamin	**Chemical Name**	**Deficiency Diseases**
B1	Thiamine	Beriberi
B2	Riboflavin	Ariboflavinosis
B3	Niacin, Niacinamide	Pellagra
B5	Pantothenic acid	Paresthesia
B6	Pyridoxine, Pyridoxamine, Pyridoxal	Anemia peripheral neuropathy
B7	Biotin	Dermatitis
B9	Folic acid, Folinic acid	Neural tube defects
B12	Cyanacobalamine	Megaloblastic anemia
C	Ascorbic acid	Scurvy

Macronutrients Diseases		
Macronutrients	**Disorder**	**Description**
Carbohydrates	Diabetes	High blood sugar due to inadequate insulin or resistance
	Hypoglycemia	Low blood sugar leading to dizziness and fatigue
Proteins	Kwashiorkor	Severe protein deficiency causing swelling, weakened immunity
	Marasmus	Severe malnutrition resulting in extreme thinness and weakness
Fats	Obesity	Excess fat accumulation linked to diabetes, heart disease
	Essential Fatty Acid Deficiency	Lack of healthy fats causing skin, vision issues

Diseases

- Disease may be defined as a **disorder** in the **physical, physiological, psychological** or **social state** of a person caused due to **nutritional deficiency, physiological disorder, genetic disorder, pathogen** or any other reason.

> World Health Organization (WHO) defines Disease as a harmful change to an organism's normal structure, function, or metabolism.
>
> The study of Diseases Is called Pathology.

- Disease outbreak is the occurrence of disease cases in excess of normal expectancy. The number of cases varies according to the disease-causing agent, and the size and type of previous and existing exposure to the agent. Outbreaks may also occur following exposure to chemicals or to radioactive materials.
- **Pathogen** : Also called infectious agents or germs, are organism such as a virus, bacteria, parasite or fungus that causes Disease . Pathogens can Pathogens can be transmitted through skin contact, bodily fluids, airborne particles, contact with feces, and touching a surface touched by an infected person. Pathogen needs to thrive and survive is a host.

Broader/ General Classification of Diseases

- **Congenital Diseases** : Disease which are present from birth. They are caused by some genetic abnormality or metabolic disorder or malfunctioning of an organ.
- **Acquired Diseases :** Diseases which may occur after birth during one's lifetime.
- **Acquired diseases can be further classified into:**
  - **Infectious Diseases :** Diseases which can be transmitted from person to person.

Examples : Flu, Measles.

  - **Degenerative Diseases :** Diseases caused by the malfunction of some vital organs of the body.

Example : Cardiovascular diseases.

  - **Deficiency Diseases :** Diseases caused due to nutritional deficiency such as that of minerals or vitamins in the diet. **Example :** anaemia (Fe, Beri- Beri (vitamin B).
  - **Cancer :** This is an abnormal, uncontrolled and unwanted growth of cells, like breast cancer.

Classification of Human Diseases

Diseases

- **Congenital diseases** (Present since birth)
- **Acquired diseases** (Develop after birth)
  - Communicable diseases (Spread from infected person to healthy person)
  - Non - communicable diseases (Do not spread from one person to another)
    - Degenerative diseases (caused due to malfunctioning of vital body organ)
    - Deficiency diseases (caused due to lack of nutrients in diet)
    - Allergies (caused due to hypersensitivity of the body to certain foreign substances)
    - Cancer (caused due to uncontrolled growth of cells/tissues)
    - Other diseases (caused due to various physical agents or any other reason)

Infectious/Communicable Diseases

- Infectious diseases are caused by **pathogenic microorganisms**, such as **bacteria**, **viruses**, **parasites** or **fungi**; the diseases can be spread, **directly** or **indirectly**, from one person to another.

Non-Infectious/ Non-communicable Diseases

- Non-infectious diseases include all diseases that are not caused by pathogens. Instead, non-infectious diseases are generally caused by **genetic** or **environmental factors** other than pathogens, such as **toxic environmental exposures** or **unhealthy lifestyle choices.**
- Most **non-infectious diseases** have a complex, multifactorial set of causes, often including a mix of **genetic** and **environmental variables.**

> The term **NCD/ Non Communicable Diseases** refers to a **group of conditions** that are not mainly caused by an acute infection, result in **long-term health consequences** and often create a need for long-term treatment and care. These conditions include **cancers**, **cardiovascular disease**, **diabetes** and **chronic lung illnesses**. Many other important conditions are also considered NCDs, including **injuries** and **mental health disorders.**

- NCDs can usually be prevented by **reducing common risk factors** such as tobacco use, harmful alcohol use, physical inactivity and eating unhealthy diets.

Vector Borne Diseases

- Diseases transmitted by vectors are called vector-borne diseases.

> **Vector** is a **living organism** that transmits an **infectious agent** from an **infected animal** to a human or another animal. Vectors are frequently **arthropods**, such as **mosquitoes, ticks, flies, fleas** and **lice.**

- **Vectors can transmit infectious diseases either actively or passively:**
  - **Biological vectors**, such as mosquitoes and ticks may carry pathogens that can multiply within their bodies and be delivered to new hosts, usually by biting.
  - **Mechanical vectors**, such as flies can pick up infectious agents on the outside of their bodies and transmit them through physical contact.
- Many vector-borne diseases are **zoonotic diseases**, i.e. diseases that can be **transmitted directly** or **indirectly** between **animals** and **humans.**

> Example of Vector Borne Diseases Lyme disease, tick-borne encephalitis, West Nile virus, Leishmaniosis and Crimean-Congo haemorrhagic fever.

- **Vectors can be introduced to new geographic areas for :**
  - Travel of humans and international trade.
  - Animal movement, for instance of livestock.
  - Migratory birds.
  - Changing agricultural practices.
  - Other factors may play a role in their establishment and persistence in new areas, including climatic conditions.
- Over the last few decades, there has been tremendous advancement in our understanding of the **biology** of **pathogenic microbes** and **viruses** and also novel approaches to combat them, though several challenges remain due to development of **drug resistant bugs** and **immune evasion.**
- On the other hand, the **genetic disorders** which are caused by inherent defect(s) in the **DNA sequence**, encoding a particular function, have been addressed.

Communicable Diseases	Non-Communicable Diseases
Caused by some biological agents or pathogens, such as viruses, bacteria, protozoans, helminths (worms) etc.	Caused to some specific factor, such as malfunctioning of some vital organ, deficiency of nutrients, etc.
Spread from one person to another through contact, water, air, food, etc.	Do not spread from one person to another by contact.
The concern of society as these are related to community health.	The concern of the individual only.

Communicable Diseases

- Diseases which spread from one person to another through **contaminated food**, **water** or **contact** or through **insecticides**, **animals** etc. These are caused by different **causative agents** (Pathogens).

Communicable Diseases →
- Viral Diseases
- Bacterial Diseases
- Protozoan Diseases
- Worm led Diseases

Modes of Transmission of Communicable Diseases

- Communicable diseases are transmitted from the infected person to a healthy person in the following ways.
- **Direct transmission :** The pathogens of diseases infect a healthy person directly without an intermediate agent. It can take place by –
  - **Direct contact between the infected person and the healthy person :** Diseases like small pox, chicken pox, syphilis, gonorrhoea spread through direct contact.
  - **Droplet infection :** The infected person throws out tiny droplets of mucus by coughing, sneezing or spitting, which may contain the pathogen. By inhaling the air containing the droplets, a healthy person may get the infection.

Diseases like **common cold, pneumonia, influenza, measles, tuberculosis** and **whooping cough** spread through **droplet infection.** Contact with **soil** contaminated with disease-causing viruses, bacteria etc.

  - **Animal bite :** Viruses of rabies are introduced through the wound caused by the bite of rabid animals, especially dogs. The virus is present in the saliva of the rabid animals.

Rabid animals include bats, foxes, skunks, cats, coyotes, dogs, rabbits, and raccoons. They are reservoirs and carriers of Rabies – a Viral / Zoonotic disease affecting central nervous system of mammals (dogs, cats, foxes, Bats), including humans. Rabies virus is present in the saliva and brain of infected animals and is transmitted by a bite.

- **Indirect transmission :** The pathogens of certain diseases reach the human body through some intermediate agents. It can take place by –
  - Vectors such as houseflies, mosquitoes, and cockroaches.

Examples: Houseflies carrying the **causative organisms** of **cholera** on their legs and mouth parts from the faeces and sputum of infected persons to food and drinks and contaminate them.

  - **Air-borne :** The pathogens may reach humans with air and dust.

The **epidemic Typhus** spreads by inhalation of dried faeces of infected fly.

  - **Object borne (Fonite borne) :** Many diseases are transmitted through the use of contaminated articles, such as clothes, utensils, toys, door handles, taps, syringes and surgical instruments, etc.
  - **Water borne :** If potable water (drinking water) is contaminated with pathogens of diseases such as cholera, diarhhoea, hepatitis or jaundice, it reaches a healthy person upon consuming such water.

Viral Diseases

Disease Name	Causative Organism	Symptoms / Organs Affected	Transmission	Vaccination
Influenza (Flu)	Influenza virus	Respiratory system, fever, cough, fatigue	Droplet infection	Flu shots- frequently updated due to mutations
Common Cold	Various rhinoviruses	Respiratory system, runny nose, sneezing	Airborne droplets	No permanent vaccine, but flu shots
Smallpox	Variola virus	Skin rashes & blisters, respiratory system and fever	Respiratory droplets, direct contact	Diseases is eradicated from the world.
Chickenpox	Varicella-zoster virus	Skin rash, fever, itching	Airborne droplets, direct contact	Varicella vaccine- A live attenuated vaccine
Mumps	Mumps virus	Salivary glands, fever, swelling of cheeks	Droplet infection	MMR vaccine - live attenuated vaccine
Measles	Measles virus	Respiratory system, fever, rash	Airborne droplets	MMR vaccine
Rubella (German Measles)	Rubella virus	Respiratory system, rash, mild fever	Droplet infection	MMR vaccine
HIV/AIDS	Human Immunodeficiency Virus (HIV)-Retrovirus	Immune system, various infections and cancers	Blood, sexual contact, mother-to-child, needles	Not available (treatment available)
Ebola	Ebola virus	Fever, bleeding, organ failure	Zoonotic Disease and later through contact, even with dead, Direct contact with bodily fluids	Not Available
Polio/ Poliomylitis	RNA/Rubeola Virus	Nervous system-paralysis	Feces and droplets : Role of contamination of water and hygiene	Oral Polio Vaccine (OPV), Inactivated Poliovirus Vaccine (IPV) : injectable

Yellow Fever	RNA virus	Mild : fever, later fatal heart liver and kidney conditions	Vector based spread : aedes mosquito	Live attenuated vaccine
Zika	Virus (RNA)	Mild illness, dengue like symptoms	Vector Bite : aedes, sometimes sexual	Not available
Rotavirus	RNA	Diarrhea : GI tract	Fecal-oral transmission	Available
Japanese Encephalitis(JE)	ssRNA	Brain swelling : severe headache. Fatal in children	Culex	Available, Part of National Schedule
Hepatitis A	Hepatitis A virus (HAV)	Liver inflammation, jaundice, fatigue, nausea	Contaminated food or water, fecal-oral route	Available (Hepatitis A vaccine)
Hepatitis B	Hepatitis B virus (HBV)	Liver inflammation, jaundice, abdominal pain	Contact with infected blood, sexual contact, mother-to-child	Available (Hepatitis B vaccine)
Hepatitis C	Hepatitis C virus (HCV)	Liver inflammation, often asymptomatic initially	Contact with infected blood, sharing needles, rarely mother-to-child	Not available.
Hepatitis D	Hepatitis D virus (HDV)	Liver inflammation, similar to hepatitis B	Co-infection with HBV or superinfection in a HBV carrier	Prevented with HBV vaccination
Hepatitis E	Hepatitis E virus (HEV)	Liver inflammation, similar to hepatitis A	Contaminated water, fecal-oral route	Available in some regions, not widely used
Dengue	Dengue virus (flavivirus), Aedes Aegypti Mosquito	High Fever, Vomiting, Muscle Pain	Bite of infected aedes mosquito.	Dengvaxia
Rabies	Rabies Virus	Nausea, Vomiting hypera activity, excessive salivation, hydrophobia, Partial Paralysis	Bite by a rabied dog	Human Diploid Cell Vaccine (HDCV), Purified Vero cell Rabies Vaccine (PVRV), Purified chick-embryo cell vaccine (PCECV) and purified duck embryo vaccine (PDEV).

Influenza Virus

- Influenza/ Flu is a contagious respiratory illness caused by flu viruses, that can cause mild to severe illness, and at times can lead to death.
- It spreada mainly by droplets containing viruses dispersed in air when people with flu cough, sneeze or talk, infecting people in close proximity.
- In temperate climates, seasonal epidemics occur mainly during winters, while in tropical regions, influenza may occur throughout the year, causing irregular outbreaks.

There are 4 types of influenza viruses: Types A, B, C and D.

- **Influenza A and B viruses** circulate and cause seasonal epidemics of disease.
- Influenza A viruses are the only influenza viruses known to cause flu pandemics. A pandemic can occur when a new influenza A virus emerges against which people have little or no immunity.
- They are further classified into subtypes based on the combinations of two surface proteins **hemagglutinin** (H) and **neuraminidase** (N). There are 18 different hemagglutinin subtypes (H1-H18) and 11 neuraminidase subtypes (NI-N11).

Currently circulating in humans are subtype A (H1N1) and A (H3N2) influenza viruses. A (H1N1) caused the pandemic in 2009 and replaced the previous A (H1N1) virus which had circulated prior to 2009

- **Influenza B** viruses are not classified into subtypes but can be broken down into lineages.
- **Influenza type B** viruses belong to either B/ Yamagata or B/Victoria lineage.
- **Influenza B** viruses generally change more slowly in terms of their genetic and antigenic properties than influenza A viruses, especially influenza A (H3N2) viruses.
- **Influenza C** virus is detected less frequently and usually causes mild infections, henceforth does not raises public health concern.
- **Influenza D** viruses primarily affect cattles and are not known to infect or cause illness in people.
- **Centers for Disease Control and Prevention** (CDC) follows an internationally accepted naming convention for influenza viruses (accepted by WHO in 1979 and published in February 1980)
    - Antigenic type (e.g., A, B, C, D)
    - Host of origin (eg., swine, equine, chicken, etc.).
    - For human-origin viruses, no host of origin designation is given.
- When humans are infected with influenza viruses that normally circulate in swine (pigs), these viruses are called variant viruses and are designated with the letter v (e.g.. an A (H3N2) v virus.
- **Duck :** Avian influenza A(H1N1), A/duck/ Alberta/35/76
- **Human:** Seasonal influenza A(H3N2), A/ Perth/16/2019
    - Geographical origin : Denver, Taiwan, etc.
    - Strain number (e.g., 7, 15, etc.)
    - Year of collection (e.g., 57, 2009, etc.)

Dengue (break-bone fever)

- A vector borne viral infection caused by the flavivirus dengue virus (DENV) that spreads through the bite of an infected Aedes aegypti mosquito to people. It is common in tropical and subtropical climates.
- The primary mode of transmission of DENV between humans involves mosquito vectors. As per WHO, there is evidence of the possibility of maternal transmission (from a pregnant mother to child).

- **Types of Dengue :** Dengue fever and Dengue hemorrhagic fever
- Dengue hemorrhagic fever is an acute infectious viral disease.

Polio

- Highly infectious contagious disease caused by a virus Picornaviridae that destroys nerve cells present in spinal cord. It invades the nervous system and can cause complete paralysis

Encephalitis

- An inflammation of the active tissues of the brain most commonly caused by viral infections, including herpes simplex virus (HSV), varicella-zoster virus (VZV), enteroviruses (such as poliovirus and coxsackievirus), arboviruses (such as West Nile virus and Japanese encephalitis virus) or an autoimmune response, causing the brain to swell, leading to headache, stiff neck, sensitivity to light, mental confusion and seizures and in extreme cases brain damage, stroke, or even death.

Encephalitis : Inflammation of the brain.
Myelitis : Inflammation of the spinal cord.
Encephalomyelitis : Inflammation of both the brain and the spinal cord.

Japanese Encephalitis Virus (JEV)

- A mosquito-borne flavivirus belonging to the same genus as dengue, yellow fever and West Nile viruses. JEV is transmitted to humans through bites from infected mosquitoes of the Cules species (mainly Culex tritaeniorhynchus). The virus exists E in a transmission cycle between mosquitoes, pigs and or water birds (Enzootic cycle).

First case of JEV was documented in Japan in 1871.

- The disease is predominantly found in rural and peri-urban settings, where humans inhabit proximity to vertebrate hosts. In temperate areas of Asia, JEV is transmitted mainly during the warm season, resulting in epidemics. In tropics and subtropics, transmission can occur year-round but often intensifies during the rainy season and pre-harvest period in rice-cultivating regions.
- **There are 4 main types of JE vaccines :** Inactivated mouse brain-derived vaccines, Inactivated Vero cell-derived vaccines, live attenuated vaccines and live recombinant (chimeric) vaccines.

Acute Encephalitis Syndrome (AES)

- The term ALS was coined by World Health Organization (WHO) in 2008 for surveillance and proper reporting of suspected encephalitis cases in India.
- WHO defines an AES case as a person of any age, at any time of the year with an acute onset of fever and a change in mental status (including symptoms such as confusion, disorientation, coma, or inability to talk) and/or new onset of seizures (excluding simple febrile seizure. In

India first AES case was clinically diagnosed in Tamil Nadu in 1955.

Zika Virus

- A mosquito-borne virus first identified in Uganda in 1947 in a Rhesus macaque monkey followed by evidence of infection and disease in humans in other African countries in the 1950s.
- Zika virus is transmitted from mother to fetus during pregnancy, through sexual contact, transfusion of blood and blood products and possibly through organ transplantation. Zika virus infection during pregnancy is a cause of microcephaly and other congenital malformations in the infant, including limb contractures, high muscle tone, eye abnormalities and hearing loss, collectively referred to as congenital Zika syndrome.

Monkeypox

- **PHEIC**, renamed as **mpox**, **zoonotic disease**, belongs to **orthopoxvirus** which also includes variola virus (smallpox), cowpox.
- India has introduced its **first quadrivalent human papillomavirus vaccine (Cervavac)**, developed by the **Serum Institute of India**. This vaccine is effective against **HPV**, a virus transmitted through **sexual contact** that can lead to cervical cancer. This step holds promise in preventing cervical cancer by targeting the root HPV infection.

Bacterial Diseases

Disease Name	Causative Organism	Symptoms / Organs Affected	Transmission	Vaccination
Tuberculosis (TB)	Mycobacterium tuberculosis	Mainly Lungs, other organs, cough, fever, weight loss	Airborne droplets, Drinking milk from infected cattle	BCG Vaccine
Cholera	Vibrio cholerae	Gastrointestinal, severe diarrhea, dehydration	Contaminated food/water	Cholera Vaccine
Diphtheria	Corynebacterium diphtheriae	Throat, breathing difficulties, swollen neck	Respiratory droplets, contact	DPT Vaccine -Toxoid vaccine
Tetanus	Clostridium tetani	Muscle stiffness, spasms, lockjaw	Bacteria in wounds, soil	DTaP vaccine Toxoid
Pertussis (Whooping Cough)	Bordetella pertussis	Severe cough, respiratory distress	Respiratory droplets, contact	DTaP vaccine- Killed Vaccine
Typhoid Fever	Salmonella typhi	Gastrointestinal, high fever, fatigue	Feco-oral-Contaminated food/water	Typhoid vaccine- Ty21a and Vi capsular polysaccharide vaccine
Bacterial Meningitis	Various bacteria	Inflammation of brain, fever, headache	Respiratory droplets, contact	Meningococcal vaccine
Haemophilus Influenza type b (HiB) disease (Pneumonia	H. Infleunzae and other bacterias	Lungs, cough, fever, difficulty breathing	Respiratory droplets, contact	Pneumococcal vaccine
Leprosy/Hansens disease	Mycobacterium Leprae	Blisters, reduced touch/temp sensation, Paralysis	Prolonged contact with infected person, nascal secretions	Dapsone, Rifampicin and clofazimine (MDT or PCT)

Tuberculosis

- **World Health Organization** (WHO) recently released new guidance to support **National Strategic Planning** (NSP) for **tuberculosis** (TB). The new document, titled **Guidance for National Strategic Planning for Tuberculosis Elimination,** provides countries with a framework for developing and implementing NSPs that are comprehensive, evidence-based, and aligned with the WHO End TB Strategy.

> **WHO End TB Strategy**, which aims to end TB as a **public health threat** by **2030.**

- The NSP for TB is a document that outlines the **country's goals** and **strategies** for **TB control** and elimination. It should be based on a comprehensive assessment of the TB situation in the country, including the burden of disease, the availability of resources, and the capacity of the health system.

Indian Initiatives to eliminate TB

- **National Strategic Plan 2017 – 2025:** A comprehensive plan to eliminate TB by **2025** through various strategies and interventions.
- **Nikshay Portal:** A national TB information system that serves as a repository for data related to TB cases.
- **Nikshay Poshan Yojana:** This scheme offers Direct Benefit Transfer (DBT) to TB patients for nutritional support, jointly funded by the Ministry of Health and Family Welfare (MoHFW) and the World Bank.
- **NTEP (National Tuberculosis Elimination Program):** Formerly known as **RNTCP**, it is a program focused on **TB control, diagnosis** and **treatment.**
- **TB Mukt Bharat:** A vision to make **India TB-free** by **2025.**
- **Patho Detect Kit:** An indigenous TB diagnostic kit developed by **Indian laboratories**, helping in **early detection** and **management** of TB cases.

Tuberculosis (TB)

TB is caused by bacteria (Mycobacterium tuberculosis) and it most often affects the lungs

Types of TB

- **Pulmonary TB** (Affects lungs)
- **Extra Pulmonary TB** (Affects both lungs and other organs)

For prevention of TB: BCG (Bacille Calmette Guerin) vaccine is used among children at the time of birth

Drug resistant TB

- **Multi-Drug Resistance TB (MDR-TB):** Does not respond to at least isoniazid and rifampicin (2 of the most powerful anti-TB drugs)
- **Extensively Drug Resistant TB (XDR-TB):** TB which is resistant to all the anti-TB drugs.
- **Totally drug resistant tuberculosis (TDR-TB):** Does not respond to at least four of the core anti-TB drugs.

> **The Pentavalent Vaccine** is a combination vaccine that provides protection against five different diseases in a single shot. It targets:
>
> Diphtheria
>
> Tetanus
>
> Pertussis (Whooping Cough)
>
> Haemophilus influenzae type b (Hib) infection
>
> Hepatitis B

Other Initiatives	
Initiative/ Declaration	**Description**
Moscow Declaration (2017)	International commitment to accelerate efforts towards TB elimination.
WHO End TB Strategy	Strategy targeting 80 % reduction in TB incidence, 90% reduction in TB deaths, and ending financial burden from TB.
Find All, Treat All, End TB	Collaborative partnership between WHO, Stop TB Partnership, and Global Fund to find, treat, and eradicate TB.
BPaL Regimen	Innovative 6-month oral TB treatment using Bedaquilline, Pretomanid, and Linezolid, significantly shortening treatment duration.
Reduced Treatment Time	TB Alliance's effort to reduce TB treatment duration from 18 months to 6 months through the BPaL regimen.

PARASITIC DISEASES

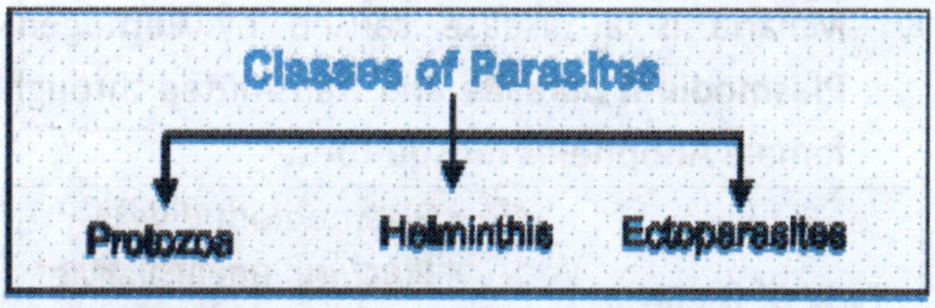

- Parasitic diseases / Parasitosis are infectious diseases caused by parasites.
- Parasitic infections are caused by organisms that live off of another living thing causing fever, fatigue, intestinal symptoms, skin rashes or neurological symptoms.

Parasite is an organism that lives on or in a host organism and gets its food from or at the expense of its host. Parasitology is the study of parasites and parasitic diseases.

Protozoa

- Protozoa are microscopic, single celled organisms that can be free-living or parasitic in nature, with an ability to multiply in humans, that contributes to their survival and allows dispersal of infections to develop from just a single organism.
- Transmission of protozoa living in human intestine to another human typically occurs through a fecal-oral route (for example, contaminated food or water or person-to-person contact).
- Protozoa that live in the blood or tissue of humans are transmitted to other humans by an arthropod vector (for example, through the bite of a mosquito or sand fly).

Protozoa (infectious to humans) are classified into 4 groups (Based on mode of movement) –

- **Sarcodina:** Amoeba – Entamoeba
- **Mastigophora:** Flagellates – Giardia, Leishmania
- **Ciliophora:** Ciliates – Balantidium.
- **Sporozoa:** Organisms whose adult stage is non motile - Plasmodium, Cryptosporidium.

Helminthis

- Large, multicellular organisms visible to the naked eye in their adult stages.
- Helminths (Greek for Worm) are most common in areas that have moist, warm climates and poor sanitation.
- **3 main groups of helminths that are human parasites:**
- **Roundworms/Nematodes:** Have cylindrical body similar to earthworms. They can lead to infection in the intestines or elsewhere in the body.

- **Flatworms/Platyhelminths:** Include Trematodes/ Flukes, having a flat body and leaf-shaped head with a sucker that helps them attach, that generally infect the bile ducts, liver or blood and Tapeworms/Cestodes which are long, segmented flatworms found in or around the intestines.
- **Thorny-headed worms/Acanthocephalans:** Having a round body which barbs around their head. They mainly infect animals and human infection is rare.
- These worms can cause parasitic infection known as helminthiasis/ helminthosis / worm infection as they get into human body.

Diseases Caused by Helminths –

- **Ascariasis:** Caused by the roundworm Ascaris lubricoides, that live in the intestines.
- **Whipworm:** An infection caused by a type of roundworm that lives in the large intestine. The symptoms include painful bowel movements, diarrhea that contains blood or mucus and frequent defecation As whipworm progresses, a person can experience anal prolapse anemia and stunted growth.
- **Hookworm Infections:** Caused by the helminths Ancylostoma duodenale and Necator americanus, which infect the small intestine.

Ectoparasites

- Blood-sucking arthropods such as mosquitoes (dependent on a blood from a human host for their survival), and also refer to organisms as ticks, fleas, lice and mites that attach or burrow into the skin and remain there for relatively long periods of time (e.g., weeks to months)

PROTOZOAN/PARASITIC DISEASES

Protozoan Diseases
- Filariasis
- Kala Azar (Leishmaniasis)
- Malaria

Filariasis

- Filariasis is a disease caused by **roundworms** called **filarial parasites**. These parasites are **transmitted to humans** through the bites of **infected mosquitoes**, particularly **Culex, Aedes,** and **Anopheles mosquitoes**.
- One of the noticeable effects of filariasis is the **swelling of lymph nodes, which can lead to a condition known as elephantiasis. Lymph nodes** are part of the **lymphatic system**, which helps to maintain **fluid balance** and **fight infections** in the body.
- When the **filarial parasites** infect the **lymphatic system**, they can **obstruct** the **normal flow** of **lymph**, leading to the **accumulation of fluid** and causing **swelling** in the affected areas, often the **limbs** or **genitals**. This severe swelling gives rise to the term **elephantiasis**.

Kala Azar (Leishmaniasis)

- Leishmaniasis, is also known as **Kala-azar**. It is transmitted by **sandflies** and is **endemic** to the **Indian subcontinent**.
- One of the most common features of Leishmaniasis is **hepatosplenomegaly**, which means the **enlargement** of both the liver and spleen. This can lead to symptoms like **abdominal discomfort, fever** and **fatigue**.

Malaria

- Malaria is a disease caused by **Pathogen-Plasmodium parasite** and transmitted through female **Anopheles mosquitoes**.

Type of Malaria
- Plasmodium Vivax
- Plasmodium Malariae
- Plasmodium Falciparum
- Plasmodium Ovale

- **Plasmodium falciparum** and **Plasmodium vivax** are the most severe types. India is home to both these types.
- Malaria leads to symptoms like **fever, chills** and **fatigue**.

- **Anopheles mosquitoes** carry the parasite from person to person, emphasizing the importance of **mosquito control** and **anti-malarial measures** in affected regions.

The **World Malaria Report 2022**, released by the **World Health Organization** (WHO), provides insights into global malaria trends.

- WHO has recommended broad use of the **RTS,S/AS01** (RTS,S) **malaria vaccine** among children living in regions with **moderate** to **high P. falciparum malaria transmission.**

Vaccine for malaria : Mosquirix.

- This **recombinant protein vaccine** has shown promising results, reducing malaria cases, severe malaria, and hospital admissions, particularly among children.

India contributes to **83%** of malaria cases in the **WHO South-East Asia Region.**

Initiatives for Malaria

- **E-2025 initiative:** Under this, WHO has identified a group of **25 countries** with the potential to **eradicate malaria** by **2025.**
- **Malaria Elimination Research Alliance (MERA)-India:** Its purpose is to **identify, articulate, prioritize** and **respond** to the research needs of the country to **eliminate malaria** from India by **2030.**
- **High Burden to High Impact (HBHI) initiative:** In 2019, WHO has initiated the HBHI initiative in 11 high malaria burden countries, including India (West Bengal and Jharkhand, Chhattisgarh and Madhya Pradesh).

National Strategic Plan for Malaria Elimination (2017-22).

- Ministerial Declaration on Accelerating and Sustaining Malaria Elimination in South-East Asia Region (SEAR).
- **National Framework for Malaria Elimination (NFME):** The NFME is a comprehensive plan that outlines the strategies and activities for malaria elimination in India. The NFME was launched in 2016 and aims to eliminate malaria by 2030.

Amoebiasis (Amoebic dysentery)

- Pathogen : Entamoeba histolytica
- Mode of transmission : Contaminated food and water

Fungal Diseases

- Fungal infections or mycosis, are diseases caused by a fungus (yeast or mold). A fungus that invades the tissue can cause a disease that's confined to the skin, spreads into tissue and organs or affects the whole body.
- Fungal infections can be on the surface of skin, nails or mucous membranes (superficial or mucocutaneous), underneath skin (subcutaneous) or inside other organs of human body like lungs, brain or heart (deep infections).
- Fungal infections are more common in places on human body that traps moisture or undergoes friction.

1. **Superficial Fungal Infections :** They affect nails, skin and mucous membranes (like your mouth, throat or vagina).
   - **Ringworm / Dermatophytosis:** A group of fungi that live off of skin, hair and nail cells (dermatophytes) caused by ringworm. They can infect feet (tinea pedis/athlete's foot), groin and inner thighs (tinea cruris/ jock itch), scalp (tinea capitis leading to baldness), hands (tinea manuum), facial hair and skin around it (tinea barbae) and other parts of human body (tinea corporis)
   - **Onychomycosis:** Many types of fungi cause infections of fingernails or toenails (onychomycosis). This can cause discolored and cracked nails.
   - **Candidiasis:** Candida (usually Candida albicans) causes skin and mucous membrane

(mucocutaneous) infections include oral thrush, types of diaper rash, vaginal yeast infections (vulvovaginitis), esophageal candidiasis and candidal intertrigo.

- **Tinea versicolor/pityriasis versicolor:** The fungus Malassezia causes skin discoloration called tinea versicolor or pityriasis versicolor.

2. **Subcutaneous Fungal Infections :** Fungal infection under the surface of skin (subcutaneous), if fungus gets into a cut or wound, usually through injury while working with plants (like a scratch from a thorn), causing rashes, ulcers and other symptoms on skin.

- **Sporotrichosis (rose gardener's disease):** Caused by Sporothrix fungus causes sporotrichosis.
- **Chromoblastomycosis:** Can cause a long-lasting (chronic) skin infections. Rarely, it spreads to other parts of human body.
- **Eumycetoma:** Most commonly affects feet

3. Deep/ Invasive fungal Infections : Found in places in human body other than skin, like lungs, blood, urinary tract or brain.

- **Histoplasmosis:** Causes histoplasmosis, can infect lungs, brain or other parts of human body.
- **Coccidioidomycosis (Valley fever):** Caused by the fungus Coccidioides, that infect lungs and rarely, move to other parts of human body.
- **Blastomycosis:** Infects bones, skin and lungs. Rarely, it can also infect brain and spinal cord.
- **Aspergillosis:** Aspergillus, the mold that causes aspergillosis, can cause lung infections, including allergic bronchopulmonary aspergillosis (ABPA) and chronic pulmonary aspergillosis. It can also infect other parts of human body or form a fungus ball (aspergilloma).
- **Candidal urinary tract infection:** Bacteria cause most urinary tract infections (UTIs), but some are caused by yeast such as Candida.
- **Invasive candidiasis:** Caused by Candida species cause, infects heart, blood (candidemia), brain, eyes (endophthalmitis), bones or other parts of human body.
- **Pneumocystis pneumonia (PJP):** Infects lungs and cause Pneumocystis jirovecii pneumonia (PJP).
- **Mucormycosis:** Infects sinuses and brain (rhinocerebral mucormycosis), lungs (pulmonary mucormycosis), intestines (gastrointestinal mucormycosis), skin (cutaneous mucormycosis) or many parts of body at the same time (disseminated mucormycosis).
- **Cryptococcosis:** They usually infect lungs, but sometimes can infect brain and spinal cord (cryptococcal meningitis).

Sexually Transmitted Diseases

- Diseases that are transmitted through sexual contact are known as sexually transmitted diseases.
- Sexually transmitted diseases are those infections that are transmitted via the mucous membrane and secretions of the sexual organ, throat and the rectum.

Examples of STDs : Syphilis, gonorrhoea, AIDS, etc.

AIDS (Acquired Immuno Deficiency Syndrome)

- **Immuno deficiency** signifies that the immune system becomes very weak. It is a disorder of cell-mediated immune system of the body.

Lymphocytes are the main cells of the immune system i.e. **T-lymphocytes** and **B-lymphocytes. Helper T lymphocytes** play a great role in regulating the immune system. Damages to or destruction of 'Helper'lymphocytes lead to the development of a cellular immune deficiency which makes the patient susceptible to wide variety of infections.

- **Mode of Transmission : AIDS may be transmitted through any of the following means :**
   - Sexual contact with the affected person. In India, the most common route of HIV transmission is through unprotected heterosexual sex.
   - Using the same syringe as that of affected person.
   - Blood transfusion which contains human immuno deficiency virus.
   - Organ transplantation of the affected person.
   - Artificial insemination.
   - From mother to new born baby during the process of giving birth.

Important Facts about HIV transmission

- HIV is a **weak virus** and hard to get infected with. It cannot be transmitted through **air** or **water outside** the **human body**.
- A person cannot get **AIDS** by hugging or sneezing of an infected person, insect bites (including mosquito), sharing the same comb, plates, glass, handkerchiefs, knives or cutlery.
- A person cannot get AIDS by using **public toilets**, **swimming pools**, **showers** and **telephones**.
- HIV does not transmit by being near to someone, touching someone or working with someone who is suffering from **AIDS**.

Syphilis

- **Causative Organism :** Treponema pallidum (a long corkscrew bacteria)
- **Mode of Spread :** Sexual contact with the infected person

Gonorrhoea

- Gonorrhoea is a **sexually transmitted disease** that often involves **urethra, vagina** or **penis, cervix, anus** and **throat**, as its **target sites.**
- **Causative Organism :** A gonococcus bacteria, Neisseria gonorrhoeae. It grows and multiplies quickly in warm moist areas of the body, such as the cervix, rectum and mouth.
- **Modes of Spread :** Having multiple sex partners increases the risk of contracting it. Any kind of unprotected sex is always a risk. Any kind of contact of sores with an infected person is also risky.

Chlamydia

- Chlamydia often referred to as a Silent infection (as most people with a chlamydia infection don't experience any symptoms) is a common sexually transmitted infection (STI) caused by bacteria.
- **Major Causes of transmission:** Unprotected Sex; In some women, the infection can spread to the fallopian tubes, which may cause a condition called pelvic inflammatory disease (PID). Newborn babies can acquire chlamydia from their mother during birth. Most prenatal testing includes a chlamydia test

Human Papilloma Virus (HPV)

- HPV is the name of a group of 200 known viruses. HPV infection is a viral infection that commonly causes skin or mucous membrane growths (warts).
- Certain types of genital HPV can cause cancer of the lower part of the uterus that connects to the vagina (cervix)
- Other types of cancers, including cancers of the anus, penis, vagina, vulva and back of the throat (oropharyngeal), have been linked to HPV infection, often transmitted sexually or through other skin-to-skin contact,
- Prophylactic vaccination against HPV can prevent these cancers.
   - 90-70-90 Targets by WHO: Aims for 90% of girls to be fully vaccinated with the

HPV vaccine by age 15, 70% of women to undergo cervical cancer screening tests by the ages of 35 and 45 and for 90% of women with cervical cancer to receive treatment by 2030.

- CERVAVAC is India's first indigenously developed quadrivalent human papillomavirus (HPV) vaccine effective against four strains of the virus-Type 6, Type 11, Type 16 and Type 18.

NON-COMMUNICABLE DISEASES

Diabetes Mellitus

- The disease can be diagnosed by blood test or urine test.
- **Causes**
  - Less secretion of insulin hormone from the pancreas.
  - Mental stress
  - Through heredity from parents to children.

Cardiovascular diseases (CVDs)

- **Cardiovascular disease** (CVD) is a general term for conditions affecting the heart or blood vessels. It's usually associated with a build-up of fatty deposits inside the arteries (atherosclerosis) and an **increased risk of blood clots.**
- It can also be associated with damage to arteries in organs such as the **brain, heart, kidneys** and **eyes.**

Types of Cardiovasular Diseases

- **Coronary Heart Disease : a disease of the blood vessels supplying the heart muscle. Coronary heart disease occurs when the flow of oxygen-rich blood to the heart muscle is blocked or reduced putting an increased strain on the heart, and can leading to:**
  - **Angina** : chest pain caused by restricted blood flow to the heart muscle
  - **Heart attacks :** where the blood flow to the heart muscle is suddenly blocked.
  - **Heart failure :** where the heart is unable to pump blood around the body properly
- **Cerebrovascular Disease** : A disease of the blood vessels supplying the brain.

Strokes and TIAs : A stroke is where the blood supply to part of the brain is cut off, which can cause brain damage and possibly death. A **transient ischaemic attack** (also called a TIA or mini-stroke) is similar, but the blood flow to the brain is only temporarily disrupted.

- **Peripheral arterial disease : A disease of blood vessels supplying the arms and legs. Peripheral arterial disease occurs when there's a blockage in the arteries to the limbs, usually the legs. This can cause:**
  - Dull or cramping leg pain, which is worse when walking and gets better with rest
  - Hair loss on the legs and feet
  - Numbness or weakness in the legs
  - Persistent ulcers (open sores) on the feet and legs
- **Aortic diseases :** They are a group of conditions affecting the **aorta.**

Aorta is the **largest blood vessel** in the body, which carries blood from the heart to the rest of the body.

- One of most common aortic diseases is an aortic aneurysm, where the aorta becomes weakened and bulges outwards. This doesn't usually have any symptoms, but there's a chance it could burst and cause life-threatening bleeding.
- **Rheumatic heart disease :** Damage to the heart muscle and heart valves from rheumatic fever, caused by streptococcal bacteria.
- **Congenital heart disease :** Birth defects that affect the normal development and functioning of the heart caused by malformations of the heart structure from birth; and
- **Deep vein thrombosis and pulmonary embolism :** blood clots in the leg veins, which can dislodge and move to the heart and lungs.

Factors leading to Cardiovascular Diseases

- The most important **behavioural risk factors** of heart disease and **stroke** are **unhealthy diet, physical inactivity, tobacco** use and **harmful use of alcohol.**
- The effects of behavioural risk factors may show up in individuals as **raised blood pressure, raised blood glucose, raised blood lipids** and **overweight and obesity.**
- These **intermediate risks factors** can be measured in **primary care facilities** and indicate an increased risk of **heart attack, stroke, heart failure** and other complications.

Prevention of CVDs

- Cessation of tobacco use, reduction of salt in the diet, eating more fruit and vegetables, regular physical activity and avoiding harmful use of alcohol have been shown to reduce the risk of cardiovascular disease

Medications for CVDs :

Aspirin;

Beta-blockers;

Angiotensin-converting enzyme inhibitors

Statins.

Surgical operations required to treat CVDs include:

Coronary artery bypass

Balloon angioplasty (where a small balloon-like device is threaded through an artery to open the blockage)

Valve repair and replacement

Heart transplantation

Artificial heart operations

- At least three-quarters of the world's deaths from CVDs occur in **low** and **middle-income countries.**
- People in **low and middle-income countries** who suffer from **CVDs** and other non-communicable diseases have less access to **effective** and **equitable health care services** which respond to their needs.
- As a result, for many people in these countries detection is often late in the course of the disease and people die at a younger age from CVDs and other non-communicable diseases, often in their most productive years.
- At the household level, evidence is emerging that CVDs and other noncommunicable diseases contribute to **poverty** due to **catastrophic health** spending and **high out-of-pocket expenditure.**
- At the macro-economic level, CVDs place a **heavy burden** on the **economies of low** and **middle-income countries.**

Hypertension High Blood Pressure

- **Symptoms**
  - Persistent high blood pressure (BP)
  - It may damage the arteries of kidney.
  - In extreme cases the arteries may burst or blindness may be caused.
  - It may also cause paralysis.

Coronary Heart Disease

- **Symptoms**
  - Severe pain in the chest gasping for breathe.
  - Intense nausea and vomiting.
  - Lot of sweating takes place.
  - Blood clot may be formed within the blood vessels.

Cancer

- Cancer is a large group of diseases that occur when abnormal cells divide rapidly and can spread to other tissue and organs. These rapidly growing cells may cause tumors. They may also disrupt the body's regular function.
- The main cause of cancer is mutations, or changes to the DNA in your cells. Genetic

mutations can be inherited. They can also occur after birth as a result of environmental forces.

- **External causes, called carcinogens, can include:**
  - Physical carcinogens like radiation and ultraviolet (UV) light.
  - Chemical carcinogens like cigarette smoke, asbestos, alcohol, air pollution, and contaminated food and drinking water.
  - Biological carcinogens like viruses, bacteria, and parasites.
- **Risk factors : Certain risk factors may increase chances of developing cancer. These risk factors include:**
  - Tobacco use.
  - High alcohol consumption.
  - An unhealthy diet, characterized by red and processed meat, sugary drinks and salty snacks, starchy foods, and refined carbohydrates including sugars and processed grains, according to a 2017 review.
  - A lack of physical activity.
  - Exposure to air pollution.
  - Exposure to radiation.
  - Unprotected exposure to UV light, such as sunlight.
  - Infection by certain viruses including H. pylori, human papillomavirus (HPV), hepatitis B, hepatitis C, HIV, and the Epstein-Barr virus, which causes infectious mononucleosis.
- The risk of developing cancer also increases with age. In general, the risk of developing cancer appears to increase until the age of **70 to 80** Trusted Source and then diminish, according to the **National Cancer Institute** (NCI).

Growth and Spread of Cancer

- **Abnormal cell division :** Normal cells in human body grow and divide. Each one has a life cycle determined by the type of cell. As cells become damaged or die off, new cells take their place. Cancer disrupts this process and causes cells to grow abnormally. It's caused by changes or mutations in the cell's DNA.
- **Creation of tumors :** Tumors can cause health problems, depending on where they grow in the body. Not all tumors are cancerous. Benign tumors are noncancerous and do not spread to nearby tissues. But sometimes, tumors can grow large and cause problems when they press against neighboring organs and tissue. Malignant tumors are cancerous and can invade other parts of the body.
- **Metastasis :** Some cancer cells can also spread through the bloodstream or lymphatic system to distant areas of the body. This is called metastasis. Cancers that have metastasized are considered more advanced than those that have not. Metastatic cancers are often harder to treat and more fatal.

According to the WHO, about **33%** of cancer deaths may be caused by tobacco, alcohol, high **body mass index** (BMI), low fruit and vegetable consumption, and not getting enough physical activity.

Types of Cancers

- **Carcinoma :** A cancer that starts in the skin or the tissues that line other organs.
- **Sarcoma :** A cancer of connective tissues such as bones, muscles, cartilage, and blood vessels.
- **Leukemia :** A cancer of the bone marrow, which creates blood cells.
- **Lymphoma and myeloma :** Cancers of the immune system.

Specific Types of Cancers	
• Appendix cancer	• Bladder cancer
• Bone cancer	• Brain cancer
• Breast cancer	• Cervical cancer

• Duodenal cancer	• Ear cancer
• Endometrial cancer	• Esophageal cancer
• Heart cancer	• Gallbladder cancer
• Kidney or renal cancer	• Laryngeal cancer
• Leukemia	• Lip cancer
• Liver cancer	• Lung cancer
• Lymphoma	• Mesothelioma
• Myeloma	• Oral cancers
• Ovarian cancer	• Pancreatic cancer
• Colon or colorectal cancer	• Penile cancer

Cancers in India

- According to a report published by the **World Health Organization** (WHO), one in ten Indians is diagnosed with cancer, and **1 in 15 dies** from it. As per reports of **Indian Council Of Medical Research India** is likely to witness a seven-fold increase in cancer cases by **2025**, caused by the increase in air pollution, the rise of chain smokers, sedentary lifestyles.
- **Lung cancer :** It is one of the most common cancers in India. According to a survey conducted by the **Indian Council of Medical Research** (ICMR), aside from being one of the most prevalent cancers in India, lung cancer accounts for **9.3%** of all death cases. There were about **70,275** lung cancer cases in **India** in **2022**.
- **Oral Cancer :** It is the most common cancer among men (11.2%) and the fifth most common cancer in women (4.3% of all cancer cases). Tobacco addiction continues to be the leading cause of oral cancer.
- **Breast Cancer:** It remains the leading cause of death among women in India. According to a 2020 report by the National Centre For Disease Informatics and Research, about 39.4% of cancer cases involving female patients tend to be breast cancer. In 2020 more than two lakh women were diagnosed with breast cancer.
- **Cervical Cancer :** According to a study published in the medical journal The Lancet, out of the **40%** of deaths that occurred due to cervical cancer globally, **23%** were from India and **17%** were from **China**. Moreover, one in four deaths caused by cervical cancer also occurs in India.
- According to a report published on cancerindia. org, esophageal cancer is the sixth most common cancer in India, as well as the sixth most common cause of death. Esophageal cancer occurs when cancerous cells grow inside your esophagus or food pipe. Men are more likely to be diagnosed with esophageal cancer.

Common types of Cancer treatment

- **Surgery :** Surgery removes as much of the cancer as possible. Surgery is often used in combination with some other therapy in order to make sure all of the cancer cells are gone.
- **Chemotherapy :** A form of aggressive cancer treatment that uses medications that are toxic to cells to kill rapidly dividing cancer cells. It may be used to shrink the size of a tumor or the number of cells in your body and lower the likelihood of the cancer spreading.
- **Radiation therapy :** It uses powerful, focused beams of radiation to kill cancer cells. Radiation therapy done inside of your body is called brachytherapy, while radiation therapy done outside of your body is called external beam radiation.
- **Stem cell (bone marrow) transplant :** This treatment repairs diseased bone marrow with healthy stem cells. Stem cells are undifferentiated cells that can have a variety of functions. These transplants allow doctors to use higher doses of chemotherapy to treat the cancer. A stem cell transplant is commonly used to treat leukemia.
- **Immunotherapy (biological therapy) :** It uses body's own immune system to attack cancer

cells. These therapies help antibodies recognize the cancer, so they can use your body's natural defenses to destroy cancer cells.

- **Hormone therapy :** It removes or blocks hormones that fuel certain cancers to stop cancer cells from growing. This therapy is a common treatment for cancers that may use hormones to grow and spread, such as certain types of breast cancer and prostate cancer.
- **Targeted drug therapy :** It uses drugs to interfere with certain molecules that help cancer cells grow and survive. Genetic testing may reveal if you are eligible for this type of therapy. It may depend on the type of cancer and the genetic mutations and molecular characteristics of the tumor.
- **Clinical trials :** Clinical trials investigate new ways to treat cancer, that may include testing the effectiveness of drugs that have already been approved by the **Food and Drug Administration** (FDA) but for other purposes. It also includes trying new drug.

Tumours

- **Tumours can be classified into two categories:**
  - **Benign tumour :** It remains confined to the place of origin and does not spread to other body parts. It is relatively harmless.
  - **Malignant tumour :** It spreads to other parts of the body and growth is rapid. This is serious and may cause death of the patient.

Deficiency Diseases

Vitamin	Diseases (due Deficiency)
Vitamin A (Retinol)	Night Blindness, Dry Skin, weak teeth and bones.
Vitamin B1 (Thiamie)	Weak memory, Disturbances in sleep, irritation.
Vitamin B2 (Riboflavin)	Sore throat, Amnesia, Skin Inflammation.
Vitamin B3 (Niacin)	Fatigue, Indigestion, Depression, Vomiting, Pellagra.
Vitamin B4 (Choline)	Blood disorder, nausea, skin disorders
Vitamin B5 (Pantothenic Acid)	Gastrointestinal problems, fatigue, headache.
Vitamin B6 (Pyridoxine)	Mood Swings, Confusion, Muscle Pains.
Vitamin B12 (Cobalamine)	Joint pain, Poor Dental health, Chronic Fatigue
Vitamin C (Ascorbic Acid)	Poor healing of wounds, Bleeding gums, Dry and scaly skin, Scurvy.
Vitamin D (Calcipherol)	Anxiety, Depression, Weak Immune System, Rickets.
Vitamin E (Tocopherol)	Visual Disturbances, General Unwellness.
Vitamin K (Phillioquine)	Haemorrhage, defective blood clotting, increased bleeding.

Degenerative Diseases

- Disease characterised by the worsening health conditions owing to increasing age, due to the deterioration of body organs and related functions causing disability, mortality and morbidity, since Neurons tend to deteriorate or degenerate over time.
- Neurodegeneration is the progressive loss of structure and function as well as the death of neurons, a condition which may lead to Neurodegenerative Diseases.

Examples of Neurodegenerative diseases: Alzheimer , Parkinson , Huntington, Amyotrophic lateral sclerosis, multiple sclerosis and Batten disease.

- **Alzheimer :** A progressive neurodegenerative disease caused by the degeneration of the neurons, with the brain progressively losing its cognitive functions as memory and language.

- **Parkinson's Disease:** A progressive neurological disease involving the melanin-containing nerve cells in the brainstem, with symptoms as shuffling gait, stooped posture, resting tremor, speech impediments. Movement difficulties and an eventual slowing of mental processes and dementia.
- **Huntington's disease:** A disease characterized by mental and physical deterioration initially lacks coordination and then eventually loses a steady gait, coordinated movement and mental abilities, ultimately leading to death.
- **Amyotrophic lateral sclerosis (ALS):** A disease caused by the death of neurons that control the voluntary muscles. Initially, there is a weakening of the arms or legs, eventually losesing the ability to use hands and feet.
- **Multiple sclerosis:** A neurodegenerative disease characterized by gradual accumulation of focal plaques of demyelination particularly in periventricular areas of the brain.
- **Batten disease:** A neurodegenerative disorder characterized by an excessive accumulation of lipofuscin in cells and tissues (due to a pathological mutation in CLN3 gene). The disease starts at the age of 5 – 8 years. Symptoms include seizures, ataxia, vision impairment.
- **Osteoporosis :** An age dependent disorder with loss of the normal density of bone. The bones become fragile and are easily fractured, even on minor fall or injury. Elderly men and women are most susceptible because of hormonal changes which occur with advancing age

FOOD BORNE DISEASES

- **Food Borne Diseases** occur when we consume **foods** or **drinks** containing **bacteria, viruses** or **parasites.** These microorganisms enter our bodies and multiply in our intestines or other tissues, causing infections that lead to various symptoms.

South-East Asia Region is responsible for a significant portion of the worldwide burden of **foodborne diseases** (FBD). Approximately **25%** of the global morbidity related to FBD and almost **42% of FBD-related mortality** can be attributed to this region.

Initiatives taken by FSSAI for Food Safety

- **Eat Right Movement:** The Eat Right Movement is a **public awareness campaign** that aims to **promote healthy eating habits** among **Indians.** The campaign focuses on the importance of eating a **balanced diet**, including plenty of **fruits, vegetables** and **whole grains.**
- **Hygiene Rating Scheme:** A **voluntary scheme** that rates **restaurants** and **other food businesses** on their hygiene standards. The scheme is designed to help consumers make **informed choices** about where to eat.
- **Blissful Hygienic Offering to God (BHOG):** The BHOG scheme is a food safety initiative that aims to improve the quality of food offered in temples and other religious places
- **Food Safety Compliance System (FoSCoS): FoSCoS** is an online platform that allows food businesses to self-assess their compliance with food safety regulations.

Food Fortification

- Food fortification is the process of adding **essential nutrients**, such as vitamins, minerals, or other beneficial substances, to foods in order to enhance their nutritional value.
- This strategy aims to address nutrient deficiencies and improve public health by providing essential elements in commonly consumed foods.

The FSSAI norms state that fortified rice should **contain iron, folic acid, and vitamin B12.** Rice may also be fortified with other **micronutrients** such as **Zinc, Vitamin A, Vitamin B1, Vitamin B2, Vitamin B3** and **Vitamin B6.**

Benefit of Rice Fortification

- Combating malnutrition and anaemia in cost effective manner.
- Preventing Cretinism, Goiter, Thyrotoxicosis, Brain damage .
- Improve foetal and neonatal health.

- The **Consumer Affairs Ministry** had issued uniform specifications for **fortified rice kernels** (FRK) for **Grade A** and common rice for procurement of **fortified rice stocks**, wherein 1% of FRK should be blended with normal rice. Fortified rice is distributed under the **public distribution system** and **midday meals.**
- The **Food Safety Standards** (Fortification of Foods) **Regulation, 2018**, is a regulation that was passed by the **Food Safety and Standards Authority of India** (FSSAI) to regulate the fortification of foods in India. The regulation specifies the foods that must be fortified, the levels of fortification, and the methods of fortification.
- The fortification of foods has been successful in **reducing micronutrient deficiencies.** For example, the **fortification of salt** with **iodine** has helped to reduce the number of **iodine-deficient countries** from 54 to 32 since 2003.

In India, **wheat flour** and **rice** are fortified with **iron, vitamin B12** and **folic acid. Milk** and **edible oil** are fortified with **vitamin A** and **D. Double fortified salt** is fortified with **iodine** and **iron.**

Genetic Diseases / Disorders

- Genetic diseases are disorders caused by abnormalities in an individual's DNA. These can be inherited from parents or result from mutations occurring spontaneously.

Types of Genetic Diseases

(A) Single-Gene Disorders (Mendelian Disorders) : Caused by mutations in a single gene. Inheritance patterns include:

- Autosomal Dominant : A single mutated copy of the gene causes disease.

Examples: Huntington's Disease, Marfan Syndrome and Neurofibromatosis

- Autosomal Recessive : Both copies of the gene must be mutated for the disease to manifest.

Examples: Cystic Fibrosis, Sickle Cell Anemia and Tay-Sachs Disease

- X-Linked Disorders : Caused by mutations in genes on the X chromosome, often affecting males more severely.

Examples: Hemophilia, Duchenne Muscular Dystrophy and Fragile X Syndrome

(B) Chromosomal Disorders : Caused by structural changes or an abnormal number of chromosomes.

Examples: Down Syndrome (Trisomy 21) – Extra copy of chromosome 21 ; Turner Syndrome (45, X0) – Affects females with a missing or incomplete X chromosome and Klinefelter Syndrome (XXY) – Males with an extra X chromosome.

(C) Multifactorial Disorders (Polygenic & Environmental Influences) : Result from mutations in multiple genes, often influenced by lifestyle or environmental factors.

Examples: Diabetes, Heart Disease, Alzheimer's Disease, Cancer (some forms like breast cancer with BRCA1/BRCA2 mutations)

D. Genetic Blood Disorders:

(A) Disorders Affecting Red Blood Cells (RBCs) : These conditions affect hemoglobin production, RBC shape, or RBC lifespan.

- **Sickle Cell Anemia :** Caused by a mutation in the HBB gene (chromosome 11), which codes for hemoglobin. It leads to the production of abnormal hemoglobin S (HbS), causing red blood cells to become rigid and crescent (sickle) shaped, reducing their ability to o carry oxygen leading to anemia and organ issues. National Mission to Eliminate Sickle Cell Anemia was launched in Union Budget 2023-24.
- **Thalassemia (Alpha & Beta) :** Caused by mutations in HBA1, HBA2 (alpha-thalassemia) or HBB (beta-thalassemia) genes. Leads to reduced hemoglobin production, causing severe anemia. Beta-thalassemia major (Cooley's anemia) requires lifelong blood transfusions.
- **Hereditary Spherocytosis :** Caused by mutations in genes affecting RBC membrane proteins (ANK1, SPTB). RBCs become spherical and get destroyed in the spleen, leading to anemia and jaundice.
- **G6PD Deficiency (Glucose-6-Phosphate Dehydrogenase Deficiency) :** Caused by mutations in the G6PD gene on the X chromosome. Leads to RBC breakdown (hemolysis) when exposed to oxidative stress (e.g., certain foods, infections, or drugs).

(B) Disorders Affecting White Blood Cells (WBCs): These disorders weaken the immune system and make individuals susceptible to infections.

- **Chronic Granulomatous Disease (CGD) :** Mutation in CYBB, NCF1, or other genes affects WBCs' ability to kill bacteria. Leads to frequent, severe bacterial and fungal infections.
- Severe Combined Immunodeficiency (SCID, "Bubble Boy Syndrome"). Caused by mutations in IL2RG or ADA genes. Leads to a lack of functional immune cells, making even minor infections life-threatening.

(C) Platelet Disorders (Bleeding & Clotting Disorders) : These conditions affect blood clotting and wound healing.

- **Hemophilia (Type A & B) Hemophilia A:** Caused by mutations in the F8 gene (deficient Factor VIII). Hemophilia B: Caused by mutations in the F9 gene (deficient Factor IX). Leads to excessive bleeding, even from minor injuries.
- **Von Willebrand Disease (VWD) :** Caused by mutations in the VWF gene. Leads to abnormal blood clotting, causing easy bruising and prolonged bleeding.
- **Bernard-Soulier Syndrome :** Mutation in genes affecting platelet adhesion. Results in excessive bleeding and easy bruising.

(D) Bone Marrow Disorders : These disorders affect blood cell production in the bone marrow.

- **Aplastic Anemia :** Can be genetic (due to mutations in TERT, TERC genes) or acquired. Causes bone marrow failure, leading to low RBCs, WBCs, and platelets.
- **Fanconi Anemia :** Caused by mutations in FA genes (FANCA, FANCC, etc.). Leads to bone marrow failure, leukemia risk, and physical abnormalities.
- **Myelodysplastic Syndromes** (MDS) : Can be caused by genetic mutations affecting bone marrow stem cells. Leads to ineffective blood cell production and a risk of leukemia.
- **Mitochondrial Disorders :** Caused by mutations in mitochondrial DNA (inherited only from the mother).

Examples: Leber's Hereditary Optic Neuropathy (LHON) and Mitochondrial Myopathy

Diagnosis of Genetic Diseases –

- **Karyotyping :** Examines chromosomal abnormalities.
- **Genetic Testing (PCR, Whole Genome Sequencing) :** Identifies gene mutations.
- **Newborn Screening :** Detects genetic disorders at an early stage in life.

Treatment

- **Gene Therapy :** Replacing faulty genes (e.g., for SCID).
- **CRISPR Gene Editing :** Emerging technology for correcting mutations.
- **Medications & Lifestyle Management :** Managing symptoms for conditions like diabetes.

Zoonotic Diseases

- Though **NCD 's** have been regarded equally threatening, **Communicable Diseases** throughout the course of human history have posed a threat to **human civilization** in form of **Pandemics**. From rats to **mosquitos**, vectors have stimulated various **viral infections** in a form or other **overpassing geographical frontiers**. With the advancement in medical technology, through Vaccinology and pharmacy, human have found vaccines and antibiotics to defeat the most threatening diseases, yet past few years have witnessed an upsurge in **Zoonotic diseases** owing to increase pace of interaction between the human and the wild posing serious threats to public health.
- In last two decades, **emerging zoonotic** diseases have been reported from **18** out of **22 countries** in the region, often, with explosive outbreaks and high fatalities. The recent emergence of **MERS-CoV** and **CoViD** exemplifies that the occurrence of these infections are unpredictable as they originate from **animals**, often these infections are caused by novel viruses and are only detected when **outbreaks occur.**
- An observation of the trend of these zoonotic diseases is that new pathogens from animals particularly viruses **remain unpredictable** and continue to emerge and spread across the countries.

- **Zoonosis** (zoonotic disease or zoonoses) is an infectious disease naturally is transmitted between species from animals to humans (or from humans to animals).
- Zoonotic disease is a disease or infection that can be transmitted naturally from vertebrate animals to **humans** or from **humans** to **vertebrate animals.**
- More than 60% of human pathogens are zoonotic in origin, which includes a wide variety of **bacteria, viruses, fungi, protozoa, parasites,** and other **pathogens.**

Classification of Zoonoses:

- **Endemic zoonoses:** Those which are present in many places and affect many people and animals.
- **Epidemic zoonoses :** Those which are sporadic in temporal and spatial distribution.
- **Emerging and re-emerging zoonoses :** Those which are newly appearing in a population or have existed previously but are rapidly increasing in incidence or geographical range.

Examples of the latter include Rift Valley fever, SARS, pandemic influenza H1N1 2009, Yellow fever, Avian Influenza (H5N1) and (H7N9), West Nile virus and the Middle East respiratory syndrome coronavirus (MERS-CoV) reported in the recent past.

- **Endemic :** A disease outbreak is endemic when it is consistently present but limited to a particular region. This makes the disease spread at predictable rates.

Example: Malaria is considered endemic in certain countries and regions.

- **Outbreak :** Outbreak is a greater-than-anticipated increase in the number of endemic cases. It can also be a single case in a new area. If it is not quickly controlled, an outbreak can become an epidemic.

Example : Dengue is endemic to certain regions of Africa, Central and South America, and the Caribbean. But in 2019 there was an outbreak of dengue fever in Hawaii, where the disease is not endemic.

- **Epidemic :** A disease that affects a large number of people within a community population, or region. It is an unexpected increase in the number of disease cases in a specific geographical area. An epidemic disease doesn't necessarily have to be contagious.

Examples: Yellow fever, Smallpox, Measles and Polio and West Nile fever.

- **Pandemic :** When a disease's growth is exponential. A viral disease, covering a wide area, affecting several countries and populations can be termed Pandemic. Pandemic is an epidemic with a passport.

Example : When COVID-19 was limited to Wuhan, China, it was an epidemic. The geographical spread turned it into a pandemic

- **Eastern Mediterranean Region** remains particularly **prone** to **zoonotic infections** owing to large number of people in the region living in **close proximity** to **animals**, increased volume of international trade, including trans-boundary mass population and livestock movement within neighbouring countries.

- As the region remains at the cross road of repeated outbreaks from **emerging infectious diseases**, **international travel** to and from the region either due to **tourism**, **business** or **religious reasons**, **globalization** and **variable levels** of **health systems capacity** to early **detect epidemics** have been identified as significant risk factors for emergence and rapid international spread of infectious diseases with zoonotic origin.

- The region has recently seen outbreaks from **Yellow fever** in **Sudan** , **Chikungunya** in **Yemen**, **West Nile fever** in **Tunisia** and **Q fever** in **Afghanistan** and **Iraq**. The region is home to a number of arbo and filoviruses. While outbreaks from **Crimean –Congo haemorrhagic fever** (CCHF) occur periodically in **Afghanistan, Iran** and **Pakistan**, as a seasonal surge, **nosocomial outbreaks** of the disease have been reported in recent years in **Iraq**, **United Arab Emirates** and **Sudan** in the region. The viral haemorrhagic fevers are perpetual risks in the region.

Modes of Transmission

- **Feco-Oral Transmission : Pathogens** from **feces** (waste) of an **infected person contaminate food, water**, or **surfaces**, and healthy individuals become infected by ingesting the contaminated items.

Examples : Hepatitis A, cholera, and some types of **gastrointestinal infections.**

- **Blood / Serum / Sexual Transmission :** Pathogens are present in **blood**, **serum**, or **body fluids** (like semen or vaginal fluids), and transmission occurs through **contact** with **infected fluids**. Can happen through **sexual contact**, **sharing needles**, or from mother to baby during **childbirth** or **breastfeeding**.

Examples : HIV, hepatitis B and **syphilis.**

- **Droplet Transmission :** Respiratory droplets containing **pathogens** are expelled when an infected person **coughs**, **sneezes**, **talks** or **breathes. Healthy individuals** can breathe in these droplets and become infected.

Examples : Flu, common cold and **COVID-19.**

- **Wound Break Transmission :** Pathogens enter the body through breaks in the skin, like cuts, scrapes, or surgical wounds. Usually occurs when **contaminated objects** or surfaces come into contact with **open wounds**.

Examples : **Tetanus** and some **bacterial skin infections.**

- **Zoonotic Transmission :** Diseases spread from **animals** to **humans**. Pathogens can be **directly transmitted** through **bites**, **scratches**, or contact with **bodily fluids** of infected animals. **Indirect transmission** can happen through contaminated food, water, or environments.

Examples : Rabies, Ebola and **COVID-19** (possibly originating from bats).

- **Direct contact:** Coming into contact with the saliva, blood, urine, mucous, feces, or other body fluids of an infected animal.

Examples : Petting or while coming in contact with animals or bites or scratches.

- **Indirect contact:** Coming into contact with areas where animals live and roam, or objects or surfaces that have been contaminated with germs.

Examples : Aquarium tank water, pet habitats, chicken coops, barns, plants, and soil, as well as pet food and water dishes.

- **Vector-borne:** Being bitten by a tick, or an insect like a mosquito or a flea.
- **Foodborne:** Eating or drinking something unsafe, such as unpasteurized (raw) milk, undercooked meat or eggs, or raw fruits and vegetables that are contaminated with feces from an infected animal. Contaminated food can cause illness in people and animals, including pets.
- **Waterborne:** Drinking or coming in contact with water that has been contaminated with feces from an infected animal.

Types of Zoonotic Diseases

- **Rabies :** Rabies is a disease that affects the nervous system of mammals. It is caused by a virus and is typically spread by an infected animal biting another animal or person. Rabies is a fatal disease; it cannot be treated once symptoms appear.
- **Leptospirosis :** A bacterial disease that affects humans & animals, caused by the bacteria genus Leptospira. It is spread through urine of infected animals, which can get into water or soil and can survive for weeks to months. Most common method of transmission is through direct contact with infected urine or other bodily fluids such as saliva, or contaminated water, soil, or food.
- **Plague (Yersinia enterocolitica, Yersinia pestis):** Plague is a zoonotic infection that has affected humans for thousands of years. In humans, the primary plague syndromes are bubonic, septicemic, and pneumonic. All of these result from infection with the gram-negative bacillus Yersinia pestis. The typical life-cycle of Y. Pestis starts within an insect vector followed by transmission to a mammalian host, typically rodents or other wild animals. Humans are only affected as **incidental hosts.**

Yersinia pestis is arguably one of the most important microbes in human history. It has caused **three documented pandemics**, with the **Black death** in **14th century Europe** leading to the death of up to **30% of the population.** The most recent **pandemic** began in the late **19th century** in **Asia** and **India**, and it continues today in **Africa**. Outside of this, the bacterium remains endemic in the Americas and Asia and also exists as a potential bioterrorism threat, spurring ongoing vaccine development.

- **Rickettsia (Rocky Mountain Spotted Fever) :** Rash associated with Rocky Mountain Spotted Fever. A disease caused by the bacterium Rickettsia rickettsii, which is carried by ticks.
- **West Nile Virus (WNV) :** It is the leading cause of mosquito-borne disease in the continental

United States. It is most commonly spread to people by the bite of an infected mosquito.

- **Blastomycosis (Blastomyces dermatitidis) :** Blastomycosis is a rare fungal infection usually acquired by inhaling the **spores** of a **fungus** (Blastomyces dermatitidis) that can be found in wood and soil.
- **Psittacosis (Chlamydophila psittaci, Chlamydia psittaci) :** Infection with Chlamydophila psittaci (formerly known as Chlamydia psittaci) is cause of systemic illness in companion birds (birds kept by humans as pets) and poultry. This illness is often referred to as avian chlamydiosis (also known as psittacosis, ornithosis, and parrot fever) in birds.

Nipah virus (NiV)

- A member of the family Paramyxoviridae, genus Henipavirus first discovered in 1999 following an outbreak of disease in pigs and people in Malaysia & Singapore. Nipah virus is also known to cause illness in pigs & people.
- The animal host reservoir for NiV is the fruit bat (genus Pteropus), also known as the flying fox. NiV is genetically related to Hendra virus (henipavirus known to be carried by bats); flying foxes were subsequently identified as the reservoir.
- Infection with NiV is associated with encephalitis (swelling of the brain), causing mild to severe illness and even death.

Chronic Wasting Disease (CWD)/ Zombie deer disease

- A neurological disorder affecting deer and other cervids (members of the deer family) caused by the abnormal growth of a misfolded protein called prion, that causes healthy brain proteins to become abnormal, leading to a range of symptoms.
- CWD is contagious; it can be transmitted freely within and among cervid populations, directly through animal-to-animal contact and indirectly through contact with objects or environments contaminated infectious material (including saliva, urine, faeces, and carcasses of CWD-infected animals).

Other Zoonotic Diseases
Trichinosis (Trichinella spiralis)
Cat Scratch Disease (Bartonella henselae)
Histoplasmosis (Histoplasma capsulatum)
Coccidiomycosis (Valley Fever)
Intestinal Illness Acquired From Animals : Including E. coli O157: H7, Cryptosporidium parvum, Campylobacter, and Salmonella.

Bioterrorism Diseases

- Diseases that may be used to **fuel bioterrorism**, divided into categories depending on the **ease of spread** and the **severity of illness** or **death** they cause.

Examples : Anthrax, Plague, Brucellosis, and Q fever.

- Ebola virus disease
- Highly pathogenic avian influenza
- Bovine spongiform encephalopathy
- CoViD

Corona Viruses (CoV)

- World Health Organisation defines Coronaviruses as a family of viruses (a group of RNA-based viruses) responsible for illness in humans or animals.
- The term Corona meant crown in Latin, derived by the spiky projections on viruses' surface resembling crowns. These viruses are known to cause mild to severe respiratory diseases, from common cold to viral pneumonia.

4 genera of Coronaviruses: Alphacoronavirus, Betacoronavirus, Gammacoronavirus & Deltacoronavirus.

7 strains of Coronaviruses (affecting Humans)

- Human Coronavirus 2296

- Human Coronavirus OC43
- SARS Coronavirus (Severe Acute Respiratory Syndrome Coronavirus)
- Human Coronavirus NL63 (New Haven Coronavirus)
- Human Coronavirus HKUI
- MERS Coronavirus (Middle East Respiratory Syndrome Coronavirus)
- 2019-Novel Coronavirus (Wuhan Coronavirus)

Severe Acute Respiratory Syndrome (SARS)

- The outbreak of a coronavirus in 2003 was identified as SARS-CoV, assumed to have transmitted through an animal virus from bats and then spread to civet cats. As per WHO, SARS was first found to have infected humans in 2002 in China. It lead to shortness of breath even leading to pneumonia.

Middle East Respiratory Syndrome (MERS)

- A novel coronavirus was identified in Saudi Arabia in 2012 and was named MERS-CoV. The virus was found to be transmitted between animals and humans and affected people from the Middle East, South Asia and Africa. As per WHO, it may have originated from bats and then camels

Coronavirus Disease 2019 (COVID-19) Pandemic

- A global outbreak of coronavirus caused by SARS-CoV-2 belonging to Betacoronavirus genus.
- CoViD-19 virus enter a person's body by getting attached to their cells and then getting inside them to duplicate RNA
- Cases of novel coronavirus (nCoV) were first detected in Wuhan, China in December 2019, which spreadedrapidly to other countries, leading WHO to declare a Public Health Emergency of International Concern (PHEIC) on 30 January, 2020 and characterize the outbreak as a pandemic on 11 March, 2020.

Name of CoVID Variants	Related Country
Alpha	United Kingdom
Beta	South Africa
Gamma	Brazil
Delta	India
Omicron (Subvariants : KP 3.3, KS 1.1, JN .1)	South Africa
XEC	Germany

- **HKU5-CoV-2 (2025):** Researchers in China identified a new bat coronavirus, HKU5-CoV-2, capable of utilizing the human ACE2 receptor for cell entry. This characteristic raises concerns about its potential to infect humans directly, similar to SARS-CoV-2. While there is no current evidence of human infection, continuous surveillance is essential.
- **COVID Mutation : Mutation** is a **natural process** where the **genetic material** of the virus changes over time. When the **virus replicates,** sometimes mistakes happen in copying its **genetic code**, leading to **new variations.**
- **ACE2 (Angiotensin Converting Enzyme 2): ACE2** is a protein found on the **surface** of **certain** cells in our body, especially in the **lungs** and other **organs**. It acts as a **keyhole** that the spike protein of the **COVID-19 virus** uses to enter **human cells**. This interaction allows the virus to infect our cells and cause illness.

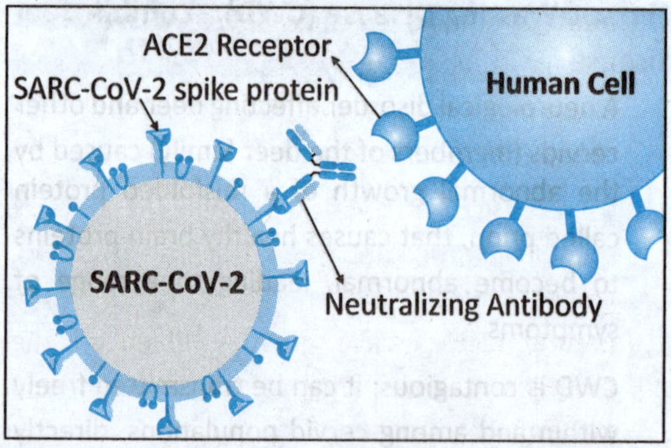

- **Hybrid Immunity** : Also known as **mixed immunity**, occurs when an **individual** is protected against a **disease** through a **combination of natural infection** and **vaccination**. For example, if someone gets infected with **COVID-19** and later receives a **vaccine**, their immune system develops a **strong defense** against the virus. This combined protection can offer a **robust shield** against the disease.
- **XBB, XBB 1 and XBB 1.5 : XBB, XBB.1** and **XBB 1.5** represent specific alterations in the **genetic code** of the **COVID-19 virus. XBB, XBB.1** and **XBB-1.5** mutations cause the COVID-19 virus to have a **weaker ability** to attach to cells in our body. This makes it less effective in infecting cells. However, these mutations also give the virus an advantage in escaping from our immune system's responses. This could potentially make our body's defenses less effective in fighting off the virus.

Factors leading to the emergence of Zoonotic Diseases

- Zoonotic disease have emerged as the result of **increased human contact** with the **animal hosts, animal tissues, vectors,** or environmental sources of the pathogens.
- It may also result from an increased prevalence of the agent in **domesticated** or wild animals or in vectors. Many currently emerging and **reemerging diseases** have **reservoirs in wildlife** or are **foodborne.**
- Other factors for their emergence include **altered human demographics** or **behavior,** ranging from **societal upheaval** (like war) that cause humans to **leave urban areas** to **simple changes** in **food preferences.**
- Factors such as **climate change, urbanization, animal migration** and **trade, travel** and **tourism, vector biology, anthropogenic factors,** and natural factors have greatly influenced the **emergence, re-emergence, distribution** and **patterns of zoonoses.**
- **Changing land use patterns** may alter the number of **reservoir hosts,** increase incidence of infection in these animals, encourage genetic changes in the pathogen (eg, recombination with other strains), or bring **animal hosts** or disease vectors into closer contact with humans.

Because many mosquitoes preferentially breed along the edges of forests rather than deep among the trees, **deforestation** can increase their numbers, potentially resulting in increased exposure to some **mosquito-transmitted diseases.**

- **Degradation of natural habitats,** as well as the **ready availability of food** near **human dwellings,** can encourage **wildlife** to move into suburban areas.
- **Growth of the human population** also exerts pressures that ultimately result in increased contact with wildlife.
- **Changing climates** can sometimes be a factor in disease emergence, particularly for arthropod-borne pathogens such as **Rickettsia spp.** A warmer climate not only allows vectors to survive the winter but also permits a longer transmission season.
- **Technological and industrial changes** in food production can contribute to disease emergence by increasing the concentration, movement, and mixing of animals.
- **Long-distance transport of animals** has been associated with increased shedding of enteric pathogens, including Salmonella. Decreased genetic diversity may eliminate species, breeds, or individuals with innate resistance to a disease.
- The development of large-scale farms and food-processing facilities has led to the exposure of greater numbers of humans to a contaminated food source.
- **Increased mobility** of humans, animals, and goods allows diseases to spread quickly.

- Viruses that formerly died out after affecting small numbers of animals or humans can now find many susceptible hosts within a short period. Severe acute respiratory syndrome (SARS), for instance, spread to nearly 30 countries on 6 continents within months of the initial outbreak.
- Occasionally, the pathogen itself may become more **virulent** or **better adapted** to humans, or it may undergo changes that affect transmission patterns.
- **Increased human susceptibility** has also contributed to the emergence or recognition of some opportunistic pathogens. The number of immunocompromised humans has been increased by factors such as the **AIDS epidemic**, the success of **organ transplantation programs**, and advancements allowing those with primary and **secondary immunodeficiencies** to live longer. Modern medicine also allows more humans, many of whom develop **chronic conditions**, to survive to an advanced age.

Climate Change and Zoonoses –

- Glacial Meltdowns due to climate change and global warming is creating new opportunities for the emergence and spread of zoonotic diseases.
- **Release of Ancient Pathogens :** Glaciers and permafrost have trapped viruses and bacteria for thousands or even millions of years. As ice melts, these ancient microbes can be released into the environment.

> Anthrax outbreak in Siberia (2016) was linked to thawing permafrost, which released spores from old reindeer carcasses.

- **Changes in Vector-Borne Disease Spread :** Warmer temperatures expand the range of mosquitoes, ticks, and other vectors that carry zoonotic diseases. Melting glaciers affect water bodies, creating breeding grounds for mosquitoes. Malaria, Dengue, and Zika are spreading to higher altitudes and previously cooler regions
- **Disruptions in Ecosystems and Food Chains :** Melting ice affects marine and terrestrial ecosystems, disturbing predator-prey relationships. Changes in food availability may lead animals to search for food in human settlements, increasing human-wildlife interactions and disease risks.
- **Contamination of Water Sources :** Melting glaciers release trapped organic material, providing nutrients for bacterial growth. Waterborne pathogens like Vibrio (which causes cholera) thrive in warmer waters.
- **Defrosting of Buried Carcasses and Human Remains :** Frozen animal and human remains from past pandemics could release pathogens.

> Scientists have detected viable smallpox and Spanish flu genetic material in permafrost samples.

- **Potential Future Risks :** Scientists fear the resurgence of unknown pathogens (Zombie viruses).

> Increased outbreaks of zoonotic diseases like rabies, hantavirus, and Lyme disease.

- Finally, some diseases are emerging not because they are more common but because they are **better recognized**. **Increased recognition** can result from improved **diagnostic techniques**, increased use of laboratories for identification of specific pathogens, and better awareness among physicians.
- **Principal means for preventing spread of zoonoses -**
  - Parasite recognition and control
  - Vaccination
  - Sanitation
  - Behavior training to prevent bites and scratches

Neglected Tropical Diseases

Neglected Tropical Diseases (NTDs) are infectious diseases prevalent in **tropical** and **subtropical regions**, affecting those in **poverty** and **lacking proper sanitation**. These diseases often spread through close contact with **infectious vectors** and **animals**. India bears the **world's largest burden of NTDs**. However, India has successfully eliminated several **NTDs**, such as **Guinea worm**, **Trachoma** and **Yaws**. Notably, the only disease ever eradicated is **smallpox**, highlighting the complexities of eliminating such diseases. Efforts to address NTDs are essential for improving public health in affected regions.

- **Important Neglected Tropical Diseases (Identified by WHO) :** Buruli ulcer; Chagas disease; dengue and chikungunya; dracunculiasis; echinococcosis; foodborne trematodiases; human African trypanosomiasis; leishmaniasis; leprosy; lymphatic filariasis; mycetoma, chromoblastomycosis and other deep mycoses; noma; onchocerciasis; rabies; scabies and other ectoparasitoses; schistosomiasis; soil-transmitted helminthiases; snakebite envenoming; taeniasis/cysticercosis; trachoma and yaws
- World Health Assembly declared 30th January as World Neglected Tropical Diseases Day.

Environment Related Diseases

- Environmental pollutants can cause health problems like respiratory diseases, heart/ cardiovascular diseases and various types of cancers.
- People with low incomes are more likely to inhabit polluted areas, consuming unsafe drinking water, making them vulnerable to environment related diseases, with Children and pregnant women at a higher risk of health problems related to pollution.
- ROE (Reports on the Environment by US Environmental Protection Agency) considers 9 indicators of health outcomes for which environmental exposures may be a risk factor Asthma, Birth Defects, Cancer, Cardiovascular Disease. Childhood Cancer, Chronic Obstructive Pulmonary Disease Infectious Diseases, Low Birth weight and Preterm Delivery.

Environment Related Diseases	Exposure to Pollutants
Mercury poisoning/ Minamata disease	High level exposure to methylmercury
Cadmium (Cd) poisoning	Kidney disease, osteoporosis Cardiovascular diseases and cancer
Lead exposure	Anaemia, hypertension, renal impairment, immunotoxicity and toxicity to reproductive organs

- **Cancers:** Environmental contaminant exposures are known risk factors for certain types of cancers. Examples include radon and lung cancer and arsenic and skin cancer. Outdoor air pollution and environmental tobacco smoke are also known risk factors for cardiovascular diseases. Particulate matter has been demonstrated to be a likely causal factor in both cardiovascular disease morbidity.
- **Respiratory Diseases:** Chronic obstructive pulmonary disease (COPD) and Asthma are two major chronic respiratory diseases. COPD is a group of diseases characterized by airflow obstruction, resulting in breathing-related symptoms.
- **Pathogenic Diseases:** Bacterial contamination of drinking water as the cause of many cases of gastrointestinal illness – leading to Waterborne diseases as typhoid fever and cholera meanwhile Legionellosis can be contracted from naturally occurring bacteria found in water

and spread through poorly maintained artificial water systems

- **Congenital Diseases:** Genetic or chromosomal aberrations resulting of exposure to chemicals, exposure to viruses and bacteria, and use of certain medications, cigarettes, or alcohol by mother during pregnancy.
- **Radioactive Radiation Exposure:** Cancers of the bile ducts, bone, brain, breast, colon, esophagus, gall bladder, liver, lung (bronchiolo, alveolar cancer), pancreas, pharynx, ovary, salivary gland, small intestine, stomach, thyroid, urinary tract (kidney/renal, pelvis, urinary bladder, and urethra), Leukemia (except chronic lymphocytic leukemia), Lymphomas (except Hodgkin's disease), Multiple myeloma (Cancer of Plasma cells), Non-malignant thyroid nodular disease, Parathyroid adenoma, Posterior subcapsular cataracts and Tumors of the brain and Central Nervous System.

Rare Diseases

- Rare disease is defined as a health condition of low prevalence affecting a small number of people as compared with other prevalent diseases.

WHO defines Rare Disease as often debilitating lifelong disease or disorder with a prevalence of 1 or less, per 1000 population.

European Union defines Rare Diseases as a life-threatening or chronically debilitating condition affecting no more than 5 in 10,000 people

In USA, Rare diseases are defined as a disease that affecting fewer than 200,000 patients in the country (6.4 in 10.000 people).

Japan identifies Rare diseases as diseases with fewer than 50,000 prevalent cases (0.04%) in the country.

Rare Disease Day is observed every year on 28 February (29 in leap years) since 2008.

- **Commonly reported Rare Diseases in India:** Primary immunodeficiency disorders, Lysosomal storage disorders (Gaucher's disease, Mucopolysaccharidoses, Pompe disease, fabry disease), Small molecule inborn errors of metabolism (Maple Syrup urine disease, organic acidemias), Cystic Fibrosis, Osteogenesis imperfecta, Forms of muscular dystrophies and spinal muscular atrophy, etc.
- Ministry of Health and family Welfare, Government of India formulated a National Policy for Treatment of Rare Diseases (NPTRD) in July, 2017 and implemented National Policy for Rare Diseases (NPRD) in March 2021 that aims at lowering the incidence & prevalence of rare diseases based on an integrated & comprehensive preventive strategy, constraints on resources and access to affordable health care to patients of rare diseases.

Allergies

- Allergy is a hypersensitivity disorder of the immune system that results in the body's negative reaction towards otherwise innocuous substances like food, common medicines, dust and pollen.
- Allergen is a substance that causes an abnormally vigorous immune response as it enters human body, triggering the immune system to fight off a perceived threat that would otherwise be harmless to the body.

Types of Allergies	Causative Agents
Airborne allergens	Dust and pollen.
Animal dander	Material shed from animal skin such as skin cells. Similar to human dandruff.
Food allergens	Shell-fish, dairy products, nuts and/or seeds and gluten, eggs and fish.

Medications	Aspirin and Penicillin.
Insect stings	Wasps and bees.
Plants	Grass and stinging nettles.
Substances	Latex.

Antimicrobial Resistance (AMR)

- AMR is the **ability of a microorganism** (like bacteria, viruses, and some parasites) to stop an **antimicrobial** (such as antibiotics, antivirals and antimalarials) from working against it.

Drivers of AMR

- Lack of access to clean water, sanitation and hygiene (WASH) for both humans and animals.
- Poor infection and disease prevention and control in health care facilities and farms.
- Poor access to quality affordable medicines, vaccines and diagnostics.
- Lack of awareness and knowledge.
- Lack of enforcement of legislation.
- Misuse and overuse of anti-microbials.

- AMR, or **Antimicrobial Resistance**, occurs when microorganisms like **bacteria**, viruses, and **parasites** become **capable of evading the effects of antimicrobial treatments** such as **antibiotics, antivirals** and **antimalarials.**
- This resistance is escalating, while the creation of **new antibiotics** has slowed. From **1980 to 2000, 63 antibiotics** were approved, but only **15 new drugs gained approval** between **2000** and **2018.**
- Among the 7 most dangerous **drug-resistant bacteria**, vaccines are solely available for those causing **pneumonia** and **tuberculosis.**
- This emphasizes the need for intensified efforts to combat AMR and enhance our arsenal against infectious diseases.

Factors leading to Antimicrobial Resistance

- **Poor Hygiene and Infection Control:** Insufficient hygiene practices can aid the spread of resistant microorganisms.
- **Antimicrobial Overuse:** Excessive use of antimicrobial drugs, like antibiotics, contributes to AMR.
- **Doctor Over-Prescription and Non-Prescription Purchases:** Over-prescribing and buying without prescriptions fuel the issue.
- **Incomplete Drug Courses:** Stopping antimicrobial treatment prematurely allows surviving microbes to develop resistance.
- **Agricultural Antibiotic Use:** Adding antibiotics to animal feed promotes resistance.
- **Environmental Impact:** Waste from farms, factories, and healthcare settings, as well as communal practices like mass bathing, can introduce AMR via the environment.

Indian Initiatives against AMR

- National programme on AMR containment
- National Action Plan on Antimicrobial Resistance (NAP-AMR)
- Red Line campaign
- Integrated One Health Surveillance Network for Antimicrobial Resistance
- FSSAI has set certain guidelines limiting the antibiotics in food products
- India's medical societies adopted the Chennai Declaration separate Schedule H-1

Fats, Transfacts and Health Concerns

Fats, also known as **dietary fats** are essential **nutrients** that provide **energy** and **play vital** roles in the body's functioning. They are a type of **macronutrient**, along with **carbohydrates** and **proteins.**

Types of Fat	
Trans Fats	• **Solid or Semi Solid at Room Temperature.** • **Sources:** Primarily artificially created through hydrogenation, found in many processed and fried foods. • **Health Implications:** Trans fats are harmful to health and can raise "bad" LDL cholesterol levels • **Recommendation:** It's best to avoid trans fats as much as possible by checking food labels and opting for healthier alternatives. • Saturated fats can **raise LDL cholesterol** and increase **heart disease risk**, unsaturated fats are considered healthier options. Trans fats are **artificial fats** that should be avoided due to their negative impact on heart health.
Saturated Fats	• Usually Solid at Room Temperature. • **Sources:** Animal products like meat, butter, full-fat dairy, and some plant sources like coconut oil and palm oil. • **Health Implications:** Consuming excessive saturated fats can raise "bad" LDL cholesterol levels, increasing the risk of heart disease. • **Recommendation:** It's advised to limit the intake of saturated fats and choose healthier sources of fat.
Unsaturated Fats	• Usually Liquid at Room Temperature. • **Types:** Monounsaturated and polyunsaturated fats. • **Monounsaturated Sources:** Olive oil, avocados, nuts, and seeds. • **Polyunsaturated Sources:** Fatty fish (omega-3s), vegetable oils (omega-6s), flaxseeds, and walnuts. • **Health Benefits:** Unsaturated fats are considered heart-healthy and can improve cholesterol levels. Omega-3 fatty acids have anti-inflammatory properties. • **Recommendation:** Replacing saturated fats with unsaturated fats in the diet is generally beneficial for health.

Initiatives to Tackle Trans- Fats

- **World Health Organization** (WHO) has undertaken significant efforts to eliminate trans fats from the **global food supply**. Their initiative is outlined in the **Countdown to 2023 report**, which aims to **phase out trans fats** to improve public health.
- To achieve this goal, WHO has introduced the **Replace action framework** that focuses on **eliminating industrially produced trans fats** from **foods**. The recommended intake of trans fats, according to WHO, should be less than **1%** of the total energy consumed.

Initiative aligns with WHO's broader Triple Billion target, which includes 3 main objectives:–

- Ensuring one billion more people benefit from universal health coverage.
- Enhancing protection for one billion more people against health emergencies.
- Ensuring one billion more people enjoy better health and well-being.

Indian Initiatives

- **TFA-Free Country Target:** India aims to become a trans fat-free country by phasing out the use of trans fats in food products.
- **Phased Reduction:** The country has implemented a phased reduction plan, aiming to limit trans fats in all food products that contain oils and fats to less than 2%. This regulation came into effect on January 1, 2022.
- **Trans Fat-Free Logo:** A distinctive logo has been introduced to indicate that a food product contains minimal trans fats. For a food product to bear the logo, it must have **less than 0.2g of trans fats per 100g or 100ml.** Edible oils or fats should contain less than **1g of trans fats per 100ml or 100g to qualify for the logo.**

IMMUNITY

- Immunity refers to the **body's ability** to prevent the **invasion** of **pathogens**.

- Pathogens are **foreign disease-causing substances**, such as **bacteria** and **viruses**, and people are exposed to them every day.
- **Antigens** are **attached** to the **surface of pathogens** and stimulate an **immune response** in the body.

- An **immune response** is the **body's defense system** to fight against **antigens** and **protect** the **body**.
- **Immunity** to a disease is achieved through the **presence of antibodies** to that disease in a person's system.
- Antibodies are proteins produced by the body to **neutralize** or **destroy toxins** or **disease-carrying organisms**. Antibodies are **disease-specific**.
- For example, **measles antibody** will protect a person who is exposed to **measles disease** but will have no effect if he or she is exposed to mumps.

Terminologies related to Immunity

- **Infection-induced immunity :** It is defined as the immune protection in an unvaccinated individual after one or more infections.
- **Vaccine-induced immunity :** It is defined as the immune protection in an individual who has not been previously infected with a virus but has completed a primary series of any vaccine, or has also received a booster vaccination.
- **Hybrid immunity :** It is defined as the immune protection in individuals who have had one or more doses of a vaccine and experienced at least one infection before or after the initiation of the vaccination.
- **Herd Immunity :** Herd Immunity also known as Population immunity is the indirect protection from an infectious disease that happens when a population is immune either through vaccination or immunity developed through previous infection.

WHO supports achieving herd immunity through vaccination, not by allowing a disease to spread through any segment of the population, as this would result in unnecessary cases and deaths.

Types of Immunity
- Innate Immunity
- Acquired Immunity

Innate Immunity

- **Innate immunity** is the **body's first line of defense**, acting rapidly to **prevent infections** regardless of the **specific pathogen.**
- **Innate immunity is a non-specific defense mechanism present from birth. It includes several types of barriers that work together to provide immediate protection against various pathogens:**
    - **Physical Barriers:** Skin forms the first protection barrier, covering the whole body.
    - **Physiological Barriers:** Stomach acid and other digestive enzymes create an inhospitable environment for pathogens.
    - **Cellular Barriers:** White blood cells (WBCs), specifically B cells and T cells, are part of the immune response. They identify and neutralize pathogens.
    - **Cytokine Barriers:** Molecules like interferons help regulate the immune response and inhibit the spread of infections.

Acquired Immunity

- **Acquired immunity develops over time in response to exposure to pathogens or vaccines. It is specific and adaptable, involving two main types:**
    - **Active Immunity:** The immune system produces its own antibodies after encountering a pathogen or receiving a vaccine.

- **Passive Immunity:** Antibodies are transferred from an external source, like a mother to her baby through breastfeeding or through medical treatments like immune globulin injections.

- Together, innate and acquired immunity help the **body recognize** and **fight off infections**, maintaining overall health.

- **Primary** and **secondary immune responses** are carried out with the help of two special types of **lymphocytes** present in our blood, i.e., **B-lymphocytes** and **T-lymphocytes**.

B Cells

- **B-lymphocytes,** also known as **B cells**, are a type of **white blood cell** that plays a vital role in the **adaptive immune system**. They are responsible for producing antibodies, which are **proteins** that **bind** to and **neutralize foreign invaders,** such as **bacteria** and **viruses.**

- **Antibodies** stick to **germs** and **mark** them for destruction by other immune cells.

- B cells are like the **intelligence agents** of our immune system, recognizing different threats.

T Cells

- T cells directly attack **infected** or **abnormal cells** in our body.

- They can also help **B cells** make more **antibodies** for a **stronger defense.**

- **T cells** play the role of **soldiers fighting** against **infections** and **cancer cells.**

B cells and **T cells** cooperate to create a **robust immune response**. When a **pathogen** enters our body, **B cells** produce **antibodies,** while T cells help **identify** and **eliminate infected cells.**

VACCINES

- The term Vaccine was derived from the **Edward Jenner's 1796** use of the term **Cow pox** (Latin **variolae vaccinae,** adapted from the Latin **vaccīn-us**, from **vacca** cow). He was the pioneer of using **cow pox vaccines** to prevent **small pox infections.**

- Vaccines take advantage of the **body's natural ability** to learn how to **eliminate** almost any **disease-causing germ**, or **microbe**, that attacks it. Once vaccinated the body remembers how to protect itself from the microbes it has encountered before.

- Vaccine is a **biological preparation** that helps the **immune system recognise** and **defend body** against **specific infectious diseases** and **improves immunity** towards a **particular disease.** It usually consists of a harmless version of disease causing microorganism or a small part of it in form of a protein or a genetic material induced within the body to develop resistance/ immunity against the infectious pathogen in due course of time.

- **Traditional vaccines** contain either **parts of microbes** or **whole microbes** that have been killed or weakened so that they don't cause disease.

TYPES OF VACCINES

Based on Medium of providing vaccine

- **Intramuscular (IM):** Injected into **muscles,** often the arm. **Examples-** include **flu shots.**

- **Intravenous (IV):** Administered directly into veins, less common due to complexity.

- **Subcutaneous (SC):** Injected under the skin, usually in the arm. **Measles vaccines** are given this way.

- **Nasal:** Sprayed into the nose, offering a **painless option** for **flu vaccines.**

- **Oral:** Swallowed as **drops** or tablets. **Polio vaccine** is an example.

Based on Pathogen

- **Types of Vaccines (based on Pathogen)**
  - Live Attenuated
  - Inactivated
  - Subunit
  - Toxoid
  - Recombinant
  - mRNA
  - DNA

Live Attenuated Vaccines

- **A live attenuated vaccine** uses weakened forms of **disease-causing germs.** These germs are still alive but not strong enough to cause illness in most people. Because they closely **resemble natural infections, live attenuated vaccines** stimulate **strong** and **long-lasting immune** responses. Just a few doses of these vaccines can offer **lifelong protection** against the germ and the disease it causes. However, they might pose risks for individuals with **compromised immune systems** and it **require refrigeration** for storage.

Live vaccines are employed to safeguard against following diseases:

- Rotavirus
- Smallpox
- Chickenpox
- Yellow fever
- Measles, Mumps, Rubella (MMR combined vaccine)

Inactivated Vaccines

- Inactivated vaccines use killed versions of **disease-causing germs.** These germs are no longer alive, but they can still stimulate the immune system. While **inactivated vaccines** might not provide immunity as strong as live vaccines, they are safer for individuals with **weakened immune systems. Multiple doses** or **booster shots** are often needed to **maintain long-term protection.**

Inactivated vaccines are used to protect against following diseases :

- Hepatitis A
- Influenza
- Polio
- Rabies

Subunit Vaccines

- **Subunit vaccines** contain **purified, antigenic parts** of a pathogen that elicit a **protective immune response.** Unlike live attenuated or inactivated vaccines, they exclude the entire pathogen and instead focus on essential parts like proteins, polysaccharides, or peptides.

Subunit Vaccines

- Subunit vaccines use only antigenic portions of the pathogen.
- They're safer and more stable as they lack **live components,** posing no **disease risk.**
- They're well-suited for immuno compromised individuals.
- Subunit vaccines have manufacturing complexity, possibly necessitating adjuvants and booster shots.
- Subunit vaccines offer a balance between **safety** and **effectiveness,** making them a valuable tool in disease prevention.

Polysaccharide Vaccines

Polysaccharides are like many **carbohydrates stuck** together. Some vaccines use these to trigger an **immune response.** Most vaccines are made from **proteins,** so vaccines with polysaccharides are unique and special. They help our body fight diseases in a different way.

Conjugate Vaccine

- A conjugate vaccine is a type of **subunit vaccine** which combines a **weak antigen** with a strong antigen as a carrier so that the immune system has a stronger response to the weak antigen.
- Conjugate vaccines use both **weak** and **strong parts** of germs to make the immune system pay better attention and fight effectively. This is because some germs have parts that the immune system doesn't notice well on their own. By connecting the weak parts to stronger ones, the immune response becomes stronger.

- Most commonly, the weak antigen is a **polysaccharide** that is attached to **strong protein antigen**. However, **peptide/protein** and **protein/protein conjugates** have also been developed.

Toxoid Vaccines

- Toxoid vaccines target **bacterial toxins** that cause diseases. Instead of using live or inactivated pathogens, these vaccines use weakened versions of toxins that have been rendered harmless through chemical treatment.

- Toxoid vaccines focus on bacterial toxins.
- Toxins are modified to be non-toxic while retaining their antigenic properties.
- Immune response to toxoid prepares the body to neutralize actual toxins.
- Examples include vaccines for tetanus and diphtheria.
- Toxoid vaccines protect against diseases caused by toxins rather than the pathogens themselves.

- **Toxoid vaccines** are crucial for **preventing diseases** where **bacterial toxins** play a significant role, **bolstering** our immune system against **harmful effects.**

Recombinant Viral Vector Vaccine

- **A recombinant viral vector vaccine** employs a harmless virus to **transport specific** parts of a pathogen, like the **spike protein** of the coronavirus. This prompts an immune response without causing illness. **Genetic instructions** for producing the **protein** are inserted into a safe virus using **recombinant DNA technology.**

- Utilizes a safe virus as a delivery vehicle.
- **Example:** Coronavirus spike protein.
- Induces immune response without causing disease.
- Genetic coding inserted into the virus.
- Various viruses, including influenza, vesicular stomatitis virus, measles virus, and adenovirus, are used as vectors.
- **Adenovirus** is a viral vector in some COVID-19 vaccine candidates.

- **Recombinant viral vector vaccines** leverage viral transport systems to **stimulate immunity,** offering a promising avenue for **disease prevention** without causing harm.

mRNA Vaccine

- An mRNA vaccine employs a copy of a molecule called **messenger RNA** (mRNA) to trigger an immune response. The vaccine introduces **antigen-encoding mRNA molecules** into **immune cells.** These cells use the provided mRNA as **instructions** to construct proteins typically produced by pathogens or cancer cells. These proteins then stimulate an **adaptive immune response,** educating the body to recognize and eliminate the **corresponding pathogens** or **cancer cells.**
- **mRNA vaccines** represent a **cutting-edge approach, capitalizing** on the body's natural processes to bolster immunity against disease.

Covid 19 Vaccines	
• mRNA	• Viral Vector
• Subunit	• DNA : Zykov-d
• Nasal	

mRNA Covid Vaccine

- It is a type of **Nucleic Acid Vaccine** which uses **genetic material** from a **pathogen** to stimulate an immune response.

How does mRNA vaccine work

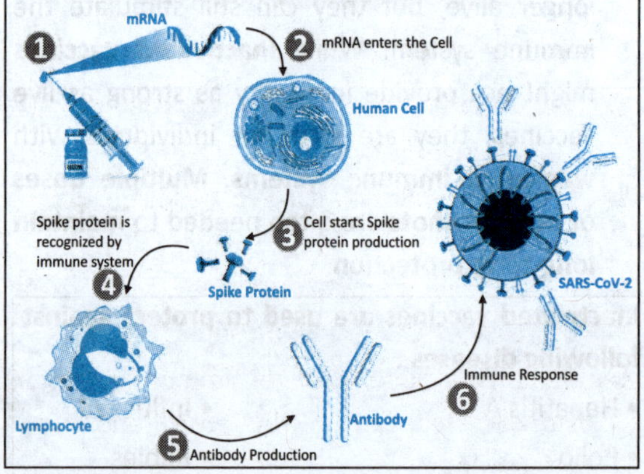

- An **mRNA vaccine** uses a copy of a molecule called **messenger RNA** (mRNA) to produce an **immune response**. The vaccine delivers molecules of **antigen-encoding mRNA** into immune cells, which use the **designed mRNA** as a **blueprint** to build foreign protein that would normally be produced by a **pathogen** (such as a virus) or by a cancer cell.

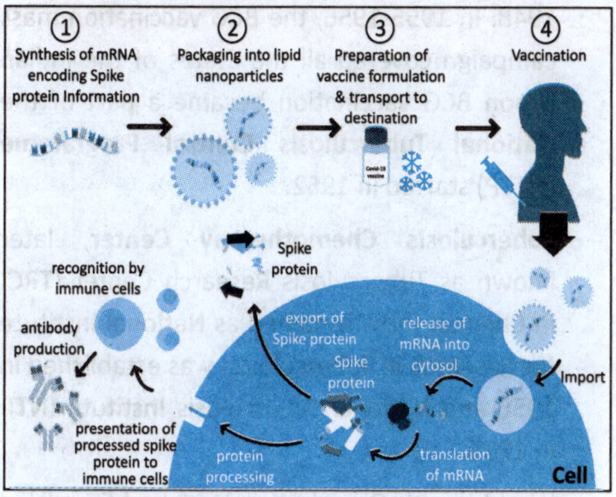

Self Amplifying mRNA vaccine for Covid

- These protein molecules stimulate an **adaptive immune response** that teaches the body to identify and destroy the corresponding pathogen or cancer cells.
- **Arcturus Therapeutics** developed **ARCT-154**, a **self-amplifying mRNA vaccine**, showing potential against COVID-19. Unlike conventional mRNA vaccines that code for the virus's spike protein, this type includes **4 extra proteins,** which enhance **mRNA replication.**

> - ARCT-154 is a self-amplifying mRNA vaccine by Arcturus Therapeutics.
> - Traditional mRNA vaccines code for the virus's spike protein.
> - Self-amplifying mRNA vaccines have extra proteins for mRNA amplification.
> - Benefits include stronger immunity, easier storage, reduced mRNA dose, and cost-effectiveness.

DNA Vaccines

- DNA vaccines involve **inserting** a **DNA piece** containing the antigen into a **bacterial plasmid.** These plasmids, along with **electroporation** (process not important), are injected into muscles. DNA vaccines are known for their **stability** and don't need **ultra-cold storage,** making them **cost-effective.**
- DNA segment **encoding antigen** inserted into **bacterial plasmid.**
- Plasmids injected into **muscles** with **electroporation.**
- DNA vaccines offer stability, eliminating the need for **ultra-cold storage.**
- This makes them **cost-effective** and **accessible.**

ZyCoV-D

- **ZyCoV-D**, developed by **Zydus Cadila,** has received emergency use **authorization.** It's the **world's first DNA vaccine** against **COVID-19.** Created in collaboration with the DBT under **Mission Covid Suraksha.** It uses a specialized delivery method called tropis, allowing needle-free administration through the skin. Tropis enables needle-free administration by using a precise stream of jet to penetrate the skin.

Covishield

- **Covishield** is a **viral vector vaccine** developed by **Oxford University** and **AstraZeneca.** This vaccine works by using a **modified virus** (viral vector) that carries genetic material from the **COVID-19 virus.** When this viral vector enters your cells, it instructs them to produce copies of the **spike protein** found on the **COVID-19 virus.** The immune system responds by creating **antibodies** and **defensive white blood cells.** If One later encounters the actual COVID-19 virus, these antibodies will fight it off.

> - Covishield is a viral vector vaccine by Oxford and AstraZeneca.
> - It employs a modified virus (viral vector) to deliver COVID-19 genetic material.

- Viral vector instructs cells to produce spike proteins.
- Immune response produces antibodies and defensive cells.
- Antibodies provide protection against COVID-19 upon exposure to the virus.

Sputnik V is also developed using similar technology to **Covishield**.

Covaxin

- **Covaxin**, developed by **Bharat Biotech**, is created using inactivated virus technology. This vaccine involves using a virus that has been rendered non-functional, so it cannot cause disease. When the inactivated virus is introduced into the body, it triggers an immune response, prompting the immune system to recognize and fight the virus if encountered in the future.
- **Covaxin's inactivated virus** approach offers a safe and proven method to stimulate immunity against COVID-19.

iNCOVACC by Bharat Biotech

- Bharat Biotech has introduced iNCOVACC, the **world's first intranasal** (Taken through nose) vaccine for COVID-19. This vaccine has obtained emergency use authorization.
- Utilizing an **adenovirus vector,** iNCOVACC represents a novel approach in the fight against the pandemic.

Vaccination in India

- The first recorded Vaccination in India was undertaken for Smallpox, that originated in India or Egypt 3,000 years ago as noted by Thucydides im 430 BC and Rhazes (Abu Bakr) in 910 AD who reported that people affected by smallpox were protected from the future infections.
- One of the first recorded smallpox epidemics was from Goa in India (1545 AD). The first doses of smallpox vaccine lymph in India arrived in May 1802, when Anna Dusthall (3 year old child from Mumbai) became the first in India to receive a smallpox vaccine on June 14, 1802. The **Compulsory Vaccination Act** was passed in India in 1892 to ensure coverage for smallpox epidemic.
- BCG vaccine laboratory was set up in Guindy in 1948. In 1955-1956, the BCG vaccination mass campaign covered all the States of the Indian Umon BCG vaccination became a part of the **National Tuberculosis Control Programme** (NTCP) started in 1962.
- **Tuberculosis Chemotherapy Center**, later known as Tuberculosis Research Center (TRC) in Chennai (now renamed as National Institute for Research in Tuberculosis) was established in 1956 and National Tuberculosis Institute (NTI) in 1959.
- World Health Organization launched Expanded Programme on Immunization (EPI) in 1974 and India launched National Immunization programme called **Expanded Programme of Immunization (EPI)** in 1978 with the Introduction BCG, OPV, DPT and typhoid-paratyphoid vaccines. Tetanus toxoid vaccine for pregnant women was added in EPI in 1983. EPI was rechristened with some major change in focus by the launch of **Universal Immunization Programme (UIP)** on November 19, 1985. The measles vaccine was added to the existing schedule.
- Immunization was given the status of one of the five National Technology Missions launched in 1986, with the objective of improving coverage with existing antigens, and developing self-sustainability in vaccine production.
- National Technology Mission on immunization helped in modernization and upgradation of vaccine facilities and by 1990-1991 India

became self-sufficient for all vaccines (including measles) except for OPV.

- An organized surveillance mechanism was established as National Polio Surveillance Project (NPSP) in 1997 (Collaboration between Indian Government and WHO). NPSP over the period built an institutional mechanism for acute flaccid paralysis (AFP) surveillance
- India reported the last case of wild polio virus (Type 1) on January 13, 2011 from Howrah district in West Benga.l On February 25, 2012, the World Health Organization removed India from polio endemic countries
- **Universal Immunization Programme** was launched in 1985 with 6 antigens (BCG, OPV, DPT and measles) in the programme and no new antigen was added to the programme for the next 16 years. During this period, globally and in India, a number of new vaccines became licensed and available in the market. The first new antigen added since the beginning of UIP was hepatitis B vaccine in 2002-2003. In 2010, India became the last country in the world to introduce second dose of measles vaccine under the national immunization programme.
- **The first Multi Year strategic Plan (MYP)** for UIP in India (2005-2010) was launched in 2005. India released the first National Vaccine Policy in 2011, that provided guiding principles for functioning of immunization programme in the country.
- **India's COVID-19 Vaccination Strategy** : India commenced its COVID-19 vaccination drive on January 16, 2021, offering free vaccinations to its citizens. The government placed advance purchase orders for vaccines like Covishield and Covaxin to ensure adequate supply. By March 2023, over 2.2 billion doses had been administered, covering a significant portion of the eligible population.

CoViD Vaccines approved in India

- **Covishield:** Non-replicating viral vector vaccine, Developed by the University of Oxford in collaboration with AstraZeneca, Covishield is manufactured under license by the Serum Institute of India (SII). Received emergency use authorization in India in January 2021.
- **Covaxin** : An indigenous vaccine – Inactivated virus vaccine, developed by Bharat Biotech in collaboration with the Indian Council of Medical Research (ICMR) and the National Institute of Virology (NIV), Granted emergency use authorization in India in January 2021.
- **Sputnik V** : Non-replicating viral vector vaccine, Developed by the Gamaleya Research Institute in Russia, Received emergency use authorization in India in April 2021.
- **Corbevax** : Protein subunit vaccine, Developed by Biological E. Limited in India, Received emergency use authorization in India in December 2021.
- **Covovax** : Protein subunit vaccine, a version of the Novavax vaccine, manufactured under license by the Serum Institute of India, Granted emergency use authorization in India in December 2021.
- **ZyCoV-D** : Plasmid DNA vaccine, Developed by Zydus Cadila, Received emergency use authorization in India in August 2021, notably for individuals aged 12 and above.
- **iNCOVACC** : Intranasal vaccine, Developed by Bharat Biotech, Granted emergency use authorization in India in September 2022.

Digital Platforms for Vaccine Management

- **CoWIN Platform:** Launched in January 2021, CoWIN is a digital platform designed to streamline COVID-19 vaccination processes, including registration, appointment scheduling, and certification. It has been pivotal in managing the large-scale vaccination drive across the country.

- **eVIN (Electronic Vaccine Intelligence Network):** This web-based system enhances vaccination efficiency by operationalizing vaccine management across various states, ensuring real-time data tracking and inventory management.
- **Oral Cholera Vaccine (Hillchol):** In August 2024, Bharat Biotech completed late-stage trials for Hillchol, an oral cholera vaccine. The company plans to produce up to 200 million doses annually to address global shortages amid rising cholera outbreaks.
- **Malaria Vaccine (R21/Matrix-M):** Developed through a collaboration between the University of Oxford and the Serum Institute of India, the R21/Matrix-M malaria vaccine received World Health Organization (WHO) recommendation in 2023. Priced under $4 per dose, the Serum Institute began supplying millions of doses to African countries where malaria is endemic.

UNIVERSAL IMMUNIZATION PROGRAM

Immunization Programme in India was introduced in **1978** as **Expanded Programme of Immunization** (EPI) by the **Ministry of Health and Family Welfare.** In **1985**, the Programme was modified as **Universal Immunization Programme** (UIP). **UIP prevents mortality** and morbidity in children and pregnant women against **12 vaccine-preventable diseases.**

- The **Universal Immunization Programme** (UIP) is a **public health programme** that provides **free vaccines to children** and **pregnant women** in India. **UIP** was launched in **1985** and has since helped to reduce the incidence of vaccine-preventable diseases in India.

UIP covers 12 vaccine-Preventable diseases:

- Tuberculosis
- Diphtheria
- Tetanus
- Poliomyelitis
- Measles
- Hepatitis B
- Rotavirus
- Rubella
- Japanese encephalitis (In some districts)
- Pertussis (whooping cough)
- Pneumococcal diseases (Pneumococcal pneumonia and meningitis) - (Bihar, Himachal)
- Meningococcal disease Haemophilus Influenza Type B (Hib)

- The vaccines are given at fixed points in a child's life, starting with the **first dose** of **BCG vaccine** at birth. The **UIP** also provides **vaccines** for **pregnant women**, such as the **tetanus toxoid vaccine.**
- The UIP is funded by the government of India and is implemented by the **Ministry of Health and Family Welfare.** The UIP is one of the most successful **public health programmes** in India and has played a major role in improving the health of **children** and **pregnant women** in the country.
- **Universal Immunization Programme** (UIP) is one of the **largest public health programmes** targeting close of **2.67 crore new-borns** and **2.9 crore pregnant women** annually.
- **Under UIP, immunization is providing free of cost against 12 vaccine preventable diseases:**
  - **Nationally against 9 diseases:** Diphtheria, Pertussis, Tetanus, Polio, Measles, Rubella, severe form of Childhood Tuberculosis, Hepatitis B and Meningitis & Pneumonia caused by Hemophilus Influenza type B
  - **Sub-nationally against 3 diseases:** Rotavirus diarrhoea, Pneumococcal Pneumonia and Japanese Encephalitis; of which Rotavirus vaccine and Pneumococcal Conjugate vaccine are in process of expansion while JE vaccine is provided only in endemic districts.

Mission Indradhanush (MI)

- Mission Indradhanush was launched by the **Prime Minister** under aegis of **Ministry of**

Health and Family Welfare on **25th December 2014** to cover the **partially** and **unvaccinated pregnant women** and **children** in pockets of **low immunization coverage**, **high-risk** and **hard-to-reach areas** and protect them from **vaccine preventable disease.**

- **Mission Indradhanush** (MI) is a special catch-up campaign under the **Universal Immunization Program** (UIP), conducted in the areas of low immunization coverage to vaccinate all the children and pregnant women left out or dropped out from **Routine Immunization** against **13 life threatening diseases.**
- It aimed to provide **immunization** against **seven life-threatening diseases** (diphtheria, whooping cough, tetanus, polio, tuberculosis, measles and hepatitis B). In addition, vaccination against **Japanese Encephalitis** and **Haemophilus influenza type B** to be provided in selected districts/states of the country. Vaccination against tetanus to be provided to the pregnant women.
- The Mission focuses on **interventions** to rapidly increase full immunization coverage of children by approximately **5% annually** and to expand full immunization coverage from **65%** in **2014** to at least **90% children** in the next five years.
- **Intensified Mission Indradhanush** was launched on **8th October 2017.** Under IMI, greater focus was given on **urban areas** which were one of the gaps of Mission Indradhanush. It focused to improve immunisation coverage in select districts and cities to ensure full immunisation to more than 90% by December 2018 instead of 2020.
- Inter-sectoral convergence along with intensive planning and monitoring are the salient features of this mission.
- **Intensified Mission Indradhanush 2.0** was a nationwide immunisation drive to mark the 25 years of **Pulse polio programme** (2019-20). It had targets of **full immunization coverage** in **272 districts** spread over **27 States**. It aimed to achieve at least **90%** PAN-India immunisation coverage by **2022.**
- **Intensified Mission Indradhanush 3.0** was launched in **2021**. Focus of the IMI 3.0 was the **children** and **pregnant women** who had missed their vaccine doses during the Covid-19 pandemic. Beneficiaries from migration areas and hard to reach areas were targeted as they might have missed their vaccine doses during Covid-19.
- **In February 2022, Health Minister virtually launched the Intensified Mission Indradhanush 4.0 portal and released the Operational Guidelines for IMI 4.0 :**
  - Strengthening Immunisation in Urban Areas
  - A framework for Action" a handbook for "Mahila Arogya Samiti on Urban Immunisation" and awareness material developed as part of the campaign.
- Three rounds of IMI 4.0 have been planned to catch up on the gaps that might have emerged due to the **COVID-19 pandemic,** it said, adding the activity will be conducted in **416 districts** across **33 States and UTs.**

One Health Approach

- **One Health** is an approach that recognizes the **interconnectedness** of **human**, **animal** and **environmental health** in wake of **Zoonotic Diseases.** It is a collaborative effort to address health challenges that arise at the intersection of these three spheres.

Human health and animal health are interdependent. At the same time, both depend on the environment.

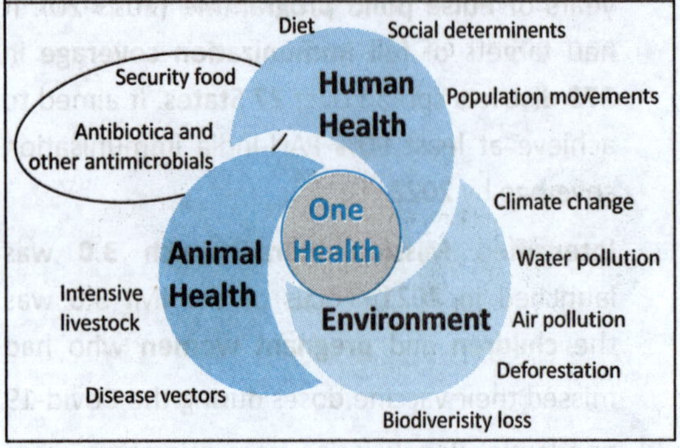

- One Health approach is based on the understanding that the **health of humans, animals** and the **environment** are inextricably linked. Diseases can spread between **humans** and **animals**, and **environmental factors** such as climate change can also **impact health**. By working together, we can better understand and address these complex health challenges.
- **The One Health approach is being used to address a wide range of health issues, including:**
  - **Zoonotic diseases:** Diseases that can spread between animals and humans, such as rabies, malaria, and HIV/AIDS.
  - **Antimicrobial resistance:** The ability of bacteria and other microbes to resist the effects of antibiotics and other antimicrobial drugs.
  - **Food safety:** The prevention of foodborne diseases.
  - **Environmental health:** The impact of environmental factors on health, such as air pollution, water pollution, and climate change.

FAO, World Organisation for Animal Health (OIE), WHO and **UNEP** are working together to mainstream **One Health**, they have recently launched the **One Health Joint Plan of Action (2022-2026).**

One Health Approach : India's initiatives

One Health Support Unit (OHSU) by the **Department of Animal Husbandry and Dairying,** to develop a national One Health Framework.

Resource allocation and **policy ecosystem** of **zoonotic diseases.**

One Health' project: By **Department of Biotechnology** to carry out surveillance of zoonotic as well as transboundary pathogens in India.

National Mission on Biodiversity and Human Well-being: Launched by **Prime Minister's Science, Technology and Innovation Advisory Council** (PM-STIAC).

- Union Ministry for Fisheries, Animal Husbandry and Dairying in April 202, launched the Animal Pandemic Preparedness Initiative and World Bank-funded Animal Health System Support for One Health to enhance India's preparedness and response to potential animal pandemics, in line with the One Health approach.
- World Bank-funded project on Animal Health System Support for One Health (AHSSOH) aims at creating an ecosystem for a better animal health management system using the One Health approach covering 5 states in India.
- Animal Pandemic Preparedness Initiative is a proactive step to protect animal resources meanwhile ensuring the safety and health of people. The initiative aims to improve veterinary services and infrastructure, disease surveillance capabilities, early detection and response, build the capacity of animal health professionals, and awareness among farmers through community outreach.

One Health Consortium

- It was launched in October 2021, comprising of medical centres at AIIMS, Veterinary Institutions, ICARS and 8 disease investigative Centres in North East, with an objective to study the prevalence of ten selected zoonotic diseases (throughout the country) and five trans-boundary animal diseases (mainly from northeast boundary states) and analyse risks so as to provide forewarning to stakeholders.

- ICAR has initiated several Programmes on One Health Approach viz Zoonotic Diseases, Indian Network for Fisheries and Animal Antimicrobial Resistance (INFAAR), programmes regarding epidemiology of animal corona viruses and residue control programmes on food safety.
- 5 Regional Disease Diagnostic Laboratories (RDDLs) and several Referral Laboratory facilities are been set up under the Department of Animal Husbandry & Dairying for surveillance and diagnosis of various livestock and poultry diseases including zoonotic diseases.

International Statistical Classification of Diseases and Related Health Problems

- International Classification of Diseases (ICD) has been the basis for comparable statistics on causes of mortality and morbidity between places and over time. Originating in the 19th century, the latest version of the ICD, ICD-11, was adopted by the 72nd World Health Assembly in 2019 with effect from 1st January 2022.
- ICD-11 allows the systematic recording analysis, interpretation and comparison of mortality and morbidity data collected in different countries or regions and at different times.
- ICD provides critical knowledge on the extent, causes and consequences of human disease and death worldwide via data that is reported & coded with it.

GAVI -The Vaccine Alliance (GAVI)

- GAVI – Vaccine Alliance is a public-private global health partnership set up as a Global Health Partnership in 2000 for creating equal access to new and underused vaccines for children living in the world's poorest countries, committed to saving children's lives and protecting people's health by increasing access to immunization in poor countries.
- GAVI aims at accelerating access to vaccines, strengthening countries health and immunization systems, and introducing innovative new immunization technology.
- In 2014. India became the first implementing country donating to GAVI, committing USS 4 million over a four-year period from 2013-2016. In 2018, India doubled its contribution to GAVI. Committing USS 8 million for a four-year period (2018-2022).
- Indian PM pledged US$ 15 million for GAVT's 2021-2025 program at the Global Vaccines Summit on 4 June 2020.
- GAVI, the Vaccine Alliance and the Government of India on 3 February 2023 established a new 3 year partnership that aims to protect millions of children by 2026 with life-saving vaccines.

Global Centre for Traditional Medicine

- WHO Director-General laid the foundation stone for **world's first** and only **Global Centre for Traditional Medicine** (GCTM) at **Jamnagar in Gujarat.**
- **Traditional medicine** (TM) is the sum of the knowledge, skill, and practices based on the theories, beliefs, and experiences indigenous to different cultures, for treatment of physical and mental illness.

Complementary medicine (CM) or **alternative medicine** refers to healthcare practices that are not part of that country's own tradition or conventional medicine and are not fully integrated into the dominant health-care system.

Indian Initiatives in Traditional Medicines

- National AYUSH Mission (NAM)
- Ayush Export Promotion Council (AEPC)
- AYUSH Information Cell
- Champion Services Sector Scheme for Medical value Travel
- The AYUR SWASTHYA YOJANA

Ayurveda Aahara

The **Food Safety and Standards Authority of India** (FSSAI) and the **Ministry of AYUSH** (MoAYUSH) have jointly formulated the **Food Safety and Standards** (Ayurveda Aahara) **Regulations, 2022.** These regulations are aimed at promoting the marketing of quality **Ayurveda Aahara products** and helping to expand the international market for Make in India.

Ayurveda Aahara will not include **Ayurvedic drugs** or **proprietary Ayurvedic medicines** and **medicinal products, cosmetics, narcotic** or **psychotropic substances** and **herbs.**

PREVIOUS YEAR QUESTIONS (2013 to 2024)

Q. What is the importance of using Pneumococcal Conjugate Vaccines in India? (2020)

1. These vaccines are effective against pneumonia as well as meningitis and sepsis.
2. Dependence on antibiotics that are not effective against drug-resistant bacteria can be reduced.
3. These vaccines have no side effects and cause no allergic reactions.

Which of the statements given above is/are correct?

(a) 1 only (b) 1 and 2 only

(c) 3 only (d) All of the above

Q. With reference to recent developments regarding 'Recombinant Vector Vaccines', consider the following statements: (2021)

1. Genetic engineering is applied in the development of these vaccines.
2. Bacteria and viruses are used as vectors.

Which of the statements given above is/are correct?

(a) 1 only (b) 2 only

(c) Both (d) None

Q. In the context of vaccines manufactured to prevent COVID-19 pandemic, consider the following statements : (2022)

1. The Serum Institute of India produced COVID-19 vaccine named Covishield using mRNA platform.
2. Sputnik V vaccine is manufactured using vector based platform.
3. COVAXIN is an inactivated pathogen based vaccine.

Which of the statements given above are correct?

(a) 1 and 2 only (b) 1 and 3 only

(c) 2 and 3 only (d) All 1, 2 and 3

Q. Which one of the following statements best describes the role of B cells and T cells in the human body ? (2022)

(a) They protect the body from environmental allergens.

(b) They alleviate the body's pain and inflammation.

(c) They act as immunosuppressants in the body.

(d) They protect the body from the diseases caused by pathogens.

Q. What do you understand by Fixed-Dose drug Combinations (FDCs)? Discuss their merits and demerits. (2013)

Q. Can overuse and the availability of antibiotics without doctor's prescription, the contributors to the emergence of drug-resistant diseases in India? What are the available mechanisms for monitoring and control? Critically discuss the various issues involved. (2014)

Q. What is the basic principle behind vaccine development? How do vaccines work? What

approaches were adopted by the Indian vaccine manufacturers to produce COVID-19 vaccines? (2022)

Q. Mission Indradhanush' launched by the Government of India pertains to: (2016)

(a) Immunization of children and pregnant women
(b) Construction of smart cities across the country
(c) India own search for Earth-like planets in outer space
(d) New Educational policy

Q. Consider the following statements: (2017)

1. In tropical regions, Zika virus disease is transmitted by the same mosquito that transmits dengue.
2. Sexual transmission of Zika virus disease is possible.

Which of the statements given above is/are correct?

(a) 1 only (b) 2 only
(c) Both 1 and 2 (d) Neither 1 nor 2

Q. Which of the following are the reasons for the occurrence of multi-drug resistance in microbial pathogens in India? (2020)

1. Genetic predisposition of some people
2. Taking incorrect doses of antibiotics to cure diseases
3. Using antibiotics in livestock farming
4. Multiple chronic diseases in some people

Select the correct answer using the code given below:

(a) 1 and 2 (b) 2 and 3 only
(c) 1, 3 and 4 (d) 2, 3 and 4

Q. Which one of the following is synthesised in human body that dilates blood vessels and increases blood flow? (2024)

(a) Nitric oxide
(b) Nitrous oxide
(c) Nitrogen dioxide
(d) Nitrogen pentoxide

Q. Consider the following pairs : 2014

Vitamin		Deficiency disease
1. Vitamin C	:	Scurvy
2. Vitamin D	:	Rickets
3. Vitamin E	:	Night blindness

Which of the pairs given above is/are correctly matched?

(a) 1 and 2 only (b) 3 only
(c) 1, 2 and 3 (d) None

Q. Consider the following diseases

1. Diphtheria 2. Chickenpox
3. Smallpox

Which of the above diseases has/have been eradicated in India?

(a) 1 and 2 only (b) 3 only
(c) 1, 2 and 3 (d) None

Q. Which of the following diseases can be transmitted from one person to another through tattooing? 2013

1. Chikungunya 2. Hepatitis B
3. HIV-AIDS

Select the correct answer using the codes given below.

(a) 1 only (b) 1 and 2 only
(c) 2 and 3 only (d) 1, 2 and 3

Q. Consider the following statements in respect of probiotics :

1. Probiotics are made of both bacteria and yeast.
2. The organisms in probiotics are found in foods we ingest but they do not naturally occur in our gut.
3. Probiotics help in the digestion of milk sugars.

Which of the statements given above is/are correct?

(a) 1 only (b) 2 only
(c) 1 and 3 (d) 2 and 3

Q. The term ACE2 is talked about in the context of [2021]

(a) Genes introduced in the genetically modified plants
(b) Development of India's own satellite navigation system
(c) Radio collars for wildlife tracking
(d) Spread of viral diseases

UNIT 4 BIOTECHNOLOGY

- *Biotechnology refers to the utilization of biological processes, organisms or systems to produce products that are anticipated to improve human lives is termed biotechnology. Broadly, this can be defined as the engineering of organisms for the purpose of human usage.*
- *Over centuries, our use and manipulation of life processes in agriculture, medicine, and manufacturing have progressed incrementally, punctuated by leaps in understanding brought about by key discoveries, such as Mendelian genetics, Germ Theory, and DNA. These leaps could not have happened without the development and acceptance of novel tools and algorithms for detecting, imaging, and manipulating biological systems.*
- *During the next 20 years, a more multidisciplinary and data-intensive approach to life sciences will shift our understanding of and ability to manipulate living matter.*
- *Scientists are increasingly treating genetic instructions as a form of computational code and incorporating insights and new tools from the rapidly advancing realm of computational science. These disciplines, combined with cognitive science, nanotechnology, physics, and others, are propelling new leaps in our understanding.*
- *It is anticipated that the collective application of these diverse technologies to the life sciences—known as bioconvergence—will accelerate discovery and predictability in biotech design and production. This multidisciplinary approach has made it possible to:*
- *Visualize, measure, identify, and manipulate biological systems at molecular scales.*
- *Treat genetic instructions in DNA, RNA, and amino acids like a language that can be written, edited, and executed with high precision to synthesize useful materials or organisms.*
- *Collect, digitize, store, and analyze genetic instructions, referred to as genomes, from many thousands of individuals, along with their physical, mental, and health traits to correlate how specific genetic instructions interact with the environment to produce distinct traits.*
- *Combine complex biological and non-biological processes, such as bioelectronic interfaces for sensing or stimulating biological systems in support of medicine, agriculture, and manufacturing.*
- *In prehistoric times, a primitive form of biotechnology was practised by agriculturalists for securing better-quality species of plants and animals through cross-pollination or cross-breeding. Previous forms of biotechnology include the training and selective breeding of animals, the cultivation of crops and the utilization of micro-organisms to produce products such as cheese, yogurt, bread, beer and wine through fermentation (which was though not understood).*
- *The advent of World War II brought the manufacture of penicillin, shifting the focus of biotechnology to pharmaceuticals. The Cold War years were ruled by work on micro-organisms for the preparation for biological products along with antibiotics and fermentation processes .*

- *Currently biotechnology places more emphasis on the establishment of hybrid genes followed by their transfer into organisms in which some, or all, of the gene is not usually present.*
- *Biotechnology is now being used in numerous disciplines including bioremediation, energy production and food processing agriculture. DNA fingerprinting is often practiced in forensics. Insulin production and other biotech-based medicines (biopharmaceuticals) are produced through cloning of vectors with genes of interest (GOIs). Immunoassays are frequently utilized in medicine for drug efficiency and pregnancy testing.*
- *Biotechnology also has vast scope in agriculture for the production of plants that are resistant to insects, weeds and plant diseases, which can be achieved through genetic engineering.*

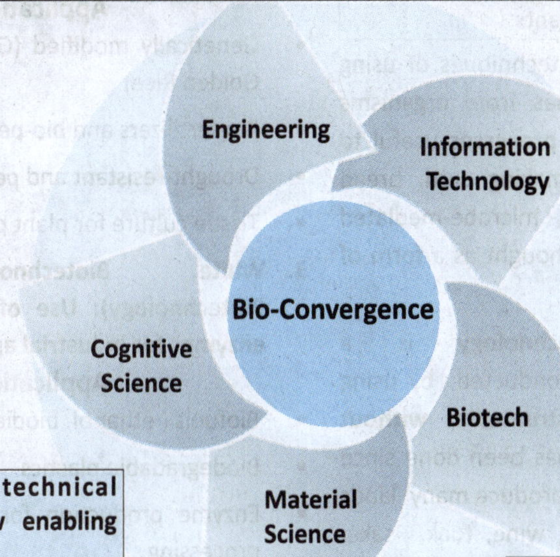

Rapidly evolving technical capabilities are now enabling researchers to :

- Visualize, measure, identify and manipulate biological systems at increasingly smaller scales.
- Read, write, edit and execute DNA, RNA and amino acids sequences with high precision to sythesize useful organisms and materials.
- Collect, digitize, analyze and store population scale volumes of biological, behavioral and environmental data to learn and predict how genes, environment and lifestyle work together.
- Create and merge biological and non-biological materials with novel properties.

Factors Shaping Biotech

- Investment
- Regulation
- Acceptance
- Collaboration and cooperation
- Demand
- Responses to environmental changes
- Geopolitical competition

Emerging Applications

- Digital/Personolized healthcare.
- Bioprinting / Xenotransplantation.
- Reproductive Engineering.
- Biosystems/Ecological Engineering.
- Computer-Human Interfaces.
- Biomanufacturing
- DNA storage
- Eradication of major diseases
- On Demand medicines.
- Synthetic organisms.
- Transformation of agriculture and food production.

Introduction to Biotechnology

United Nation Convention on Biological Diversity, defines **Biotechnology** as any **technological application** that uses **biological systems, living organisms** or **derivatives** there of, to make or **modify products** or **processes** for specific use.

India has become the world's 12th biggest biotechnology economy having the second highest number of USFDA-approved plants.

- Biotechnology deals with techniques of using **live organisms** or **enzymes** from organisms to produce **products** and **processes** useful to humans. In this sense, making curd, bread or wine, which are all microbe-mediated processes, could also be thought as a form of biotechnology.
- **Conventional biotechnology** is a **biotechnology practice** conducted by using simple **methods** and **instruments, without genetic manipulation.** It has been done since thousands of years ago to produce many kinds of products such as beer, wine, tuak, sake, yogurt, bread, cheese, soy sauce, tempe,tapai, and oncom.
- **Modern biotechnology** is a biotechnology practice developed with **genetic manipulation technique,** in which transfer of **genetic material** (transfer of gene) from **one living organism** to the other occurs. Through this technique, humans can control the production according to his desire. For examples, the production of pest and disease resistant plants, imperishable fruits, and cattle which are able to produce more milk.

Types of Biotechnology

1. **Red Biotechnology (Medical Biotechnology): Deals with healthcare, medicine, and pharmaceuticals.**

Applications:

- Vaccine development (e.g., COVID-19 vaccines)
- Gene therapy (e.g., CRISPR-Cas9)
- Stem cell research
- Production of antibiotics and insulin

2. **Green Biotechnology (Agricultural Biotechnology) : Focuses on improving agriculture and food production.**

Applications:

- Genetically modified (GM) crops (Bt Cotton, Golden Rice)
- Bio-fertilizers and bio-pesticides
- Drought-resistant and pest-resistant crops
- Tissue culture for plant propagation

3. **White Biotechnology (Industrial Biotechnology): Use of microorganisms and enzymes for industrial applications.**

Applications:

- Biofuels (ethanol, biodiesel)
- Biodegradable plastics
- Enzyme production for detergents and food processing
- Waste management and recycling

4. **Blue Biotechnology (Marine Biotechnology) : Utilisation of marine and aquatic resources**

Applications:

- Pharmaceuticals from marine organisms
- Aquaculture (fish farming)
- Bio-remediation of oil spills
- Algae-based biofuels

5. **Yellow Biotechnology (Food & Nutrition Biotechnology) : Focuses on food production and processing.**

Applications:

- Fermentation technology (e.g., probiotics, yogurt, beer).
- Artificial meat and lab-grown food.
- Nutraceuticals and functional foods.

6. **Grey Biotechnology (Environmental Biotechnology) : Deals with environmental protection and sustainability.**

Applications:

- Bioremediation (cleaning up pollutants using microorganisms)
- Waste treatment and sewage management
- Biodegradable packaging materials

7. **Gold Biotechnology (Bioinformatics & Computational Biology) : Involves data analysis and software tools in biotechnology.**

Applications:

- Genomic sequencing (e.g., Human Genome Project)
- Drug discovery using AI and machine learning
- Personalized medicine

8. **Violet Biotechnology (Legal & Ethical Aspects of Biotechnology) : Focuses on ethical, legal, and social issues in biotechnology.**

Applications:

- Biotechnology patent laws
- Ethical concerns in genetic modification
- Bioethics in cloning and stem cell research

Introduction to Basics : Cells

- Cells are the basic, fundamental unit of life, that provide **structure** and **support** to an organism.
  - Anton Von Leeuwenhoek first observed and described a living cell.
  - **Robert Brown** later discovered the nucleus.
- The **cell interior** is organised into different individual organelles surrounded by a separate membrane.

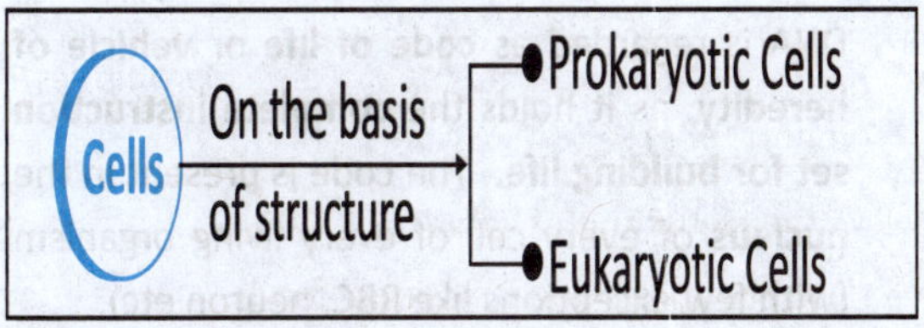

Prokaryotic Cells

- Prokaryotic cells are a type of cell that **lacks a true nucleus and other membrane-bound organelles**. They are simple and structurally less complex as compared to eukaryotic cells.

Eukaryotic Cells

- Eukaryotic cells are a type of cell that **possesses a true nucleus and other membrane-bound organelles**. They are **more complex** structurally as compared to prokaryotic cells.
- They contain a **true nucleus**, where the genetic material (DNA) is enclosed within a **double membrane** and various **membrane-bound organelles**, such as **mitochondria, endoplasmic reticulum, Golgi apparatus** etc.

Structural Organisation of a Cell

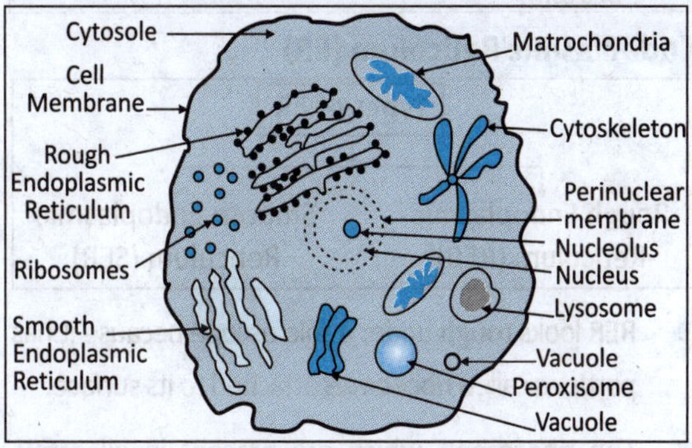

Plasma Membrane or Cell Membrane

- This is the **outermost covering** of the cell that **separates the contents** of the cell from its external environment.
- It is mainly **composed of lipids and proteins**.
- Found in both **plant** and **animal cells**.

Cell Wall

- **Plant cells**, in addition to the plasma membrane, have another **rigid outer covering** called the cell wall, **lying outside the plasma membrane** and composed of **cellulose**.

- It **protects the cell** from **mechanical damage** and **infection** and **facilitates cell-to-cell interaction** and provides a **barrier** to **undesirable macromolecules.**

Cytoplasm

- The cytoplasm is the **fluid content** inside the plasma membrane. It contains many **specialised cell organelles.**

Nucleus

- The nucleus contains **chromosomes,** which are visible as **rod-shaped structures** only when the cell is about to divide.
- Chromosomes contain **information** for **inheritance of characters** from parents to the next generation in the form of **DNA** (Deoxyribo Nucleic Acid) molecules.

> **Chromosomes** are composed of **DNA** and protein.

Endoplasmic Reticulum (ER)

Types of ER

- Rough Endoplasmic Reticulum (RER)
- Smooth Endoplasmic Reticulum (SER)

- RER looks **rough** under a microscope because it has particles called **ribosomes** attached to its surface.
- The ribosomes, which are present in all active cells, are the **sites of protein manufacture.** The manufactured proteins are then sent to various places in the cell depending on need, using the ER.
- The **SER** helps in the **manufacture of fat molecules**, or **lipids**, **important for cell function.** Some of these proteins and lipids help in building the cell membrane. This process is known as **membrane biogenesis.**
- An important one function of the ER is to serve as **channels** for the **transport of materials** (especially proteins) between various regions of the **cytoplasm** or between the **cytoplasm** and the **nucleus.**

Golgi Apparatus

- The material synthesized near the ER is **packaged and dispatched to various targets** inside and outside the cell through the Golgi apparatus.

> **Functions :** Storage, modification and packaging of products in vesicles.

Lysosomes

- Lysosomes are a kind of **waste disposal system** of the cell and also known as **suicide bags.**
- These help to keep the cell clean by **digesting any foreign material** as well as **worn-out cell organelles.**

Mitochondria

- Mitochondria are known as the **powerhouses of the cell.**
- The energy required for various chemical activities needed for life is released by mitochondria in the form of ATP (Adenosine triphopshate) molecules.

> **ATP** is known as the **energy currency of the cell.**

Plastids

- Plastids are present only in **plant cells.**
- There are two types of plastids – **chromoplasts** (coloured plastids) and **leucoplasts** (white or colorless plastids).

> Chromoplasts containing the **pigment chlorophyll** are known as **chloroplasts.**

Vacuoles

- Vacuoles are **storage sacs** for **solid** or **liquid contents.** Vacuoles are **small sized** in **animal cells** while plant cells have very large vacuoles.

BASICS OF GENETICS

DNA

- DNA is regarded as **code of life** or **vehicle of heredity**, as it holds the **complete instruction set for building life.** The code is present in the **nucleus** of every cell of every living organism (with few exceptions like RBC, neuron etc).

- **DNA is a molecule that carries the genetic information in all living organisms. It consists of a double helix structure made up of four nucleotide bases: adenine (A), thymine (T), cytosine (C), and guanine (G).**

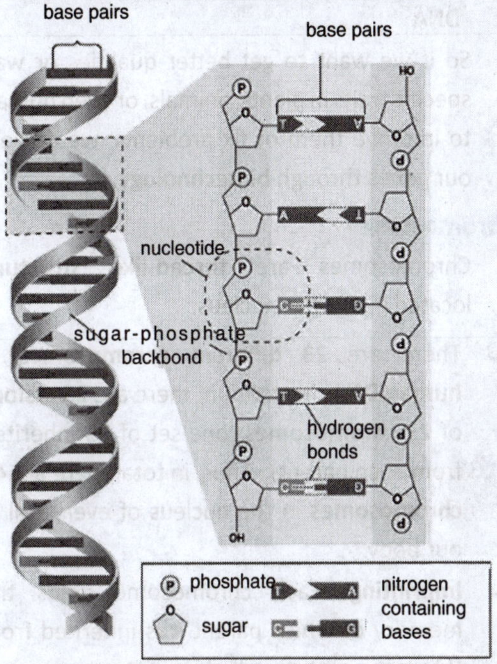

- The specific sequence of these bases in a gene **encodes the instructions** for **building proteins** and **carrying** out various **biological functions**.
- Apart from being responsible for the **inheritance of genetic information** in all living beings, DNA also plays a crucial role in the production of proteins.
- The DNA present in the **mitochondria** of the cell is termed **mitochondrial DNA**. It is inherited from the mother to the child.
- DNA is converted into **proteins in cells** because proteins perform many important functions in our bodies. They help **build** and **repair tissues**, carry out **chemical reactions**, and controls our bodily functions.
- **The process of turning DNA into protein happens in two steps: transcription and translation.**

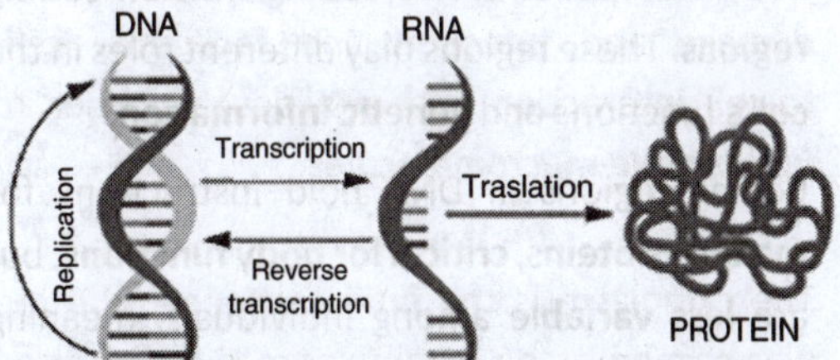

Transcription	Translation
Copying DNA to RNA Imagine DNA as a recipe book for making proteins. Transcription is like copying a recipe from the book onto a piece of paper (RNA).	Making Proteins from RNA Think of RNA as the copied recipe paper. Translation is like following the instructions on the paper to cook a dish (make a protein). Ribosomes act like cooking stations where the recipe (RNA) is read and the dish (protein) is assembled.
An enzyme called RNA polymerase reads the recipe (DNA) and writes down the instructions on the paper (RNA).	Transfer RNA (tRNA) molecules bring the ingredients (amino acids) needed to make the dish.
The paper (RNA) now has a copy of the recipe (gene) needed to make a protein.	The ribosome reads the instructions (codons on mRNA) and adds the right ingredients (amino acids) in the correct order.
When the ribosome reaches the end of the recipe (stop codon), the dish (protein) is complete and ready to use.	

- DNA is composed of **two-coding** and **non-coding regions**. These regions play different roles in the cell's functions and **genetic information**.
- Coding regions in DNA hold instructions for **making proteins, critical for body functions**, but are **less variable** among individuals, meaning **Human A** and **Human B** would have very less difference in their coding DNA.

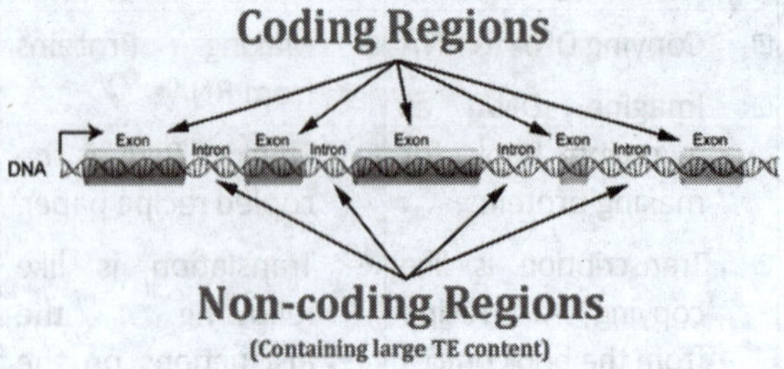

- While, **Non-coding regions don't make proteins** but have **repeating sequences** (STRs) that differ in how many times they repeat, which varies a lot among people. (in simple words, this part is highly variable in human beings).
- Since **non-coding regions of DNA** are different in different people, they are used in **DNA fingerprinting, enabling unique genetic profiles** for **identification, forensic analysis,** and **relationship establishment** due to their **distinctive** and **heritable nature.**
- These **coding parts** of **DNA** can be understood as **Genes.**

Genes

- Genes are **segments of DNA** (deoxyribonucleic acid) that **contain instructions** for **building** and **maintaining an organism.** They determine an organism's traits, such as **eye color, height** and **susceptibility** to certain **diseases.**

> - **Gene** is a **DNA segment** carrying **instructions** for **protein/RNA synthesis,** influencing traits. **Genome** is an **organism's complete genetic material,** encompassing **all genes** and **non-coding DNA**. Genes collectively shape the **genome**, dictating an organism's characteristics and functions.
> - **Gene** = Coding part/ region of DNA
> - **Genome** = Coding + Non- Coding region of DNA

- So if we want to get better qualities or want specific traits in plants, animals, or even humans to improve them or fix problems, we can edit our genes through **biotechnology.**

Chromosomes

- Chromosomes are **thread-like structures** located inside the nucleus.

> - There are **23 different chromosomes** in **human DNA**. In addition, there are **2 versions** of **23 chromosomes** (one set of 23 inherited from each parent). Thus, in total there are **46 chromosomes** in the nucleus of every cell in our body.
> - **Imprinting:** Each chromosome holds the memory of which parent it is inherited from through a process called imprinting.

Cell Division

- New cells are formed in organisms in order to grow, to replace old, dead and injured cells, and to form **gametes** required for **reproduction.**
- **The process by which new cells are made is called cell division. There are two main types of cell division:** mitosis and meiosis.
  - **Mitosis :** Types of cell division for somatic cells for the a sexual reproduction of unicellular eukaryotic cells. Involves division of body cells 2 daughter cells (diploid) are produced which are genetically identical.
  - **Meiosis :** Type of cell division for production of gametes in sexual reproduction. Involved division of sex cells 4 daughter cell (haploid) are produced which are genetically diverse.

Human Reproduction

- Human fertilization is the process that happens when a tiny, special cell from a man's body called a **sperm** meets a tiny, special cell from a woman's body called an **egg** or **ovum**.

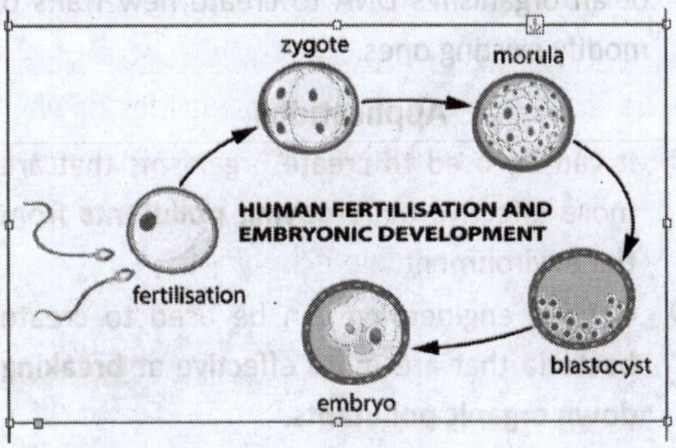

Features of Zygote

- It has **nuclei** containing **chromosomes** from both parents.
- The **mitochondria** present in the zygote come from the **egg cell** (oocyte) contributed by the mother.
- **Mitochondria** have their own DNA, and this **mitochondrial DNA** (mtDNA) is inherited exclusively from the mother.
- During **fertilization**, while the father's sperm contributes genetic material to the nucleus of the zygote, the mitochondria in the sperm are usually located in the tail and are not typically involved in the formation of the zygote. Therefore, the **mitochondria** in the **zygote** are primarily derived from the mother's egg.

Mitochondrial Replacement therapy

- If a mother's mitochondria is defective, a special method called **Mitochondrial Replacement Therapy** (MRT) is used to fix it. MRT is like getting healthy mitochondria from another person and putting them into the mom's cells. This helps in **preventing sickness** caused by bad mitochondria.
- MRT originated as a special form of in **vitro fertilization** in which some or all of the future baby's mitochondrial DNA (mtDNA) comes from a third party. This technique is used in cases when mothers carry genes for **mitochondrial diseases.**
- Mitochondrial disease can affect a **child's energy production, leading to fatigue**, muscular weakness, and organ problems due to **faulty mitochondria** not providing enough energy for the bodily functions.

Methods of treating Mitochondrial diseases

- **Pronuclear transfer :** Pronuclear transfer involves taking the **nucleus** from a **mother's egg** with **faulty mitochondria** and placing it into a **healthy donor egg**, which has had its nucleus removed. This **combined egg** is then **fertilized** with the **father's sperm** and **implanted** for **pregnancy**, reducing the **risk of mitochondrial** disease in the child.

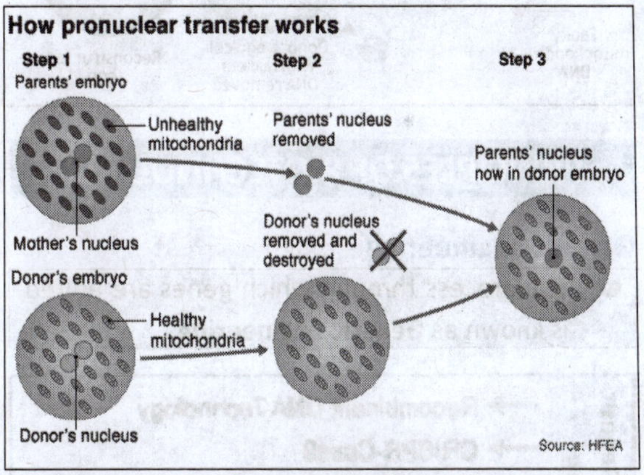

- **Reconstructed Egg Technology:** Reconstructed Egg Technology involves transferring the nucleus from a mother's egg into a donor egg with healthy mitochondria. The combined egg is then fertilized with the father's sperm, helping prevent certain inherited diseases carried by the mother's mitochondria. This is also known as **maternal spindle transfer technique.**

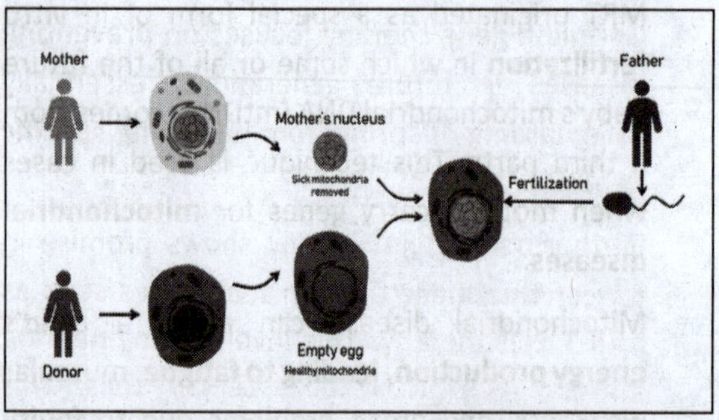

- Baby born from MRT is called **3 parent baby** because in this process, genetic material from three individuals is used: the nuclear DNA from the mother and father, and healthy mitochondria from a female donor.

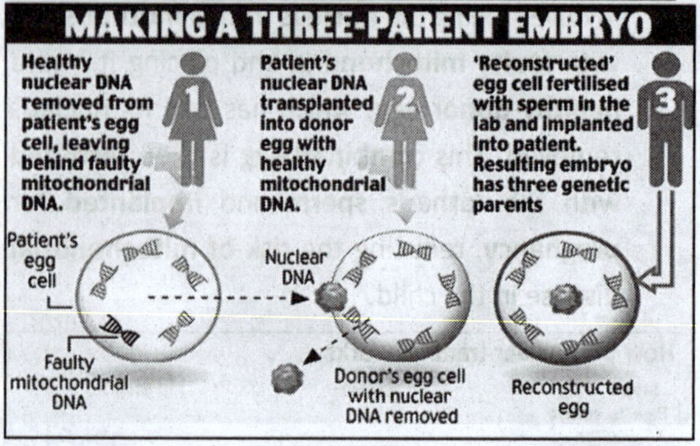

PRINCIPLES OF BIOTECHNOLOGY

Genetic engineering

- The process through which genes are edited, is known as **Genetic Engineering.**

Techniques of Genetic Engineering

- → Recombinant DNA Technology
- → CRISPR-Cas9
- → Gene Cloning
- → Polymerase Chain Reaction
- → Gene Therapy
- → Gene Silencing (RNA Interference)-RNAi
- → Transgenic Technology

- Techniques to alter the chemistry of genetic material by introducing traits of one species into host organism subsequently changing the phenotype of organism.
- Genetic engineering is another important aspect of biotechnology that can be used in **pollution control.**
- Genetic engineering involves the manipulation of an organism's DNA to create new traits or modify existing ones.

Applications

- It can be used to create organisms that are more effective at **removing pollutants** from the environment.
- Genetic engineering can be used to **create bacteria** that are more effective at **breaking down organic pollutants.**
- Scientists can introduce new genes into the bacteria that **encode enzymes** that **break down** specific pollutants.

Bioprocess engineering

- **Maintenance of sterile** (microbial contamination-free) **ambience** in **chemical engineering** processes to enable growth of only the desired **microbe/eukaryotic** cell in large quantities for the manufacture of **biotechnological products** like **antibiotics, vaccines, enzymes**, etc.

GENE THERAPY

- Gene therapy is a **medical approach** aimed at **addressing genetic defects** in individuals.
- When a child is born with a **crucial gene** that isn't functioning properly, gene therapy offers a solution. It involves **introducing healthy copies** of the **malfunctioning gene** into the **child's cells.**
- In essence, gene therapy encompasses a range of techniques designed to rectify genetic issues. It achieves this by inserting functional genes into the cells and tissues of a person to combat specific diseases.
- The goal of correcting a **genetic flaw entails**

introducing a functional gene to an individual or even to an embryo, thus compensating for the defective gene's inability to perform its intended role.

- Gene therapy involves using biotechnological methods to replace defective genes with properly functioning ones.

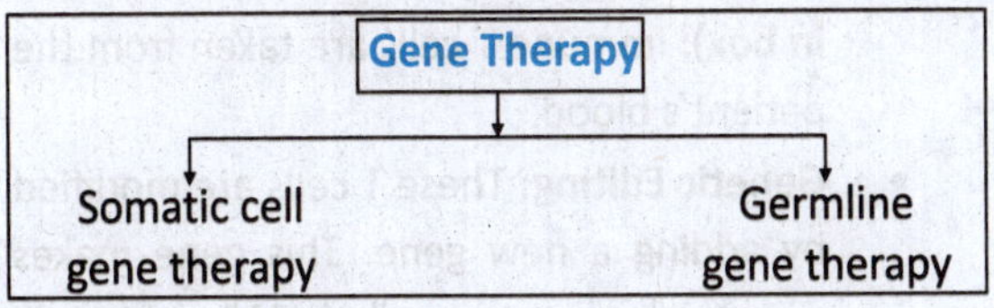

Somatic Cells

- **Somatic Cells:** Somatic cells are the regular cells that make up our body tissues and organs. They **form** the **structure of our body** and perform various functions.
- Changes or mutations in somatic cells do not affect the genetic makeup of future generations. In other words, these changes are not passed onto offspring.

> **Example :** Skin Cells, Neck Cells, Liver cells etc

- In somatic gene therapy, **genetic disorders** in individuals can be effectively treated. For instance, conditions like **hemophilia** and **sickle cell anemia** can be addressed using this approach.

Germline Cells

- Germline cells are **special cells** that give rise to **eggs in females** and **sperm in males.** These cells carry genetic information that can be passed onto the **next generation.**
- **Changes** or **mutations** in **germline cells** can be **inherited** by **offspring.** If a germline cell has a mutation, it can affect the genetic makeup of future generations.

> **Example :** Egg Cell in females, Sperm Cells in Male.

- **Germline gene therapy** focuses on **preventing diseases** in future generations, essentially **safeguarding offspring** from **inheriting specific health issues.**
- Furthermore, gene therapy shows promise in **cancer treatment** through techniques such as **CAR-T cell therapy.** This involves **engineering immune cells** to combat cancer cells. This underscores gene therapy's diverse potential in addressing a range of complex medical challenges.

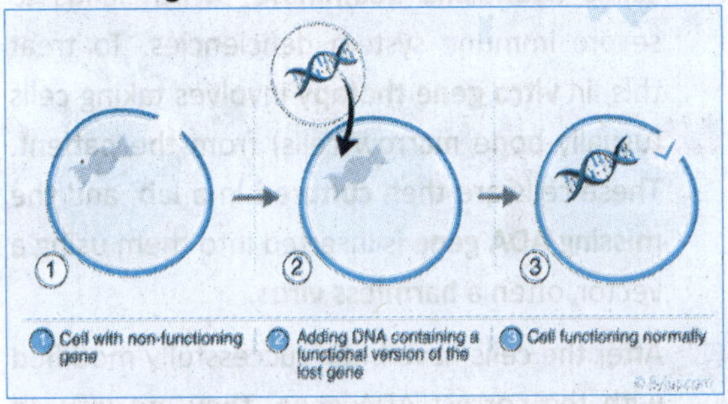

- **Identify the Problem Gene:** First, doctors figure out which gene is causing the health issue.
- **Introduce the Correct Gene:** They create a good copy of the faulty gene and put it into a special carrier called a **vector.** This vector is usually a harmless virus that won't make us sick.
- **Deliver the Vector:** The vector, with the corrected gene inside, is put into our body. It can be injected into the bloodstream or directly into the target cells.
- **Fixing the Gene:** Once inside our cells, the corrected gene takes over and starts working properly. It helps make the missing protein or fixes what was wrong.
- **Gene therapy** can be done inside and outside our body. Inside therapy is done through the help of vectors called **In Vivo** while therapy done outside our body called **In Vitro** therapy.

In Vitro Gene therapy : ADA - SCID

- **In vitro gene therapy** refers to a type of gene therapy where the **corrective gene** is **modified** or **added to cells outside the body** before being introduced back into the patient.

> **Example:** Treatment of Adenosine Deaminase Deficiency - Severe Combined Immunodeficiency (ADA-SCID) also known as bubble boy disease.

- In **ADA-SCID**, patients lack a functional enzyme called **adenosine deaminase**, which leads to severe immune system deficiencies. To treat this, in **vitro gene therapy** involves taking cells (usually bone marrow cells) from the patient. These cells are then **cultured** in a lab, and the **missing ADA gene** is inserted into them using a vector, often a **harmless virus**.
- After the cells have been successfully modified with the correct ADA gene, they are infused back into the patient's body. Once inside, these **genetically corrected cells** can produce the missing enzyme, restoring the immune system's function and improving the patient's overall health.
- This approach allows scientists to precisely modify the gene in a controlled environment before reintroducing the corrected cells into the patient, offering a potential cure for genetic disorders like **ADA-SCID**.

Gene Therapy for ADA-SCID

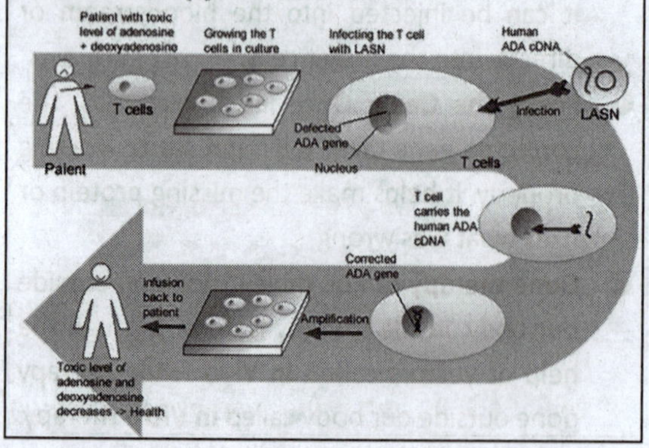

CAR-T Cell therapy

- CAR-T cell therapy is a revolutionary approach in cancer treatment. It involves modifying the patient's own immune cells, known as **T cells**, to **target** and **fight cancer cells** effectively.
- **Process of CAR–T cell therapy :**
  - **Collecting T Cells (T -cell explained below in box):** Immune T cells are taken from the patient's blood.
  - **Genetic Editing:** These T cells are modified by adding a new gene. This gene makes a special receptor called CAR (chimeric antigen receptor.
  - **Cancer Detection:** CAR helps T cells recognize proteins on cancer cells.
  - **Attacking Cancer:** Modified T cells are infused back into the patient. They spot and attack cancer cells.
  - **Curing Specific Cancers:** This therapy can cure certain types of cancer.
  - **Different from Chemotherapy:** Unlike chemotherapy, which may be ongoing, CAR-T therapy is a one-time treatment.
- **CAR-T cell Therapy** offers shorter treatment and **faster recovery**, with targeted action against cancer cells.

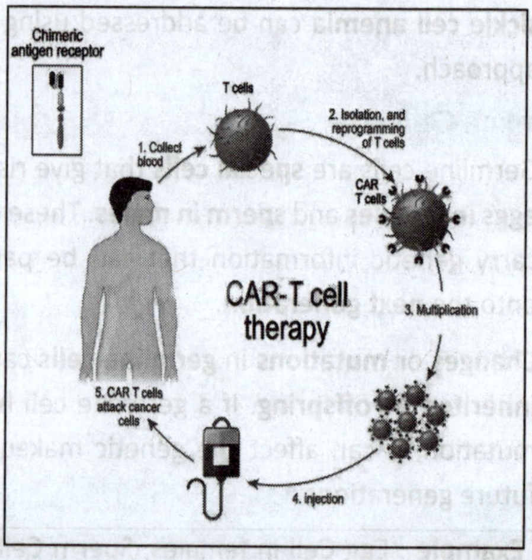

Concerns of Gene Therapy

- **Immune Responses and Side Effects:** The body's

immune system might react to the introduced gene, leading to **potential side effects**. These immune reactions can **impact** the therapy's success and safety.

- **Short-Lived Effects:** Gene therapy might require multiple treatments over time.

> - Conditions like **ADA-SCID** need repeated interventions to maintain the desired effect.

- **Limited Applicability:** Gene therapy is effective for disorders caused by a single gene defect, not for conditions involving multiple genes or chromosomal abnormalities.
- **Chromosomal Disorders:** Gene therapy can't correct large-scale chromosomal abnormalities/ disorder, limiting its scope to specific gene-related disorders.
- **Virus Alteration and Manipulation:** Modified viruses are used as carriers for gene delivery. Ensuring these viruses are safe and effectively contained is a critical concern to prevent unintended outcomes.

Down's Syndrome

- Down's Syndrome is a **chromosomal disorder** characterized by a person having **three copies** of **chromosome number 21** instead of the usual **two copies.** This **extra genetic material leads** to various **developmental** and **intellectual challenges.**
- Gene therapy is not an effective solution for Down's Syndrome. This is because gene therapy primarily focuses on **replacing** or **correcting individual genes**, but Down's Syndrome involves a complex **chromosomal abnormality**. The additional chromosome 21 cannot be simply removed or altered through gene therapy.

GENOME EDITING

- **Gene Editing:** Gene editing refers to precise changes made to the DNA sequence of a specific gene using techniques like CRISPR-Cas9. It aims to modify or correct the genetic information within an organism's existing genome(doesn't introduce foreign genes). Gene editing allows for targeted alterations, such as removing, adding, or editing individual DNA bases, with the goal of influencing specific traits.
- **Genetic Modification:** Genetic modification involves broader changes to an organism's genetic makeup, often by introducing foreign genes from another organism or making significant alterations to the genome.

Techniques of Genome Editing

- CRISPR-Cas9
- TALENs (Transcription Activator-Like Effector Nucleases)
- ZFNs (Zinc Finger
- Prime Editing/ Site Directed Nuclease
- Homologous Recombination
- Cpf1 (Cas12) Editing
- PEG-Mediated Editing.

CRISPR CAS9: REVOLUTION IN GENETIC ENGINEERING

- **CRISPR:** It stands for **Clustered Regularly Interspaced Short Palindromic Repeats.** These are **repeated sequences** in the **DNA of bacteria.**
- **Cas9:** This is a protein associated with CRISPR. It acts like **molecular scissors** and **glue,** allowing scientists to **cut** and paste **DNA.**

- CRISPR-Cas9 was originally discovered in **bacteria.** It is a **defence system** that bacteria uses to **defend** against **viruses** that infect bacteria. These viruses are called **bacteriophage.**
- This technique of Bacteria was used through gene therapy to edit genes or to cure the **gene disorder.**
- The CRISPR-Cas9 gene editing process in humans involves following steps-

- **Target Identification:** Scientists identify the specific gene or DNA sequence they want to modify.
- **sgRNA Design:** A single guide RNA (sgRNA) is designed to match the **target DNA sequence**. The sgRNA serves as a **molecular guide** to direct the **Cas9 protein** to the desired location.
- **Cas9 and sgRNA Complex Formation:** The Cas9 protein is combined with the sgRNA, creating a Cas9-sgRNA complex.
- **Cutting DNA:** Cas9 acts as molecular scissors, making a precise cut at the chosen location in the DNA.

Applications of CRISPR

- **Gene Editing and Gene Therapy:** CRISPR-Cas9 has vast potential for correcting genetic defects and treating diseases through gene therapy, offering hope for conditions like cystic fibrosis and sickle cell anemia.
- **Genetically Modified Organisms (GMOs):** CRISPR enables precise modification of plant and animal genomes for enhanced agricultural traits, disease resistance and improved nutritional content in food.
- **Designer Babies:** While controversial, CRISPR raises possibilities of selecting traits in offspring, but ethical and safety concerns abound, exemplified by the case of a Chinese scientist imprisoned for unethical human germline editing.
- **Germline Editing:** Altering genes in **reproductive cells** (germline) could potentially **prevent genetic diseases** from passing to future generations. However, this approach raises significant **ethical** and **social considerations**.

Precision Guided Sterile Insects

- A **CRISPR-based system** has been developed **for controlling mosquito populations** by using **precision gene editing techniques.**
- **Precision-Guided Sterile Insect Technique (pgSIT):** This technique involves **altering** the **genes of mosquito species**, specifically **Aedes aegypti**, which are responsible for spreading diseases like **malaria, dengue, chikungunya** and **Zika.** The goal is to control these disease vectors by manipulating their genetics.

Zinc Finger Nuclease (ZFN)

- Zinc finger nucleases (ZFNs) serve as **DNA scissors**, using a **zinc finger protein** for specific **DNA recognition** and the **FokI nuclease** for cutting. The zinc finger protein attaches precisely to the target DNA region, while the **nuclease cuts** it. The success rates of this technology ranges from **1% to 20%**. ZFNs predate **CRISPR-Cas9**, an advanced genome editing tool, and are less efficient.

TALEN

- TALENs are genome editing tools utilizing **Transcription activator-like effectors** (TALEs) from **Xanthomonas bacteria** as the DNA binding domain.
- Coupled with the **FokI nuclease** domain, they act as **DNA scissors**, enabling targeted DNA cutting.
- While an improvement over zinc finger nucleases, **TALEN's complexity** limited their use. The advent of **CRISPR-Cas9** surpassed both due to its efficiency and ease of design.

Site-directed nucleases (SDNs)

- **Site-directed nucleases** (SDNs) represent a category of genome editing methodologies.
- **SDN** refers to **cleaving DNA strands** to affect subsequent genome editing, taking advantage of natural repair mechanisms to introduce small changes.

> **Two prominent SDN technologies: Zinc Finger Nucleases** (ZFNs) and **Transcription Activator-Like Effector Nucleases** (TALENs).

- These methods exploit the **natural DNA repair pathways,** allowing for **controlled modification** by introducing **subtle changes** at **specific genomic sites.**
- **Site-directed nucleases (SDNs) encompass three variations: SDN 1**, **SDN 2** and **SDN 3**.
- **SDN 1** and **SDN 2** involve make changes in organisms without adding foreign genes, resembling natural variations. **SDN 3**, however, integrates genes from external sources. SDN 3 introduces foreign genes.

> - **SDN 1** and **SDN 2** have been exempted from 1989 regulations governing genetically modified (GM) crops due to their similarity to traditional breeding outcomes.
> - **SDN 3** comes under these rules if the introduced foreign **DNA exceeds 20 base pairs.**

Homing endonucleases

- Homing endonucleases, also known as **meganucleases**, is also a type of **molecular scissors** used in **genetic engineering**. These enzymes cut DNA at specific locations, offering the flexibility to subsequently insert or omit specific genes as needed for targeted modifications.

Recombinant DNA Technology

- This is like mixing ingredients from different recipes to create a new dish. Scientists can **combine DNA** from different sources, such as **inserting a human gene** into **bacteria** to make them produce a human protein.
- The construction of the **first recombinant DNA** emerged from the possibility of **linking a gene of E-Coli encoding antibiotic resistance** with a **native plasmid** (autonomously replicating circular extra- chromosomal DNA) of **Salmonella typhimurium.**

> - **Stanley Cohen** and **Herbert Boyer** in **1972** cut out the **gene** from a **plasmid** that made **Salmonella resistant** to **antibiotics.** The cutting of DNA at specific locations became possible with the discovery of the so-called **molecular scissors– restriction enzymes.**

- The cut piece of DNA was then linked with the

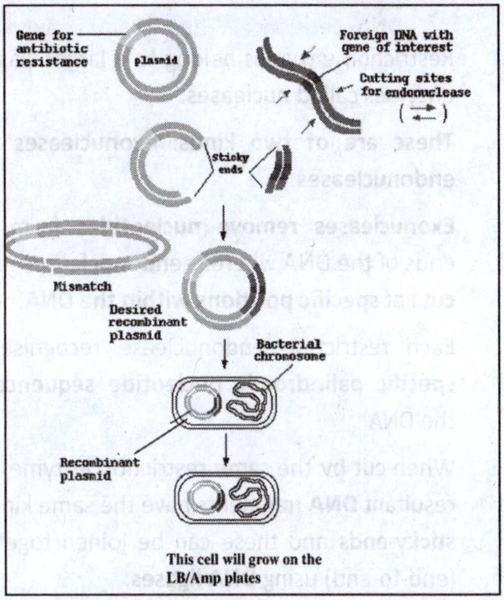

plasmid DNA. These plasmid DNA act as vectors to transfer the piece of DNA attached to it.

- As mosquito acts as an **insect vector** to **transfer** the **malarial parasite** into the human body. In the same way, a plasmid can be used as **vector** to **deliver** an **alien piece** of **DNA** into the **host organism.**
- The **linking** of **antibiotic resistance gene** with the plasmid vector became possible with the **enzyme DNA ligase**, which acts on cut **DNA molecules** and joins their ends. This makes a new combination of circular autonomously replicating DNA created in vitro and is known as **recombinant DNA.**

Steps in Genetic Modifying

- Identification of DNA with desirable genes;
- Introduction of the identified DNA into the host;
- Maintenance of introduced DNA in the host and transfer of the DNA to its progeny.

Restriction Enzymes

Tool of RDT

- Restriction Enzymes
- Cloning Vectors

- Restriction enzymes belong to a larger class of enzymes called **nucleases**.
- **These are of two kinds: exonucleases and endonucleases.**
- **Exonucleases remove nucleotides** from the ends of the DNA whereas **endonucleases** make **cuts at specific positions within the DNA.**
- Each restriction endonuclease recognises **a specific palindromic nucleotide sequence** in the DNA.
- When cut by the same restriction enzyme, the resultant **DNA** fragments have the same kind of **sticky-ends** and these can be joined together (end-to-end) using **DNA ligases.**

Cloning Vector

- Vectors in recombinant DNA techniques serve as **delivery vehicles, transporting foreign DNA** into **host cells**. These molecular tools enable the **replication** and **expression** of **inserted DNA**, aiding in **gene manipulation** and **protein production.**
- In the same way, **Cloning vectors** are essential **tools in genetic engineering,** serving as **carriers** for **introducing** and **replicating foreign DNA** in **host cells**. Their primary functions include transporting foreign **DNA** into **host cells,** replicating the **inserted DNA.**

> **Bacteriophages** (viruses that infect bacteria) and **plasmids** (small, circular DNA molecules) are commonly employed as **cloning vectors** due to their **ability to replicate** within **host cells.**

- **Bacteriophages have high copy numbers (understand as replication number only) within bacteria** because they generate numerous viral particles during their **replication cycle.**
- By linking **foreign DNA** with plasmid or **bacteriophage** DNA, scientists can exploit their **replication mechanisms** to rapidly increase the number of copies of the inserted DNA, providing ample material for further research, protein production, or other applications.

Steps in Recombinant DNA Technique

- **Isolation of DNA:** Extract pure DNA.
- **Cutting:** Use restriction enzymes (RE) to cut at specific sites, then analyze using gel electrophoresis.
- **PCR:** Amplify desired gene via Polymerase Chain Reaction.
- **Ligation:** Join foreign DNA with vector DNA.
- **Insertion:** Introduce into host with selectable marker.
- **Protein Production:** Host creates recombinant protein.
- **Downstream Processing:** Refine and purify the protein.

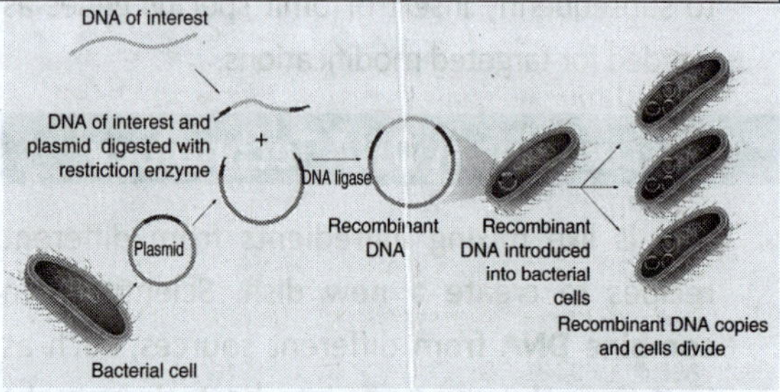

RDT applications in Medicine- Genetically Engineered Insulin

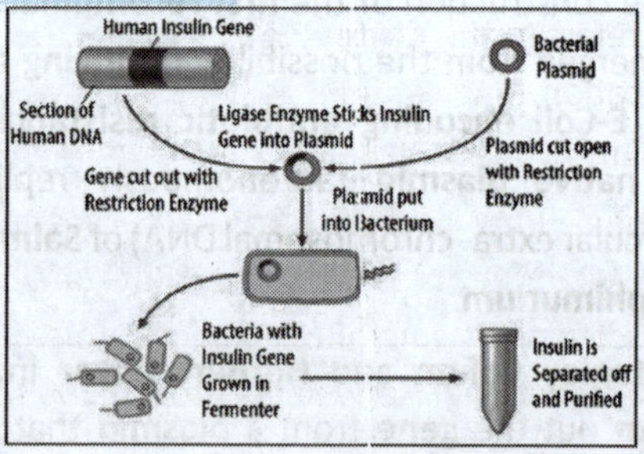

- Earlier we had to take insulin from other animals by killing them. This led to unwanted immune responses. But, genetic engineering made it possible to use bacteria to make human insulin. In **1983** a company called **Eli Lilly** did this, improving diabetes treatment.

Challenges and Concerns of Gene editing

- **Mutation and Cancer Risk:** Gene editing may inadvertently introduce **unintended mutations**, potentially leading to increased cancer risk or other health problems.
- **Ethical Concerns and Designer Embryos:** Altering human genes raises ethical questions, especially with regard to **designer babies** with **selected traits**, posing complex **moral dilemmas.**
- **Impact on Human Variation:** Gene editing might **homogenize human genetic diversity**, potentially diminishing the richness of human diversity.
- **Abuse of Gene Editing:** Misuse or unethical application of gene editing could lead to unintended consequences and harm to individuals or societies.
- **Justice and Equity: Accessibility** and **affordability** issues must be addressed to ensure **fair** and **equitable access** to gene editing therapies.
- Issues related to **Gene doping** that involve the use of **gene transfer** to **increase** or **decrease gene expression** and **protein biosynthesis** of a **specific human protein.**

Gene Regulation

- It refers to the process that controls the timing, location, and amount in which genes (out of many genes in a genome) are expressed.
- Nobel Prize in Physiology 2024 was awarded to Victor Ambros and Gary Ruvkun for their discovery of microRNA and its role in post-transcriptional Gene Regulation in 1993.
- Till 1993, it was believed that gene regulation is limited to specialized proteins called transcription factors, which bind to specific regions in DNA and determine which messenger Ribonucleic acid (RNA) (mRNA) is produced.
- **Gene Expression:** Human organs and tissues consist of different cell types, the chromosomes in the cell contain the same set of genes with the same set of instructions. However, due to gene regulation, these different cells (like muscle cells, nerve cells, etc.) express unique sets of proteins, enabling them to perform their specialized function.
- microRNA (miRNA) is a small non-coding RNA that helps cells regulate gene expression. It controls gene expression by binding with mRNA and preventing them from being translated into proteins or by degrading or destroying mRNA altogether. Proteins in the nucleus regulate RNA transcription and splicing while microRNAs control the translation and degradation of mRNA in the cytoplasm.

Significance/Applications of Gene Regulation –

- **Understanding Cellular Development:** Self-renewal and differentiation of stem cells
- **Immune Response:** Regulate innate and adaptive immune responses.
- **Oncogenesis:** To avoid healthy cells conversion to cancer cells.
- **Disease diagnostics:** Cancer

RNA (Ribonucleic acid) Editing

- A process that modifies genetic information on RNA sequences through insertion, deletion or substitution. Scientists used a technique called 'Adenosine Deaminase Acting on RNA (ADAR)' with guide RNA (gRNA).
- gRNA are small RNA molecules that direct editing machinery by base-pairing with mRNA in specific regions for modification.

RNA & DNA editing

- **Form of change:** DNA editing makes permanent changes while RNA editing makes temporary changes.
- RNA editing is safer and flexible compared to DNA editing which may result in irreversible errors.
- **Allergic and immune reactions:** DNA editing has a higher risk of undesirable reactions compared to RNA editing.
- DNA editing tools use proteins from certain bacteria to perform cutting functions while RNA editing relies on ADAR enzymes, already occurring in the human body
- **DNA Repair :** Mechanism of a cell to maintain the integrity of its genetic code. It exists in both prokaryotic and eukaryotic organisms.

Jumping Genes

- Jumping genes also known as transposable elements are DNA sequences that move from one location on the genome to another.
- These small DNA segments contain recombinase enzyme along with extra DNA segments at the ends of the genes that bind and manipulate DNA. They can replicate themselves and insert copies at new locations. Their movement can cause genetic mutations and contribute to genome evolution.

Bridge Recombinase Mechanism (BRM)

- Extra DNA at the ends of jumping genes gets joined together and converts the DNA double helix structure into a single-stranded RNA molecule. This bridge RNA molecule can bind to two DNA segments (donor and target), allowing for flexible DNA modifications.

Genome editing tool – ISDra2TnpB

- Derived from bacteria called Deinococcus radiodurans (which can survive extreme environmental conditions).
- It belongs to a family of jumping genes.
- TnpB proteins are considered the evolutionary ancestors of Cas 12 nucleases.

Significance –

- TnpB can target unique regions in the genome that Cas9 and Cas12 cannot.
- Facilitates the creation of fusion proteins (chimeric protein), created by joining two or more genes that originally coded for separate proteins..
- **Exosomes :** Naturally occurring membrane-enclosed vesicles actively released into the extracellular space that have the potential to be manipulated to become promising drug delivery vehicles.

Recombinant Proteins (RPs)

- Proteins that are artificially produced using genetic engineering techniques. These are modified or manipulated proteins encoded by recombinant DNA (DNA).
- rDNA is an artificially made DNA strand that is formed by the combination of two or more DNA molecules.
- DNA technology can be used to combine (or splice) or transfer DNA from different species or to create genes with new functions.
- RPs such as monoclonal antibodies (moAbs or mAbs), are mass-produced by growing modified bacterial, viral, or mammalian cells in large bioreactors.
- mAbs are lab-made proteins mimicking natural antibodies.
- Applications of Recombinant Proteins -
- **Production of biotherapeutics:** Such as insulin. Growth hormones, and monoclonal antibodies.
- **Development of vector Vaccines: vector vaccines:** Considered safer than traditional vaccines, as they do not contain live pathogens.

- **Agricultural:** Used in development of genetically modified crops, increase nutritional value of animal feed etc.
- **Environmental:** Used in bioremediation (process of using microorganisms to break down pollutants in the environment)

Genetic Modification (GM)

- GM refers to **insertion of a gene** in an **organism**. The method can **introduce traits** from a **different** organism which is impossible to obtain via conventional breeding.
- **Modern biotechnological techniques** can directly **manipulate** the gene of an organism, by modifying the **DNA** of the **organism** by **inserting genes** from the same or another (foreign) species.
- The introduced gene is integrated into the organism's genome but its **location** in the DNA is not known.
- This technique is referred to as **genetic engineering** and is also often called **Genetic Modification** (GM). The overall objective is similar to **conventional breeding**, i.e., to **obtain desired traits**.
- One of the methods of doing **genetic modification** is to use a **biolistic gun** (also called a gene gun). **Particles of a heavy metal** are coated with the gene to be introduced, and then fired with mechanical force into cells, where they get integrated.
- Another method uses **bacteria** or **virus** (containing the gene) to **infect** the **target cells**. In both these methods, the gene is introduced randomly within the **target DNA**, i.e., its location cannot be specified.
- A recently invented technique is **gene editing**, a much more precise form of **genetic modification**, which often uses **CRISPR technology**. It can modify a small fragment of a specific gene at a specific location in an organism's DNA.

> **Examples** : Gene-edited tomato which helps lower blood pressure and gene-edited soybean oil with enhanced nutritional quality.

- Common GM traits in plants are **herbicide tolerance** (corn), **insect resistance** (cotton) and **virus resistance** (papaya).

> Potential concerns regarding GM crops include **impact on biodiversity**, **soil** and **genetic diversity among crops.**

- GM technology has been used to introduce traits to boost crop production as following –
    - **Herbicide tolerance (HT):** The application of herbicides to kill weeds can damage the crop too. GM crops are created with resistance to specific herbicides which can be used to manage weeds. HT crops reduce soil erosion as weed removal requires ploughing, leading to erosion. They can also be planted in weedy fields.

> **HT crops** include corn, cotton and soybeans.

-
    - **Insect resistance:** Crops are created with insecticidal protein which is only harmful to certain pests that feed on them, this removes the need for the external application of chemicals.

> **Bt-crops** (cotton and corn) contain such **insect-resistant traits.**

-
    - **Virus resistance:** Virus-resistant traits are introduced in susceptible plants which do not possess natural resistance.

> In 1990s, **GM Papaya** was created to resist the papaya ringspot virus in **Hawaii** (US).

-
    - Traits like **herbicide tolerance** and **insect resistance** can also be combined, i.e., crops can have **multiple traits** (e.g., HT-Bt cotton). Other GM traits include **aesthetic changes** (non-browning Arctic apples) and **enhanced nutritional quality** (Vitamin

A-rich crops such as Golden Rice).

Advantages of Application of GM methods in agricultural plants :

- Increased yield
- Enhanced yield protection, i.e., resistance to pests and diseases
- Reduced costs for food
- Reduced usage of environmentally damaging pesticides
- Enhanced nutritional value
- Tolerance to drought hence reducing the use of groundwater

Genetically Modified (GM) Crops

Transgenic crops

- Plants that have been modified through genetic engineering techniques. These crops have had specific genes inserted into their DNA to give them new characteristics or traits that are not naturally found in the species through traditional breeding methods.
- **GM plants have been useful in many ways. Genetic modification has:**
  - Made crops more tolerant to abiotic stresses (cold, drought, salt, heat).
  - Reduced reliance on chemical pesticides (pest-resistant crops).
  - Helped to reduce post harvest losses.
  - Increased efficiency of mineral usage by plants (this prevents early exhaustion of fertility of soil).
  - Enhanced nutritional value of food, e.g., golden rice, i.e., Vitamin A enriched rice.
- In addition to these uses, GM has been used to create **tailor-made plants** to supply alternative resources to industries, in the form of starches, fuels and **pharmaceuticals**.

Example : GM Algae for biofuels

Pest Resistance

- In agriculture, biotechnology helps create plants resistant to pests, reducing pesticide use.
- A bacterium, **Bacillus thuringiensis** (Bt), produces **Bt toxin** that's deadly to insects like bollworms. These toxins stay as **protoxins** in bacteria but become **active** when eaten by pests.
- Scientists cloned the **Bt toxin gene** and placed it in plants, giving them insect resistance. This made **bio-pesticides**, like **Bt cotton, corn, rice**, etc.

Different **Cry genes** target specific pests; like **CryIAC** and **CryIIAB work** against **cotton bollworms**, while **CryIAB fights** corn borers. This technique has created plants that protect themselves without the need of insecticides.

Protection from Parasites

- Certain **nematodes**, like **Meloidogyne incognita**, harm plants and animals, even humans. For instance, **Meloidogyne incognita attacks tobacco roots, reducing yield.**
- RNAi takes place in all **eukaryotic organisms** as a method of **cellular defense**. This method involves silencing of a specific mRNA due to a **complementary dsRNA molecule** that binds to and **prevents translation** of the mRNA (silencing). The source of this complementary RNA could be from an **infection** by **viruses** having **RNA genomes** or **mobile genetic elements** (transposons) that replicate via an RNA intermediate.
- Using **Agrobacterium vectors**, **nematode-specific genes** were introduced into the host plant. The introduction of DNA was such that it produced both sense and anti-sense RNA in the host cells.
- These two RNA's being complementary to each other formed a **double stranded** (dsRNA) that initiated RNAi and thus, silenced the specific mRNA of the nematode. The consequence was that the parasite could not survive in a **transgenic host** expressing **specific interfering RNA**. The transgenic plant therefore got itself protected from the parasite.

GM Mustard : DMH 11

- It is a Genetically Modified Mustard
- DMH = Dhara Mustard Hybrid
- Developed by the Centre for Genetic Manipulation of Crop Plants of Delhi University
- It is herbicide tolerant mustard
- It was created by using **barnase/barstar** technology for genetic modification by adding genes from soil bacterium that makes mustard self-pollinating plants. It also allows for cross pollination and hybridisation.
- **DMH -11** contains three genes **Bar gene, Barnase and Barstar** sourced from soil bacterium.
- The bar gene had made plants resistant to herbicide named **Basta.**

Utilization of Mycorrhiza

- **Mycorrhiza** is a **symbiotic association** between **a fungus and a plant's root system.**

- This relationship involves **fungus filaments** enveloping the **developing roots** or directly accessing root cells. These filaments possess a **substantial surface area**, enabling them to **extract water** and **mineral ions** from a **broader soil region** than the **roots alone.**
- As a result, **mycorrhizal plants** exhibit **enhanced resilience** to **adverse soil conditions**, varying pH levels, high temperatures, drought, and even **toxic heavy metals.**
- Mycorrhiza also contributes to plant disease resistance. In this collaboration, the **fungus gains sugars** and **nitrogen-based components** from the roots, while providing **water** and **minerals** to the roots. This intricate partnership fosters improved plant vigor, particularly in challenging environments.

Challenges of GM Crops

- **Human Consumption Safety:** Ensuring that GM crops are safe for people to eat without causing harm or allergies.
- **Biosafety:** Concerns include eradicating wild species and contaminating the gene pool due to GM crop release.
- **Legal disputes with respect to trait fees:** Disagreements arise over fees for using patented GM technologies, like Monsanto's Bt cotton.
- **Terminator Gene:** Introducing plants that yield sterile seeds, compelling farmers to buy new seeds every planting season, impacting their autonomy.
- **Resistance:** Pests or weeds could develop resistance to GM crop traits.
- **Long-Term Effects:** Limited understanding of long-term consequences on health and environment.
- **Genetic Divide:** Differences between small and large farmers' access to and affordability of GM technologies, potentially deepening existing inequalities.
- **Unintended Effects:** Genetic modifications might have unforeseen impacts on organisms or environments.

Concerns related to Transgenic Crops

- **Lack Nutritional Value:** GM foods can sometimes lack nutritional value despite their increased production and pest resistance focus. This is because the emphasis is often placed on enhancing certain traits rather than nutritional content.
- **Risks to Ecosystems:** GM production can also pose risks to ecosystems and biodiversity. It may disrupt gene flow and harm indigenous varieties, leading to a loss of diversity in the long run.
- **Trigger Allergic Reactions:** Genetically modified foods have the potential to trigger allergic reactions since they are biologically altered. This

can be problematic for individuals accustomed to conventional varieties.

- **Endangered Animals:** Wildlife is also at risk due to GM crops. For instance, genetically modified plants used for producing plastic or pharmaceuticals can endanger animals like mice or deer that consume crop debris left in fields after harvest.
- **Economic issues:** The use of genetically modified organisms may be costly for farmers, as they may need to purchase new seeds or pay for licensing fees.
- **Reduced genetic diversity:** The widespread use of genetically modified organisms could reduce genetic diversity in crops, which could make them more susceptible to diseases or pests in the long term.
- **Environmental risks:** There is a risk that genetically modified organisms could escape into the environment and potentially disrupt natural ecosystems.
- **Health risks:** There are concerns that genetically modified organisms could have unknown effects on human health, although there is no scientific evidence to support these claims.
- **Ethical concerns:** There have been ethical concerns about the use of genetic modification to alter living organisms, particularly when it involves inserting genes from unrelated species.

Regulatory Mechanisms of GM Technology

- **United Nations Cartagena Protocol on Biosafety (2000) :** Signatory countries may take a decision to minimise potential adverse effects on biological diversity and risks to human health with regard to import of **living** (genetically) **modified organisms** (LMOs).
- **Environment Protection Act, 1986:** Regulation of GM Crops is primarily governed by The Manufacture, Use, Import, Export and Storage of Hazardous Micro Organisms Genetically Engineered Organisms or Cells Rules, 1989.
- **Review Committee on Genetic Manipulation (RCGM):** Under the Department of Biotechnology (DBT), this committee monitors various aspects of R & D projects involving GM organisms.
- **Genetic Engineering Appraisal Committee (GEAC) :** Earlier known as the Genetic Engineering Approval Committee, is the topmost biotech regulator in India which functions as a statutory body under the Environment Protection Act 1986 of the Ministry of Environment & Forests (MoEF).
- Under the **EPA 1986**, **Rules for Manufacture, Use**, **Import**, **Export** and **Storage** of Hazardous Microorganisms / Genetically Engineered Organisms or Cells 1989, GEAC is responsible for granting permits to conduct experimental and large-scale open field trials and also approving commercial release of biotech crops.

> The **Rules of 1989** define **5 competent authorities** i.e. the **Institutional Biosafety Committees** (IBSC), **Review Committee of Genetic Manipulation** (RCGM), **Genetic Engineering Approval Committee** (GEAC), **State Biotechnology Coordination Committee** (SBCC) and **District Level Committee** (DLC) for handling of various aspects of the rules.

- **GEAC Safety Assessment tests:** Molecular characterisation (study of inserted genes), food safety studies (protein analysis, toxicity and allergenicity tests) and Environmental safety studies (field trials, Biosafety Research Level trials, impact on soil, pollen flow studies)

> GMOs and the products thereof are regulated under the **Rules for the manufacture, use, import, export & storage of hazardous microorganisms, genetically engineered organisms or cells, 1989** under the **Environment (Protection) Act, 1986.**

- The rules include within its purview all molecular genetics techniques including **R-DNA**, **gene editing techniques, gene drive** etc.

- The rules are enforced by the **MOEFCC, DBT** and **State Governments**.
- **Food Safety and Standards Act, 2006:** Prohibits import, manufacture, use, or sale of GM food without FSSAI's approval.
- **Review Committee on Genetic Manipulation (RCGM):** Under the Department of Biotechnology (DBT), this committee monitors various aspects of R & D projects involving GM organisms.
- **State Biotechnology Coordination Committee (SBCC):** Reviews the safety and control measures in various institutions handling Genetically Modified Organisms (GMOs).
- **District Level Committee (DLC):** Inspects, investigates, and reports to the SBCC or the GEAC about compliance.
- **Genetic Engineering Appraisal Committee (GEAC) :** A Statutory committee under Ministry of Environment, Forest and Climate Change (MOEF&CC) constituted under the "Rules for Manufacture, Use, Import, Export and the Storage of Hazardous Micro-organisations, Genetically Engineered Organisms or Cells, 1989". The rules are framed under the Environment (Protection) Act, 1986. It deals with the ppraisal of proposals relating to the release of Genetically engineered (GE) organisms and products and Appraisal of activities involving large-scale use of hazardous microorganisms and recombinants in research and industrial production.

Ministries Involved in GM CROPS

Ministries	Responsibilities
Ministry of Environment Forest and Climate Change	• Primarily responsible for conservation and protection of environment, ensuring environmental and human health safety before release of GMOS/LMOS • Nodal agency for implementing Rules, 1989 and the Cartagena Protocol on Biosafety
Department of Biotechnology (Ministry of Science & Technology)	• Nodal department for promoting biotechnology programs • Provides scientific support in implementation of biosafety regulations. • Provide services in areas of research, infrastructure, generation of human resource.
Ministry of Commerce and Industries	• Enhance trade with other countries through export/import policies. • Nodal agency for implementing DGFT notification on GMOs
Ministry of Agriculture	• Policies aimed at agriculture growth. • Indian Council of Agricultural Research (ICAR) responsible for monitoring agronomic benefits of GM technology. • Monitoring post-release performance of GM crops.
Ministry of Health and Family Welfare	• Policies aimed at protecting and monitoring human health. • Food Safety and Standards Authority of India responsible for regulating genetically engineered foods.
Central Board of Excise and Customs ,Department of Revenue Ministry of Finance	• Enforcement of regulation pertaining to transboundary movement of GMOS/LMOS at point of entry

Major regulatory committees related to GM Crops	
Committee	**Function**
Recombinant DNA Advisory Committee (RDAC)	Reviews biotechnology developments at national and international levels under DBT.
Institutional BioSafety Committee	Ensures safe research in GM crops at institutes ,approving low-risk experiments.
Review Committee on Genetic Modification	Regulatory body inside DBT, responsible for bringing out manuals/ guidelines specifying procedures for research/ use /applications in GMOs. Reviews all projects involving high risk field experiments.
Genetic Engineering Appraisal Committee	Apex regulatory committee under MOEFCC, grants approval for commercial release of GM crops.
State Biotechnology Coordination Committee	Monitors GM crop activities as per regulations at the state level. Assesses damage caused by GM crops. Serves as a state-level nodal agency.
District Level Committee	Monitors GM crop activities at the district level, chaired by the District Collector (DC).

Genetic Engineering Appraisal Committee

- The Genetic Engineering Appraisal Committee (GEAC) is a **statutory body** constituted under the **Rules for the Manufacture, Use / Import /Export and Storage of Hazardous Microorganisms/Genetically Engineering Organisms or Cells, 1989** notified under the Environment (Protection) Act, 1986. It functions under the **Ministry of Environment, Forests & Climate Change.**
- The body **regulates the use, manufacture, storage, import** and **export** of **hazardous microorganisms** or **genetically-engineered organisms** and **cells** in India.
- The Committee is chaired by the **Special Secretary/Additional Secretary** of the **Ministry of Environment, Forests and Climate Change, GOI**. A representative of the Department of Biotechnology is a co-chair.
- It is responsible for the **appraisal of activities that involve** the **large scale use of hazardous microbes** and **recombinants** in **research** and **industrial production.**
- The GEAC also assesses proposals regarding the **release of genetically engineered products** and **organisms** into the environment, which includes **experimental field trials** as well.
- The body also looks into proposals regarding the use of **living modified organism** that comes in the **risk category III** and above in the **import/ manufacture of recombinant pharma products**, or where the end-product of the recombinant pharma product is a **modified living organism.**
- The Committee has the power to take punitive action against people/body under the Environment (Protection) Act.
- The approval of the GEAC is **mandatory** before **genetically modified organisms** and **products** derived from them can be used commercially.
- The Ministry of Environment, Forest and Climate Change (MoEFCC) holds the authority to provide exemptions to specific handlers of genetically modified organisms (GMOs) from the stipulated regulations. These exemptions serve various purposes.

- **Exemption can be granted for :**
  - Indigenous development of **recombinant pharmaceuticals** that have less risk (risk group 1 and 2)
  - Exemptions can be granted for the import and marketing of products derived from **living modified organisms** (LMOs) when the final product is not itself an LMO.
  - **Event based approval mechanism for Bt Cotton Hybrids :** BT cotton hybrids expressing approved events developed through conventional hybridization are exempted from conduct of detailed biosafety trials.

> Recently, GEAC has given approvals for biosafety trials of **Event 142** : a new variety of **Bt Brinjal.**

GM Crops in India

GM Crops of India		
BT Cotton	GEAC Recommended	Ministry Approved
BT Brinjal	GEAC Approved	Ministry Rejected
GM Mustard	GEAC Recommended	Ministry Rejected
GM Soymeal	Import Allowed	
GM Rubber	Trials : Going on	

- The import of genetically modified (GM) soymeal has been permitted, with the **Genetic Engineering Appraisal Committee** (GEAC) bypassed due to an exemption granted by the **Ministry of Environment, Forest and Climate Change** (MoEFCC). This exemption was based on the classification of the final product as non-living.

> **Soymeal**, derived from soybean seeds after oil **extraction**, serves as a protein-rich solid residue and is a significant component of poultry feed.

- In parallel, trials for **genetically modified rubber** are underway. Notably, the **world's first GM rubber plant** was cultivated in **Assam**, tailored specifically for the **Northeast region of India.**
- This variety contains additional copies of the **MnSOD gene**, which encodes for **Manganese-containing Superoxide Dismutase**. This genetic addition aids the plant in enduring cold winter conditions. This innovative **GM rubber strain** was developed by the **Rubber Research Institute of India**, located in **Kerala.**

> The **Agharkar Research Institute**, operating under the **Department of Science and Technology** (DST), has successfully identified and mapped **two genes in wheat**, known as **Rht14 and Rht18.**

- These genes contribute to enhanced **seedling vigor** and **longer coleoptiles**, which serve as a protective sheath. This advancement holds the potential to enable deeper planting of wheat seeds and subsequently reduce the need for crop residue burning.
- In the context of genetically modified (GM) **food imports**, a dual regulatory process is employed. The **Genetic Engineering Appraisal Committee** (GEAC) provides clearance by considering **environmental aspects**, while the **Food Safety and Standards Authority of India** (FSSAI) grants approval based on the human health perspective.
- This dual evaluation process aligns with the regulatory frameworks of the Environmental Protection Act of 1986 and the Food Safety and Standards Act of 2006, ensuring comprehensive scrutiny of GM food imports.

Important GM Crops in News

- **Flavr Savr Tomato :** first commercial GM food crop
- **Golden Rice :** Provitamin A
- **BT Crops : Cry 1 AC gene :** Protection against Bollworms

Significance of Genetic Modified Crops (GM)

- **Increased crop yields:** Genetic modification can enhance the ability of crops to resist pests, diseases, and environmental stresses, leading to higher crop yields.
- **Improved nutritional content:** Genetic modification can also improve the nutritional content of crops, such as increasing the amount of vitamins and minerals in the food.
- **Reduced use of pesticides:** Crops engineered to be resistant to pests can reduce the need for harmful pesticides, leading to less environmental damage.
- **Control Weeds:** GM technology has also played a crucial role in developing herbicide-tolerant crops. Crops like soybean, maize, cotton, and canola have been genetically modified to withstand specific broad-spectrum herbicides, allowing farmers to effectively control weeds while preserving the cultivated crop.
- **Ensuring Food Security:** GM crops are being developed to adapt to changing environmental conditions. Researchers are working on strains of rice, maize, and wheat that can tolerate longer droughts and wetter monsoon seasons, ensuring food security in challenging climates.
- **Greater efficiency in industrial processes:** Genetic modification can also be used to create microbes or enzymes that can be used in industrial processes, such as producing biofuels.
- **Creation of new products:** Genetic modification can also be used to create entirely new products, such as crops that produce pharmaceuticals.
- **Deals with challenges related to cultivation of Crops in Salty soils:** GM has also been used to create salt-tolerant plants, offering a potential solution for growing crops in salty soils. By inserting genes that remove sodium ions from water and maintain cell balance, plants can thrive in high-salt environments.

Transgenic/Genetically Modified Organisms (GMOS)

- In the **genetic manipulation process**, organisms whose body contains **foreign genes** are called transgenic organisms. They can be **transgenic plants, transgenic animals** and **transgenic bacteria.**
- **Genetically Modified Organisms** (GMO) are **living organisms** whose **genetic material** has been **artificially manipulated** in a **laboratory** through **genetic engineering** in order to favour the expression of **desired physiological traits** or the generation of desired biological products.

> **Genetically Modified Organism** (GMO) and **Transgenic Crganism** are often used interchangeably.

- However, there is a slight difference between GMO and transgenic organism. Although both have altered genomes, a transgenic organism is a GMO containing a DNA sequence or a gene from a different species. While a GMO is an animal, plant, or microbe whose DNA has been altered using genetic engineering techniques.

> **All transgenic organisms** are **GMOs**, but **not all GMOs** are **transgenic.**

- **Transgenic** and **cisgenic** are terms used to describe **genetically modified organisms** (GMOs) that have been **altered** through the introduction of **foreign genetic material.**
- **Transgenic organisms** have genes from other organisms **inserted** into their **genome** using **genetic engineering techniques**. These foreign genes may come from different species or even different kingdoms of life.

> A transgenic plant may have a gene from a bacteria inserted into its genome to make it resistant to certain pests or herbicides.

- **Cisgenic organisms,** on the other hand, have genes from **related organisms inserted** into their **genome**. These related organisms may be of the same species or a closely related species.

- A cisgenic potato may have a gene from another potato variety inserted into its genome to make it resistant to a particular disease.
- Cisgenic modifications only use genetic material from closely related organisms, while transgenic modifications can use genetic material from unrelated organisms.

One Day One Genome Initiative

- Launched by Department of Biotechnology (DBT) and Biotechnology Research and Innovation Council (BRIC).
- An annotated microbial genome will be publicly released every day to make microbial genomics data more accessible to researchers and will highlight the unique bacterial species found in our country.

Microbial Genomics

- It is the scientific field that studies the complete genetic material of microorganisms to understand their structure, function, evolution, and interactions with other organisms. Microbes (or microorganisms) are too small to see with the naked eye. E.g., bacteria, algae, etc.

Significance of Microbial Genomics –

- **Human health:** Understanding the relationship between disease-causing bacteria and their genetic makeup.
- **Advancing biotech applications:** Biofuel production, bio-manufacturing, etc.
- **Environmental sustainability** : Ideonella sakaiensis produces an enzyme that degrades PET plastic into reusable monomers.
- **Human health and disease management:** Genome sequencing of Mycobacterium tuberculosis helps in detecting drug-resistant strains.
- **Agriculture:** Nutrient cycling, nitrogen fixation, maintaining soil fertility, etc.

Heritable Human Genome Editing (HHGE)

- Unlike somatic cell editing, which affects only individuals, HHGE introduces changes in germline cells (sperm, eggs, or embryos), enabling these alterations to be inherited by offspring.

Applications –

- **Disease Prevention: These include Heritable diseases, Huntington's disease, and sickle cell anemia. Assisted reproductive technology:** Can improve technologies, such as in vitro fertilization (IVF).
- South Africa becomes the first country to allow Heritable Human Genome Editing (HHGE).

Concerns:

- Germline genome edits would be heritable, and their effects could be multigenerational.
- Creation of "designer babies," where traits like intelligence, etc. might be engineered

Stem cells

- Stem cells are **special cells** with the **unique ability** to **transform** into different types of cells in the body. They can **self-renew** and **differentiate**, aiding in **tissue repair** and **growth**.
- Stem cells have the unique ability to develop into specialised cell types in the body. They can divide over and over again to produce new cells andand replace specialised cells that are damaged or lost. As they divide, they can change into the other types of cells that make up the body.
- **Major sources of Stem Cells:** Embryos and adult tissues (adult stem cells).

Types of Stem Cells –

- **Totipotent:** Can make all three embryonic germ layers. Ex – Zygote.
- **Pluripotent:** Can make multiple lineages from all three embryonic germ layers. Ex – Embryonic stem cells (ESCs).

- **Multipotent:** Can make at least two different lineages, usually from the same embryonic germ layer. Ex – Hematopoetic stem
- **Unipotent:** Can produce only one cell type but have the property of self-renewal. Ex - Skin cell
- **Stem cells are distinguished from other cell types by 2 important characteristics:**
  - First, they are unspecialized cells capable of renewing themselves through cell division, sometimes after long periods of inactivity.
  - Second, under certain physiologic or experimental conditions, they can be induced to become tissue- or organ-specific cells with special functions. In some organs, such as the gut and bone marrow, stem cells regularly divide to repair and replace worn out or damaged tissues. In other organs, however, such as the pancreas and the heart, stem cells only divide under special conditions.
- Stem cells have the **remarkable potential** to develop into many different cell types in the body during early life and growth.
- In addition, in many tissues they serve as a sort of **internal repair system**, dividing essentially without limit to replenish other cells as long as the person or animal is still alive.
- When a stem cell divides, each new cell has the potential either to remain a stem cell or become another type of cell with a more specialized function, such as a muscle cell, a red **blood cell**, or a **brain cell**.

Embryonic vs Adult Stem Cells

Types of Stem Cells

Embryonic | Adult

- One major difference between adult and Embryonic stem cells is their **different abilities** in the **number** and **type of differentiated cell** types they can become.
  - **Embryonic stem cells** can become all cell types of the body because they are pluripotent.
  - **Adult stem cells** are thought to be limited to differentiating into different cell types of their tissue of origin.
- **Embryonic stem cells** can be grown relatively easily in culture. **Adult stem cells** are rare in **mature tissues**, so isolating these cells from an **adult tissue** is challenging, and methods to expand their numbers in cell culture have not yet been worked out. This is an important distinction, as large numbers of cells are needed for **stem cell replacement therapies.**

> Scientists have discovered **Induced Pluripotent Stem Cells (iPSCs)** which can be helpful in **personalized disease modeling** and **potential for cell-based therapies**, enabling **tailored treatments** and advancing our understanding of **diseases** and **regenerative medicine.**

Regulatory status in India

- **National Guidelines for Stem Cell Research** jointly formulated by **Department of Biotechnology** and the **Indian Council of Medical Research** was released by the **Hon'ble Minister for Health & Family Welfare** on **11th October, 2017.**
- As per the **National Guidelines for Stem Cell Research** (2017), at present, there are no approved indications for **stem cell therapy** other than the **hematopoietic stem cell transplantation** (HSCT) for **hematological disorders.**
- Accordingly, all stem cell therapy other than the above shall be treated as investigational and conducted only in the form of a **clinical trial** after obtaining necessary regulatory approvals. Use of stem cells for any other purpose outside the domain of clinical trials is considered unethical and hence is not permissible.

Stem Cell Therapy

- Stem cell therapy offers the potential to replace **impaired tissues** with **healthy cells** generated from stem cells. It holds promise in addressing conditions like **thalassemia, leukemia, osteoarthritis, osteoporosis, and even blindness.**
- **Advantages :** Minimal Immune rejection because cells are derived from the body itself.

Applications of Stem Cell Therapy

Stem Cell Applications

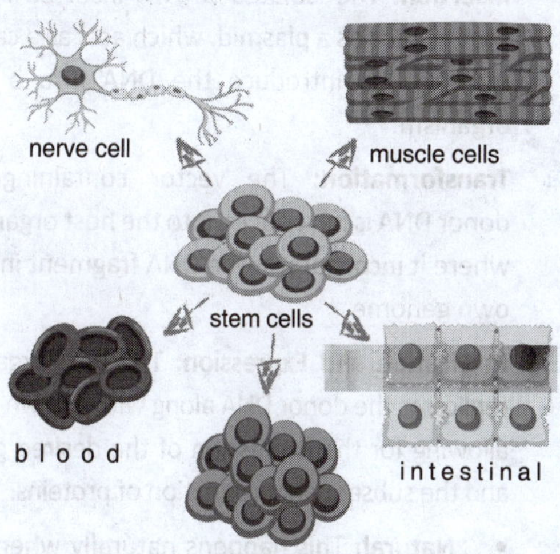

- **Blood Disorders:** Treats leukemia with bone marrow transplants.
- **Musculoskeletal Issues:** Regenerates cartilage and bone for osteoarthritis relief.
- **Autoimmune Diseases:** Manages lupus by modulating immune responses.
- **Cardiac Diseases:** Restores heart tissue after heart attacks or for heart failure treatment.
- **Tissue Healing:** Aids in wound and burn healing, accelerating tissue regeneration.
- **Genetic Disorders:** Potential for gene replacement to address genetic diseases.
- **Organ Regeneration:** Research ongoing for growing replacement organs like kidneys and liver.
- **Personalized Medicine:** Creates patient-specific treatments using induced pluripotent stem cells.
- **Drug Testing:** Helps assess drug safety and effectiveness on specific cell types before human trials.

Challenges and Concerns in Stem Cell Therapy

- **Concerns Regarding Biosafety:** Ensuring safe use of engineered cells to prevent unintended consequences or harm to patients and the environment.
- **Genetic Disparities:** Access to advanced therapies could create a gap between affluent and less privileged populations.
- **Synthetic Biology Perception:** Manipulating biology can be viewed as tampering with natural processes, raising ethical debates.
- **Misuse of Technology:** Possibility of misuse or unintended consequences, demanding strict regulations.
- **Ethical Dilemmas:** Balancing scientific advancement with ethical considerations, especially when using embryonic stem cells.

Organ-on-Chip (OoC) Technology

- It refers to micro-scale system used for mimicking the human body environment.
- Cells are placed chip and allowed to grow into 3D structures with the help of a polymer that resembles real tissue in the human body. It uses tiny fluid channels that simulate blood flow, oxygen delivery, nutrient transport, etc. to create miniature models of biological organs (lung, heart, etc.) on a chip-sized device
- One of the human-relevant 3D culture models, also known as 'New Approach Methods' (NAMs). 3D culture system allows researchers to recreate human organs and diseases in one dish. It control the movement and behaviour of materials and cells by using channels, chambers, membranes, etc.

- **Organoids:** Created by growing cells from a tissue.
- **Spheroids:** Believed to mimic tumor behavior more effectively than regular two-dimensional (2D) cell cultures.
- **Bio printing:** Uses 3D printing to create living tissues and organs.

Significance –

- **Precision Therapeutics:** Researchers con test how specific drugs will affect that individual/ Group.
- **Simulation:** Replicate the structure and function of human organs more accurately.
- **Complex Organ Interactions:** Multiple organ models can be linked together.

Cloning

Cloning refers to the process of **creating genetically identical copies** of an organism. It involves replicating the entire genetic blueprint of an **individual** and **producing offspring** with the **same genetic makeup**. Genes, cells, tissues, and even whole animals can all be cloned.

Types of cloning
- Reproductive Cloning
- Therapeutic Cloning
- DNA Cloning

- **Reproductive Cloning:** Reproductive cloning aims to create an **identical copy** of an **existing organism**. This process involves **transferring the DNA** from a **donor cell** into an **egg cell** without its nucleus. The embryo is then **implanted** into a **surrogate mother**, resulting in the birth of an organism genetically **identical** to the donor.
- **Therapeutic Cloning:** Therapeutic cloning is a procedure specifically employed for medical purposes. It involves the **creation of embryonic stem cells** that can be used to **regenerate tissues** and potentially treat a range of diseases.
- **DNA Cloning:** DNA cloning is the technique of **making multiple copies** of a **specific DNA segment**, typically a gene or a particular sequence, using various **molecular biology methods**.

Methods of Cloning

- **Isolation:** The first step involves extracting the donor DNA containing the desired genes. This DNA is selected carefully, ensuring it possesses the required traits.
- **Insertion:** The isolated DNA is inserted into a vector, such as a plasmid, which acts as a carrier molecule to introduce the DNA into a host organism.
- **Transformation:** The vector containing the donor DNA is introduced into the host organism, where it incorporates the DNA fragment into its own genome.
- **Replication and Expression:** The host organism replicates the donor DNA along with its own DNA, allowing for the expression of the desired genes and the subsequent production of proteins.
  - **Natural:** This happens naturally when one embryo spontaneously divides into two or more embryos, thus creating identical twins or, sometimes, triplets or even more. Happens in case of Identical twins.
  - **Artifical:** An existing embryo is mechanically divided into two or more embryos that are then allowed to develop naturally.
  - **Artifical and Donor:** Through use of somatic cell of Donor.

Steps Involved

- **DNA Extraction:** The target DNA is isolated from the source organism using various extraction techniques.
- **DNA Amplification:** The isolated DNA is amplified through the polymerase chain reaction (PCR) method, producing numerous copies of the desired DNA segment.

- **Vector Preparation:** A vector is prepared by isolating a circular piece of DNA, often a plasmid, which will hold the desired gene or DNA segment.
- **Ligation:** The amplified DNA segment and the vector are chemically linked, creating a recombinant DNA molecule.
- **Transformation and Selection:** The recombinant DNA molecule is introduced into host cells, which are then subjected to selection methods to identify cells successfully incorporating the desired DNA.
- **Reproductive cloning** is a very **inefficient technique** and most cloned animal embryos cannot develop into healthy individuals. For instance, Dolly was the only clone to be born live out of a total of 277 cloned embryos. This very low efficiency, combined with safety concerns, presents a serious obstacle to the application of reproductive cloning.

Therapeutic Cloning

- **Therapeutic cloning** offers the potential to **revolutionize medicine** through its unique approach.
- By producing a **healthy replica** of a human organ, it provides a promising solution to the organ transplant crisis, eliminating the need for immunosuppressant drugs due to the matching DNA. The process resembles reproductive cloning until the creation of an embryo, which is then allowed to develop in a laboratory environment.
- Subsequently, stem cells are extracted from the embryo, enabling the treatment of various diseases by replacing **damaged cells.**
- However, ethical concerns arise, encompassing viewpoints such as the **Divine Command Theory** and the **Christian belief** that life begins at **conception**. Additionally, debates surrounding violations of natural laws further shape the discourse on therapeutic cloning's ethical dimensions.

Potential applications of therapeutic cloning

- Applications range from addressing **age-related conditions** and **cancer to enhancing implant surgeries.**
- Researchers hope to use **embryonic stem cells,** which have the **unique ability to generate** virtually all types of cells in an organism, to grow healthy tissues in the laboratory that can be used **replace injured** or **diseased tissues.**
- In addition, it may be possible to learn more about the molecular causes of disease by studying embryonic stem cell lines from cloned embryos derived from the cells of animals or humans with different diseases.
- **Differentiated tissues** derived from ES cells are excellent tools to test new therapeutic drugs
- An embryo made by cloning can be turned into a **stem cell factory.** Stem cells are an early form of cells that can grow into many different types of cells and tissues.

> Scientists can turn them into **nerve cells** to fix a **damaged spinal cord** or **insulin-making cells** to **treat diabetes.**

- The **cloning of animals** has been used in a number of different applications. Animals have been cloned to have gene mutations that help scientists study diseases that develop in the animals.

> **Livestock** like cows and pigs have been cloned to produce more milk or meat.Example India is doing this project on **Indigenous breeds.**
>
> Cloning might one day **bring back extinct species** like the **woolly mammoth** or **giant panda.**

- It overcomes the problem of immune rejection which is major concern during organ transplantation

- It can help in understanding process of ageing
- **Biopharmaceuticals:** Human proteins with biomedical uses are created using DNA cloning.

> **E. coli-based insulin synthesis** is one instance. Additional examples are tissue plasminogen activator, which is used to treat strokes, and human growth hormones, which are used to treat people who cannot naturally make this hormone.

- **Gene Therapy:** A specific gene that is missing from a patient's body as a result of a genetic condition is provided by gene therapy.

> It was possible to create plasmids with a normal copy of the cystic fibrosis gene via DNA cloning.

- The lung function deterioration rate was reduced in **cystic fibrosis patients** after plasmids were administered to their lungs.

Significance of Cloning

- Replication of Desirable Traits
- Medical Advancements
- Repopulation of Endangered Species
- Research and Drug Development

Concerns of Cloning

- Ethical Considerations
- Genetic Diversity
- High Failure Rates
- Psychological and Social Implication
- May Lead to Cancer
- Researchers have observed some **adverse health effects in sheep** and **other mammals** that have been cloned. These include an increase in birth size and a variety of defects in vital organs, such as the liver, brain and heart. Other consequences include premature ageing and problems with the immune system.
- Another potential problem centers on the **relative age of the cloned cell's chromosomes.** As cells go through their normal rounds of division, the tips of the chromosomes, called **telomeres**, **shrink**. Over time, the **telomeres** become so **short** that the cell can no longer divide and, consequently, the cell dies. This is part of the natural aging process that seems to happen in all cell types. As a consequence, clones created from a cell taken from an adult might have chromosomes that are already shorter than normal, which may condemn the **clones** cells to a **shorter life span.**
- **Gene cloning** is a carefully regulated technique that is largely accepted today and used routinely in many labs worldwide. However, both reproductive and therapeutic cloning raise important ethical issues, especially as related to the potential use of these techniques in humans.
- **Reproductive cloning** would present the potential of creating a human that is **genetically identical** to another person who has **previously existed** or **who still exists.** This may conflict with **long-standing religious** and **societal values** about **human dignity, possibly infringing** upon **principles of individual freedom, identity** and **autonomy**. However, some argue that reproductive cloning **could help sterile couples** fulfill their dream of **parenthood**. Others see human cloning as a way to **avoid passing** on a **deleterious gene** that runs in the family without having to undergo embryo screening or embryo selection.
- **Therapeutic cloning**, while offering the potential for treating humans suffering from disease or injury, would require the **destruction of human embryos** in the **test tube**. Consequently, opponents argue that using this technique to collect embryonic stem cells is wrong, regardless of whether such cells are used to benefit sick or injured people.

Assisted Reproductive Technology

- **Assisted reproductive technologies** (ART) refer to a range of **fertility treatments** aimed at **aiding reproduction** for couples suffering from infertility or to persons who may wish to have a child through **artificial methods.**
- According to the **Indian Society of Assisted Reproduction** (ISAR), roughly **10-14 percent** of **Indian couples** are currently experiencing **infertility.**
- The issue is exacerbated by late **marriages, demanding lifestyles, obesity, excessive consumption of fast food, smoking, drinking,** and **drug addiction.**
- The desire to conceive a child through biotechnological intervention lays ground for demand of **Assisted Reproductive Technology.**

- ART procedures involve **surgically removing eggs from a woman's ovaries, combining** them with **sperm** in the **laboratory** and **plaiting** them to the **woman's body** or **donating** them to another woman (called Surrogacy).
- **Assisted Reproductive Technology fertility treatments** handle both a **woman's egg** and a **man's sperm.**
- ART does not include treatments in which only sperm are handled or procedures in which a woman takes medicine only to **stimulate egg production** without the intention of having eggs retrieved. It works by removing eggs from a woman's body which are then mixed with sperm to make embryos. The embryos are then put back in the woman's body.

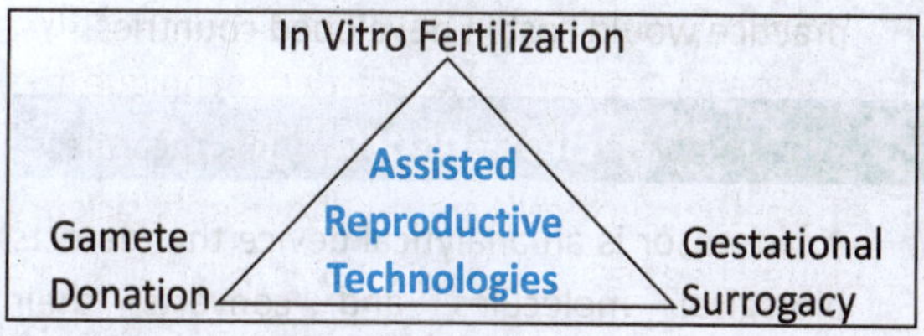

- **In-vitro fertilization (IVF) :** IVF involves the **retrieval of eggs** from a **woman's ovaries**, which are then fertilized with sperm in a laboratory setting. The resulting embryos are cultured for a few days before being transferred back into the woman's uterus.
- **Gamete donation :** This refers to the use of donated sperm, eggs, or both, to achieve fertilization.
- **Gestational Surrogacy :** In gestational surrogacy, an embryo created through IVF, using either the intended parents' or donated gametes, is transferred into the uterus of a surrogate (also known as a gestational carrier). The surrogate carries the **pregnancy to term** and **delivers** the **baby**, but the child is **genetically unrelated** to the surrogate.

Surrogacy

- Surrogacy is a practice where a woman agrees to **carry** and **give birth** to a **child** on behalf of another person or couple who are unable to conceive or carry a pregnancy of themselves.
- The woman who carries the pregnancy is known as a **surrogate**, and she may use her own eggs or the eggs of the intended mother or a donor, fertilized by sperm from the intended father or a donor.
- Surrogacy is often used by couples who struggle with **infertility** or **medical conditions** that make it difficult or impossible for them to conceive and **carry a pregnancy.**
- In some cases, surrogacy may also be used by **same-sex couples** (homosexuals) or **single parents** who wish to have a child.
- In India, **commercial surrogacy** is not allowed, and surrogacy can only be carried out for **altruistic purposes** with strict restrictions and no monetary consideration allowed.

Assisted Reproductive Technology (Regulation) [ART] Act, 2021

- The Act defines ART to include **all techniques** that seek to obtain a pregnancy by handling the sperm or the oocyte (immature egg cell) outside the **human body** and **transferring the gamete** or the embryo into the **reproductive system** of a woman.

> ☯ As per the **ART Act**, **Infertility** means the **inability to conceive a child after one year of unprotective intercourse or other proven medical condition preventing a couple** from **conception.**

- ART services will be provided through **ART Clinics** and **Banks.**

> ☯ **ART Clinics:** ART clinics are specialized medical facilities that provide a range of services related to assisted reproductive technologies.
>
> ☯ **ART Banks:** Also known as **gamete banks** or **cryobanks**, are the facilities that store and supply gametes (sperm and eggs) for use in assisted reproductive procedures.

- A bank can **obtain semen** from males between 21 and 55 years of age, and oocytes from females between 23 and 35 years of age.
- An **oocyte donor** should be a married woman having at least one alive child of her own (minimum three years of age).
- The woman can **donate oocytes only once in her life** and not more than **seven oocytes** can be retrieved from her.
- A **bank cannot supply the gamete** of a single donor to more than one couple seeking services.
- A child born through ART will be deemed to be a **biological child of the couple** (commission couple) and will be entitled to the rights and privileges available to a natural child of the commissioning couple.
- A donor will not have any parental rights over the child.
- The Act allows **only married couples** and single women to avail ART services.
- The **Health ministry** clarified that **single women** (includes the LGBTQ community) will have **access to ART services** and other benefits specified as per the Act.
- However, **single men will not be able to avail such services** as they are not allowed to adopt a child as per the current adoption rules.
- Prior the ART Act, **Surrogacy remained unregulated** in India. The absence of legislation to govern this space has led to the mushrooming of surrogacy clinics and rampant exploitation of women who choose to become surrogates, often due to abject poverty, leading to commercialisation of womb.
- **Unconscionable practices** are frequently employed by surrogacy clinics, and owing to their illiteracy and indigence, surrogates are usually excluded from the decision-making process, which remains **restricted** between the **intended parent(s)** and **medical professionals.**
- In the past, disputes regarding **conflict of laws** have arisen in cases where the intended parent(s) were not Indian citizens and withdrew from the arrangement at an advanced stage, as India no longer grants **birth right** (jus soli) **citizenship.**
- Further, considering the **taboo around assisted reproduction in India**, surrogates are typically constrained to carry the foetus in secrecy, in deplorable physical conditions, and for sums of money approximately a third of what the practice would cost in developed countries.

Biosensors

- A biosensor is an analytical device that detects biological molecules and converts their presence or concentration into a measurable signal.

- Biosensors are widely used in healthcare, environmental monitoring, food safety, and biotechnology.

Components of a Biosensor –

Bioreceptor : A biological element that recognizes the target analyte.

Examples:

- Enzymes (e.g., glucose oxidase in glucose sensors)
- Antibodies (e.g., in pregnancy tests)
- DNA/RNA (e.g., for genetic testing)
- Microorganisms (e.g., for detecting pollutants)

Transducer : Converts the biological response into an electrical signal. Types include:

- Electrochemical transducers (measure voltage, current, or resistance)
- Optical transducers (detect changes in light absorption, fluorescence, etc.)
- Piezoelectric transducers (detect changes in mass or vibration)

Signal Processor : Converts and displays the signal in a readable format, such as graphs or digital readouts.

Types of Biosensors

A. Based on Transduction Method

- **Electrochemical Biosensors :** Measure electrical signals (current, voltage, or impedance) caused by biochemical reactions.
  - **Example:** Glucose biosensors for diabetes monitoring.
- **Optical Biosensors :** Detect changes in light absorption, fluorescence, or luminescence.
  - **Example:** Surface Plasmon Resonance (SPR) biosensors for detecting biomolecular interactions.
- **Piezoelectric Biosensors :** Measure mass changes by detecting shifts in frequency due to molecular binding.
  - **Example:** Quartz crystal microbalance (QCM) for detecting bacterial pathogens.
- **Thermal Biosensors :** Measure heat changes produced by biochemical reactions.
  - **Example:** Used in calorimetric assays for enzyme activity detection.

B. Based on Bioreceptor Type

- **Enzyme-based Biosensors :** Use enzymes to recognize specific substrates.
  - **Example:** Glucose oxidase in blood glucose monitoring.
- **Immunosensors (Antibody-based Biosensors) :** Use antibodies to detect specific antigens.
  - **Example:** COVID-19 rapid test kits.
- **DNA Biosensors (Genosensors) :** Use complementary DNA strands to detect genetic sequences.
  - **Example:** PCR-based biosensors for genetic disorder detection.
- **Microbial Biosensors:** Use bacteria or microorganisms to detect pollutants or toxins.
  - **Example:** Bacteria-based biosensors for arsenic detection in water.

Applications of Biosensors

A. Medical & Healthcare

- **Glucose Monitoring:** Used by diabetic patients.
- **Cancer Biomarker Detection:** Early cancer diagnosis through biomarker detection.
- COVID-19 & Infectious Disease Detection: Rapid antigen tests.

B. Environmental Monitoring

- **Water Quality Testing:** Detects heavy metals, toxins, and pathogens.
- **Air Pollution Sensors:** Detect harmful gases like CO_2, NO_2, and VOCs.

C. Food Industry

- **Pathogen Detection:** Identifies bacteria like E. coli and Salmonella in food.
- **Toxin Detection:** Monitors pesticides and contaminants in agricultural products.

D. Industrial & Military Applications

- **Biodefense & Bioterrorism Detection:** Detects biological warfare agents.
- **Quality Control in Pharmaceuticals:** Ensures purity of drugs.

Advantages of Biosensors –

- High sensitivity & specificity
- Rapid detection & real-time monitoring
- Miniaturization (portable biosensors)
- Cost-effective (compared to traditional lab methods)

Challenges and Limitations –

- Limited lifespan of biological components
- Environmental factors affecting accuracy
- Complex manufacturing & calibration

Emerging Trends in Biosensors

- **Wearable Biosensors:** Smartwatches and patches for continuous health monitoring.
- **Nano-biosensors:** Enhanced sensitivity using nanotechnology.
- **AI-Integrated Biosensors:** Machine learning for predictive diagnostics.
- **Lab-on-a-Chip Technology:** Miniaturized portable diagnostic tools.

Bioinformatics

- Bioinformatics is the application of computational tools to store, analyze, and interpret biological data, particularly in genomics and molecular biology.
- It integrates biology, mathematics, and computer science to solve complex biological problems.

Applications of Bioinformatics

- **Genomics & Proteomics :** Analyzing DNA and protein sequences.
- **Drug Discovery :** Designing new drugs using molecular docking.
- **Evolutionary Biology :** Understanding genetic relationships between species.
- **Personalized Medicine :** Tailoring treatments based on genetic profiles.

Biological Databases

- Biological databases store genomic, proteomic, and structural information, allowing researchers to retrieve and analyze data efficiently.

Types of Databases –

- **Nucleotide Sequence Databases:**
  - GenBank (NCBI)
  - EMBL (European Molecular Biology Laboratory)
  - DDBJ (DNA Data Bank of Japan)
- **Protein Sequence Databases:**
- UniProt (Swiss-Prot & TrEMBL) – Stores protein sequences with functional annotations.
- **Structural Databases :**
- Protein Data Bank (PDB) – Stores 3D structures of biomolecules.
- **Metabolic Pathway Databases:**
- KEGG (Kyoto Encyclopedia of Genes and Genomes) – Pathway mapping of genes and proteins.

Tools for Searching Databases:

- **BLAST (Basic Local Alignment Search Tool):** Compares DNA/protein sequences to find similarities.
- **FASTA :** Another tool for sequence alignment and similarity search.

Sequence Alignment & Analysis

- Sequence alignment compares two or more biological sequences to identify similarities and differences, helping in evolutionary studies and functional annotation.

Types of Sequence Alignment –

1. Pairwise Sequence Alignment:

- Global Alignment (Needleman-Wunsch Algorithm) – Aligns full-length sequences.
- Local Alignment (Smith-Waterman Algorithm) – Finds regions of high similarity.
- **2 Multiple Sequence Alignment (MSA):**
- **ClustalW and MUSCLE :** Align multiple sequences to find conserved regions.

2. Substitution Matrices

- **PAM (Point Accepted Mutation) :** Measures evolutionary distance between sequences.
- **BLOSUM (Blocks Substitution Matrix) :** Scores alignments based on conserved protein blocks.

Genomics

- **Genome Sequencing & Annotation :** Identifying and labeling genes in a genome.
- **Functional Genomics :** Studying gene functions using high-throughput technologies.
- **Comparative Genomics :** Comparing genomes of different species to understand evolutionary relationships.

Proteomics

- **Protein Structure & Function Prediction :** Understanding protein roles in biological processes.
- **Protein-Protein Interactions (PPI) :** Studying how proteins interact to form cellular networks.

Structural Bioinformatics

- Focuses on the 3D structure of biomolecules (proteins, DNA, RNA).

Major Techniques:

- **Homology Modeling :** Predicts protein structure based on known templates.
- **Ab Initio Methods :** Predicts structures without using templates.
- **Molecular Docking:** Predicts interactions between molecules (used in drug design).
- **Molecular Dynamics Simulations:** Studies biomolecular movements over time.
- **Systems Biology & Computational Biology:** Studies complex biological systems using computational models.
- **Network Biology:** Analyzing biological networks (gene-regulatory, metabolic, protein interactions).
- **Pathway Analysis (KEGG, BioCyc) :** Mapping biochemical pathways to understand metabolism.
- **AI & Machine Learning in Bioinformatics:** Using deep learning to predict gene expression, disease risks, and protein folding.

Algorithms in Bioinformatics

- Computational algorithms are crucial for sequence analysis, pattern recognition, and data mining.

Common Algorithms:

1. Dynamic Programming Algorithms:

- Needleman-Wunsch (Global Alignment)
- Smith-Waterman (Local Alignment)

2. Hidden Markov Models (HMMs): Used in gene prediction and sequence alignment.

3. Phylogenetic Tree Construction:

- **Neighbor-Joining Method:** Builds evolutionary trees.
- **Maximum Likelihood Method :** Estimates probability of evolutionary relationships.

Applications of Bioinformatics

- **Personalized Medicine & Pharmacogenomics:** Designing drugs based on genetic profiles.
- **Vaccine Development:** Using computational models to identify vaccine targets.
- **CRISPR Gene Editing :** Improving genome editing accuracy.
- **Evolutionary Biology & Phylogenetics:** Studying species evolution using genetic data.

Applications of Biotechnology

Medicine and Pharmaceuticals

- Biotechnology techniques are used in **medicine for diagnosis** and **treating different diseases.** It gives opportunities for the people to protect themselves from dangerous diseases.
- The field of Biotechnology, genetic engineering has introduced techniques like **gene therapy,** recombinant **DNA technology** and **polymerase chain** reaction which use genes and DNA molecules to diagnose diseases and insert new and healthy genes in the body which replace the damaged cells.
- Genetic modification in mosquitoes can solve the problems of epidemic diseases such as **dengue** and **malaria.**
- **Artificial insemination** is the artificial introduction of semen into the reproductive tract of a female animal. It is used extensively in breeding animals, such as sheep and cattle
- Medical researchers believe that **stem cell therapy** has the potential to dramatically change the treatment of human disease. A number of adult stem cell therapies already exist, particularly bone marrow transplants that are used to treat leukaemia.
- **Stem cell transplantation** was first used in the treatment of **blood disorders** and it was a breakthrough. Conventionally known as **bone marrow transplantation,** the stem cells responsible for production of the blood cells reside in the bone marrow
- **Drug Development:** Biotechnology is used to discover and develop new drugs, including the identification of potential drug targets, screening of compounds, and optimizing drug delivery systems. Techniques like genomics, proteomics, and high-throughput screening accelerate the drug discovery process.
- **Gene Therapy:** Modification of genetic material for therapeutic purposes. Biotechnology enables the insertion, deletion, or replacement of genes to treat genetic disorders.
- **Personalized Medicine:** Biotechnology allows for tailored medical treatments based on an individual's genetic makeup and molecular profiles.
- **Antibody Production:** Techniques like hybridoma technology and recombinant DNA technology are employed.
- **Vaccine Development:** Techniques like genetic engineering and protein expression systems are used to create safe and effective vaccines.
- **Stem Cell Therapies:** Instrumental in the field of regenerative medicine, utilizing stem cells for tissue repair and replacement in conditions like spinal cord injuries, heart disease, and neurodegenerative disorders.
- **Biopharmaceuticals:** Biotech methods are used to produce therapeutic proteins, hormones, and vaccines using living organisms, such as bacteria or mammalian cells.

Research and Diagnostics

- **DNA Sequencing:** Biotechnology tools like next-generation sequencing have revolutionized genomics and genetic research.
- **Diagnostic Tests:** Techniques such as polymerase chain reaction (PCR) are used for the detection of diseases and genetic disorders.

Agriculture

- Biotechnology has played a major role in agriculture by altering genes, studying and cloning various crops in order to provide better quality products of foods ultimately improving our lives.
- **Hybrid Seeds, Artificial Seeds, Photosynthesis improver, Stress resistant crops and plants, Biofertilizers, Bio-pesticides** are some of the potential applications.

- **Potential advantages** that biotechnology can confer across a wide range of agricultural applications are in areas such as livestock management, storage of agricultural products and sustaining current crop yields, while reducing the use of fertilizers, herbicides and pesticides.
- **Biotechnology** offers a very promising alternative to synthetic foods and an improvement on conventional plant-breeding technologies. Combined with other advanced agricultural technologies, it offers an exciting and environmentally responsible way to meet consumer demand for sustainable agriculture.
- **Genetically Modified Organisms (GMOs):** Biotechnology is used to create genetically engineered crops with enhanced traits, such as pest resistance, disease resistance, and improved nutritional content.

Example : BT- Cotton, BT Brinjal, GM Mustard.

- **Crop Improvement:** Techniques like marker-assisted breeding and genetic modification help develop crops with higher yields, better nutritional content, and increased tolerance to environmental stress.

Ex- GM Golden Rice contains higher vitamin A

Industrial Applications/ Industrial Biotechnology

- Industrial biotechnology (White biotechnology) uses biological processes, microorganisms, and enzymes to produce industrial goods such as biofuels, pharmaceuticals, food products, and biodegradable plastics. It aims to create sustainable and eco-friendly alternatives to chemical-based industrial processes.

Key Areas of Industrial Biotechnology

A. Fermentation Technology

- **Fermentation is the metabolic process where microorganisms convert organic compounds into useful products. It is widely used in:**
  - Food & Beverage Industry – Producing yogurt, cheese, beer, and vinegar
  - Pharmaceuticals – Manufacturing antibiotics (penicillin), vaccines, and insulin.
  - Biofuels – Producing ethanol and biogas.

Types of Fermentation:

- Aerobic Fermentation – Requires oxygen (e.g., citric acid production).
- Anaerobic Fermentation – No oxygen required (e.g., ethanol production).
- Batch Fermentation – Microbes grow in a closed system with limited nutrients.
- Continuous Fermentation – Continuous nutrient supply maintains microbial growth.

B. Bioprocess Engineering

- **Bioprocess engineering involves designing and optimizing biological processes for industrial applications. It includes:**
- 1. Upstream Processing – Preparing raw materials, microbial cultures, and media.
- 2. Bioreactor Operation – Controlling temperature, pH, and oxygen levels for optimal microbial growth.
- 3. Downstream Processing – Purification and recovery of the final product (e.g., protein purification).

Types of Bioreactors

- Stirred Tank Bioreactors : Commonly used for microbial fermentation.
- Airlift Bioreactors : Used for shear-sensitive cells like mammalian cultures.
- **Membrane Bioreactors** : Used for wastewater treatment.

C. Enzyme Technology & Biocatalysis

- Industrial biotechnology uses enzymes as biocatalysts to speed up chemical reactions in various industries.

Applications of Enzymes in Industry –

- Detergent Industry : Proteases and lipases in laundry detergents for stain removal.
- Textile Industry : Cellulases for fabric softening.
- Paper & Pulp Industry : Laccases for eco-friendly bleaching.
- Food Industry : Amylases for starch processing in baking and brewing.

D. Bio-based Chemicals & Materials

- Industrial biotechnology is replacing petroleum-based chemicals with bio-based alternatives.
- **Examples of Bio-based Products:**
  - Bioplastics – PLA (Polylactic Acid) and PHA (Polyhydroxyalkanoates).
  - Biodegradable Packaging – Made from starch or cellulose.
  - Bio-based Polymers – Used in textiles and adhesives.

E. Biofuels & Renewable Energy

- Biofuels are an eco-friendly alternative to fossil fuels and are derived from biomass.

Industrial Applications –

- Ethanol (Bioethanol) : Used as a fuel additive.
- Biodiesel : Made from vegetable oils or animal fats.
- Biogas (Methane) : Produced from organic waste through anaerobic digestion.

- F. **Waste Management & Environmental Biotechnology** : Industrial biotechnology helps in environmental sustainability by reducing pollution and recycling waste.

Applications –

- Bioremediation : Using microbes to clean up oil spills and heavy metal pollution.
- Waste-to-Energy : Converting organic waste into biofuels.
- Industrial Wastewater Treatment : Using microbes to degrade toxic substances.

Advantages and Significance –

- Reduces reliance on fossil fuels
- Environmentally friendly & sustainable
- Increases efficiency & reduces production costs
- Produces biodegradable and non-toxic products

Challenges and Limitations –

- High initial investment and production costs
- Scaling up from lab to industrial level is complex
- Regulatory hurdles for genetically modified organisms (GMOs)
- Competition with petroleum-based industries
- Emerging Trends in Industrial Biotechnology
- Synthetic Biology: Designing microbes for custom biochemical production.
- CRISPR & Genetic Engineering: Improving microbial strains for higher yield.
- AI & Machine Learning in Bioprocessing: Optimizing fermentation and enzyme reactions.
- Carbon Capture & Utilization: Converting CO_2 into biofuels and chemicals.

Environmental Protection

- **Biological Pest Control:** Biotechnology aids in the development of natural and environmentally friendly methods for pest control, reducing the need for chemical pesticides.
- **Waste Treatment:** Microorganisms are used to break down organic waste and sewage, leading to more sustainable waste management.

Food Processing

Application of Biotechnology in Food Processing

- Biotechnology has a major application in the food sector.
- Bread, cheese, wine, beer, yogurt, and vinegar are all made by culturing microorganisms and are really the oldest products of biotechnology.

- It helps in improving the **edibility**, **texture** and **storage of the food**; in preventing the attack of the food, mainly dairy, by the virus like **bacteriophage**.
- **Biotechnologists** are also developing tests that will allow the detection of food-contaminating microorganisms and the toxins they produce, which may be present only in minute quantities.
- **Biotechnology** also has applications in the detection of **mutagens** (substances that cause genetic mutations) in individual food products.
- GM crops which have been approved for use in food items in select countries include **corn**, **maize**, **soya**, **tomato**, **potato** and **papaya**.
- Latest innovations in biotechnology that fortify major staples with micro nutrients like **vitamin A**, **zinc** and **iron** can be game changers for hunger problem in **India**.
- **Fermentation:** Biotechnology is used in the production of fermented foods and beverages like yogurt, cheese, beer, and bread.
- **Food Safety:** Biotech methods are employed to develop rapid and sensitive methods for detecting foodborne pathogens.

Forensics

- DNA fingerprinting uses biotechnology to identify individuals by analyzing **variable number of tandem repeats** (VNTR) in their DNA. This creates unique patterns of bands on a gel through gel **electrophoresis**, **helping solve crimes**, **determine paternity**, **handle immigration cases**, **address child swapping** and **identify disaster victims**.
- **DNA Profiling:** Biotechnology plays a crucial role in **forensic investigations** by **analyzing DNA** evidence to **identify individuals** and **establish relationships**.
- **DNA Barcoding :** DNA barcoding is a molecular technique that involves identifying and distinguishing species by analyzing a short, standardized DNA sequence from a specific gene region. This method is used for rapid and accurate species identification in various fields such as biodiversity research, conservation, and food safety.

Bioinformatics

- **Data Analysis:** Biotechnology involves the use of computational methods to analyze large biological datasets, aiding in genomics, proteomics, and drug discovery.

Synthetic Biology

- **Creating Novel Organisms:** Synthetic biology combines biology and engineering to design and construct new biological systems for specific applications.

Application of Biotechnology in Environment

- Biotechnology can be used to tackle environmental issues like deforestation and air pollution.
- Biotechnology can help in finding out the level of **Particulate Matter 2.5** in the air.
- Biotechnology is already providing a clean and **renewable alternative** to **traditional fossil fuels**, the burning of which contributes to global warming.
- The benefit of environmental biotechnology helps us to **avoid the use of hazardous pollutants** and wastes that affect the natural resources and the environment.
- **Biosensors**, which combine a biological component (such as an enzyme) with various electronic components to trigger a circuit when a particular type of chemical is detected. Biosensors are capable of detecting extremely low levels of proteins, hormones, pollutants, gases, and other molecules.

Environmental Biotechnology

Bioremediation

- One of the most important roles of biotechnology in pollution control is **bioremediation.** Bioremediation is the use of microorganisms, such as bacteria, fungi, and algae, to remove pollutants from the environment.
- Microorganisms have the ability to break down organic and inorganic compounds into harmless byproducts, and they can be used to clean up contaminated soil, water, and air.
- In **soil bioremediation**, microorganisms are used to break down organic pollutants, such as petroleum products and pesticides. The microorganisms convert the pollutants into harmless substances, such as carbon dioxide and water.
- In water bioremediation, microorganisms are used to break down organic and inorganic pollutants. They can also be used to remove nutrients, such as nitrogen and phosphorus, from wastewater, which can cause eutrophication if left untreated.
- In air bioremediation, microorganisms are used to remove **volatile organic compounds** (VOCs) from the air.
- **Advabtages of Bioremediation :** It is **cost-effective**, **environmentally friendly** and can be used to treat a **wide range of pollutants.** It also has the potential to be used in situ, which means that the contaminated site does not need to be excavated and transported to another location.

Phytoremediation

- Another important role of biotechnology in pollution control is phytoremediation.

> **Phytoremediation** is the use of plants to remove pollutants from the environment. Plants have the ability to absorb and accumulate pollutants in their tissues, which can then be removed from the site. They can be used to clean up **contaminated soil, water** and **air**.

- In **Soil phytoremediation**, plants are used to remove heavy metals, such as lead and mercury, from the soil. The plants **absorb** the **heavy metals** through their **roots** and **accumulate** them in their tissues. The plants can then be harvested and removed from the site, along with the pollutants.
- In **water phytoremediation, plants** are used to remove nutrients, such as nitrogen and phosphorus, from the water. They can also be used to remove organic and inorganic pollutants.
- In **air phytoremediation, plants** are used to remove **VOCs** from the air.

Advantages of Phytoremediation : It is cost-effective, environmentally friendly, and can be used to treat a wide range of pollutants. It also has the potential to be used in situ, which means that the contaminated site does not need to be excavated and transported to another location.

Biofuels

- Biotechnology can also be used to **develop biofuels**, which can help **reduce pollution** from fossil fuels. Biofuels are fuels made from renewable biological resources, such as crops, algae, and waste materials. They can be used to power vehicles, generate electricity, and heat homes and buildings.
- Biofuels are **less polluting** than fossil fuels because they **produce fewer emissions** of **greenhouse gases**, such as **carbon dioxide.** They can also be produced locally, which **reduces** the need for **long-distance transportation** and **associated pollution.**

Bioplastics

- Biotechnology can also be used to develop **bioplastics**, which are **plastics made from renewable biological resources**. Bioplastics can help **reduce pollution** from **conventional plastics**, which are made from **non-renewable fossil fuels** and can persist in the environment for hundreds of years.
- Bioplastics can be made from a variety of **renewable resources**, such as **corn, sugarcane** and **algae**. They can be used in a wide range of applications, from packaging to automotive parts. Bioplastics can also be designed to biodegrade in the environment, reducing the impact of plastic pollution.
- However, the production of bioplastics also has **potential environmental impacts**, such as land use **changes, water use** and the displacement of food crops. It is important to carefully evaluate the **sustainability of bioplastic production** and use to ensure that they provide a net benefit for the environment.

Emerging Concepts in Biotechnology

- **1. Artificial Intelligence (AI) in Drug Discovery:** AI is revolutionizing the pharmaceutical industry by expediting drug discovery processes, predicting molecular interactions, and optimizing clinical trials. Companies like Exscientia and BenevolentAI are at the forefront, leveraging AI to accelerate the development of new therapeutics.
- **2. Synthetic Biology and Gene Editing:** Advancements in synthetic biology enable the design and construction of new biological parts and systems. Techniques like CRISPR-based gene editing are being refined for precision medicine applications, offering potential cures for genetic disorders.
- **3. Microbiome Research:** Understanding the human microbiome's role in health and disease has led to novel therapeutic approaches. Recent studies have uncovered diverse bacteriophages in everyday items, such as toothbrushes, which could be harnessed for future biotech applications.
- **Molecular De-Extinction :** Researchers are exploring the recreation of ancient molecules from extinct species using AI. This approach aims to discover new antimicrobial compounds, potentially offering solutions to combat antibiotic-resistant bacteria.
- **Advancements in Genomic Techniques :** New genomic techniques are producing faster and more precise results than conventional methods. These advancements allow scientists to design traits of interest, an approach referred to as synthetic biology.

Indian Government Initiatives in Biotechnology

- **Genome India Project (GIP):** 10,000-genome Database will be available to researchers across the globe under it. Launched in January 2020 by the Department of Biotechnology. Indian Biological Data Centre (IBDC), the first national repository for life science data, will facilitate a database to researchers. The project aims to sequence at least 10,000 Indian genomes to develop predictive diagnostic indicators for various diseases. The research focuses on understanding genetic diversity and its implications for public health, with future phases targeting specific disease categories such as cardiovascular diseases, mental illness, and cancer.
- **Phenome India Project:** By CSIR, for generating a comprehensive phenome database. Phenome is the entire set of phenotypes (set of observable characteristics or traits) in a cell, tissue, organ, organism, or species.
- **Unified Genomic Chip :** A Single Nucleotide Polymorphism (SNP) chip, designed for genomic

profiling and evaluation of Indian cattle breeds. It enables the direct application of DNA technologies to enhance the genetic potential (genetic improvement) of diverse dairy animal.

- Gau chip for cattle.
- Mahish chip for buffaloes.

BioE3 Policy/ Biotechnology for Economy, Environment and Employment Policy

- Union Cabinet, chaired by PM Narendra Modi, approved 'BioE3 (Biotechnology for Economy, Environment and Employment) – Policy for Fostering High-Performance Biomanufacturing' of the Department of Biotechnology on August 24, 2024.
- **Objective:** Establish a framework to adopt advanced technologies and align research to revolutionize biomanufacturing processes.
- **Implementation Agency:** Department of Biotechnology (DBT)
- **Salient features of BioE3 policy :** Innovation-driven support to R&D & Entrepreneurship across thematic sectors to accelerate technology development and commercialization by establishing Biomanufacturing & Bio-AI hubs and Biofoundry.
- Along with prioritizing regenerative Bio-Economy models of green growth, the policy will facilitate expansion of India's skilled workforce and provide a surge in job creation.
- High Performance Biomanufacturing is the ability to produce products ranging from medicine to materials, address farming and food challenges, and promote manufacturing of bio-based products, through integration of advanced biotechnological processes.
- **BioE3 Policy would broadly focus on the following strategic/thematic sectors:**
  - High-value bio-based chemicals, biopolymers & enzymes.
  - Smart proteins & functional foods
  - Precision biotherapeutics
  - Climate resilient agriculture
  - Carbon capture & its utilization
  - Marine and space research.

The policy aims to achieve a US $300 billion bioeconomy by 2030.

- Biomanufacturing refers to using engineered microbial, plant, and animal (including human) cells with increasing precision and control to produce commercially important products on scale.
- Bioeconomy is the production, use and conservation of biological resources, including knowledge, science, technology, and innovation to provide information, products, proces services to all economic sectors.

Salient Features:

- Innovation-driven support to R&D and entrepreneurship across six thematic sectors.
- The research and translational activities under thematic sectors will be catalyzed by Bio-Artificial Intelligence (AI) Hubs: Integrating AI, and Biomanufacturing Hubs.

Biotechnology Research Innovation and Entrepreneurship Development (Bio-RIDE) Scheme

- Nodal Department: DBT, Ministry of Science & Technology
- Components: it combines two existing schemes with a new third component:
- Biotechnology Research and Development (R&D)
- Industrial and Entrepreneurship Development (I&ED)
- Biomanufacturing and Biofoundry (B&B) component aims at furthering India's goal of creating a Circular Bioeconomy in alignment with the Lifestyle for the Environment (LIFE) mission.

National Biotechnology Development Strategy (2020-2025)

- This strategy aims to make India globally competitive in biotechnology research, innovation, and industrial growth, targeting a bioeconomy of USD 150 billion by 2025. It focuses on sectors like healthcare, agriculture, and clean energy, promoting the translation of research into viable commercial products.

National Biopharma Mission

- Supported by the World Bank, this mission facilitates collaboration between industry and academia to develop biopharmaceuticals. Its objectives include developing new vaccines and therapeutics, strengthening bio-clusters, attracting foreign direct investment (FDI), and delivering 6 to 10 new biopharmaceutical products over five years.

Biotechnology Industry Research Assistance Council (BIRAC) Initiatives

- **BIRAC, a public sector enterprise under the Department of Biotechnology, offers several programs to support innovation and research:**
- **Biotechnology Ignition Grant (BIG):** Provides funding to scientist-entrepreneurs from research institutes, academia, and startups to establish and validate proof of concept for innovative ideas.
- **Small Business Innovation Research Initiative (SBIRI):** Supports early-stage, pre-proof-of-concept research in biotechnology by industry, focusing on societal needs in healthcare, food and nutrition, agriculture, and other sectors.
- **Biotechnology Industry Partnership Programme (BIPP):** A cost-sharing partnership with industries for advanced research in frontier technology areas with significant economic potential, aiming to make Indian industry globally competitive.

Atal Jai Anusandhan Biotech Mission

- This mission aims to transform the health, agriculture, and energy sectors over five years, with components focusing on maternal and child health, affordable vaccines, antimicrobial resistance, and clean energy.

Biotech-KISAN Scheme

- The initiative connects farmers with scientists and institutions, focusing on sustainable agricultural practices, soil health, irrigation, and new agri-technologies. It aims to empower farmers through knowledge and innovation, enhancing productivity and income.

Important Terminology

- **T cells :** Type of **white blood cell** in our **immune system** that play a key role in **fighting infections** and **diseases**.
- **Chimeric antigen receptor-** A **chimeric antigen receptor**, or CAR, is like a special antenna that we add to immune cells. This antenna helps these cells find and fight cancer cells in our body. It's a bit like giving our immune cells superhero powers to target and destroy the cancer cells.
- **Gene doping :** Athletes manipulating their genes to enhance their performance in sports. This can involve altering their DNA to improve traits like strength or endurance. It's considered unethical and is banned in sports because it gives unfair advantages and can have health risks. **World Anti-Doping Agency** (WADA) look into such matters.
- **Somatic cells :** All the cells that make up an organism, but that are not sperm or egg cells. **Sperm** and **egg cells** contain only one set of **chromosomes**, and when they join during fertilization, the mother's chromosomes merge with the father's. **Somatic cells**, on the other hand, already contain two full sets

of chromosomes. To make a clone, scientists transfer the DNA from an animal's somatic cell into an egg cell that has had its nucleus and DNA removed. The egg develops into an embryo that contains the same genes as the cell donor. Then the embryo is implanted into an adult female's uterus to grow.

Previous Year Questions

Q. Recombinat DNA technology (Genetic Engineering) allows genes to be transferred.

1. Across different species of plants.
2. From animals to plants.
3. From microorganisms to higher organisms.

Select the correct solution using the codes given below.

(a) 1 Only (b) 1 and 2 only
(c) 2 and 3 only (d) 1, 2 and 3

Q. With reference to the Genetically Modified mustard (GM mustard) developed in India, consider the following statements : (2018)

1. GM mustard has the genes of a soil bacterium that gives the plant the property of pest-resistance to a wide variety of pests.
2. GM mustard has the genes that allow the plant cross-pollination and hybridization.
3. GM mustard has been developed jointly by the IARI and Punjab Agricultural University.

Which of the statements given above is/are correct?

(a) 1 and 3 only (b) 2 only
(c) 2 and 3 only (d) 1, 2 and 3

Q. 'RNA interference (RNAi)' technology has gained popularity in the last few years. Why? (2019)

1. It is used in developing gene silencing therapies.
2. It can be used in developing therapies for the treatment of cancer.
3. It can be used to develop hormone replacement therapies.
4. It can be used to produce crop plants that are resistant to viral pathogens.

Select the correct answer using the code given below:

(a) 1, 2 and 4 (b) 2 and 3
(c) 1 and 3 (d) 1 and 4 only

Q. Recombinant DNA technology (Genetic Engineering) allows genes to be transferred (2013)

1. Across different species of plants.
2. From animals to plants.
3. From microorganisms to higher organisms.

Select the correct Solution using the codes given below.

(a) 1 only (b) 1 and 2 only
(c) 2 and 3 only (d) 1, 2 and 3

Q. Mycorrhizal Biotechnology has been used in rehabilitating degraded sites because mycorrhiza enables the plants to - (2013)

1. Resist drought and increase absorptive area
2. Tolerate extremes of pH
3. Resist disease infestation

Select the correct answer using the codes given below:

(a) 1 only (b) 1 and 2 only
(c) 1, 2 and 3 only (d) 2 and 3 only

Q. With reference to agriculture in India, how can the technique of 'genome sequencing', often seen in the news, be used in the immediate future? (2017)

1. Genome sequencing can be used to identify genetic markers for disease resistance and drought tolerance in various crop plants.
2. This technique helps in reducing the time required to develop new varieties of crop plants.
3. It can be used to decipher the host-pathogen relationships in crops.

Q. Bollgard I and Bollgard II technologies are mentioned in the context of: (2021)

A. clonal propagation of crop plants
B. developing genetically modified crop plants
C. production of plant growth substances
D. production of biofertilizers

Q. In the context of hereditary diseases, consider the following statements: (2021)

1. Passing on mitochondrial diseases from parent to child can be prevented by mitochondrial replacement therapy either before or after in vitro fertilization of the egg.
2. A child inherits mitochondrial diseases entirely from mother and not from father.

Which of the statements given above is/are correct?

(a) 1 only (b) 2 only
(c) Both 1 and 2 (d) Neither 1 nor 2

Q. In the context of recent advances in human reproductive technology, "Pronuclear Transfer" is used for: (2020)

(a) Fertilization of egg in vitro by the donor sperm
(b) Genetic modification of sperm producing cells
(c) Development of stem cells into functional embryos
(d) Prevention of mitochondrial diseases in offspring

Q. Which of the following statements are correct regarding the general difference between plant and animal cells? (2020)

1. Plant cells have cellulose cell walls whilst animal cells do not.
2. Plant cells do not have plasma membranes unlike animal cells which do.
3. Mature plant cell has one large vacuole whilst animal cell has many small vacuoles.

Select the correct answer using the code given below:

(a) 1 and 2 only (b) 2 and 3 only
(c) 1 and 3 only (d) 1, 2 and 3

Q. Which organelle in the cell, other than the nucleus, contains DNA? (2001)

(a) Centriole (b) Golgi apparatus
(c) Lysosome (d) Mitochondrion

Q. Which of the following cell organelles play the most significant role in protein synthesis? (2001)

(a) A.Lysosome and Centrosome
(b) B.Endoplasmic reticulum and Ribosome
(c) C.Golgi apparatus and Mitochondria
(d) D.Lysosome and Mitochondria

Q. In which of the following are hydrogels used? (2024)

1. Controlled drug delivery in patients
2. Mobile air-conditioning systems
3. Preparation of industrial lubricants

Select the correct answer using the code given below:

(a) 1 only
(b) 1 and 2 only
(c) 2 and 3 only
(d) 1, 2 and 3

Q. 1. Some microorganisms can grow in environments with temperatures above the boiling point of water.
2. Some microorganisms can grow in environments with temperatures below the freezing point of water.
3. Some microorganisms can grow in a highly acidic environment with a pH below.

How many of the above statements are correct?

(a) Only one
(b) Only two
(c) All three
(d) None **(2023)**

Q. With reference to the role of bio-filters in Recirculating Aquaculture System, consider the following statements:

1. Bio-filters provide waste treatment by removing uneaten fish feed.
2. Bio-filters convert ammonia present in fish waste to nitrate.
3. Bio-filters increase phosphorus as a nutrient for fish in water.

How many of the statements given above are correct?

(a) Only one
(b) Only two
(c) All three
(d) None **(2023)**

Q. Microsatellite DNA' is used in the case of which one of the following?

(a) Studying the evolutionary relationships among various species of fauna
(b) Stimulating 'stem cells' to transform into diverse functional tissues
(c) Promoting clonal propagation of horticultural plants
(d) Assessing the efficacy of drugs by conducting series of drug trials in a population **(2023)**

Q. Wolbachia method' is sometimes talked about with reference to which one of the following?

(a) Controlling the viral diseases spread by mosquitoes
(b) Converting crop residues into packing material
(c) Producing biodegradable plastics
(d) Producing biochar from thermo-chemical conversion of biomass **(2023)**

Q. Stem cell therapy is gaining popularity in India to treat a wide variety of medical conditions including leukaemia, Thalassemia, damaged cornea and several burns. Describe briefly what stem cell therapy is and what advantages it has over other treatments? (150 words, 10 marks) (2017)

Q. Stem cell therapy is gaining popularity in India to treat a wide variety of medical conditions including leukaemia, Thalassemia, damaged cornea and several burns. Describe briefly what stem cell therapy is and what advantages it has over other treatments? (2017)

Q. Why is there so much activity in the field of biotechnology in our country? How has this activity benefitted the field of biopharma? (2018)

Q. How is the Government of India protecting traditional knowledge of medicine from patenting by pharmaceutical companies?(2019)

Q. How can biotechnology help to improve the living standards of farmers? (2019)

Q. What are the research and developmental achievements in applied biotechnology? How will these achievements help to uplift the poorer sections of the society? (2021)

Q. How can biotechnology help to improve the living standards of farmers? (250 words, 15 marks) (2019)

Q. Why is there so much activity in the field of biotechnology in our country? How has this activity benefitted the field of biopharma? (2018)

Q. The world is facing an acute shortage of clean and safe freshwater. What are the alternative technologies which can solve this crisis? Briefly discuss any three such technologies citing their key merits and demerits. (2024)

UNIT 5 INFORMATION AND COMMUNICATIONS TECHNOLOGY

- *Information and Communications Technology (ICT) is the infrastructure and components that enable modern computing. ICT refers to the integration of digital technologies for data processing, storage, communication, and information exchange. It includes computers, the internet, telecommunications, artificial intelligence (AI), and cloud computing.*
- *The internet, internet of things, metaverse, virtual reality and social media are also part of ICT, as are cloud computing services, video conferencing and collaboration tools, unified communications systems and mobile communication networks. Emerging, work-in-progress or still-nascent technologies like 5G/6G, Web3, and quantum computing are also in the ICT universe.*
- *ICT has significantly transformed industries, economies, education, and social structures by enabling faster and more efficient information flow. ICT encompasses the internet-enabled sphere and the mobile one powered by wireless networks. It includes antiquated technologies, such as landline telephones, radio and television broadcast – all of which remain widely used alongside today's cutting-edge ICT pieces, such as artificial intelligence and robotics.*
- *ICT has evolved from basic computing and telecommunication systems to advanced AI-driven and quantum computing technologies. As innovations continue, ICT will further transform industries, economies, and daily life, making global connectivity and automation more seamless. The future of ICT promises breakthroughs in human-computer interaction, space communication, and digital security.*
- *ICT has transformed the landscape of science and technology, making research faster, more collaborative, and accessible worldwide. From space exploration to healthcare innovations, the synergy between ICT and science continues to drive human progress into the future.*

Evolution of Computers

1. **Early Mechanical Computers (19th Century)**
   - Analytical Engine (1837) – Charles Babbage
   - Considered the first concept of a modern computer.
   - Used mechanical gears for calculations.
   - Had memory (store) and processing unit (mill) like today's computers.
   - Ada Lovelace wrote the first algorithm for it, making her the first programmer.
   - **Limitations** : Never built due to lack of technology.
2. **First Generation (1940s–1950s) – Vacuum Tube Computers**
   - ENIAC (1945) – First Electronic Computer
   - Used vacuum tubes instead of mechanical parts.
   - Occupied a large room (~27 tons).
   - Speed: 5,000 calculations per second (slow by today's standards).
   - **Limitation:** Needed manual rewiring for programming.
   - **EDVAC (1949)** – First Stored-Program Computer : Introduced Von Neumann Architecture (instructions stored in memory). Allowed computers to be reprogrammed easily.

- **UNIVAC I (1951)** – First Commercial Computer : Used in government and businesses. Used magnetic tape for storage.

3. **Second Generation (1950s–1960s) – Transistor-Based Computers**
   - Transistors replaced vacuum tubes – Smaller, faster, and more reliable.
   - Examples:
   - IBM 1401 (1959) – First mass-produced computer.
   - PDP-1 (1960) – First computer with a keyboard and monitor.
   - **Advancements:** More storage capacity, Faster processing and Lower power consumption.

4. **Third Generation (1960s–1970s) – Integrated Circuits (ICs) : ICs (chips) replaced transistors, making computers even smaller and more powerful.**
   - **IBM System/360 (1964)** – First computer family (compatible models).
   - **PDP-8 (1965)** – First affordable "minicomputer".
   - **Impact:** More businesses and governments started using computers. Led to the development of supercomputers.

5. **Fourth Generation (1970s–Present) – Microprocessors & Personal Computing**
   - Microprocessors (CPU on a single chip) revolutionized computing.

Key Innovations:

- **Intel 4004 (1971)** – First microprocessor (4-bit).
- **Intel 8086 (1978)** – Led to modern x86 processors.

Personal Computers (PCs):

- **IBM PC (1981)** – Standard for business computing.
- **Apple Macintosh (1984)** – First popular GUI-based computer.
- **Memory & Storage Growth:** Early PCs had few KBs of RAM, now GBs & TBs are common.
- Shift from floppy disks → hard drives → SSDs.

Supercomputers (1960s–Present)
CDC 6600 (1964) – First Supercomputer: Developed by Seymour Cray. Speed: 3 million calculations per second.
Cray-1 (1976) – First Vector Supercomputer: Used for weather forecasting, nuclear research, and defense.

Usage:

- Climate modeling.
- Space exploration.
- AI and big data analysis.

6. **Fifth Generation (2000s–Present) – AI & Cloud Computing**
   - Artificial Intelligence (AI): AI-powered computing for automation and decision-making.
   - Cloud Computing: Services like AWS, Google Cloud, Microsoft Azure store and process data remotely.
   - Neuromorphic Chips: Mimic the human brain for faster AI processing (Intel Loihi, IBM TrueNorth).

7. **Quantum Computing**
   - Instead of classical bits (0 or 1), it uses qubits (can be 0, 1, or both at the same time – superposition).
   - **Quantum Entanglement:** Instant communication between qubits.
   - **Quantum Supremacy:** Can solve problems in seconds that would take classical computers thousands of years.

Major Quantum Computers
Google Sycamore (2019)
IBM Quantum System One (2019)
D-Wave Advantage (2020)

Applications of Quantum Computing

- **Drug Discovery:** Simulating molecules for new medicines.
- **Cryptography:** Breaking and developing secure encryption.
- **AI & Machine Learning:** Faster and more efficient computing models.

Internet : An Introduction

Internet is a short form for Inter connected Network developed by **Bob Kahn** and **Vint Cerf** in **1970's**. Internet is defined as an **Information super Highway**, to **access information** over the web. Internet is a **world-wide global system** of interconnected computer networks.

- The concept of Internet originated in **1969** devised from the concept of **Advanced Research Project Agency Network** (ARPANET) developed by **United States Department of Defense**. Basic purpose of **ARPANET** was to provide **communication** among the various bodies of **government**. Initially, there were only **four nodes**, formally called **Hosts**.

In **1972**, the ARPANET spread over the globe with **23 nodes** located at different countries and thus became known as **Internet**.

- Internet uses the **standard Internet Protocol** (TCP/IP). Every computer in internet is identified by a **unique IP address**.

IP Address is a **unique set of numbers** (such as 110.22.33.114) which identifies a computer location.

- A special computer **DNS** (Domain Name Server) is used to give name to the **IP Address** so that user can locate a computer by a name.

Tim Berner Lee who led development of **World Wide Web** (WWW), **Hyper Text Transfer Protocol** (HTTP), **Hypertext Markup Language** (HTML) and **Universal Resourse Locator** (URL) is known as the **Father of Internet**.

Computer Network

- A computer network is a system that connects two or more computing devices for transmitting and sharing information. Computing devices include everything from a mobile phone to a server, which can be connected through physical wires as fiber optics, or can be wireless.
- A simple network is a collaboration software as Google Drive to share documents with colleagues working remotely.

An example of a complex computer network is the traffic monitoring systems in urban cities, used to alert officials and emergency responders with information about traffic flow and incidents.

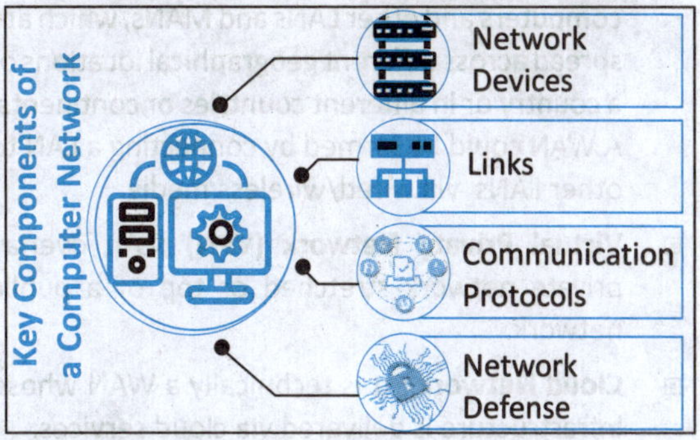

Types of Network

- **Nanoscale Networks :** They enable communication between minuscle sensors and actuators.
- **Personal Area Network (PAN) :** It is a network formed by connecting a few personal devices like computers, laptops, mobile phones, smart phones, printers etc, lying within an approximate range of 10 metres. A personal area network may be wired or wireless.

Example : A mobile phone connected to the laptop through USB forms a wired PAN while two smartphones communicating with each other through Bluetooth technology form a wireless PAN or WPAN.

- **Local Area Network (LAN) :** It is a network that connects computers, mobile phones, tablet, mouse, printer, etc., within geographical area from a room to a building. The connectivity is done by means of wires, Ethernet cables, fibre optics, or Wi-Fi.
- **Storage Area Network :** A dedicated network that facilitates block level data storage like storae divices disc arrays and tape libraries.
- **Metropolitan Area Network (MAN) :** It is an extended form of LAN which covers a larger geographical area like a city or a town. Data transfer rate in MAN also ranges in Mbps, but it is considerably less as compared to LAN.

Cable TV network or cable based broadband internet services are examples of MAN. This kind of network can be extended up to 30-40 km.

- **Wide Area Network (WAN) :** It connects computers and other LANs and MANs, which are spread across different geographical locations of a country or in different countries or continents. A WAN could be formed by connecting a LAN to other LANs via wired/wireless media.
- **Virtual Private Network (VPN) :** An overlay private network stretched or top of a public network.
- **Cloud Network :** It is technically a WAN whose infrastructure is delivered via cloud services.

Based on organizational intent, Networks can be classified as:

- **Intranet:** A set of networks that is maintained and controlled by a single entity. It is generally the most secure type of network, with access to authorized users alone. An intranet usually exists behind the router in a local area network.
- **Internet:** Also known as the internetwork is a collection of multiple networks connected by routers and layered by networking software. This is a global system that connects governments, researchers, corporates, the public, and individual computer networks.
- **Extranet:** It is similar to the intranet but with connections to particular external networks. It is generally used to share resources with partners, customers, or remote employees.
- **Darknet:** An overlay network that runs on the internet and can only be accessed by specialized software. It uses unique, customized communication protocols.

Network Devices

- To communicate data through different transmission media and to configure networks, devices like **Modem**, **Hub**, **Switch**, **Repeater**, **Router**, **Gateway** are required and are called **Network Devices.**
- **Computers, mobiles, and other consumer devices:** End devices that users directly and frequently access. For example, an email originates from the mailing application on a laptop or mobile phone.
- **Gateways:** They are hardware devices that act as gates between two distinct networks. They can be firewalls, routers, or servers.
- **Servers:** Application or storage servers where the main computation and data storage occur. All requests for specific tasks or data come to the servers.
- **Router :** It is a network device that can receive the data, analyse it and transmit it to other networks. A router connects a local area network to the internet. Compared to a hub or a switch, a router has advanced capabilities as it can analyse the data being carried over a network, decide/alter how it is packaged, and send it to another network of a different type.
- **Switch :** A switch is a networking device that plays a central role in a Local Area Network (LAN). Like a hub, a network switch is used to connect multiple computers or communicating devices. When data arrives, the switch extracts the destination address from the data packet and looks it up in a table to see where to send the packet. Thus, it sends signals to only selected devices instead of sending to all. It can forward multiple packets at the same time. A switch drops the noisy and corrupted signals and asks the sender to resend it.
- **Modem- MOdulator DEModulator :** It refers to a device used for conversion between analog signals and digital bits. To transmit data from a sender to a receiver, or while browsing the internet, digital data are converted to an analog signal and the medium (be it free-space or a physical media) carries the signal to the receiver. There are modems connected to both the source and destination nodes. The modem at the sender's end acts as a modulator that converts the digital data into analog signals. The modem at the receiver's end acts as a demodulator that converts the analog signals into digital data for the destination node to understand.

- **Ethernet Card:** Also known as Network Interface Card is a network adapter used to set up a wired network. It acts as an interface between computer and the network. It is a circuit board mounted on the motherboard of a computer

> The Ethernet cable connects the computer to the network through NIC. Ethernet cards can support data transfer between 10 Mbps and 1 Gbps (1000 Mbps). Each NIC has a MAC address, which helps in uniquely identifying the computer on the network.
>
> **RJ45 - Registered Jack-45 :** An eight-pin connector used exclusively with Ethernet cables for networking. It is a standard networking interface that can be seen at the end of all network cables.

- **Repeater :** Data are carried in the form of signals over the cable, which may lose their strength beyond 100m limit and become weak. In such conditions, original signals need to be regenerated. A repeater is an analog device that works with signals on the cables to which it is connected, and regenerates the weakened signal.
- **Hub :** An Ethernet hub is a network device used to connect different devices through wires. Data arriving on any of the lines are sent out on all the others. The limitation of Hub is that if data from two devices come at the same time, they will collide.

Links

- Links are the transmission media which can be of two types –
- **Wired:** Examples of wired technologies used in networks include coaxial cables, phone lines, twisted-pair cabling, and optical fibers.

> Optical fibers based on Total Interanl Reflection carry pulses of light to represent data.

- **Wireless :** Network connections can also be established through radio or other electromagnetic signals. The most common examples of wireless links include communication satellites, cellular networks, and radio and technology spread spectrums. Wireless LANs use spectrum technology to establish connections within a small area.

Communication Protocols

- A communication protocol is a set of rules followed by all nodes involved in the information transfer.

> **Common protocols** include the internet protocol suite (TCP/IP), IEEE 802, Ethernet, wireless LAN, and cellular standards.

- TCP/IP is a conceptual model that standardizes communication in a modern network. It suggests **four functional layers** of these communication links:
  - **Network access layer:** This layer defines how the data is physically transferred. It includes how hardware sends data bits through physical wires or fibers.
  - **Internet layer:** This layer is responsible for packaging the data into understandable packets and allowing it to be sent and received.
  - **Transport layer:** This layer enables devices to maintain a conversation by ensuring the connection is valid and stable.
  - **Application layer:** This layer defines how high-level applications can access the network to initiate data transfer.

Network Defense

- While nodes, links, and protocols form the foundation of a network, a modern network cannot exist without its defenses.
- Security is critical when unprecedented amounts of data are generated, moved, and processed across networks.

> **Examples of network defense tools :** Firewall, intrusion detection systems (IDS), intrusion prevention systems (IPS), network access control (NAC), content filters, proxy servers, anti-DDoS devices and load balancers.
>
> **Key Objectives of Deploying a Computer Network :**
>
> - Resource Sharing
> - Resource availability and reliability
> - Performance management
> - Cost saving
> - Increased storage capacity
> - Streamlined collaboration & communication
> - Reduction of errors
> - Secured remote

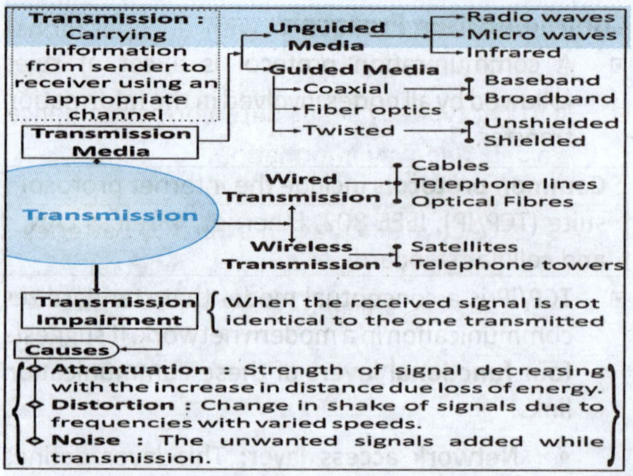

Spectrum

- It is collection of waves with particular frequencies arranged in order.
- Invisible Radio Frequencies that wireless signals travel over. It is the range of radiowaves used for communication purposes.
- Spectrum as a range of frequencies is divided into different forms of technology.
- **Band width** : A subsection of a portion of spectrum. It is the maximum rate of data transfer with in a period of time.

Types of Wireless Technologies

	Near Field Communication Technology (NFCT)	Radio Frequency Identification (RFID)	Quick Response (QR) Code
About	A short-range wireless connectivity technology that allows NFC-enabled devices to communicate with each other and transfer information quickly and easily with a single touch	A wireless system comprised of two components: tags and readers.	A two dimensional version of a barcode that can be read easily by a digital device.
Working Range	NFC-enabled devices must be either physically touching or within a few centimeters from each other for data transfer.	Read distance depends upon the frequency (Ranging from 300 gigahertz to as low as 9 kilohertz) used.	Ideal scanning size to distance ratio is 1:10.
Other Key Information	Transfer information quickly and easily with a single touch.	• Do not require direct line of sight to be read. • Data stored in an RFID tag can be updated in real-time.	• Require a line of sight to scan. • No real-time tracking.

Near Field Communication

- NFC is the technology that allows **compatible devices** to establish **radio communication** with each other by touching them together or bringing them into a distance maximum of **10 cm**.
- NFC works on **Radio Frequency Identification** (RFID) **technology** and **Magnetic induction principle.**
- **Near Field Communication** (NFC) is a technology where your smartphone or an NFC reader generates a **magnetic field. NFC tags**, such as **cards** or **chips**, harness energy from this field.

NFC works on Magnetic induction

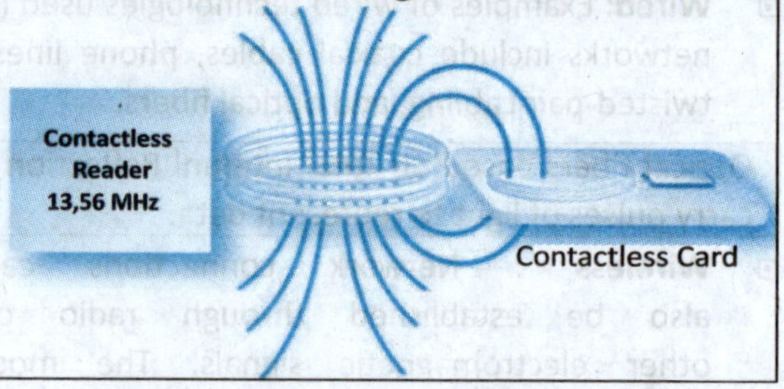

- They then communicate by altering the field's properties. This enables actions like payments, data transfer, or access control, all within close proximity. It is a method for secure and convenient interactions between devices and objects.

Bluetooth

- Bluetooth is universal for short-range wireless voice and data communication. It is a **Wireless Personal Area Network** (WPAN) technology used for exchanging data over smaller distances.
- Bluetooth simply follows the principle of transmitting and receiving data using radio waves. Here, a device can be paired with the other device which has also Bluetooth but it should be within the estimated communication range to connect. When two devices start to share data, they form a network called piconet which can further accommodate more than five devices.
- The technology was invented by Ericson in 1994. It operates in the unlicensed, **industrial, scientific, and medical** (ISM) band from **2.4 GHz to 2.485 GHz**.
- Maximum devices that can be connected at the same time are 7. Bluetooth ranges up to 10 meters. It provides data rates up to 1 Mbps or 3 Mbps depending upon the version.
- The spreading technique that it uses is **FHSS** (Frequency-hopping spread spectrum). A Bluetooth network is called a piconet and a collection of interconnected piconets is called scatternet.

Radio Frequency Identification (RFID) Technology

- Radio Frequency Identification (RFID) technology is a system that uses **wireless communication** to **identify** and **track objects, people** or **animals** using **RFID tags** or **transponders.**
- It is an **electronic tag** that can **exchange data** with an **RFID reader** through **radio waves.**
- These tags contain **electronic information** that can be read by an **RFID reader** or **scanner** via **radio waves.**
- In this, an **antenna broadcasts energy** to **tag,** which in turn **returns modulated energy** back in the form of back-scatter.
- It is a **faster connection** with an **operational range** of about **100m.**
- RFID tag typically sends out information hence is a only **one-way information.**

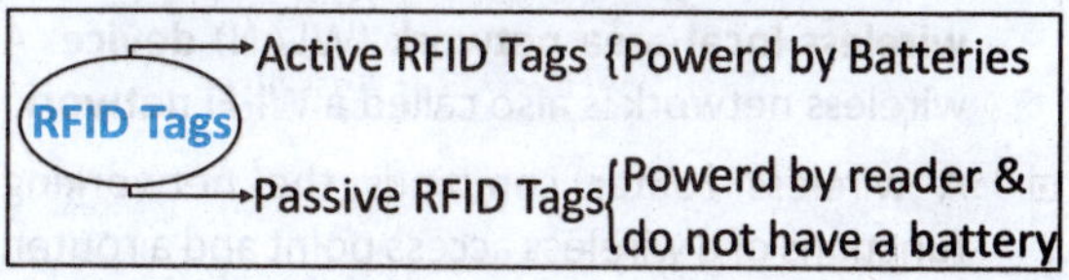

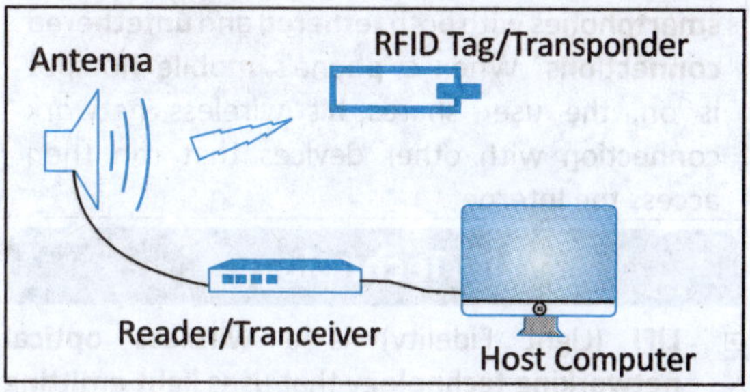

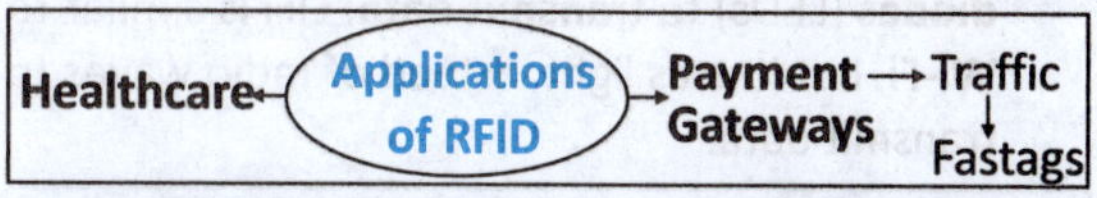

Wi-Fi Technology

- Wi-Fi is a **wireless technology** used to connect **computers, tablets, smartphones** and other devices to the internet.

> Wi-Fi is not an acronym; but a brand name created by a marketing firm that is meant to serve as an **interoperability** seal for marketing efforts.

- Wi-Fi is the **radio signal** sent from a **wireless router** to a nearby device, which **translates** the **signal** into **data.** The device transmits a **radio signal** back to the router, which connects to the internet by a **wire** or **cable.**
- Wi-Fi uses **radio waves** to transmit data from wireless router to Wi-Fi enabled devices like **TV, smartphone, tablet** and **computer.** Because they communicate with each other over airwaves, personal devices and information can become **vulnerable to hackers, cyber-attacks** and other threats especially in public **WiFi networks** and **hotspots.**

- **Wireless routers**, commonly found in homes are the **hardware devices** that Internet service providers use to connect the users to their cable or **xDSL Internet network**.
- A wireless router is sometimes referred to as a **wireless local area network** (WLAN) **device**. A wireless network is also called a **Wi-Fi network**.
- A wireless router combines the networking functions of a wireless access point and a router.

Mobile hotspot is a common feature on **smartphones** with both **tethered** and **untethered connections**. When a phone's mobile hotspot is on, the user shares his wireless network connection with other devices that can then access the Internet.

LiFi Technology

- **LiFi** (Light Fidelity) is a **wireless optical networking technology** that uses **light emitting diodes** (LEDs) to **transmit data**. LiFi is similar to **Wi-Fi**, but it uses light instead of radio waves to transmit data.

Visible Light Communication (VLC) technology

- **VLC** uses electromagnetic spectrum wave lengths **375 to 780 nm**.
- It is possible to achieve **illumination** and **data transfer** simultaneously by means of **LEDs** that is the prominent lighting equipment lately.
- VLC can transmit large amounts of data faster than Bluetooth.
- VLC has no electromagnetic interference.

- LiFi can transmit data at **very high speeds**, up to **224 gigabits per second.**

The human eye cannot see the light pulses that are used to transmit data, so LiFi is invisible to humans.

Advantages of LiFi over Wi-Fi

- **LiFi** is more secure than **Wi-Fi**, as it is difficult to intercept light signals.
- LiFi is also more energy-efficient than **Wi-Fi**, as LED uses less power than radio waves.
- LiFi is also less likely to be affected by **interference** from other devices, as the light spectrum is less crowded than the radio spectrum.

- LiFi is still a **developing technology**, but it has the potential to revolutionize **wireless networking**. LiFi could be used in a variety of applications, such as **smart homes, healthcare**, and **industrial automation**.

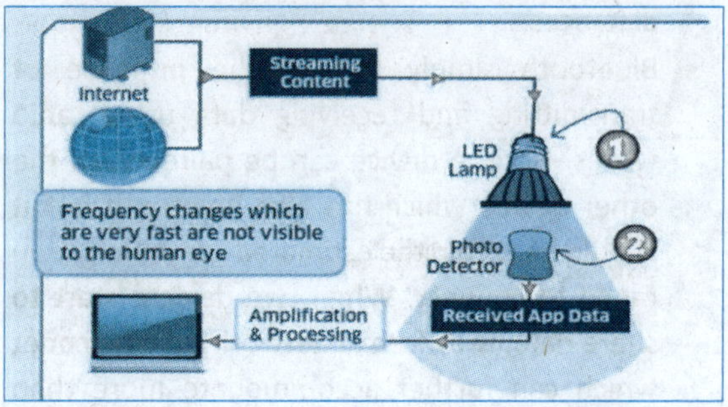

Difference between WiFi and LiFi		
Features	**LiFi**	**WiFi**
Operation	LiFi transmits data using light with the help of LED bulbs.	WiFi transmits data using radio waves with the help of WiFi router.
Interference	Do not have any intereference issues similar to radio frequency waves.	Will have intereference issues from nearby access points (routers).
Privacy	In LiFi, light does not penetrates/ passes thorugh the walls and hence provides a much secure data transfer	In WiFi, Radio frequencies signal passess thorugh the walls and hence there is a need to deploy techniques to achieve secure data transfer.
Data transfer speed	About 1 Gbps	About 150 Mbps.
Frequency of operation	10 thousand times frequency spectrum of the radio	2.4GHz, 4.9GHz and 5GHz

Coverage distance	About 10 meters	About 32 meters (vary based on transmit power and antenna type)
Data density	work with high dense environment	work in less dense environment due to interference related issues

Satellite based Internet Connectivity

- Satellite Internet Services utilize **satellites** in **space** to **transmit internet signals** from **Internet Service Providers** (ISPs) to users on Earth.
- This wireless internet connection is particularly valuable in **remote** or **rural areas** where **traditional broadband infrastructure** is limited, providing access to a **wide range of online services** and **information**.

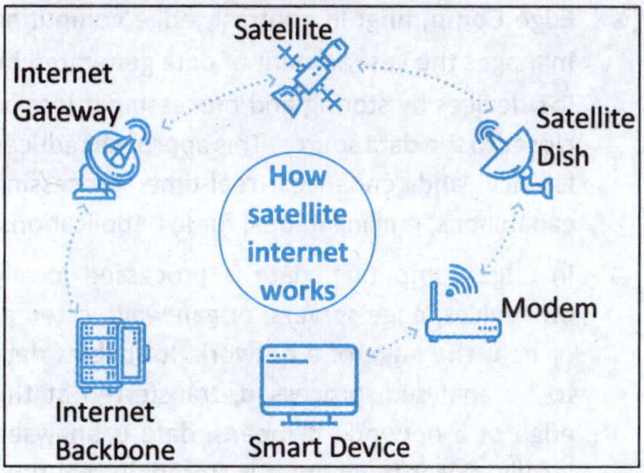

- **It has two main types:** one where the **device communicates directly to the satellite**, and another where the **device communicates to a satellite dish** on the **ground**.
- These satellites can be **closer to Earth** (faster but need more Satellites) or far away (slower but need fewer). The satellite dishes are called **Very Small Aperture Terminal** (VSAT).

Types of Satellites

- **Satellite Internet services** can be facilitated by two types of satellites:
  - **Low Earth Orbit Satellites** (LEO): These satellites orbit closer to Earth, providing **lower latency** but requiring a larger number of satellites for global coverage.
  - **Geostationary Earth Orbit Satellites** (GEO): These satellites orbit at higher altitudes, remaining fixed relative to Earth's surface. They offer broader coverage with fewer satellites but may have **higher latency** due to their distance.

Models for Satellite based connectivity

- **Hybrid (LPWAN + Satellite):** In this method, each sensor or device initially connects to a **sink node** using **LPWAN** (Low-Power Wide-Area Network). The sink node then serves as an intermediary to connect to the satellite. This hybrid approach combines the benefits of LPWAN (low power, long-range connectivity) with the broader coverage of satellite communication.
- **Direct to Satellite:** With this approach, devices communicate directly with the satellite without the need for an intermediate ground gateway. It simplifies the communication process but may have limitations in terms of coverage and latency, depending on the satellite's orbit.

D2M Technology

- D2M stands for **Direct-to-Mobile technology**. It is a **new technology** that allows **mobile phones** to receive **digital TV signals** directly, without the need for an **internet connection**. This is made possible by using a **combination of broadband** and **broadcast technologies**.

> **Broadband** refers to the **high-speed internet connection** that we use to **access the internet**. **Broadcast** refers to the traditional way of **distributing TV signals**, which is through **radio waves**.

- D2M technology combines these two technologies to allow **mobile phones** to receive **digital TV signals** directly, without the need for an internet connection. This is done by using a special receiver that is built into the mobile phone. The **receiver converts** the **radio waves** into **digital signals** that can be decoded by the phone's processor.

Application of DM Technology	
Application	**Examples**
IoT Device Networks	Smart home devices, Sensors, Automation systems
Emergency Services	Police radios, First responder equipment
Vehicle-to-Vehicle (V2V)	Automotive safety, Traffic management
Industrial Automation	Manufacturing robots, Machines, Production lines
Healthcare	Medical devices, Patient monitoring
Agriculture	Precision farming, Irrigation control
Retail and Inventory Management	Inventory tracking, Supply chain optimization
Energy Management	Smart grids, Energy meters
Asset Tracking	Shipping containers, High-value equipment
Environmental Monitoring	Air and water quality sensors, Weather stations
Military and Defense	Tactical equipment, Communication in the field
Entertainment and Gaming	Multiplayer gaming, Reduced latency

Serverless Computing

- A **computing model** that offloads all the backened infrastructure management tasks to the **cloud provider** freeing developers to focus on **coding** and **business specifics**.

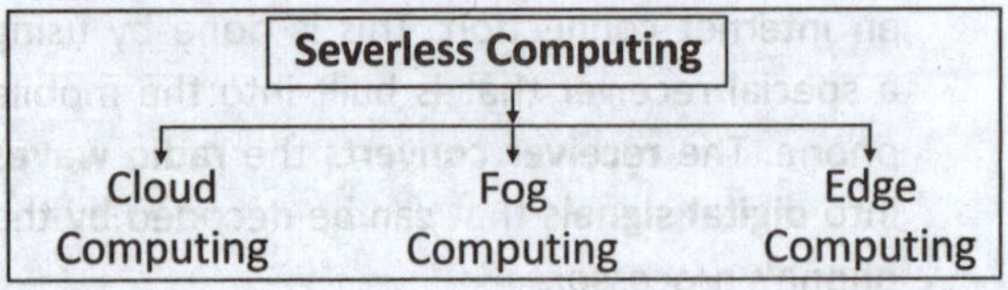

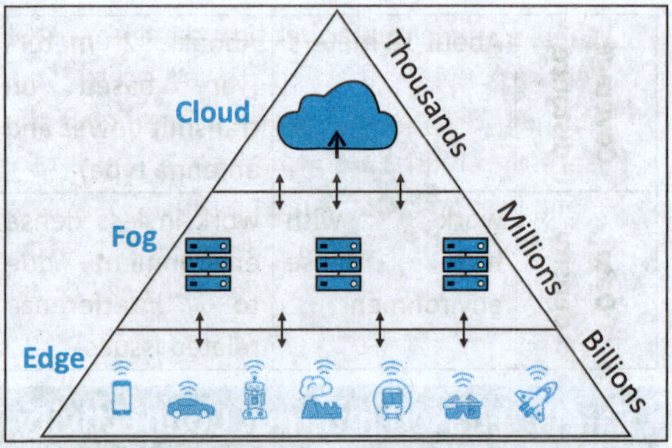

- **Cloud Computing:** This involves storing and accessing data and programs over the internet, eliminating the need for local storage. It often utilizes data centers for processing.
- **Fog Computing :** A decentralised computing infrastructure in which data, compute, storage and applications are located somewhere between data source and cloud.
- **Edge Computing:** In contrast, edge computing manages the vast amount of data generated by IoT devices by storing and processing it locally, closer to the data source. This approach reduces latency and enhances real-time processing capabilities, making it ideal for IoT applications.
- In edge computing, data is processed locally on devices, edge servers, or gateways, often at or near the **edge** of a network. It enables data to be analysed, processed, transferred at the edge of a network. It means, data is analysed locally, closer to where it is stored, in real-time without latency. Basic difference between edge computing and cloud computing lies in where data processing takes place.

Content Delivery Network (CDN)

- A **content delivery network** (CDN) is a geographically distributed group of servers that caches content close to end users.
- A CDN allows for the **quick transfer** of assets needed for **loading Internet content**, including **HTML pages, JavaScript files, stylesheets, images and videos.**

- When a user visits a website, data from that website's server has to travel across the internet to reach the user's computer. If the user is located far from that server, it will take a long time to load a large file, such as a video or website image. Instead, the website content is stored on **CDN servers** geographically closer to the users and reaches their computers much faster.
- The **primary purpose** of a content delivery network (CDN) is to **reduce latency**, or reduce the delay in communication created by a network's design. Because of the global and complex nature of the internet, communication traffic between **websites** (servers) and their **users** (clients) has to move over large physical distances. The communication is also **two-way,** with requests going from the client to the server and responses coming back.
- A CDN improves efficiency by **introducing intermediary servers** between the client and the website server. These CDN servers manage some of the **client-server communications**. They decrease web traffic to the web server, **reduce bandwidth consumption** and improve the **user experience.**
- Today the majority of web traffic is served through CDNs, including traffic from major sites like Facebook, Netflix, and Amazon.

Advantages of CDN
• Reduce page load time • Reduce bandwidth costs • Increase content availability • Improve website security

- **Distributed denial-of-service** (DDoS) attacks attempt to take down applications by sending large amounts of fake traffic to the website. CDNs can **handle** such **traffic spikes** by distributing the load between **several intermediary servers,** reducing the impact on the origin server.

Important Terminologies associated with Internet

- **Intranet vs Extranet:**
  - **Intranet** is defined as **private network** of computers **within an organization** with its **own server** and **firewall.** Intranet is system in which **multiple PCs** are networked to be **connected** to each other. PCs in intranet are not available to the world outside of the intranet. Usually each company or organization has their own Intranet network and members/employees of that company can access the computers in their intranet.
  - **Extranet** refers to network **within an organization**, using internet to **connect to the outsiders** in controlled manner. It helps to **connect businesses** with their **customers** and **suppliers** and therefore allows working in a **collaborative manner.**
- **IP address** : It is **a unique logical address** assigned to a machine over the network, assigned to each host present on Internet. IP address consists of two components: **network component** and **host component.**

IP address is 32 bits (4 bytes) long.

- **Uniform Resource Locator (URL):** It refers to a web **address** which uniquely identifies a document over the internet.
- **Domain Name:** It is a **symbolic string** associated with an IP address. There are several domain names available; some of them are generic such as **com, edu, gov, net** etc, while some country level domain names such as **au, in, za, us etc.**

The domain name space refers a **hierarchy** in the internet naming structure.

- **Name server** : It contains the **DNS database**. This database comprises of various **names** and their **corresponding IP addresses.**

- **Internet Service Provider (ISP):** It is a company offering access to internet. They offer various services like **Internet Access, Domain name registration, Dial-up access** and **Leased line access.**
- **Satellite Internet Connection :** Satellite Internet connection offers **high speed connection** to the internet. In **one way connection**, we can only download data but if we want to upload, we need a **dialup access** through ISP over telephone line. In **two way connection**, we can download and upload the data by the satellite. It does not require any dialup connection.

There are two types of satellite internet connection: **one way connection** or **two way connection.**

- **Wireless Internet Connection :** Wireless Internet Connection makes use of **radio frequency bands** to connect to the internet and offers a **very high speed.** The wireless internet connection can be obtained by either **WiFi** or **Bluetooth.**
- **WiFi wireless technology:** It is based on **IEEE 802.11 standards** which allow the electronic device to connect to the internet. **Bluetooth wireless technology:** It makes use of short-wavelength radio waves and helps to create personal area network (PAN).
- **Internet Protocol:** It is connectionless and unreliable protocol. It ensures no guarantee of successfully transmission of data. In order to make it reliable, it must be paired with reliable protocol such as TCP at the transport layer.
- **Transmission Control Protocol (TCP):** It is a connection oriented protocol and offers end-to-end packet delivery. It acts as back bone for connection.
- **File Transfer Protocol (FTP):** It is used to copy files from one host to another. FTP creates two processes such as Control Process and Data Transfer Process at both ends i.e. at client as well as at server. FTP establishes two different connections: one is for data transfer and other is for control information.
- **Hyper Text Transfer Protocol (HTTP):** It is a communication protocol. It defines mechanism for communication between browser and the web server. It is also called request and response protocol because the communication between browser and server takes place in request and response pairs.
- **Web Browser :** A software application for accessing the information on World Wide Web.

Examples : Google Chrome, Internet Explorer, Mozilla Firefox, Safari etc.

Generations of Internet

First Generation of Internet

Web 1.0 was invented in **1989** and functioned between **1993-99**. It was a **closed system**, where the users could not create any content or post, they were just at the receiving end.

- First Generation Internet was conceived in the era of **time sharing** in **1965.**
- In **1969**, the **Department of Defense Advanced Research Projects Agency** (ARPA) developed an **experimental network** called **ARPAnet** to link together **four supercomputing centres** for **military research.** This network had the many and difficult design requirements that it had to be **fast, reliable** and **capable** of **withstanding** a **nuclear bomb** destroying any one computer centre on the network.
- From those original four computers, this network evolved into the sprawling network of millions of computers known today as the Internet.

Features of First Generation Internet	
• Used IPv4	• Lacked Quality Service
• Unreliable	• No assured Bandwidth
• Low speeds	

Second Generation of Internet

Web 2.0 functioned from **1990's to 2004**. During this phases, users could create content, interact or contribute by sharing and uploading **photos** and **videos** paving way for social media.

- The Second generation Internet adds **quality of service**, multimedia and other advanced services to the current Internet. The second generation Internet initiatives are **I2, NGI, CAnet2** and other **Asian networks**.

Features of Second generation Internet	
• Used IPv6	• QoS provided
• Multicast provided	

- Second Generation Internet is a **collaborative effort** to develop **advanced Internet technology** and **applications** vital to the **research** and **education missions** of **higher education**.
- Second Generation Internet is working to **enable applications**, such as **telemedicine**, **digital libraries** and **virtual laboratories** that are not possible with the technology underlying Today's Internet.

Third Generation of Internet

Web 3.0 was coined by **Gavin Wood** in **2014**. Internet was **decentralised** where the users could control their content.

- The third generation Internet provides all the **advanced features** at a **very fast speed**. The third generation Internet is mainly in the **research stage**. It involves many ambitious projects that are being done in the level of a local area network and are expected to be implemented in a global way.
- The third generation internet initiatives are the **CAnet3, SUPERNet**.

Features of Third generation Internet
• Use of DWDM and other optical technologies.
• Usage of optical layer routing and switching.

- In this generation Internet is being commercialized, privatized and has broader access capacity.
- The Third Generation Internet created an avenue where people can be connected, share information, data transmission becomes easier. Services like online adverts, ecommerce and Internet banking are easily rendered.

Fourth Generation of Internet

- The era of Fourth Generation Internet is supposed to have emerged form **2020** in backdrop of **Artificial Intelligence** and **Metaverse**. It is believed to pave way for **Internet Decentralisation**.
- The Fourth Generation Internet seeks to provide **better services**, **more intelligence**, **greater involvement** and **participation**. It should be looking at worlds social and **ethical values**, **interoperable** and **transparent**.

Types of Services provided by Internet

- Internet Services allows us to **access huge amount of information** such as **text**, **graphics**, **sound** and **software** over the internet.
- **Communication Services:** There are various Communication Services available that offer exchange of information with individuals or groups.
  - **Electronic Mail :** Used to send electronic message over the internet.
  - **Telnet :** Used to log on to a remote computer that is attached to internet.
  - **Newsgroup :** Offers a forum for people to discuss topics of common interests.
  - **Internet Relay Chat** (IRC) : Allows the people from all over the world to communicate in real time.
  - **Mailing Lists :** Used to organize group of internet users to share common information through e-mail.
  - **Internet Telephony** (VoIP) : Allows the internet users to talk across internet to any PC equipped to receive the call.
  - **Instant Messaging :** Offers real time chat between individuals and group of people. **Ex.** Yahoo messenger, MSN messenger.

- **Information Retrieval Services :** There exist several Information retrieval services offering easy access to information present on the internet.
  - **File Transfer Protocol (FTP) :** Enable the users to transfer files.
  - **Archie :** It's updated database of public FTP sites and their content. It helps to search a file by its name.
  - **Gopher :** Used to search, retrieve, and display documents on remote sites.
  - **Very Easy Rodent Oriented Netwide Index to Computer Achieved (VERONICA):** VERONICA is gopher based resource. It allows access to the information resource stored on gopher's servers.
- **Web Services :** Web services allow exchange of information between applications on the web. Using web services, applications can easily interact with each other.
- **World Wide Web (WWW) :** WWW is also known as **W3**. It offers a way to **access documents** spread over the several servers over the internet. These documents may contain **texts, graphics, audio, video, hyperlinks.**

> **Hyperlinks** allow the **users** to **navigate** between the **documents.**

- **Video Conferencing :** Video conferencing or **Video teleconferencing** is a method of communicating through a **two-way video** and **audio transmission** with help of telecommunication technologies.

Generations of Cellular Technology

1G: Voice calls

- **1G refers** to the **first generation of wireless cellular technology** and they enabled communication between **two supported devices** using a **wireless network.**
- Based on the analog system, 1G supported **only voice calls**, and those too of **poor quality** because of **interference** and it worked in a **fixed area** because of a **lack of roaming support** by the network.

2G: Telephony services

- The **analog system** was now replaced by a much more advanced digital technology for wireless transmission called the **Global System for Mobile communication** (GSM).
- With digital underpinning, the 2G supported better quality voice calls and data services such as **short message service** (SMS) and **multimedia messaging service** (MMS).
- Besides, this mobile network enabled roaming facility, allowing users to attend calls, and send and receive texts and multimedia content on the go.
- It later received internet support by way of **GPRS** (General Packet Radio Service) and **EDGE** (Enhanced Data GSM Evolution), but that alone wasn't enough for a generational shift.

> The main difference between first two mobile cellular generations is that the **audio transmissions** of **1G networks** were **analog,** while **2G networks** were **entirely digital.**

3G: Age of Applications

- The third generation mobile network introduced **high speed internet services,** which set the stage for **smartphones** and **application ecosystems.**
- While 3G enabled the concept of **mobile television, online radio services** and emails on phones.

> **Video calling** and **mobile phone** apps defined the **3G era.**

4G: Internet calling

- 3G set the base for 4G, which is the **current generation** of the mobile network. The concepts introduced by 3G such as **high definition voice calls, video calls,** and **other internet services** become a reality in 4G on account of a higher data rate and **advanced multimedia services** that the mobile network supports.
- It perfected the **LTE** (Long Term Evolution) system, which significantly improves **data rate** and allows simultaneous transmission of voice and data.

- Internet calling, or **VoLTE** (Voice over LTE), is one of the many advantages of the 4G mobile network. It also **enables voice over WiFi** (VoWiFi) that allows voice calls in areas with low or no network reception.
- VoLTE requires the **4G LTE** mobile core network (Evolved Packet Core – EPC) to work with another network entity **IP Multimedia Subsystem** (IMS).

> **WiFi calling** or **Voice over WiFi** (VoWiFi) is an **IP technology** that requires the **mobile phone** to connect to a **local WiFi network** to establish a connection with a mobile network entity **ePDG** (Evolved Packet Data Gateway).

- **ePDG** works with the mobile core network and **IMS** to ensure secure communication.
- **VoWiFi** allows any cellular device to connect to the **4G LTE network** as long as it is connected to the internet.
- Mobile networks require a new network entity called **Evolved Packet Data Gateway** (ePDG) as an adapter to connect any online cellular device to the **4G LTE network ecosystem**.
- The role of ePDG is to make sure that the cellular devices are connected to the mobile network in a highly secure way.

> **VoNR stands or Voice over New Radio (NR)**
> - VoNR is the capability in the **fifth generation** (5G) of **mobile networks** that requires a 5G mobile core network that can work with another network entity **IP Multimedia Subsystem** (IMS).
> - It is a **packet-switched IP** technology that requires the mobile phone to be connected to a **5G radio base station – gNodeB**.

5G : IoT and Enterprises

- The 5G network operates in the **millimeter-wave spectrum** (30-300 GHz) which can send large amounts of data at very high speeds as the **frequency is very high**, and it experiences **little interference** from surrounding signals.
- For consumers, the network would deliver **high internet speeds** and would likely play a crucial role in **enabling technologies** such as the metaverse.
- It uses **OFDM** (Orthogonal Frequency-Division Multiplexing) and **millimeter wireless** that enables a data rate of **20Mbps** and a frequency band of **2-8 GHz**. It can be used for streaming high-quality videos, more **accurate location tracking**, **low-latency communication** and better ability for **real-time analytics**.

3G vs 4G vs 5G vs 6G

	Deployment	Bandwidth	Latency	Average Speed
3G	2004–06	2mbps	100–150 milli second	144 kbps
4G	2006–10	200mbps	20–30 milli second	25 mbps
5G	2020	>1gbps	<10 milli second	200–400 mbps
6G	2028–2030	1tbps	<1 micro-second	about 50 times faster than 5G

6G : Connected ecosystem

- 6G is touted to drive the **adoption of 5G** use cases at scale through **optimisations** and cost **reduction**, especially at the **enterprise level**.
- **Metaverse** is one of the 5G use cases, which promises to disrupt both traditional and digital spaces.

> With 6G, the metaverse would not just evolve into a final model but is also likely to unify with the **physical world** with the help of **artificial intelligence** and machine learning.

5G technology

- 5G represents a significant advancement in **mobile communication technology, offering faster speeds, lower latency,** and the capability to connect a vast array of devices and objects.

5G Spectrum Types	
5G Spectrum	**Features**
Low band	• Lower than 1 Ghz on the spectrum chart. • Wider coverage but limited improvement in speed and latency. • For thinly populated areas and provides indoor coverage in built-up areas.
Mid band	• 1 GHz – 6 GHz range. • Ideal for 5G because it can carry plenty of data while also traveling significant distances.
High-band	• 24 GHz band and higher. • It delivers super-fast speeds over short distances.

Features of 5G
• Higher Frequency • Higher bandwidth • Lower Latency (time taken to respond)

Spectrum	Uses/ Advantages	Challenges
Low band	• Great **coverage** and **speed of internet** and **data exchange.** • Maximum speed is limited to **100 Mbps** (Megabits per second). • For commercial cellphone users who may not have specific demands for very high speed internet.	May not be optimal for specialised needs of the industry.
Mid-band	• Higher speeds compared to the low band. • May be used by industries and specialised factory units for building captive networks.	In terms of coverage area and penetration of signals.
High-band	• Offers the highest speed (as high as 20 Gbps (giga bits per second)) of all the three bands.	Extremely limited coverage and signal penetration strength.

- **5G** has the potential to **revolutionize industries** and **enable innovative applications** that were not feasible with earlier generations of cellular networks. 5G operates at **higher frequencies** to offer a new kind of network that is designed to **connect virtually everyone** and **everything** together including **machines, objects** and **devices.**

5G mainly works in **3 bands**, namely **low, mid** and **high frequency spectrum.**

- **Challenges to 5G evolution in India**
  - **Lack of infrastructure** : Inadequate optical fiber infrastructure and backhaul, interrupted power supply, etc.
  - **High Base Price for Aution.**
  - **Telco issues** : Low average revenue per user, Lack of skillset etc.
  - **Consumer constraints** : Network coverage issue, handset availability, data privacy etc.
  - **Technological Challenges** : High import dependency on complete 5G supply chain etc.
  - **Others** : Connectivity with critical infrastructure, National security issue from chinese vendors like ZTE, huawel etc.

Important Terms associated with 5G technology

- **Fiberisation :** Connecting radio towers with each other via optical fiber cables. Connects core of network to edge facilitating large amounts of data used in 5G services.
- **5G airwave interference** : 5G uses the same spectrum as **aircraft radio altimeters** leading to interference.

- **Network Slicing** : Multiple networks to be created on top of a common physical infrastructure. Each slice can be allocated based on the specific needs of the application, use case or customer.

> **5G** is a **Massive Multi User MIMO** (multiple input multiple output) enabled network.

- **Beamforming** - Beamforming involves focusing the transmit and receive antenna arrays' energy in a specific direction, rather than broadcasting signals uniformly in all directions. This directional approach allows for more precise targeting of wireless signals.
- **Open Radio Access Network (O-RAN)** is a new approach to **5G network architecture** that decouples the hardware and software components of the **radio access network** (RAN). **O-RAN** is based on the **principle of disaggregation**, which means that the different components of the RAN are separated from each other. This makes it possible to use different vendors' equipment for different components, which can lead to lower costs and more flexibility.
- **Long term Evolution (LTE) and Voice over LTE (VoLTE)** : LTE is a **4G wireless communication** technology that focuses on **high-speed data transmission**. Under LTE, the **infrastructure** of telecom players only allows **transmission** of **data** while voice calls are routed to their older **2G** or **3G networks. VoLTE** (Voice over LTE) is an extension of LTE that enables high-quality voice calls to be made over LTE networks, providing improved voice quality and faster call setup times while still supporting data services.

Challenges associated with the adoption of 5G/6G in India

- **Last mile connectivity:** India lacks optical fiber infrastructure and greenfield deployment. Thus, providing last-mile connectivity to tier 2 and 3 cities and rural India owing to the digital divide becoming the greatest challenge.
- **Affordable 5G devices:** The biggest roadblock in India's electronics manufacturing industry is that it **lacks world-class semiconductor fabricating units** (FAB) which is the notable denominator for device affordability.
- **High Spectrum Pricing:** India's 5G/6G spectrum pricing is many times costlier than the global average. This will be of disadvantage to India's debt-ridden telecom companies.
- **Security and Privacy:** The new generations needs to ensure the protection of personal data. It will have to define the **uncertainties related to security threats including trust**, **privacy** and **cybersecurity**, which are growing across the globe.
- **Fiber Connectivity:** India lacks a strong backhaul for the transition to the new generations.

> - **Backhaul** is a **network** that **links cell sites** to the **central exchange**.
> - However, **80%** of cell sites in India are connected through **microwave backhaul** (high latency + limited capacity) and only **20%** of sites are connected through **fiber communication** (low latency + unlimited capacity).

- **Lack of regulatory bodies in India's Telecom Sector:** 5G/6G implementation in India will not become a reality until there is a proper regulatory body that will develop the roadmap.
- **Replacement of older devices:** 6G technology would require newer handsets with the latest hardware, which would mean the replacement of older phones with new and costlier phones, which is undesirable for low-income people.

Applications of Internet

- Internet allows us to **communicate** with people at **remote locations.**
- Informations regarding various topics such as **Technology, Health & Science, Social Studies, Geographical Information, Information Technology** and various products can be surfed / browsed with help of a search engine.

- Internet also serves a medium for entertainment like Online Television and Online Gaming.
- **Browsing Social Media** like Facebook, Twitter, Yahoo, Google, Flickr etc.
- With the expansion of **digital services**, Internet acts as a **basic infrastructure** like accessing Internet Banking, Matrimonial Services, Online Shopping, Online Ticket Booking, Online Bill Payment, Data Sharing, E-mail.
- Internet paves way for e commerce / electronic commerce, that allows the business deals to be conducted on electronic systems.

Concerns of Internet

- Creates Digital Divide.
- Privacy and Security concerns.
- Cybercrimes.
- Threat to critical infrastructure.
- Concerns of Metaverse and Artificial Intelligence.

Virtual Private Network/ VPN uses **Internet Protocol Security Architecture** (IPSEC) Protocol to provide secure transactions by adding an additional security layer to **TCP/IP protocol**. This layer is created by **encapsulating** the **IP packet** to a **new IP packet**.

Emerging Technologies in Internet Technology (IT)

- Super Computers
- Quantum Computing
- Artificial Intelligence (AI) & Machine Learning (ML)
- Big data
- 6G Technology
- Internet of Things (IoT)
- Blockchain and Cryptocurrency
- Augmented Reality (AR) and Virtual Reality (VR)
- Edge Computing
- Robotics and Automation

SUPERCOMPUTERS

- Supercomputers are **specialized large systems** built to tackle **intricate scientific** and **industrial problems** that require **massive computational power.**
- Unlike traditional computers, supercomputers use more than one **central processing unit** (CPU).
- Supercomputing performance is gauged by the **number of floating-point operations** it can perform per second **(FLOPS)**, reflecting its **processing capability**.

Petaflops is a unit measuring a **computer's speed**, equivalent to **one quadrillion FLOPS**, highlighting its immense **computational prowess**.

- **Floating-point** is a method of **encoding real numbers** within the limits of **finite precision available** on computers.
- Supercomputers can have one million times more processing power than the **fastest laptop**. They work on **parallel computing** or **parallelism** where many processors work together.

National Supercomputing Mission (NSM)

- Initiated in **2015**, NSM is a collaborative effort involving **Ministry of Electronics & Information Technology**, **Department of Science and Technology**, **C-DAC** and **Indian Institute of Science, Bangalore**.
- NSM aims to strengthen **India's academic** and **research institutions** across the nation by establishing a widespread supercomputing grid. This grid encompasses over **70 high-performance computing** (HPC) **facilities**, fostering technological advancement.
- Till now **C-DAC** has deployed **11 such facilities** under **NSM Phase-1** and **Phase-2** with a **CCP** of more than 20 Petaflops. Eg: **PARAM Shivay** [IIT (BHU)], **PARAM Shakti** (IIT Kharagpur), **PARAM Brahma** (IISER, Pune) etc. These supercomputers will also be networked on the National Supercomputing Grid over **National Knowledge Network** (NKN).

Four major pillars of NSM

- Infrastructure
- Applications
- R&D
- Human resource development

- NSM serves various purposes including **genomics**, **drug discovery**, **urban modeling**, **flood prediction**, **river basin warnings**, **seismic imaging** for oil and gas exploration.

NSM aims to deploy **70 supercomputers** with a combined computational power of **1 exaflop by 2030.**

Indian Agencies involved in Supercomputers

- Centre for Development of Advanced Computing (C-DAC), Centre for Development of Telematics (C-DOT), National Aerospace Laboratories (NAL), Bhabha Atomic Research Centre (BARC), and Advanced Numerical Research and Analysis Group (ANURAG) took the lead in this direction.

> - **C-DOT** developed "CHIPPS", a high-performance Parallel Processing System.
> - **BARC** created the Anupam series of supercomputers.
> - **ANURAG** created the PACE series of supercomputers.

- **Param Series:** PARAM supercomputers are designed and assembled by the Centre for Development of Advanced Computing (C-DAC) in Pune, India.
- PARAM means supreme in Sanskrit, and also creates an acronym for **"PARAllel Machine"**.
- The PARAM 8000 was a success for C-DAC in delivering a gigaFLOPS range Parallel computer. It was launched in 1991.

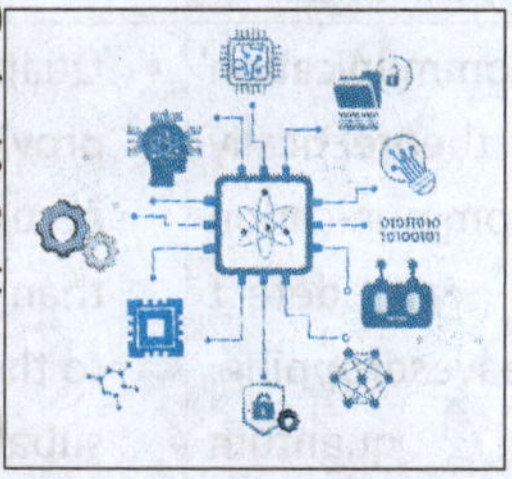

- In 1993, the PARAM 9000 series was released, which had a peak computing power of 5 GFLOPS.
- In 1998, the **PARAM 10000** series had a sustained performance of 38 GFLOPS on the LINPACK benchmark.
- The AI Supercomputer **'AIRAWAT'** and **PARAM Siddhi** – AI are currently the fastest supercomputers in India.

Top Ranking Supercomputers (TOP 500)

1. El Capitan (USA)
2. FRONTIER (USA)
3. Aurora (USA)
4. Eagle (USA)
5. HPC 6 (Italy)
6. Fugaku (Japan)
7. Alps (Switzerland)
8. LUMI (Finland)
9. Leonardo (Italy)
10. Tuolumne (USA)

TOP RANKING Supercomputers in India

136. AIRAWAT – PSAI
188. Arka
189. Arunika
268. Pratyush (Cray XC40)
400. Arka AI/ML
431. Mihir (Cray XC40)

- As of November 2024, India has deployed a total of 33 supercomputers with a combined compute capacity of 32 petaflops.
- In October 2024, India unveiled three PARAM Rudra supercomputers, each with a peak computing speed of over 5 petaflops. These systems have been deployed in Pune, Delhi, and Kolkata to support advanced scientific research in areas such as physics, cosmology, and earth sciences
- Companies like Lenovo are contributing to India's HPC landscape by manufacturing AI servers at their plant in Puducherry. Lenovo plans to produce 50,000 AI rack servers and 2,400 GPU servers annually, catering to both local consumption and export markets

Quantum Technology

- Quantum Technology is based on the principles of Quantum mechanics developed in the early 20th century to describe nature at the scale of atoms and elementary particles.
- Using quantum superposition, a set of unbreakable codes or super-speedy information processing, quantum computers are able to mimic several classical computers working in parallel.
- Quantum Technology is based on the principles of quantum theory, which explains the nature of energy and matter on the atomic and subatomic level. It concerns the control and manipulation of quantum systems, with the goal of achieving information processing beyond the limits of the classical world.

Quantum Technology
• Quantum Key Distribution
• Quantum Networks
• Quantum Simulators
• Post-Quantum Cryptography
• Quantum Sensors Particle Generators Atomic Clocks
• Quantum Cloud Computing
• Quantum Memories
• Quantum Repeaters
• Quantum Chips
• Quantum Software
• Quantum Computing
• Quantum Annealers
• Quantum Materials

- Quantum principles will be used for engineering solutions to extremely complex problems in **computing**, **communications**, **sensing**, **chemistry**, **cryptography**, **imaging** and **mechanics**. Quantum field has not yet matured for commercialization, due to the extreme scientific challenges involved.
- Quantum computers store and process information using quantum two level systems (quantum bits or qubits) which unlike classical bits, can be prepared in superposition states. This key ability makes quantum computers extremely powerful compared to conventional computers when solving certain kinds of problems like finding prime factors of large numbers and searching large databases.
- The prime factorization quantum algorithm has important implications for security as it can be used to break RSA encryption, a popular method for secure communication.

Three key Quantum Use Cases : Computing, Communication and Sensing		
Quantum Computing	**Quantum Communication**	**Quantum sensing**
• Quantum computing solves advanced computational problems by leveraging quantum phenomena to process information and make calculations. • Enterprice use of quantum computers is expected to ramp up over the next several year, likey growing dramtically within a decade with the appearance of fault-tolerant quantume machines.	• Quantum communication creates secure, theorectically tamper-proof communication networks that can detect interception or eavesdropping. • Several quantum communication networks either have been deployed or are in progress, but it likely will be several years before they can overcome the unpredictability of quantum particles.	• Quantum sensing devices provide, higher reponsiveness, accuracy, and performance than conventional sensors, due to the nature and sensitivity of subatomic particles. • Quauntum sensors are available today for limited production use cases and their availability and capability likely will increase substantially withing five to 100 years.

Stalwart quantum Indians in quantum Science : Professor Satyendra Nath Bose, Sir Chandrasekhara Venkata Raman and Professor Meghnad Saha.

- India is currently at the forefront of tapping the second quantum revolution through massive investments in the field.

Union Budget 2020-21 proposed to spend **₹8,000 crore** ($ 1.2 billion) on the newly launched **National Mission on Quantum Technologies and Applications** (NMQTA) and **₹3660 Crore** for **National Mission on Interdisciplinary Cyber Physical Systems** (NM-ICPS).

- **Budget 2020 allocated Rs 8000 Crore** to a National Mission on Quantum Technologies & Applications (NM-QTA) for a period of five years.

Potential applications of Quantum technology

Quantum Computing
Uses qubits (typically subatomic particles as it's the basic unit of information instead of binary bits.

Quantum Communication
Uses quantum bits, typically photons of light, for transmitting data along optical cables. Includes technologies like– Quantum key distribution and Quantum Random Number Generation (QRNG).

Quantum Simulation
Specially designed quantum computer constructed for the purpose of simulating materials or chemical reactions of the physical world.

Quantum sensing and metrology
Uses individual particles such as photons and electrons as highly sensitive sensors in current technologies related to measurements of forces, gravitation, electric fields etc.

Quantum Computing

Quantum computing is a type of **computing** that uses the **principles of quantum mechanics to perform calculations.** Quantum mechanics is the **study of the behavior of matter** and **energy** at the **atomic** and **subatomic level.** Unlike classical computers that use bits as the smallest unit of data (0 or 1), **quantum computers** use quantum bits or qubits.

- **Classical computers** operate using **binary physical state**, meaning its operations are based on one of two positions (1 or 0).

1 : Electricity is being passed through the wire
0 : No electricity is being passed through the wire

- Classical computers process information in a binary format, called **bits,** which can represent either a 0 or 1.
- **Quantum computers** use **logical units** called **quantum bits**, or **qubits** in short, that can be put into a **quantum state** where they can simultaneously represent both **0** and **1** and their correlations.

Qubits have a **special ability**: they can exist in **multiple states at once**, sort of like being both on and off at the same time.

Principles of Quantum Computing
- Superposition
- Entanglement

Superposition

- Superposition is a fundamental concept in quantum mechanics where a **quantum system**, such as a **particle** or an atom, can exist in multiple states simultaneously.
- In the **quantum world**, particles can be in a **combination** or **superposition of states**, like being in two places at once or having two different properties at the **same time.**

Superposition means that **each quantum bit** (basic unit of information in a quantum computer) can represent both a **1** and a **0** at the **same time.**

- An analogy might be thinking of a spinning coin that's both heads and tails until you actually observe it. In a similar way, until you measure a quantum system, it can be in a **superposition of states.**
- This property is harnessed in quantum computers, where **qubits** can hold **multiple possibilities at once**, allowing for **parallel**

processing and **potentially solving complex problems** more **efficiently** than classical computers.

Entanglement

- Entanglement is a remarkable phenomenon in quantum physics where **two** or **more particles** become **deeply connected** in a way that their **states are interdependent**, no matter how far apart they are.
- This means that the state of one particle instantly affects the state of the other, even if they're light-years apart. It's as if they're **communicating faster than the speed of light**, though this doesn't **violates Einstein's theory of relativity.**

> Imagine you have a pair of gloves – one is left-handed, and the other is right-handed. You separate these gloves and send one to a friend on the other side of the world. When your friend opens their box and sees that they have a left-handed glove, they instantly know that the glove you have is right-handed, even though you haven't opened your box yet.

- In the quantum world, particles can be entangled in a similar way. The properties of one particle (electron) become tied to the **properties of another** (electron), regardless of how far apart they are. Changing the state of one particle(electron) immediately changes the state of the other, as if they're connected in an invisible and instantaneous way.
- Entanglement creates a **remarkable phenomenon** known as **superlinkages.** Even when separated by **immense distances,** a disturbance in one electron will cause an instant change in another electron it's entangled with. This property holds immense potential for **communication and cryptography.**
- **Alain Aspect** (France), **John F. Clauser** (USA) and **Anton Zeilinger** (Austria) were accorded **Nobel Prize** in **Physics 2022** for experiments with entangled photons, establishing the violation of Bell inequalities and pioneering quantum information science.

Advantages of Quantum Computing

- **Speed:** Perform quick and easy calculations that are time consuming on conventional computers.
- **Storage:** Drastically bring down the space needed to store data.
- **Simulation:** Doing data simulation involving multiple parameters like weather forecasting, chemical simulation.
- **Privacy:** Impossible to break the security of quantum entanglement-based cryptography

Quantum Computing in India

- **National Mission on Quantum Technologies and Applications (NMQTA) :** Union Budget 2020 allocated Rs. 8000 Crore to the National Mission on Quantum Technology for a period of **5 years.**
- **Quantum Frontier Mission:** It is an initiative of the **Prime Minister's Science, Technology, and Innovation Advisory Council** (PM-STIAC) which aims to initiate work in the understanding and control of quantum mechanical systems.
- **DRDO Young Scientist Laboratory for Quantum Technologies** (DYSLQT) is located in **Mumbai**.
- **Quantum-Enabled Science & Technology (QuEST)** is a research program by the Department of Science & Technology.
- **Quantum Information and Computing (QuIC)** lab is located at **Raman Research Institute, Bangalore.**

National Mission on Quantum technology

- The areas of focus for the NM-QTA mission will be in fundamental science, translation, technology development and towards addressing issues conceming national priorities.
- The mission can help prepare next generation skilled manpower, boost translational research and also encourage entrepreneurship and start-up ecosystem development.
- Quantum principles will be used for engineering solutions to extremely complex problems in computing, communications, sensing, chemistry, cryptography, imaging and mechanics.

- Their applications which will be boosted include those include those in aero-space engineering, numerical weather predictions, simulations, securing the communications and financial transactions, cyber security, advanced manufacturing, health, agriculture, education.
- It can bring India in the list of few countries with an edge in this emerging field will have a greater advantage in gamarig multifold **economic growth** and **dominent leadership role.**

- **Quantum applications** which will receive boost include those in aero-space engineering, numerical weather prediction, simulations, securing the communications & financial transactions, cyber security, advanced manufacturing, health, agriculture, education and other important sectors with focus on creation of high skilled jobs, human resources development, start-ups & entrepreneurship leading to technology lead economic growth.

Applications of Quantum Computing

- **Secure Quantum Communication:** Utilizing **quantum cryptography** holds immense importance for satellite communication, military operations, and cybersecurity due to its potential to provide **ultra-secure channels and unhackable encryption methods.**

In **March 2021, ISRO** demonstrated **free space Quantum communication** and **China demonstrated secure quantum communication** between **terrestrial stations and satellites.**

- **Cryptography and Cybersecurity:** Quantum computers can both break and enhance encryption methods, leading to advancements in secure communication and data protection.
- **Agriculture:** Using advanced tools to predict meteorological events like rains, cyclones and soil type, which helps farmers decide what crops to grow and which fertilizers to use. This smart planning boosts harvests and efficiency. There are even clever algorithms to spot weeds and improve farming further (Precision agriculture).
- **Pharmaceutical Advancements:** Quantum computing's powerful data processing **speeds accelerate vaccine development**, **predict outbreaks, simulate drug reactions** and analyze genes for **precision medicine.** It has potential to shorten molecule discovery timeframes, as seen with Covid-19 variant analysis, leading to more effective treatments and faster responses to health challenges.
- **Empowering Industry 4.0:** Quantum computing is a key player in **Industry 4.0**, collaborating with technologies like the **Internet of Things** (IoT), **machine learning**, **robotics** and **AI.** It enhances their capabilities, enabling smarter decision-making, optimized operations, and innovative solutions that drive the next wave of industrial transformation.
- **Weather and Climate Forecasting:** Quantum computing improves **weather modeling,** leading to highly accurate predictions of changing weather patterns. Scientists can generate **detailed climate models,** offering deeper insights into **climate change** and **strategies for mitigation**. This advancement holds promise for better understanding and addressing environmental challenges.
- **Disaster Management:** Quantum computing streamlines **climate change data collection,** integrating it with **advanced weather models.** This fusion could potentially enhance the **predictability** of **natural disasters** like tsunamis, **droughts**, **earthquakes** and **floods**, aiding in better disaster preparedness and response.

Important Terminology related to Quantum Computing

- **Quantum Supremacy** - It's the point at which a **quantum computer** can complete a **mathematical calculation** that is beyond the reach of even the most powerful supercomputer. Recently, **Sycamore** (Google's quantum computer) took **200 seconds** to perform a calculation that the world's fastest supercomputer would have taken 10,000 years to do.

Challenges to Quantum Computing

- **Qubit Stability and Error Correction:** Maintaining **qubit reliability** and developing methods to **correct errors** caused by **external interference**.
- **Scalability:** Ensuring the technology can handle increasing numbers of **qubits** while maintaining their **performance**.
- **Decoherence:** Preventing rapid **loss of quantum states** due to interactions with the environment.
- **Hardware Complexity:** Designing, building, and maintaining the intricate hardware components necessary for quantum computing.
- **Energy Consumption:** Addressing the high energy requirements for cooling quantum systems.
- **Designing Quantum Algorithms:** Quantum algorithms require specialized design approaches that differ significantly from **traditional classical algorithms** due to the unique properties of **quantum computation**.
- **Cybersecurity Concerns:** Quantum computers have the potential to break many of the encryption methods currently used in cybersecurity, raising concerns about data security on the internet.
- **Limited Applicability:** Quantum computers are not suited for all tasks; tasks like **word processing** and **email** are not suitable for quantum computers due to their specific computational strengths and limitations.

Quantum Communication

- Quantum communication takes advantage of the laws of quantum physics to protect data. These laws allow particles—typically photons of light for transmitting data along optical cables—to take on a state of superposition, which means they can represent multiple combinations of **1 and 0 simultaneously**. The particles are known as **quantum bits** or **qubits**.
- The beauty of qubits from a cybersecurity perspective is that if a hacker tries to observe them in transit, their super-fragile quantum state collapses to either **1 or 0**. This means a hacker can't tamper with the qubits without leaving behind a telltale sign of the activity.
- Some companies have taken advantage of this property to create networks for transmitting highly sensitive data based on a process called quantum key distribution, or QKD. In theory, at least, these networks are ultra-secure.

Quantum Key Distribution (OQD)

- Quantum key distribution is a fundamental concept in quantum cryptography. **Traditional cryptography** relies on **mathematical problems** that are computationally hard to solve, while **quantum key distribution** (QKD) leverages the principles of **quantum physics** to achieve security.

Quantum key distribution allows user to agree on a way of **transmitting their data** without the worry that someone is listening in : • Sender instructs satellite to generate 2 entangled photons of particular quantum state. • **Photons** are beamed to both **ground stations**. • **Sender** and **receiver** compare the quantum states of the photons to check if they have been intercepted. If not they use the photons to create a code to encrypt the date. • **Encrypted data** can then be sent securely via conventional means.
Quantum cryptography is considered future proof : It is believed that no future changes in technology can crack quantum cryptography.

Challenges of QKD

- **Transmission Loss :** Quantum signals are sensitive to external factors during transmission, leading to degradation of quantum information, limiting communication range, and requiring techniques like quantum repeaters to extend distances.
- **Lower Communication Rates :** Quantum communication has slower data rates due to the time needed for qubit preparation, transmission and measurement, hindering its throughput compared to classical methods.

- **Infrastructure Shortfalls :** Quantum communication demands controlled environments and specialized hardware due to qubits' sensitivity.
- **Implementation Complexity :** QKD necessitates precise control over quantum states and advanced error correction techniques.
- **Standardization and Interoperability:** Establishing common protocols and standards is essential to ensure seamless communication between different QKD systems, enhancing compatibility and widespread adoption.
- **Cost :** Quantum communication networks require significant investment in specialized hardware and secure infrastructure, making cost a key barrier to achieving practical and scalable implementation.

Quantum Sensing

- Subatomic particles are sensitive to such external effects as rotation; acceleration; time; and electric, magnetic, and gravitational fields, which allow them to be used to make highly responsive sensors whose accuracy and performance exceed that of conventional sensors.
- Quantum sensors have the potential to replace existing sensors in many applications, including locating and monitoring oil, gas, and mineral deposits; surveying construction sites; and detecting the slightest environmental, seismic, or weather changes.
- In the transportation sector, quantum sensors promise to dramatically improve precise navigation and positioning systems.
- In the medical field, they likely will be used to analyze temperature, heart rate, and other vital signs and to advance the accuracy of magnetic resonance imaging.
- Quantum sensors are available today for limited production use cases; their availability and capability likely will grow dramatically within **5 to 10 years.**

Semantic Communication: A Paradigm Shift in ICT

- Traditional communication systems focus on transmitting raw data bits (0s and 1s) as accurately as possible, without considering the actual meaning of the data. In contrast, **Semantic Communication** (SC) is an advanced paradigm that emphasizes the meaning and purpose of transmitted information, reducing redundant data transmission while maintaining communication effectiveness.
- Instead of transmitting entire data packets, Semantic Communication extracts the essential "meaning" (semantics) from information before transmission. This reduces bandwidth usage, improves efficiency, and enables intelligent communication.

> **Traditional Communication:** Transmits every letter of the sentence as raw data.
>
> **Semantic Communication:** Transmits only the meaning of the sentence using AI-driven models, drastically reducing the data size.

- Semantic Communication relies on Artificial Intelligence (AI) and Natural Language Processing (NLP) to extract, process, and optimize messages.
- **Example in a smart home system:** A sensor detecting "room temperature is rising" may send just "Increase AC cooling" instead of raw temperature data.

Applications of Semantic Communication

- **6G Networks:** Future wireless networks will integrate semantic communication for ultra-efficient data exchange.
- **IoT (Internet of Things):** Smart devices can share summarized data instead of raw readings.
- **Healthcare:** AI-based communication in telemedicine can prioritize essential medical details over redundant data.
- **Autonomous Vehicles:** Vehicles can communicate intent (e.g., "changing lane") instead of full sensor data.

Big Data

- Big data is a combination of **structured, semi-structured** and **unstructured data** collected by organizations that can be **mined** for **information** and used in **machine learning projects, predictive modeling** and other **advanced analytics applications.**
- Systems that **process** and **store big data** have become a common component of **data management architectures** in organizations, combined with tools that support big data analytics uses.
- Big data is often characterized by the **3 V's:**
  - The large **Volume** of data in many environments.
  - The wide **Variety** of data types frequently stored in big data systems.
  - The **Velocity** at which much of the data is generated, collected and processed.
- These characteristics were first identified in **2001** by **Doug Laney; Gartner** further popularized them after it acquired **Meta Group** in **2005**. More recently, several other V's have been added to different descriptions of big data, including veracity, value and variability.

The Six Vs of Big Data
• **Volume :** The **amount** of data from myriad sources.
• **Variety :** The **types of data**- structured, semi-structured, unstructured.
• **Velocity :** The **speed** of which big data is generated.
• **Veracity :** The **degree** to which big data can be trusted.
• **Value :** The **business value** of the date collected.
• **Variability :** The **ways** in which the big data can be used and formatted.

Types of Big Data
Structured data : Transactions and financial records.
Unstructured data : Text, documents and multimedia files.
Semi-structured data : Web server logs and streaming data from sensors.

- **Big data comes from multiple digital sources like -** transaction processing systems, customer databases, documents, emails, medical records, internet clickstream logs, mobile apps and social networks. It also includes machine-generated data, such as network and server log files and data from sensors on manufacturing machines, industrial equipment and internet of things devices.
- Big data environments often incorporate **external data** on consumers, financial markets, weather and traffic conditions, geographic information, scientific research and more. Images, videos and audio files are forms of big data, too, and many big data applications involve streaming data that is processed and collected on a continual basis.

Applications of Big Data

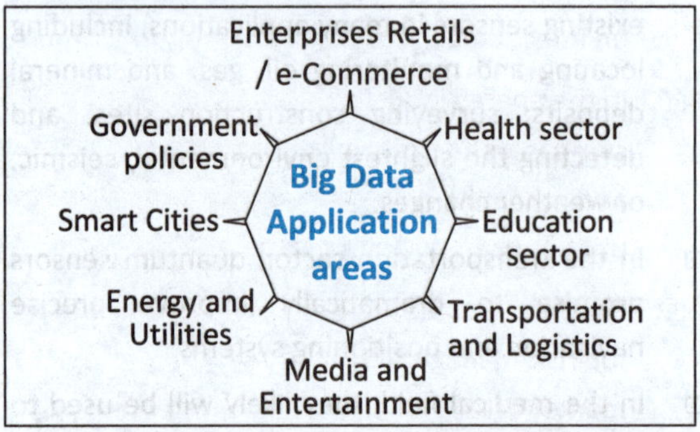

Data is the new form of currency.

- Industry-wide, as well as government-wide, business practises are being transformed by technological advancements and an ever-increasing amount of **data digitization** and **data generation** in government are on the rise.

- **Public sector transactions, employment, education, manufacturing and agriculture**, to name a few, generate a large amount of publicly available information. In addition to boosting productivity and growth, applications of big data analytics can help the government achieve **greater efficiency** and **combat fraud**.
- Companies use big data in their systems to improve **operations**, provide **better customer service**, create **personalized marketing campaigns** and take other actions that, ultimately, can increase revenue and profits.
- Businesses that use it effectively hold a potential **competitive advantage** over those that don't because they're able to make faster and more informed business decisions.
- Big data is used by **medical researchers** to **identify disease signs** and risk factors and by doctors to help diagnose illnesses and medical conditions in patients.
- A combination of data from **electronic health records, social media sites**, the web and other sources gives **healthcare organizations** and government agencies up-to-date information on infectious disease threats or outbreaks.
- In the energy industry, big data helps oil and gas companies identify potential drilling locations and monitor pipeline operations; likewise, utilities use it to track electrical grids.
- **Financial services** firms use big data systems for risk management and real-time analysis of market data.
- **Manufacturers and transportation companies rely** on big data to manage their supply chains and optimize delivery routes.
- **Government/ Public Institutions** may use the Big Data for emergency response, crime prevention and smart city initiatives.
- **Governments** can use big data and analytics to unlock key information and improve transparency and efficiency in public management. Government agencies can benefit from implementing big data platforms by improving the way they utilise **IT**, discovering **new capabilities** and **services**, understanding **correlations** and trends in underlying data, and improving **decision making**.

To **combat terrorism, MI5** (British Secret Service) has launched a new data sharing scheme that will allow the **NHS** and other social service providers to share more information.

Virtual Private Networks (VPN)

- A **Virtual Private Network** (VPN) is a technology that establishes a **secure computer network** over the **public internet**, allowing users to access their **organization's network** while safeguarding the **confidentiality** and **integrity** of **transmitted information**.
- VPNs also enhance **online privacy** and **anonymity** by creating a **private network** within the **public internet**, **protecting user data** from **potential surveillance**.

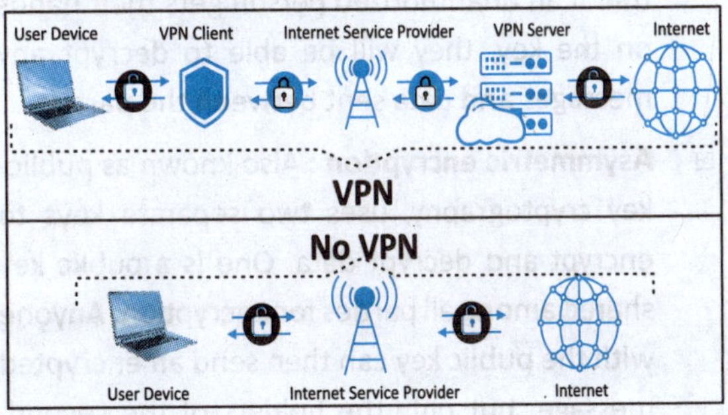

Types of VPN

- **Secure Sockets Layer :** It enables individual users to access an organization's network and client-server applications without the need for specialized software.

- **Site-to-site-VPN :** A private network designed to hide private intranets and allow users of these secure networks to access each other's resources.
- **Client-to-Server VPN :** User is not connected to the internet via his own ISP (Internet service provider), but establishing a direct connection through VPN provider.

Encryption

- Encryption is the process of **protecting information** or **data** by using **mathematical models** to scramble it in such a way that only the parties who have the key to unscramble it can access it.
- Encryption works by **encoding plaintext** into **ciphertext**, typically through the use of **cryptographic mathematical models** known as **algorithms**. To decode the data back to plaintext requires the use of a **decryption key**, a **string of numbers** or a **password** also created by an **algorithm**.

Types of Encryption

- **Symmetric encryption :** Also known as a shared key or private key algorithm, uses the same key for encryption and decryption. The drawback is that if an unauthorized person gets their hands on the key, they will be able to decrypt any messages and data sent between the parties.
- **Asymmetric encryption :** Also known as public-key cryptography, uses two separate keys to encrypt and decrypt data. One is a public key shared among all parties for encryption. Anyone with the public key can then send an encrypted message, but only the holders of the second, private key can decrypt the message.

Computer Viruses and Cyber threats

Malware

- Malware is the shortened form of **malicious software**. Malware is an umbrella term used to refer to a variety of forms of hostile or intrusive softwares including **Ransom wares, Computer Viruses, Worms, Trojan Horses, Spyware, Adware, Scareware** etc.

Malware is any program or file that is **harmful** to a **computer user**. The term refers to **software** that is deployed with malicious intent.

- Malware can be deployed even **remotely**, and tracking the source of malware is hard. It can take the form of executable code, scripts, active content, and other software.
- These malicious programs can perform a variety of functions, including **stealing, encrypting** or **deleting sensitive data, altering or hijacking core computing functions** and monitoring users' computer activity without their permission.

The term **Malware** was first used by computer scientist and security research **Yisrael Radai** in **1990**. Before the term malware, **malicious software** was referred to as **computer viruses.**

- One of the **first known examples** of malware was the **Creeper virus** in **1971**, which was created as an experiment by **BBN Technologies** engineer **Robert Thomas.**
- **Applications of Malware :**
  - To **steal information** that can be readily **monetized**, such as **login credentials**, credit card and bank account numbers,
  - To **steal intellectual property** such as computer software, financial algorithms, and trade secrets.
  - To **ransom money** in **Bitcoin** as Wannacry Ransomware.
  - Spy on computer users for an extended period without their knowledge, for example, **Reign Malware.**
  - To cause harm, or sabotage, for example **Stuxnet.**
  - **Extort payment** for example Cryptolocker.

Important Malwares

- **Adware:** The least dangerous and most lucrative Malware. Adware displays ads on computer.
- **Spyware:** Spyware is software that spies on user, tracking internet activities in order to send advertising (Adware) back to the user system.
- **Virus:** A virus is a contagious program or code that attaches itself to another piece of software, and then reproduces itself when that software is run. Most often this is spread by sharing software or files between computers.
- **Spam:** Spamming is a method of flooding the Internet with copies of the same message. Most spams are commercial advertisements which are sent as an unwanted email to users. Spams are also known as Electronic junk emails or junk newsgroup postings.
- **Worm:** A program that replicates itself and destroys data and files on the computer. Worms work to **eat the system operating files** and data files until the drive is empty.
- **Trojan:** A Trojan horse or Trojan is a type of malware that is often disguised as legitimate software. Trojans are written with the purpose of **discovering financial information** of the user taking over your computer's system resources, and in larger systems creating a **denial-of-service attack** which is making a machine or network resource unavailable to those attempting to reach it. Like making network services unavailable.
- **Backdoors:** Backdoors are much the same as **Trojans** or **worms**, except that they open a backdoor on a computer, providing a network connection for hackers or other Malware to enter or for **viruses** or **SPAM** to be sent.
- **Rootkit:** It is the hardest of all Malware to detect and therefore to remove; many experts recommend completely wiping your hard drive and reinstalling everything from scratch. It is designed to permit the other information gathering Malware in to get the identity information from computer without the user realising anything is going on.
- **Keyloggers:** Records everything you type on PC in order to glean log-in names, passwords, and other sensitive information, and send it on to the source of the keylogging program. Many times keyloggers are used by corporations and parents to acquire computer usage information.
- **Rogue security software:** This one deceives or misleads users. It pretends to be a good program to remove Malware infections, but all the while it is the Malware. Often it will turn off the real Anti-Virus software.
- **Ransomware:** If you see this screen that warns you that you have been locked out of your computer until you pay for your cybercrimes. Even if you pay to unlock the system, the system is unlocked, but you are not free of it locking you out again.
- **Browser Hijacker:** When your homepage changes to one that looks like those in the images inserted next, you may have been infected with one form or another of a Browser Hijacker. This dangerous Malware will redirect your normal search activity and give you the results the developers want you to see. Its intention is to make money off your web surfing. Using this homepage and not removing the Malware lets the source developers capture your surfing interests.

Modes of Malware infection

- **Email: Cybercriminals** are notorious for including **malicious attachments** and **links** in **emails** that appear to come from friends, reputable organisations, or other trusted sources. Some malicious emails can even infect the computer from the email client's preview pane, without the user opening or downloading an attachment or a link.

- **Internet: Surfing the Web** may feel like a private activity, but in fact, exposing computer to unwanted contact with anyone else who has a computer and Internet access.
- **Outdated software:** Malwares can crawl the Internet, looking for **vulnerabilities** of **outmoded** software to spread its influence over computer systems.
- **Local Area Networks (LANs):** A LAN is a group of **locally connected computers** that can share information over a private network. If one computer becomes infected with malware, all other computers in the LAN may quickly become infected as well.
- **Instant messaging (IM) and peer-to-peer (P2P) file-sharing systems:** If one is using a client for these online activities, malware may spread to the users computer.
- **Social networks:** Malware authors take advantage of many popular social networks, infecting the massive user-data networks with worms. If a social website account is infected with a worm, just about anyone who visits a poster's profile page could **catch** the worm on their system.
- **Pop-ups:** Some of the most sophisticated malware spreads through well-disguised screen pop-ups that look like genuine alerts or messages. One particularly devious and widespread **hoax pop-up** claims to have scanned your computer and detected malware. An attempt to remove the malware ends up, actually installing the malware.
- **Computer storage media:** Malware can be easily spread if you share computer storage media with others, such as **USB drives**, **DVDs**, and **CDs**. While it may seem safe to open a CD of photos from a colleague, it's always best to scan unfamiliar files first for possible corruptions or security risks before you copy or open them.
- **Mobile devices:** Mobile malware threats have become increasingly prevalent, as more people use their smartphones and tablets as mini-computers, helping malware problems proliferate across additional platforms.

Wannacry Ransomware

- **Ransomware:** A type of computer malware that encrypts the files, **storage media** on **communication devices** like **desktops**, **Laptops**, **Mobile phones** etc., holding data/ information as a hostage. The victim is asked to pay the demanded ransom to get his device decrypts.
- WannaCry is **Encrypting Ransomware** or **Crypto Locker type of ransomware** that is programmed to attack Microsoft Windows software.
- According to some statistics, hackers extorted business and institutions for more than $209 million in Ransomware payments in the first three months of 2016. The business of Ransomware is on pace to be a $1 billion a year crime.

In **2017 May**, there was a massive global ransomware attack. The attack infected more than **230,000 computers** in **150 countries** including India, demanding ransom payments in bitcoin in 28 languages.

- **Shadow Brokers:** People (Hackers) behind these attacks call themselves by this term.
- Another type of ransomware that is frequently circulated is **Locker ransomware**, which locks the victim out of the operating system, making it impossible to access the desktop and any apps or files.

CryptoLocker, like **WannaCry**, is a malware when injected into a host system, scans the hard drive of the victim and targets specific file extensions and encrypts them.

- **Wannacry encrypts the files** on an infected computer. It spreads by using a **vulnerability** in implementations of **Server Message Block** (SMB) of **Windows systems**. This exploit is known as **ETERNALBLUE**. It encrypts hard disk/drive and then spread laterally between computers on the same LAN. It also spreads through the malicious Email-attachment.

Cybercrimes

Cybercrime refers to any **unlawful act** where **computer** or **communication device** or computer network is used to commit or facilitate the commission of a crime.

Types of Cybercrimes

- **Child Pornography OR Child sexually abusive material (CSAM)** : It refers to a material containing **sexual images** in any form, of a child who is abused or sexually exploited.

Section 67 (B) of the **IT Act** states that it is punishable for **publishing** or **transmitting** of **material depicting children** in the **sexually explicit act**, etc. in **electronic form**.

- **Cyber Bullying** : A form of harassment or bullying inflicted through the use of electronic or communication devices such as computers, mobile phones, laptops, etc.
- **Cyber Stalking** : Cyberstalking is the use of electronic communication by a person to follow a person, or attempts to contact a person to foster personal interaction repeatedly despite a clear indication of disinterest by such person; or monitors the internet, email or any other form of electronic communication commits the offence of stalking.
- **Cyber Grooming** : Cyber Grooming is when a person builds an online relationship with a young person and tricks or pressures him/ her into doing a sexual act.
- **Online Job Fraud** : It is an attempt to defraud people who are in need of employment by giving them false hope/ promise of better employment with higher wages.
- **Online Sextortion** : It occurs when someone threatens to distribute private and sensitive material using an electronic medium if he/ she doesn't provide sexual favours gratification or money.
- **Phishing** : Phishing is a type of fraud that involves stealing personal information such as Customer ID, IPIN, Credit/Debit Card number, Card expiry date, CVV number, etc. through emails that appear to be from a legitimate source.
- **Vishing** : Vishing is an attempt where fraudsters try to seek personal information like Customer ID, Net Banking password, ATM PIN, OTP, Card expiry date, CVV etc. through a phone call.
- **Smishing** : Smishing is a type of fraud that uses mobile phone text messages to lure victims into calling back on a fraudulent phone number, visiting fraudulent websites or downloading malicious content via phone or web.
- **Sexting** : Sexting is an act of sending sexually explicit digital images, videos, text messages, or emails, usually by cell phone.
- **SIM Swap Scam** : SIM Swap Scam occurs when fraudsters manage to get a new SIM card issued against a registered mobile number fraudulently through the mobile service provider. With the help of this new SIM card, they get One Time Password (OTP) and alerts, required for making financial transactions through the victim's bank account. Getting a new SIM card against a registered mobile number fraudulently is known as SIM Swap.
- **Credit Card Fraud or Debit Card Fraud** : It involves the unauthorized use of another's credit or debit card information for the purpose of purchases or withdrawing funds from it.

- **Impersonation and identity theft :** An act of fraudulently or dishonestly making use of the electronic signature, password or any other unique identification feature of any other person.
- **Spamming :** Spamming occurs when someone receives an unsolicited commercial message sent via email, SMS, MMS and any other similar electronic messaging media. They may try to persuade the recipient to buy a product or service, or visit a website where he can make purchases, or they may attempt to trick him/ her into divulging bank account or credit card details.
- **Data Breach :** A data breach is an incident in which information is accessed without authorization.
- **Denial of Services (DoS) attack :** A denial of Services (DoS) attack is an attack intended for denying access to computer resources without the permission of the owner or any other person who is in charge of a computer, computer system or computer network.
- **Website Defacement :** Website Defacement is an attack intended to change the visual appearance of a website and/ or make it dysfunctional. The attacker may post indecent, hostile and obscene images, messages, videos, etc.
- **Cyber-Squatting :** Cyber-Squatting is an act of registering, trafficking in or using a domain name with an intent to profit from the goodwill of a trademark belonging to someone else.
- **Pharming :** A cyber-attack aiming to redirect a website's traffic to another, bogus website.
- **Cryptojacking :** Unauthorized use of computing resources to mine cryptocurrencies.
- **Online Drug Trafficking :** A crime of selling, transporting, or illegally importing unlawful controlled substances, such as heroin, cocaine, marijuana, or other illegal drugs using electronic means.
- **Cyber Espionage :** An act or practice of obtaining data and information without the permission and knowledge of the owner.

Dark Net

- Part of the internet that is readily available to general public and searchable on standard search engines is called as **Surface Web.**

- **Dark net** refers to a part of the internet that is intentionally hidden and not indexed by search engines like Google. It is a subset of the deep web, which encompasses all web content that is not indexed by traditional search engines and includes things like private databases, password-protected websites, and other non-public information.
- It generally uses **non-standard communication protocols** which make it **inaccessible to internet service providers** (ISPs) or government authorities.

> Content on Dark Net is encrypted and requires specific browser such as **TOR (The Onion Router)** browser to access those pages.

- The darknet raises concerns due to **anonymity**, enabling **illicit activities** like drug dealing and terrorist communication, posing privacy and ethical dilemmas.
- It offers both legitimate uses and opportunities for illegal acts, necessitating vigilance to balance

personal privacy with combating criminality and potential security threats.

Cyberspace and Cyber attacks

- **Cyberspace** occupies a key position in national security, and comprises of an **interactive domain** made up of **digital networks** that is used to **store**, **analyse**, **modify** and **communicate information**.
- Our dependence on cyberspace has immensely increased in all fields: **economic**, **military**, **diplomatic**, **social interactions**, **transportation**, **banking transactions**, **education** and **science & technology**.
- Alongside, cyberattacks on **critical infrastructure** have also increased. The cyberattacks can **disable official websites and networks**, **disrupt**, or **disable essential services**, **steal**, or **alter classified data**, and **cripple financial and military systems**, i.e., they can affect all components of national power. More importantly, it can also push the hostile narrative through influence operations to weaponize the public opinion in favour of a rival state.
- India is in a **critical phase of digitalisation**, with a growing digital presence in the **government and private sectors** providing **services** to its citizens, as well as in **economic** and **national security infrastructures**.
- The digital surface has significantly expanded, which gives more opportunities for cyber-attackers. All critical infrastructures, both in private and governmental sectors, are totally dependent on cyber technologies for management, control, and operations.
- Even **physical security depends** on **CCTV cameras**, which are dependent on cyberspace. These infrastructures are being increasingly targeted, and the attacks are becoming more sophisticated and devasting.
- India is witnessing increasing cyberattacks on its critical infrastructure.
    - In 2019, **Kudankulum Nuclear Power Plant** (KKNPP) was under cyberattack.
    - In **2020**, the **Mumbai Power Grid** was attacked, causing a massive power outage, stopping trains on tracks, and disrupting economic operations. Later, it was found that 14 Trojans were placed on the server and the attack was traced to a **Chinese entity**.
    - In **2021**, **Airtel** and **Air India** servers were attacked.
    - In **2022**, several ransomware attacks were reported, which included Oil India Limited, and Spice Jet servers.
    - A serious cyberattack occurred on the Goa Flood Monitoring System, which was traced to a Chinese entity, **RedEcho**.
    - A cyberattack on **Delhi's AIIMS** impacted its five servers and about **1.3 TB data** was encrypted. While the banking system reported **248 serious attacks** on its sector between **2018** and **2022**,
    - Cert-In **tracked 13.91** lakh incidents in **2022**. Significantly, cyberattacks on governmental agencies more than doubled in 2022, indicating an increase in state-sponsored attacks.

Critical Infrastructure

- Those **assets**, **systems**, and networks that provide functions necessary for our way of life.
- There are **16 critical infrastructure sectors** whose **assets**, **systems** and **networks** (both physical and virtual) are part of a complex, interconnected ecosystem, are considered so vital to a country that their incapacitation or destruction would have a debilitating effect on security, national economic security, national public health or safety, or any combination thereof.

16 Critical Infrastructure Sectors	
• Communications	• Chemical
• Critical Manufacturing	• Comercial Facilities
• Defence Industrial Base	• Dams
• Emergency Services	• Energy
• Government Facilities	• Financial
• Transportation Systems	• Water
• Information Technology	• Food and Agriculture
• Healthcare and Public Health	
• Nuclear Reactors, Materials and Waste	

- The damage to a critical infrastructure, its **destruction** or **disruption** by **natural disasters, terrorism, criminal activity** or **malicious behaviour**, may have a significant negative impact for the security of the country and the well-being of its citizens.
- The **Information Technology Act, 2000** defines **Critical Information Infrastructure** (CII) as those computer resource, the destruction of which, shall have debilitating impact on national security, economy, public health or safety.

National Critical Information Infrastructure Protection Centre (NCIIPC) has identified the following as Critical Sectors:

- Power & Energy
- Banking, Financial Services & Insurance
- Telecom
- Transport
- Government
- Strategic & Public Enterprises

Government Initiatives

- **National Cyber Security Policy 2013:** Indian Government already have a National Cyber Security Policy in place. The National Cyber Security Policy document outlines a roadmap to create a framework for comprehensive, collaborative and collective response to deal with the issue of cyber security at all levels within the country.
- **Computer Emergency Response Team** (CERT-In) has been designated to act as a nodal agency for coordination of crisis management efforts. CERT-In will also act as an umbrella organisation for coordination actions and operationalization of sectoral CERTs. CERT-in will also issue early warnings.
- **Cyber Swachhta Kendra:** The **Cyber Swachhta Kendra** is a **Botnet Cleaning and Malware Analysis Centre** (BCMAC), operated by the **Indian Computer Emergency Response Team** (CERT-In) as part of the Government of India's Digital India initiative under the Ministry of Electronics and Information Technology (MeitY). Its goal is to create a secure cyberspace by detecting botnet infections in India and to notify, enable cleaning and securing systems of end users so as to prevent further infections.

PRACTICE PYQs-

Q. With reference to 'LiFi', recently in the news, which of the following statements is/are correct? 2016

1. It uses light as the medium for high-speed data transmission.
2. It is a wireless technology and is many times faster than 'WiFi.

Select the correct answer using the code given below:

(a) 1 only (b) 2 only
(c) Both 1 and 2 (d) Neither 1 nor 2

Q. With reference to Visible Light Communication (VLC) technology, which of the following statements are correct? 2020

1. VLC uses electromagnetic spectrum wavelengths 375 to 780 nm.
2. VLC is known as long-range optical wireless communication.
3. VLC can transmit large amounts of data faster than Bluetooth
4. VLC has no electromagnetic interference.

Select the correct answer using the code given below:

(a) 1, 2 and 3 only (b) 1, 2 and 4 only
(c) 1, 3 and 4 only (d) 2, 3 and 4 only

Q. Consider the following pairs : 2018

Terms sometimes seen in news	Context /Topic
1. Belle II experiment	-Artificial Intelligence
2. Blockchain technology	-Digital/Cryptocurrency
3. CRISPR — Cas9	- Particle Physics

Which of the pairs given above is/are correctly matched ?

(a) 1 and 3 only (b) 2 only
(c) 2 and 3 only (d) 1, 2 and 3

Q. Consider the following communication technologies:

1. Closed-circuit Television
2. Radio Frequency Identification
3. Wireless Local Area Network

Which of the above are considered of Short-Range devices/technologies?

(a) 1 and 2 only (b) 2 and 3 only
(c) 1 and 3 only (d) 1, 2 and 3

Q. When the alarm of your smartphone rings in the morning, you wake up and tap it to stop the alarm which causes your geyser to be switched on automatically. The smart mirror in your bathroom shows the day's weather and also indicates the level of water in your overhead tank. After you take some groceries from your refrigerator for making breakfast, it recognises the shortage of stock in it and places an order for the supply of fresh grocery items.When you step out of your house and lock the door, all lights, fans, geysers and AC machines get switched off automatically. On your way to the office, your car warns you about traffic congestion ahead and suggests an alternative route, and if you are late for a meeting, it sends a- message to your office accordingly.

In the context of emerging communication technologies, which one of the following terms " best" applies to the above scenario? 2018

(a) Border Gateway Protocol
(b) Internet of Things
(c) Internet Protocol
(d) Virtual Private Network

Q. "3D printing" has applications in which of the following? 2018

1. Preparation of confectionery items
2. Manufacture of bionic ears
3. Automotive industry
4. Reconstructive surgeries
5. Data processing technologies

Select the correct answer using the code given below :

(a) 1, 3 and 4 only (b) 2, 3 and 5 only
(c) 1 and 4 only (d) 1, 2, 3, 4 and 5

Q. With reference to communication technologies, what is/are the difference/ differences between LTE (Long-Term Evolution) and VoLTE (Voice over Long-Term Evolution)? 2019

1. LTE is commonly marketed as 3G and VoLTE is commonly marketed as advanced 3G.
2. LTE is data-only technology and VoLTE is voice-only technology.

Select the correct answer using the code given below.

(a) 1 only (b) 2 only
(c) Both 1 and 2 (d) Neither 1 nor 2

Q. In the context of digital technologies for entertainment, consider the following statements: 2019

1. In Augmented Reality (AR), a simulated environment is created and the physical world is completely shut out.
2. In Virtual Reality (VR), images generated from a computer are projected into real-life objects or surroundings.
3. AR allows individuals to be present in the world and improves the experience using the camera of smart-phone or PC.
4. VR closes the world, and transposes an individual, providing complete immersion experience.

Which of the statements given above is/are correct?

(a) 1 and 2 only (b) 3 and 4
(c) 1, 2 and 3 (d) 4 only

Q. In the context of wearable technology, which of the following tasks is/are accomplished by wearable devices? 2019

1. Location identification of a person
2. Sleep monitoring of a person
3. Assisting the hearing impaired person

Select the correct answer using the code given below:

(a) 1 only (b) 2 and 3 only
(c) 3 only (d) 1, 2 and 3

Q. Consider the following activities: 2020

1. Spraying pesticides on a crop field
2. Inspecting the craters of active volcanoes
3. Collecting breath samples from spouting whales for DNA analysis

At the present level of technology, which of the above activities can be successfully carried out by using drones?

(a) 1 and 2 only (b) 2 and 3 only
(c) 1 and 3 only (d) 1,2 and 3

Q. In India, the term "Public Key Infrastructure" is used in the context of (2020)

(a) Digital security infrastructure
(b) Food security infrastructure
(c) Health care and education infrastructure
(d) Telecommunication and transportation infrastructure

Q. With reference to "Blockchain Technology", consider the following statements: 2020

1. It is a public ledger that everyone can inspect, but which no single user controls.
2. The structure and design of blockchain is such that all the data in it are about cryptocurrency only.
3. Applications that depend on basic features of blockchain can be developed without anybody's permission.

Which of the statements given above is/are correct?

(a) 1 only (b) 1 and 2 only
(c) 2 only (d) 1 and 3 only

Q. 'Project Loon', sometimes seen in the news, is related to (2016)

(a) Waste management technology
(b) Wireless communication technology
(c) Solar power production technology
(d) Water conservation technology

Q. With reference to Web 3.0, consider the following statements: 2022

1. Web 3.0 technology enables people to control their own data.
2. In Web 3.0 world, there can be blockchain-based social networks.
3. Web 3.0 is operated by users collectively rather than a corporation

Which of the following given above are correct?

(a) 1 and 2 only (b) 2 and 3 only
(c) 1 and 3 only (d) 1, 2 and 3

Q. With reference to "Software as a Service", Consider the following statements. 2022

1. SaaS buyers can customise the user interface and can change data fields.
2. SaaS users can access their data through their mobile devices.
3. Outlook, Hotmail and Yahoo! Mail are forms of SaaS.

Which of the statements given above are correct?

(a) 1 and 2 only (b) 2 and 3 only
(c) 1 and 3 only (d) 1, 2 and 3

Q. With reference to 'Near Field Communication (NFC) Technology', which of the following statements is/are correct? 2015

1. It is a contactless communication technology that uses electromagnetic radio fields.
2. NFC is designed for use by devices which can be at a distance of even a metre from each other
3. NFC can use encryption when sending sensitive information.

Select the correct answer using the code given below.

(a) 1 and 2 only (b) 3 only
(c) 1 and 3 only (d) 1,2 and 3

Q. Discuss the advantage and security implications of cloud hosting of servers vis-à-vis in-house machine-based hosting for government businesses. (2015)

Q. What are the different elements of cyber security? Keeping in view the challenges in cyber security examine the extent to which India has successfully developed a comprehensive National Cyber Security Strategy. (2022)

Q. Social media and encrypting messaging services pose a serious security challenge. What measures have been adopted at various levels to address the security implications of social media? Also suggest any other remedies to address the problem. (UPSC Mains 2024)

Q. Describe the context and salient features of the Digital Personal Data Protection Act, 2023. (UPSC Mains 2024)

UNIT 6

INDUSTRIAL REVOLUTION 4.0, ARTIFICIAL INTELLIGENCE AND RELATED TECHNOLOGIES

- *Prior to the **Industrial Revolution**, which began in **Britain** in the **late 1700s**, manufacturing was done in people's homes known as **Cottage Industries**, using hand tools or basic machines, which were enormously labour intensive. Industrialization marked a shift to powered, special-purpose machinery, factories and mass production. **Ion** and **textile industries** became the mainstay of Industrial revolution. From cooking appliances to ships, all had components of iron and steel. The process went in hyper drive with the advent of steam engine and ships.*
- ***Industry 4.0** also called the **Fourth Industrial Revolution/ 4IR** is the next phase in the digitization of the manufacturing sector, driven by disruptive trends including the rise of data and connectivity, analytics, human-machine interaction, and improvements in robotics.*
- ***Fourth Industrial Revolution** (4IR or Industry 4.0) is the ongoing automation of traditional manufacturing and industrial practices, using modern smart technology.*
- *Industry 4.0 concepts and technologies can be applied across all types of industrial companies, including discrete and process manufacturing, as well as **oil** and **gas**, **mining** and **other industrial segments**.*

Industry 4.0

Industry 1.0
Water and steam power to mechanise production (1765).

Industry 2.0
Electric power to create mass production (1870).

Industry 3.0
Electronics & information technology to automate production (1969).

Industry 4.0
Cyber physical system, internet of things, networks. (Present time)

- **4IR** builds on the inventions of the Third Industrial Revolution or digital revolution which unfolded from the 1950s and to the early 2000s and brought us computers, other kinds of electronics, the Internet, and much more.
- Industry 4.0 brings these inventions beyond the previous realm of possibility with four foundational types of disruptive technologies (examples below) that can be applied all along the value chain:
  - **Connectivity, data, and computational power** : Cloud technology, the Internet, blockchain, sensors analytics and intelligence: advanced analytics, machine learning, artificial intelligence.
  - **Analytics and intelligence** : Advanced analytics, machine learning, artificial intelligence.
  - **Human machine interaction** : Virtual reality (VR) and augmented reality (AR), robotics and automation, autonomous guided vehicles.
  - **Advanced engineering** : Additive manufacturing (such as, 3-D printing), renewable energy, nanoparticles.

Industrial Revolution 4.0

- Fourth Industrial Revolution (IR 4.0) is a term that describes **present technological age.**

> The term **Industry 4.0** was coined by the **German government** in **2011. Industry 4.0** refers to a new phase in the Industrial Revolution that focuses heavily on **interconnectivity, automation, machine learning** and **real-time data.**

- The key elements of the fourth revolution are the **fusion of technologies** ranging from the **physical, digital to biological spheres.**

> As described by the founder and executive chairman of **World Economic Forum, Klaus Schwab**, - the Fourth Industrial Revolution is a **technological revolution** that will fundamentally alter the way we live, work and relate to one another.

- Industry 4.0, which encompasses **IoTs** and **smart manufacturing**, integrates **physical production** and **operations** with **smart digital technology, machine learning** and **big data.**
- **Processed artificial intelligence** has broken the distinction between **Man, Machine** and **Intelligence.**

Important Concepts under 4IR

- **Enterprise resource planning (ERP) :** It is an essential tool for business process management. It is used for managing information across the organization.
- **The Internet of Things (IoT) :** It refers to connections between physical industrial objects, such as machines or sensors, and the internet.
- **Industrial Internet of Things (IIoT) :** It is the link between human resources, data, and machines/ equipment related to manufacturing.
- **Big Data:** A large set of structure and unstructured data compiled, stored, analyzed, and organized to disclose patterns, associations, trends, and opportunities.
- **Artificial Intelligence :** It refers to the computer's ability to perform tasks and make decisions historically requiring human intelligence.
- **Digitization:** It refers to the method of collecting information and converting them into a digital format.
- **Machine-to-machine (M2M) :** It is a communication taking place between two distinct machines through wired or wireless networks.
- **Smart Factory :** It is a facility that invests in and leverages Industry 4.0 technologies, approaches, and solutions.
- **Cloud Computing:** The act of using multiple interconnected remote servers on the internet for storing, managing, and processing information.
- **Real-time Data Processing:** Computer systems and machines can automatically and continuously process data to provide real-time or simply near-time outputs plus insights.
- **Ecosystem:** In manufacturing, an ecosystem means the potential connection or connectedness of the entire operation, including inventory planning, financials, supply chain management, customer relationships, manufacturing execution, etc.
- **Cyber-physical System (CPS):** Also called cyber manufacturing, is the Industry 4.0-enabled environment for manufacturing, which provides real-time data collection and analysis, with transparency across different aspects of the manufacturing operations. Cyber-Physical Systems form the backbone of Industrial Revolution 4.0. They are defined as the merge of our physical, virtual and digital systems into an intelligent system. They create a tighter integration between humans, machines and information technology systems.

- **3 progressive stages of Industry 4.0 transformation :**
  - **STAGE 1: Digital connectivity and sensors -** Integration and automation, IoT solutions, AI, cloud and advanced analytics.
  - **STAGE 2: Digital engineering** - Using Industry 4.0 technologies to enhance product design and supply chains, develop smart products and cultivate upstream and downstream connected ecosystems. Full digital engineering process, includes increasingly intelligent automation and blockchain-based smart contracts.
  - **STAGE 3: Digital Operations-** Using Industry 4.0 capabilities to carve out greater differentiation in fields involving bioinformatics, nanotechnology and quantum technologies.
- **4 design principles identified as integral to Industry 4.0 :**
  - **Interconnection** : Aility of machines, devices, sensors, and people to connect and communicate with each other via the Internet of things or the internet of people (IoP).
  - **Information transparency** : Transparency afforded by Industry 4.0 technology provides operators with comprehensive information to make decisions. Inter-connectivity allows operators to collect immense amounts of data and information from all points in the manufacturing process, identify key areas that can benefit from improvement to increase functionality.
  - **Technical assistance** : Technological facility of systems to assist humans in decision-making and problem-solving, and the ability to help humans with difficult or unsafe tasks.
  - **Decentralized decisions** : Ability of cyber physical systems to make decisions on their own and to perform their tasks as autonomously as possible. Only in the case of exceptions, the tasks are delegated to a higher level.

Characteristics of IR 4.0

- **IR 4.0** is characterized by a fusion of technologies that is blurring the lines between the **physical, digital**, and **biological spheres.**
- It brings together **digital technology** and the **physical world** to create a new **range of products** and **services.**
- It explores unlimited possibilities of billions of people connected by **mobile devices**, with **unprecedented processing power, storage capacity** and **access to knowledge**, multiplied by emerging technology breakthroughs in fields such as **Cognitive computing, artificial intelligence, robotics, the Internet of Things, autonomous vehicles, 3-D printing, nanotechnology, biotechnology, materials science, energy storage** and **quantum computing.**
- Product customisation/personalisation and comparatively greater automation.

Significance of IR 4.0

- It has the **potential to raise global income levels** and improve the **quality of life for populations around the world.**
- It will lead to **supply-side miracle**, with **long-term gains** in **efficiency** and **productivity.**
- **Transportation and communication costs** will **drop, logistics** and **global supply chains** will become more **effective**, and the **cost of trade** will diminish, opening new markets driving **economic growth.**
- Governments will **gain new technological powers** to increase their control over populations, based on **pervasive surveillance systems** and the ability to **control digital infrastructure.**
- Advances in technology will create the potential to **reduce the scale** or **impact of violence,** through the development of new modes of threat perception protection, greater precision targeting.

Scope and Dimensions of IR 4.0

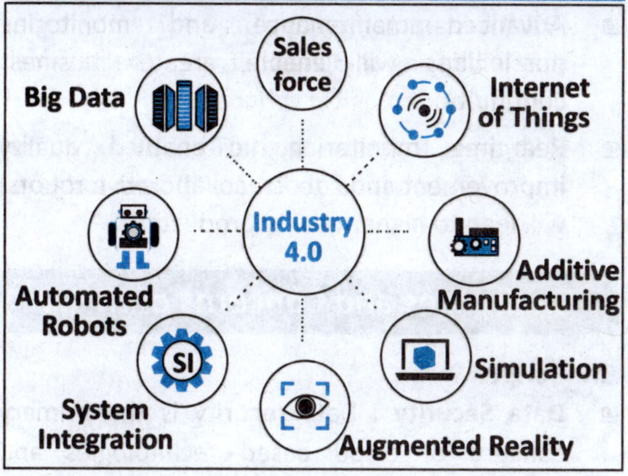

- Synonymous with smart manufacturing, Industry 4.0 is the realization of the digital transformation of the field, delivering real-time decision making, enhanced productivity, flexibility and agility.
- Industry 4.0 is revolutionizing the way companies manufacture, improve and distribute their products. Manufacturers are integrating new technologies, including Internet of Things (IoT), cloud computing and analytics, and AI and machine learning into their production facilities and throughout their operations.
- These smart factories are equipped with advanced sensors, embedded software and robotics that collect and analyze data and allow for better decision making.
- Even higher value is created when data from production operations is combined with operational data from ERP, supply chain, customer service and other enterprise systems to create whole new levels of visibility and insight from previously siloed information.
- This digital technologies have lead to increased automation, predictive maintenance, self-optimization of process improvements and, above all, a new level of efficiencies and responsiveness to customers not previously possible.
- Developing smart factories provides an incredible opportunity for the manufacturing industry to enter the fourth industrial revolution. Analyzing the large amounts of big data collected from sensors on the factory floor ensures real-time visibility of manufacturing assets and can provide tools for performing predictive maintenance in order to minimize equipment downtime.
- Using high-tech IoT devices in smart factories leads to higher productivity and improved quality.
- Replacing manual inspection business models with AI-powered visual insights reduces manufacturing errors and saves money and time. With minimal investment, quality control personnel can set up a smartphone connected to the cloud to monitor manufacturing processes from virtually anywhere.
- By applying machine learning algorithms, manufacturers can detect errors immediately, rather than at later stages when repair work is more expensive.
- Advanced data analysis will help its **manufacturing capacity** and increase the **quality** of the **product**.
- **Business Analytics** will work on the prediction and prevention of production defects.
- **Digitization of numerous manufacturing processes** will lead to **cost reduction** with an improved experience for consumers.
- The implementation of automation will **reduce manufacturing cycles, decrease cycle time** and reduce wasteful use of capital.
- **IoT** and **man-machine connectivity** will help supply chains to **decrease lead times.**
- India is moving towards becoming a hub of **global manufacturing, 3D printing, machine learning, data analytics** and **IoT** are key to promoting industrial growth,

> • In **November 2020, Modern Coach Factory** (MCF) at **Raebareli, Uttar Pradesh**, rolled out **smart railway coaches** that are fitted with a **battery of sensors** to provide a comfortable experience to passengers.

- In **May 2020**, the **Union Ministry of Heavy Industries** launched the **Smart Advanced Manufacturing** and **Rapid Transformation Hub** (SAMARTH) **scheme**, which brings together **manufacturers**, **vendors** and **customers** to make them aware of **4IR technologies.**
- In **2022's budget speech**, the Union Finance Minister announced a slew of new **4IR-driven projects,** including **Drone Shakti**, to encourage **start-ups** that will facilitate the use of drone services.

- India even has a **4IR centre** in **Mumbai** run by **WEF**, working closely with several state governments.
- The Centre has recently come up with the **Fourth Industrial Revolution for Sustainable Transformation** (FIRST) **Cancer Care model** in which 4IR technologies would be used to provide **better healthcare** for cancer patients

In **February 2022**, Government launched the **pan-India 3D maps programme** by **Genesys International** for the **100 smart cities.**

Advantages of 4IR

- **Competitive Advantage :** Industry revolution 4.0 could make your business more competitive, typically against disruptors such as Amazon.
- **Enhanced Appeal :** Industry 4.0 technologies also make you attractive and presentable to the youth workforce as well as clients.
- **Enhanced Efficiency :** Increases efficiency, enables prescriptive and predictive analysisa and lets the enterprise leverage the real-data for best insights.
- **Address Threats :** It empowers businesses to address potential threats and issues before they turn into more significant problems.
- **Cut Costs :** Cut costs, boost profit and increase growth with industry 4.0 technologies that optimize each and every aspect of the business.
- Optimization and automation leading to enhanced productivity.
- Real-time data for real-time supply chains in a real-time economy.
- Advanced maintenance and monitoring possibilities will enable greater business continuity.
- Real-time monitoring, IoT-enabled quality improvement and cobots (collaborative robots) will lead to higher quality products.

Challenges and Concerns of IR 4.0

Challenges

- **Data Security :** Data security is the primary concern of cloud based technologies and industry 4.0 technologies.
- **Human resources :** To adopt new technology, the frontline executives need training which can prove expensive.
- **Team Support :** Having team support is highly crucial when moving to new technology. The new model may be challenging to accept and adopt.
- **Leveraging Data :** You need training, knowledge, and documentation to understand the pottern to use data and improve, change or grow a business.
- **Inadequate digital infrastructure and Interlinking current skills with required level of digitalisation :** To adopt new technology, training is the prerequisites for frontline executives. Investing in Industry 4.0 incorporates both the structural and human resource investment (for training and skill upgradation).
- **Concerns regarding cyber security :** There is a constant threat of cybercrimes regarding customer data. Switching to the cloud makes the data vulnerable. There are also concerns regarding location of massive amounts of Data (to the server country or the host country, raising debates on Data Localisation). Data security is the primary concern of cloud-based technologies and Industrial 4.0 technologies.

- **Data Sensitivity :** Concerns over data and IP privacy, ownership, and management.
- **Handling Data Growth:** As more companies become dependent on AI usage, companies will be faced with more data that is being generated at a faster pace and presented in multiple formats. To wade through these vast amounts of data, AI algorithms need to be easier to comprehend.
- **Security Concerns over Interoperability :** Smart factories make real-time interoperability possible, however, it comes with the risk of an expanded attack surface. When numerous machines and devices are connected to single or multiple networks in a smart factory, vulnerabilities in any one of those pieces of equipment could make the system vulnerable to attack.

Concerns

- **IR 4.0** creates immediate threat of **job loss**, particularly in the **informal sector**.
- It could **yield greater inequality** owing to **digital divide**, particularly in its potential to **disrupt labor markets.**
- There are several other critical concerns surrounding **safety, ethics** and the **short- and long-term socio-economic impact** that remain unanswered.
- There is a growing concern that the **existing fallacies** in humans might only get more accentuated after 4IR.
- There are several studies that show how **facial recognition technologies** have a higher chance of **misidentifying African** and **Asian people** compared to their **Western counterparts**. It is also going to be skewed as developing and least developed countries **lack the data framework** and **infrastructure.**
- It will also profoundly impact the **nature** of **national** and **international security**, affecting both the **probability** and the **nature** of the **conflict**, leading to new **fears** and **threats.**

- One of the greatest individual challenges posed by **new information technologies is privacy.**

Biometric

Biometrics are **physical** or **biological characteristics** that identify a specific human being. The term biometrics is derived from the **Greek words- bio** meaning **life** and **metric** meaning to **measure.**

- Biometrics are **biological measurements** or **physical characteristics** that can be used to identify individuals.

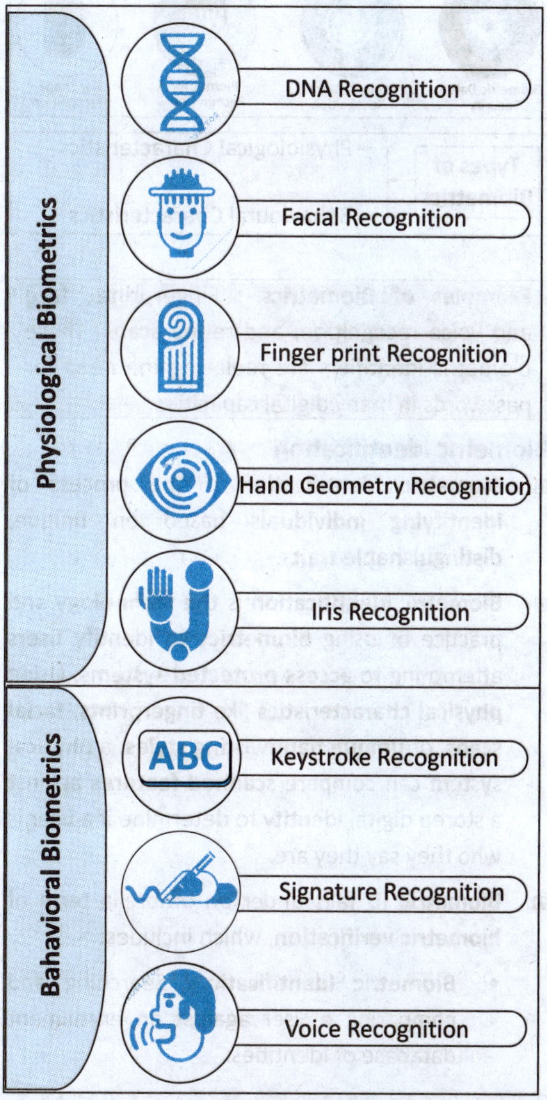

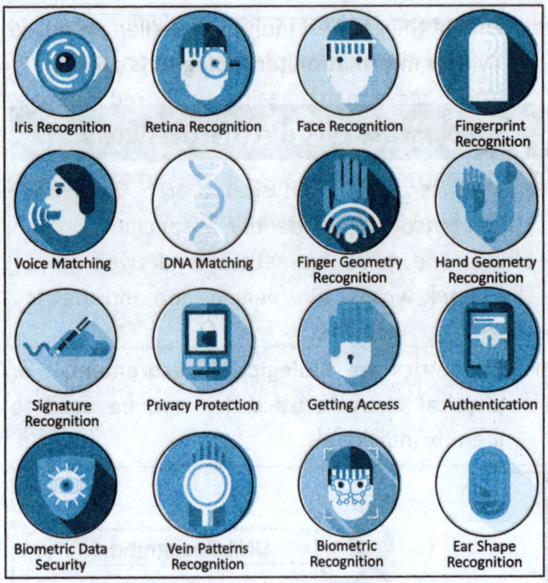

Types of Biometrics
- Physiological Characteristics
- Behavioural Characteristics

Examples of Biometrics : Fingerprints, face and voice recognition, and retina scans. These biometric identifiers are replacing the need for passwords in many digital capacities.

Biometric Identification

- **Biometric identification** is the process of **identifying individuals** based on unique, **distinguishable traits.**
- **Biometric identification** is the **technology** and practice of using **biometrics** to identify users attempting to **access protected systems**. Using **physical characteristics** like **fingerprints**, **facial scans**, or **unique handwriting styles**, a **physical system** can compare **scanned features** against a stored digital identity to determine if a user is who they say they are.
- **Biometric ID** falls under an umbrella term of **biometric verification**, which includes:
  - **Biometric Identification:** Searching and comparing a user against an enrollment database of identities.
  - **Biometric Verification:** Comparing user-submitted biometric information against the database information to verify identity.

Biometric Authentication

- Biometric authentication is defined as a security measure that matches the biometric features of a user looking to access a device or a system. Access to the system is granted only when the parameters match those stored in the database for that particular user.

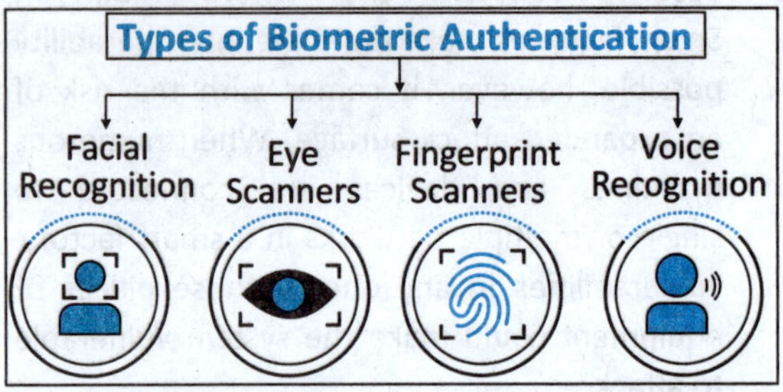

Biometric Verification	Biometric Authentication
Verification is the process of associating data stored with the individual seeking access.	Authentication ascertains whether the individual trying to gain access is who he/she is claiming to be.
Verification is where the data provided by the user is matched against previously collected and stored data.	In authentication, individuals answer dynamic questions that only they have the answers to. This determines whether they have the necessary credentials to access a system.
Verification is just an additional layer of security used by businesses.	Authentication adds a layer to the identity confirmation process and is particularly important in determining the authenticity of online transactions.

Benefits of Biometric Authentication for Enterprise security :
- Restricts access
- Records timeliness
- Enhances security measures

- Replaces passwords
- Minimizes human error
- Eases installation
- Offers reasonable coasts

Multi-Factor Authentication (MFA)

- MFA is defined as a form of security that necessitates two or more credentials to authenticate an individual's identity. They can be passwords, hardware tokens, numerical codes, biometrics, specific times, or even locations. The main benefit of multiple credentials is that even if one factor is compromised, the overall authentication process remains secure.
- The most common MFA factors are **one-time passwords** (OTPs) which are **4 to 8 digit codes** received through email, SMS, or even through mobile apps. There are three main types of MFA authentication methods:
  - **Knowledge:** A password or a pin.
  - **Possession:** A badge with a code or a smartphone to receive OTPs.
  - **Inherence:** Biometric recognition methods of fingerprints, voice, or eye scanners.

Types of Biometric Security

- **Biological biometrics :** It use traits at a genetic and molecular level. These may include features like **DNA** or **blood**, which might be assessed through a sample of body's fluids.
- **Morphological biometrics :** It involves the structure of body. More **physical traits** like your eye, fingerprint, or the shape of one's face can be mapped for use with security scanners.
- **Behavioral biometrics :** They are based on patterns unique to each person. How one walks, speaks, or even types on a keyboard can be an indication of his identity if these patterns are tracked.
- **Biometrics scanners** are hardware used to capture the biometric for verification of identity. These scans match against the saved database to approve or deny access to the system.
- **Biometric security** means the body becomes the **key** to unlock one's access.
- Biometrics are largely used because of two major benefits:
  - **Convenience of use:** Biometrics are always with you and cannot be lost or forgotten.
  - **Difficult to steal or impersonate:** Biometrics can't be stolen like a password or key can.

Types of Biometric Identification

Facial Recognition | Fingerprint verification | DNA matching

- **Fingerprint recognition** software verifies an **individual's identity** by comparing their fingerprint against one or more fingerprints in a database.
- **DNA matching** identifies an individual by analyzing segments from their **DNA**. The technology sequences the DNA in a lab and compares it with samples in a database.
- **Eye Recognition:** Analyzes features in the **iris** or patterns of the **veins** in the **retina** to determine a match and identify an individual.
- **Hand geometry recognition :** Individuals can be identified through the **geometric features / patterns** of their hands, such as the length of the fingers and width of the hand. A camera captures a silhouette image of the hand and compares it against a database.
- **Voice recognition systems :** They extract the characteristics that distinguish an individual's speech from others. It creates a **voiceprint** that is similar to a fingerprint or faceprint and matches it to samples in a database.

- **Signature recognition :** The technology to can be used analyze handwriting style or compare two scanned signatures using advanced algorithms.

Facial Recognition

- A face analyzer is **software** that **identifies** or **confirms** a **person's identity** using their face. It works by **identifying** and **measuring facial features** in an image.
- **Facial recognition** can **identify human faces** in **images** or **videos**, determine if the face in two images belongs to the same person, or search for a face among a large collection of existing images.
- **Biometric security systems** use **facial recognition to uniquely identify individuals** during user **onboarding** or **logins** as well as strengthen user **authentication activity.** Mobile and personal devices also commonly use face analyzer technology for device security.

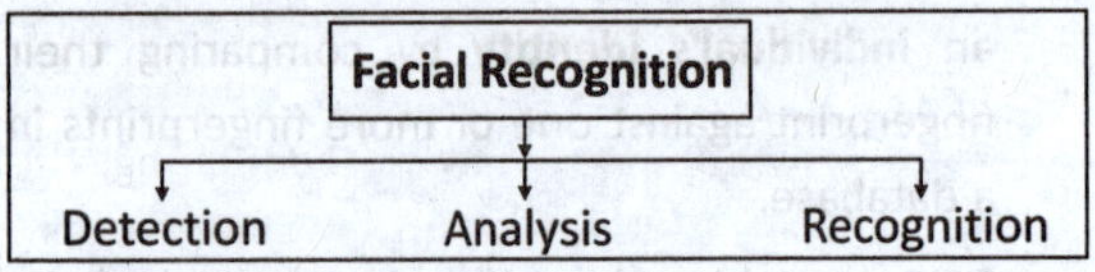

- **Detection :** Detection is the process of finding a face in an image. Enabled by computer vision, facial recognition can detect and identify individual faces from an image containing one or many people's faces in both front and side face profiles.

> **Computer Vision :** Machines use computer vision to identify people, places, and things in images with accuracy at or above human levels and with much greater speed and efficiency. Using complex **artificial intelligence** (AI) **technology**, computer vision automates **extraction, analysis, classification**, and understanding of useful information from image data.

- **Analysis :** The facial recognition system then analyzes the image of the face. It **maps** and **reads face geometry** and **facial expressions.** It identifies **facial landmarks** that are key to distinguishing a face from other objects. The system then converts the face recognition data into a **string of numbers** or **points** called a **faceprint.** Each person has a unique faceprint, similar to a fingerprint. The information used by facial recognition can also be used in reverse to digitally reconstruct a person's face.
- **Recognition :** Facial recognition can identify a person by comparing the faces in two or more images and assessing the likelihood of a face match.

Scope and Dimensions of Biometrics

- **Financial Services:** Biometrics can provide additional protection against fraud and theft in financial industries.

> **Electronic Know Your Customer** (eKYC) **technology** uses digital verification (including fingerprint and/or facial scans) as verification forms through software.

- **Healthcare:** Similarly to eKYC, healthcare providers implement digital identification systems that allow doctors and nurses to ID patients through their physical characteristics and link that verification to their complete medical history. This provides **no-touch service** for essential administrative work.
- **Automotive:** With the onset of innovation in automobiles with **electric** and **self-driving vehicles**, some manufacturers and third-party companies are developing biometric verification systems that can work in cars alongside, or in place of, traditional key starts. Here, physical verification can help prevent theft.
- **Travel and Hospitality:** Increased demand for no-touch check-in and service drives the adoption of biometrics in hospitality. These advances include using facial scans as part of no-touch service and instant check-ins with fingerprint biometrics as part of MFA that can serve as a door key.

> - Facial recognition is a part of everyday life in **Chinese cities**, where it's used for **routine purchases**, and **London** is famously dotted

with **CCTV cameras. New York, Chicago** and **Moscow** are linking **CCTV cameras** in their cities to **facial recognition databases** to help local police fight crime. Ramping up the technology **Carnegie Mellon University** is developing a camera that can scan the **irises** of people in crowds from a distance of **10 meters.**

- In **2018, facial recognition** was introduced in **Dubai airport**, where travelers are photographed by **80 cameras** as they pass through a tunnel in a **virtual aquarium.**

Concerns of Biometrics

- Biometric authentication is convenient, but **privacy advocates** fear that **biometric security erodes personal privacy.** The concern is that personal data could be **collected easily** and **without consent**.
- An early attack on fingerprint biometric authentication was called the gummy bear hack, and it dates back to 2002 when Japanese researchers, using a gelatin-based confection, showed that an attacker could lift a latent fingerprint from a glossy surface. The capacitance of gelatin is similar to that of a human finger, so fingerprint scanners designed to detect capacitance would be fooled by the gelatin transfer.
- **Storing biometric data on a device :** like the **iPhone's TouchID** or **Face ID** is considered **safer** than storing it with a **service provider**, even when the data is encrypted. That risk is similar to that of a **password database**, in which hackers may breach the system and steal data that's not effectively secured. The ramifications, however, are significantly different. If a password is compromised, it can be changed.
- **Ethics and Privacy:** More widespread biometrics do introduce **questions of privacy**. It bears noting that the implementation of **biometric ID**, like **face scans** in public places, raises questions about the **ethical impact** of the technology. However, in most enterprise contexts using biometrics for authentication in a reasonable capacity isn't typically a moral problem.
- **False Security:** Biometrics are incredibly resistant to theft or fakery—but they **aren't immune** to it. There have been cases of hacker groups breaking through scans using **software combinations**, information stolen from databases, and fake models of physical body parts. Relying on biometrics alone as a form of authentication could create **security gaps** that hackers can exploit. Biometrics work best as part of an **MFA system** alongside another ID such as a **public/private keypair, PINs** or **external authenticator apps.**
- **Hesitancy:** Some users, including your employees, could be hesitant to provide physical information like fingerprints. Their fears are rooted in an anxiety about giving up personal attributes in ways where they don't understand how they are used or protected. **Transparency** and **education** are vital to addressing this challenge.
- **Reusability:** One of the strengths of biometrics, immutability, is also a drawback. If fingerprint information is compromised in a database, you can't just replace that information. Instead, the user will have to provide some other form of ID (even if it is an entirely different fingerprint).
- **Hygiene:** Some biometrics aren't as useful in certain situations. With COVID-19, we've seen how public touch scans might not be helpful in specific contexts, and facial scans might limit how we access devices while wearing masks. Careful planning and flexibility (and a robust MFA system) can mitigate this challenge.

Blockchain Technology and Cryptocurrency

- A blockchain is a **sequence of blocks**, each containing **data or transactions** (contains details of transactions executed over the **network**, **hash** (address) of the previous block, timestamp etc.).

- **Blockchain** is a method of recording information that makes it impossible or difficult for the system to be **changed**, **hacked** or **manipulated**. A blockchain is a distributed ledger that duplicates and distributes transactions across the network of computers participating in the **blockchain.**
- **Blockchain technology** is a structure that stores transactional records, also known as the **block**, of the public in several databases, known as the **chain**, in a network connected through **peer-to-peer nodes**. Typically, this storage is referred to as a **Digital ledger**.
- Every transaction in this ledger is authorized by the digital signature of the owner, which authenticates the transaction and safeguards it from tampering. Hence, the information the digital ledger contains is highly secure.
- It's designed to **ensure security**, **transparency**, and **immutability** in **digital records** by linking these blocks **cryptographically**.

Popular blockchain platforms : Hyperledger, Cosmos, Polkadot, Redbelly, Ethereum.

Decentralized Ledger

- A decentralized ledger refers to a **record-keeping system** where **multiple participants** (nodes) maintain copies of the **same ledger**.
- It doesn't rely on a single central authority, **enhancing transparency** and **security** in various applications like cryptocurrencies.
- Blockchain operates in a **decentralized manner**, unlike centralized tech giants such as **Google**, where data is stored on **individual computers** rather than **centralized servers**. In essence, a blockchain is essentially a **ledger comprising records of transactions**. These transactions are grouped into **blocks**, each with a unique identifier called a **hash**.
- What makes blockchain distinct is its decentralized nature, where this ledger is **distributed across a network of computers**, or **nodes**. This network verifies and **validates transactions** using **complex algorithms**, reaching **consensus** before adding a new block to the chain.

Working of Blockchain Technology

A transaction is requested

1 The transaction is broadcasted to a peer-to-peer (P2P) network that consists of computers (otherwise knows as nodes)

2 The network of nodes uses known algorithms to validate the transaction and user's status

3 A verified transaction can involve cryptocurrency, contracts, records or other information

4 The transaction is combined with other transactions, once verified, to create a new block of data for the ledger

5 The new block is added to the existing blockchain (which is permanent and unalterable

6 The transaction is now finished.

- **Blockchain is a combination of three leading technologies :**

Cryptographic keys

- A peer-to-peer network containing a shared ledger.

- A means of computing, to store the transactions and records of the network.
- Cryptography keys consist of two keys – Private key and Public key. These keys help in performing successful transactions between two parties. Each individual has these two keys, which they use to produce a secure digital identity reference.
- The digital signature is merged with the peer-to-peer network; a large number of individuals who act as authorities use the digital signature in order to reach a consensus on transactions, among other issues. When they authorize a deal, it is certified by a mathematical verification, which results in a successful secured transaction between the two network-connected parties.

Types of Blockchains

- **Private Blockchain Networks :** They operate on closed networks, and tend to work well for private businesses and organizations. Companies can use private blockchains to customize their accessibility and authorization preferences, parameters to the network, and other important security options. Only one authority manages a private blockchain network.
- **Public Blockchain Networks :** Public Blockchain is a kind of blockchain which is open for the public and allows everyone to join the network to perform transactions and to participate in the consensus process. Public blockchains are transparent, because all transactions are publicly recorded.
- Bitcoin and other cryptocurrencies originated from public blockchains, which also played a role in popularizing **distributed ledger technology** (DLT). Public blockchains also help to eliminate certain challenges and issues, such as security flaws and centralization. With DLT, data is distributed across a peer-to-peer network, rather than being stored in a single location. A consensus algorithm is used for verifying information authenticity; **proof of stake** (PoS) and **proof of work** (PoW) are two frequently used consensus methods.
- **Permissioned Blockchain Networks :** They are private blockchains that allow special access for authorized individuals. Organizations typically set up these types of blockchains to get the best of both worlds, and it enables better structure when assigning who can participate in the network and in what transactions.
- **Consortium Blockchains :** They have both public and private components, except multiple organizations will manage a single consortium blockchain network. Although these types of blockchains can initially be more complex to set up, once they are running, they can offer better security and are optimal for collaboration with multiple organizations.
- **Hybrid Blockchains :** A combination of both public and private blockchains. In a hybrid blockchain, some parts of the blockchain are public and transparent, while others are private and accessible only to authorized and specific participants. This makes hybrid blockchains ideal for use in those cases where a balance is required between transparency and privacy. For example, in supply chain management multiple parties can access certain information, but sensitive data can be kept private.
- **Sidechains :** They are different blockchains that run parallel to the main blockchain, allowing for additional functionality and scalability. Sidechains enable developers to experiment with new features and applications without affecting the main blockchain's integrity. For example, sidechains can be used for creating decentralized applications and to implement specific consensus mechanisms. Sidechains can also be used to handle transactions of the main blockchain to reduce congestion and increase scalability.

- This structure ensures **security** & **immutability**, as altering one block would require changing subsequent blocks across the network.
- All records in a blockchain are **linked**, preventing random changes to any individual record. This makes it **resistant to alteration** and **highly secure** against hacking attempts.
- Transactions recorded in the blockchain can be validated or invalidated by anyone in the network, **ensuring transparency** and trust in the system.
- One notable aspect is that while blockchain provides **security** and **transparency**, it doesn't **guarantee accountability** if data is missing or incorrect. Ensuring accurate input is crucial to maintaining reliability in the system.

Validation in Blockchain Technology

- Validation in blockchain technology is the process of **verifying the authenticity** and **accuracy of transactions** before they are added to the **blockchain ledger**. This is done by a network of nodes, or computers, that are all running the same software.
- There are **two main types of validation** in blockchain technology:
  - **Proof-of-work (PoW):** Proof of work means calculation of work number for validation of new transactions. It is a highly complex problem requiring lots of computational power and electricity. The first node to solve the puzzle get certain tokens for demonstrating proof of work
- **Proof-of-stake (PoS):** In PoS, nodes are randomly selected to validate blocks based on the amount of cryptocurrency they hold. Staking is the process of locking up cryptocurrency in order to participate in the validation process. This is a more energy-efficient consensus mechanism than PoW.

Ethereum is a blockchain network that is currently transitioning from a **proof-of-work** (PoW) consensus mechanism to a **proof-of-stake** (PoS) consensus mechanism.

Proof of authority : **Proof of authority** (PoA) is a **consensus mechanism** that is based on the **value of identity**. In PoA, only a select group of nodes, called **validators**, are allowed to validate transactions and add new blocks to the blockchain. The validators are chosen based on their reputation or stake in the network.

Advantages of Block chain Technology

- **Highly Secure :** It uses a digital signature feature to conduct fraud-free transactions making it impossible to corrupt or change the data of an individual by the other users without a specific digital signature.
- **Decentralized System :** With Blockchain, transactions are done with the mutual consensus of users resulting in smoother, safer, and faster transactions.
- **Automation Capability :** It is programmable and can generate systematic actions, events, and payments automatically when the criteria of the trigger are met.

Applications of Blockchain Technology

Social

- Blockchain helps individuals have **control over** their **digital identities, reducing identity theft** and **fraud.**
- **Transparent donation tracking** ensures that funds reach their intended beneficiaries in charitable organizations.
- **Digital Land Records** (Property record management).

Political

- **Voting:** Blockchain-based voting systems enhance election security, reduce fraud, and improve voter trust.
- **Government Transparency:** Public sector transactions on blockchain increases transparency and reduces corruption.

Economic

- **Cross-Border Payments:** Blockchain simplifies and accelerates cross-border transactions, reducing fees and settlement times.
- **Financial Inclusion:** Cryptocurrencies and blockchain enable financial services for the unbanked population.

Legal

- **Smart Contracts:** Self-executing smart contracts automate legal agreements, reducing the need for intermediaries.
- **Intellectual Property:** Blockchain ensures transparent ownership and copyright protection for creative content. Ex- Open Law Platform

Health

- **Medical Records:** Blockchain securely stores and shares medical records, ensuring data accuracy and patient privacy.
- **Drug Traceability:** It verifies the authenticity and origins of pharmaceuticals in the supply chain, improving drug safety.
- Pharmaceutical Supply Chain.

Education

- **Credential Verification:** Blockchain verifies educational credentials, simplifying the hiring process and reducing credential fraud.
- **E-Learning:** Blockchain can incentivize e-learning platforms and reward learners with digital tokens.

Infrastructure

- **Smart Cities:** Blockchain enables secure, automated transactions in smart grids, transportation, and waste management.
- **Property Records:** Property ownership records on blockchain reduce fraud and streamline property transactions.

Agriculture

- **Supply Chain Tracking:** Blockchain tracks the journey of agricultural products, enhancing food safety and transparency.
- **Crop Insurance:** Smart contracts automatically trigger insurance payouts based on weather or yield data.

Environmental

- **Carbon Credits:** Blockchain verifies and trades carbon credits, encouraging environmental conservation.
- **Renewable Energy:** Peer-to-peer energy trading platforms use blockchain for transparent and efficient energy sharing.

Technological

- **Decentralized Apps:** Developers build decentralized applications (DApps) on blockchain networks for various purposes.
- **Tokenization:** Physical assets like real estate or art can be tokenized for easier transfer and investment.

Challenges of BlockChain Technology

- **Scalability :** Bitcoin's blockchain has a limited transaction processing capacity, leading to slower transaction at times during high demand periods.
- **Energy Consumption :** Proof of Work (PoW) consensus mechanisms, used by cryptocurrencies like Bitcoin, consume significant energy due to the computational power required for mining.
- **Regulatory and Legal Uncertainty :** Many countries are still formulating regulations for blockchain and cryptocurrencies, creating uncertainty for businesses operating in the space.
- **Privacy Concerns :** While transactions on a public blockchain are pseudonymous, they can still be traced, potentially compromising user privacy.
- **Lack of Governance :** Disputes within a blockchain community on protocol upgrades, as seen in the Bitcoin scaling debate, can lead to forks.

- **Cost of Implementation :** Building and maintaining a private blockchain network infrastructure can be costly, especially for small businesses or startups.
- **Education and Awareness :** Many individuals and organizations still lack a clear understanding of how blockchain works and its potential applications.

National Strategy for Blockchain Technology

- The **National Blockchain Framework** (NBF) is a **strategy** for the **next five years** to promote the **adoption** and **use of blockchain technology** in **India**. The NBF was initiated by the **Ministry of Electronics and Information Technology** (MeitY) in **2022**.

Objectives and Vision of National Strategy on Blockchain :

- To create **trusted digital platforms** through **shared blockchain infrastructure.**
- **Promoting research** and **development, capacity, skill** and **innovation, technology** and **application development**.
- Making **India a global leader** in **blockchain technology**.
- Facilitating state of the art, transparent, secure and trusted digital service delivery to citizens and businesses.

- NBF will initially be used for e-governance applications, such as **land records management, supply chain management** and **education records management**. Over time, the NBF will be expanded to include other use cases, such as **financial services, healthcare** and **logistics**.
- The NBF is a significant step forward for India's blockchain adoption journey. The NBF will help to create a more **secure, transparent** and **efficient digital ecosystem** in India.

Cryptocurrency

- Cryptocurrency is a digital currency that is secured by **cryptographic techniques** and is built on **blockchain technology**.

Some popular Crypto Currencies : Bitcoins (BTC), Ethereum (ETH), Litecoin (LTC), Dash and Ripple

Key terms associated with Cryptocurrency

- **Cryptography:** Cryptocurrencies use cryptographic techniques to **secure transactions** and **control the creation** of **new units. Public** and **private keys** are used to **verify ownership** and **facilitate secure transfers.**
- **Wallet:** the account addresses of the user which is accessible only by a **private and** a **public key**; the private key is unique and known only to the owner of the wallet.

Challenges

- **Vulnerability to Illegal Activities:** The pseudonymous nature of cryptocurrency transactions can be exploited for illegal activities such as **money laundering, tax evasion** and funding of **illegal organizations.**
- **Regulatory Concerns:** Many governments and regulatory authorities have expressed concerns about the use of cryptocurrencies. Some countries have imposed strict regulations, while others have banned cryptocurrencies altogether. No protection is assured under **FEMA.**
- **Frauds and Scams:** The cryptocurrency space has been plagued by frauds and scams, including **Ponzi schemes, phishing attacks** and fraudulent **initial coin offerings** (ICOs).
- **Irreversible Transactions:** Once a cryptocurrency transaction is confirmed and added to the blockchain, it is irreversible.
- Lack of Consumer Protections.
- Limited Acceptance.

Legal Status of Cryptocurrencies

- **El Salvador** was the first country in the world to accept **Bitcoin** as a legal tender.
- **Singapore, France, Switzerland, Thailand** have legalized **Bitcoins.** Bitcoin was accepted by

the **US government** in **2013** as a decentralised virtual currency that can be used for performing transactions. **Canadian government** in **2017** accepted **Impak Coin** as its first legalised **cryptocurrency**.

- Indian government has made some special provisions and regulations and levied a tax on virtual currency trading and came up with its own digital currency.
- **Digital Rupee** (e₹) or eINR or E-Rupee is a tokenised digital version of the Indian Rupee, issued by the Reserve Bank of India (RBI) as a **central bank digital currency** (CBDC) launched on 1 December 2022.

WEB 3.0

- **Web 1.0**, often referred to as the **Static Web**, represents the **earliest stage** of the **World Wide Web's development**. It emerged in the late **1980s** and **gained momentum** throughout the **1990s**.
- **Web 2.0**, the **Social Web**, transformed the internet with **interactive technologies** like **Javascript**, **HTML5** and **CSS3**. This era fostered platforms like **YouTube**, **Facebook** and **Wikipedia**, allowing users to **actively create** and **share content**, ushering in a new era of **user engagement** and **collaboration** on the web. In the **Web 2.0 era**, many online services are built around **collecting** and **monetizing** user data. Users often trade their **personal data** and attention for access to these services, making them the product that companies sell to **advertisers** and **marketers**.
- **Web 3.0**, often referred to as the **Semantic Web** or the **Decentralized Web**, represents the next phase in the evolution of the internet. In the envisioned **Web 3.0**, there's a shift towards **decentralization** and **user empowerment**. Users have greater control over their data and digital assets, often represented as **tokens** on **blockchain networks.** This model aims to give users **ownership of their online identities** and **assets, reducing reliance** on **centralized intermediaries.**
- **Web 3.0** aims to provide a **more user-centric, decentralized** and **economically inclusive internet experience** compared to the data-centric model of Web 2.0.
- **Challenges of Web 3.0 :**

  - Regulation
  - Data privacy
  - Malafide use
  - Consensus approach
  - Not decentralized
  - Business models
  - Finance sernet Of Things (IoT)

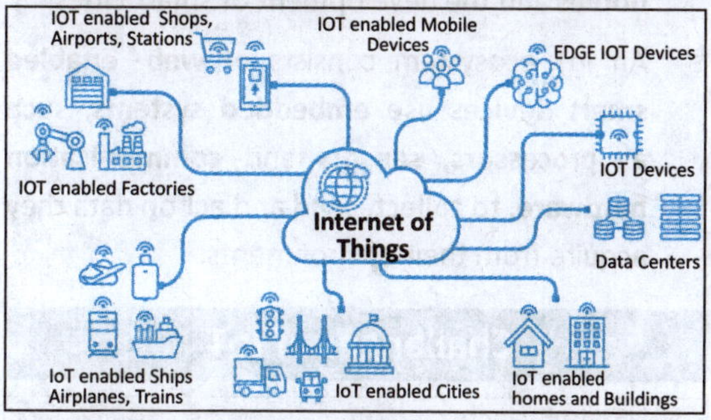

- The **Internet of Things** (IoT) is a system of **interconnected devices, vehicles, buildings**, and other objects that are embedded with **sensors, software** and **network connectivity** to enable them to collect and exchange data.
- The IoT allows objects to be sensed and controlled remotely across **existing network infrastructure, creating opportunities** for more **efficient operations, better decision-making,** and **new business models.**
- The IoT is often confused with **M2M** (Machine to Machine) **communication**, which is a subset of the IoT.

  - **M2M communication** is the **exchange of data** between two or more devices without **human intervention.**

- **Example** : A smart thermostat that **automatically adjusts** the **temperature based on the weather.**

- **Phones**, **tablets** and **PCs** are not typically considered part of the IoT because they are not embedded with sensors and actuators that allow them to interact with the physical world. However, they can be used to control and monitor IoT devices.
- IoT is a **key enabler** for **creating smart infrastructure** across various industries and verticals. This includes areas such as **power management**, **automotive technology**, **safety** and **surveillance systems**, **remote health monitoring**, **precision agriculture**, **smart homes** and the development of smart cities.
- An IoT ecosystem consists of **web- enabled smart devices** use **embedded systems**, such as **processors**, **sensors** and **communication hardware**, to **collect**, **send** and act on data they acquire from their environments.

Challenges of IoT

- Data Breach
- Increased Dependence on Technology
- Complexity in Operation
- Issue of Compatibility in Tagging and Monitoring
- Lesser Employment of Menial Staff
- Internet Consumption
- Bandwidth Issues
- Privacy Concerns
- Energy Efficiency

Applications of Internet of Things

Sector	Application
Home	• Smart Temperature control
	• Optimized Energy use
Industrial	• Machine to Machine communication
	• Quality Control
Automotive	• Vehicle Auto-Diagnosis
	• Optimized Traffic Flow
	• Smart Parking
Agriculture	• Off spring care
	• Crop Management
	• Soil Analysis
Military	• Situation awareness
	• Threat anyalysis
Medical	• Optimized patient care
	• Wearable fitness devices
	• Quality data reporting
Environmental	• Forest fire detection
	• Species Tracking
	• Weather prediction
Retail	• Theft protection
	• Inventory Control
	• Focused Marketing

Metaverse

- Metaverse projects refer to **blockchain-based games** and **applications** that are set in virtual **worlds.** Such games follow a play-to-earn model, where gamers are rewarded for being invested in the game.
- Metaverse can be understood as a combination of multiple elements of technology, including virtual reality, augmented reality and video where users **live** within a digitally enhanced surroundings.

Technologies of Metaverse

- Virtual Reality
- Augmented Reality
- Hologram
- Avatar

Virtual Reality (VR)

- **Virtual Reality** (VR) employs **computer-generated simulations** to **immerse individuals in artificial 3D environments.** It offers **complete immersion**, isolating users from the real world.

Applications span **gaming, education, healthcare** and **training**, aiming to create a vivid sense of presence within the virtual realm, exemplified by games like **World of Warcraft**.

Augmented Reality

- It is an **enhanced** version of the **real physical world** that is achieved through the use of **digital visual elements**, sound, or other **sensory stimuli** delivered via technology. E.g., games like **Pokemon Go.**

Holograms

- Holograms are **three-dimensional virtual images** formed through the **interference of light** beams that accurately **replicate real physical objects**, providing a **compelling** and **realistic visual representation.**

Avatar

- An avatar in the metaverse serves as a **digital representation** of an **individual**, allowing them to interact and engage within **virtual environments** as if they were physically present. These **digital avatars** enable a range of **human-like activities** and experiences in **digitally constructed worlds, spanning social interaction, gaming** and **virtual commerce.**

Artificial Intelligence

- The term Artifical Intelligence was coined by John Mocarthy in 1956 during Dartmouth Conference which is considered to be the birth of AI John McCarthy is known as father of AI as he developed LISP Progamming Language that be came fundamental for AI research.
- It refers to the **ability of machines** to perform **cognitive tasks** like **thinking, perceiving, learning, problem solving** and **decision making.**

Important terms related to AI

- **Artificial Intelligence (AI) :** Techniques and mechanism that enable machines to solve a task in a way like humans do.
- **Machine Learning (ML) :** Algorithms that allows computers to learn, without being explicityl programmed.
- **Artificial Neural Networks (ANN) :** Brain-inspired machine learning models.
- **Deep Learning (DL) :** A subset of ML which uses deep artificial neural networks as models and automatically builds a hierarchy of data represemtatopms.

- AI with incredible advances made in **data collection, processing** and **computation power**, intelligent systems can now be deployed to take over a variety of tasks, enable connectivity and enhance productivity.

Types of Artificial Intelligence (AI)

Based on Capabilities	Description
Weak AI or Narrow AI	AI designed for specific tasks like playing chess, recognizing faces, or making recommendations. Examples include Siri, Watson, AlphaGo.
General AI	AI with the ability to perform any intellectual task that a human can, including reasoning, learning, and planning. No current examples, but researchers are working on it.
Super AI	Speculative AI that surpasses human intelligence, excelling in tasks with cognitive abilities like creativity, self-awareness, and emotion. No current examples, only future possibilities.

Based on Functionality	Description
Reactive Machines	AI that reacts to the current situation but lacks memory or past experience storage. Examples include Deep Blue, AlphaGo.
Limited Memory	AI that stores some data or past experience for a short time, using it for decision-making. Examples include self-driving cars, chatbots.
Theory of Mind	AI that understands and simulates the mental states, emotions, and beliefs of others. No current examples, research is ongoing.
Self-Aware	AI with a sense of self, consciousness, and self-reflection. No current examples, subject to philosophical and scientific debates.

Artificial General Intelligence (AGI)

- It refers to intelligence that is not limited or narrow. Think of it as human common sense but absent in AI systems.
- Common sense will make a human save his life in a life-threatening situation while a robot may remain unmoved. There are no credible efforts towards building AGI yet. Many experts believe AGI will never be achieved by a machine; others believe it could be in the far future.

Generative AI

- **Generative AI** is a branch of **artificial intelligence** focused on **creating original content** or **data rather** than **analyzing** or making decisions based on **existing data.**
- It uses **algorithms** and **models to generate content**, such as **text**, **images**, **music** or even **videos**, that can be **realistic** and **creative.**
- **Generative AI** find applications in various fields, including **art**, **content creation**, **natural language processing** among others.

Examples of generative AI : GPT-3 for text generation and deep learning models for image and video synthesis.

Type of Generative AI frameworks

- **Generative Adversarial Networks (GANs):** GANs consist of **two neural networks, a generator** and a **discriminator**, which compete in a **game-like fashion**. The generator produces new data samples based on a given dataset, while the discriminator evaluates these samples, distinguishing between real and generated data.

GANs are used for tasks like image generation and data synthesis.

- **Variational Autoencoders (VAEs):** VAEs utilize an **encoder-decoder architecture**. The encoder maps input data into a latent space, effectively compressing it. The decoder then **reconstructs** the original data from this compressed representation.

VAEs are commonly used for tasks like **image generation**, **data denoising** and **anomaly detection.**

Transformer Based Models

- **Transformer-Based Models:** Transformers are a class of deep learning models originally developed for natural language processing tasks. They excel at **understanding** and **generating sequences of data**, such as text.
- Transformer-based models read and learn from large corpora of text and use this knowledge to generate new content, like generating stories, poems, or language translations.

GPT (Generative Pre-trained Transformer) is an example of a widely used transformer-based model.

- TBMs find application in various tasks such as question answering, text summarization, and creative writing.

Prominent programs based on TBMs include **OpenAI's ChatGPT, Google's BARD AI, and DALL-E.** They rely on **natural language processing (NLP)** to understand and generate text data. NLP helps these models handle synonyms, remove redundant words, and simplify sentences, enhancing their training and comprehension abilities.

Natural Language Processing (NLP)

- Natural Language Processing (NLP) is a branch of **artificial intelligence** (AI) that focuses on the interaction between computers and human languages.
- It involves the development of algorithms and models that enable machines to understand, interpret, and generate human language in a way that is both meaningful and useful.

Evolution of AI in various spheres

- AI is embedded in the recommendations we get on our **favourite streaming** or **shopping** site; in **GPS mapping technology**; in the predictive text that completes our sentences when we try to send an email or complete a web search.
- It promises to be even more **transformative** than the **harnessing of electricity**. And the more we use AI, the more data we generate, the smarter it gets.
- Just as electricity allowed us to tame time, enabling us to radically alter virtually every aspect of existence, AI can leapfrog us toward **eradicating hunger**, **poverty** and **disease** opening up new and hitherto unimaginable pathways for climate change **mitigation**, **education** and **scientific discovery**.

Applications of Artificial Intelligence

Applications of AI in Agriculture

- AI can be used to **predict advisories** for **sowing, pest control, input control** can help in **ensuring increased income** and **providing stability** for the agricultural community.
- **Precision agriculture** uses AI technology to aid in **detecting diseases** in **plants, pests** and **poor plant nutrition** on **farms.**
- AI sensors can detect and **target weeds** and then decide which **herbicides** to apply within the right buffer zone.
- **Climate pattern** and **effects** on different crops can be analysed using AI software which will help in prediction of the best crop for the season and the possible outcomes.
- **Image classification tools** combined with **remote** and local sensed data can bring a revolutionary change in utilization and efficiency of farm machinery, in areas of **weed removal, early disease identification, produce harvesting** and **grading.**

Applications of AI in Manufacturing sector

- **Robots** are being used for **manufacturing** since a long time now; however, more advanced **exponential technologies** have emerged such as **additive manufacturing** (3D Printing) which with the help of AI can revolutionize the entire manufacturing supply chain ecosystem.
- The **predictive maintenance** of machineries would lead to **reduced operational cost.**
- IR technologies would be helpful in **minimizing deterioration** in the quality of the machinery.
- By having a **repository of data** regarding **machines** and **equipment's** will aid in managing them well.
- Robots can perform the tasks given by a human because of **sensors** to **detect physical** data from the real world such as **light, heat, temperature, movement, sound, bump** and **pressure.** Moreover, they have **efficient processors, multiple sensors** and **huge memory**, to exhibit intelligence.
- Further, they are capable of learning from their errors and therefore can adapt to the new environment.

Applications of AI in Education

- AI in education is already creating personalised learning experiences. Adaptive learning platforms use AI algorithms to tailor educational content to cater to individual student's needs.
- AI-driven assessment tools provide immediate feedback, empowering educators to optimise their teaching strategies.
- Today, whether it's understanding complex grammar or understanding the nuances of a foreign language, AI can do it pretty much all in a short amount of time.

Applications of AI in Arts

- AI's foray into the world of music composition is exciting. Machine learning algorithms analyse vast datasets of musical compositions, learning patterns and styles to compose original songs. From classical to contemporary music, **AI-generated music** has made its mark, sparking debates about the authenticity and emotional depth of algorithmic compositions.
- Whether used as a tool for inspiration by human composers or as a standalone creator, AI has undeniably etched its name in the musical landscape so much so that recently the **Grammy** awards announced that only human creators are eligible to be considered for the nomination.

Applications of AI in Scientific Research

- AI is making waves in industries traditionally associated with innovation and problem-solving. In scientific research, **AI algorithms** are analysing vast datasets to identify patterns, predict outcomes, and even propose hypotheses.
- The speed and efficiency with which AI processes information have the potential to accelerate scientific discovery, opening new frontiers in fields such as medicine, materials science, and environmental research, doing complicated codes or making websites.

Concerns and Challenges of AI

- **Predictative Algorithms :** Algorithms based on our **past digital searches** creates and provides us **probable solutions** or **alternatives** which we are looking for but also raises concerns in certain aspects.
- **Data Privacy and Security:** Gathering and storing massive amounts of data for AI applications raises concerns about **data breaches**, **privacy violations** and the **misuse of personal information**. Concerns resents serious data **privacy concerns**. The algorithm's never-ending quest for data has led to our digital footprints being harvested and sold without our knowledge or **informed consent.**
- **Bias and Fairness**: AI algorithms can perpetuate biases present in training data, leading to unfair or **discriminatory outcomes**, especially in areas like hiring and lending.

Types of bias in AI
Data bias : When the data used to develop and train an AI is incomplete, skewed, or invalid. This can be because the data is incorrect, excludes certain groups, or was collected in bad faith.
Societal bias : When the assumptions and biases present in everyday society make their way into AI through blind spots and expectations that the programmers held when creating the AI.

- **Ethical Concerns:** Ethical dilemmas arise in AI applications, such as autonomous weapons, surveillance and decisions that may harm individuals or groups.
- **Lack of Regulation:** The absence of clear regulations and standards for AI technologies can lead to misuse and ethical dilemmas.
- **Job Displacement:** Automation through AI can lead to job displacement in various industries, raising concerns about unemployment and economic inequality.
- **Cost of Implementation:** Developing and implementing AI systems can be expensive, particularly for smaller businesses and organizations.
- **Data Quality and Availability:** AI models require high-quality and diverse data, which may not always be readily available or may be biased.
- **Human-AI Collaboration:** Balancing the roles of humans and AI in decision-making processes presents challenges in various fields, including healthcare and law.

In **2018**, a self-driving car used by the rideshare company **Uber** hit and killed a pedestrian in a driving accident. In that particular case, the court ruled that the backup driver of the self-driving car was at fault, as she was watching a show on her phone instead of paying attention to her surroundings.

- **AI Safety:** Ensuring that AI systems operate safely and do not pose risks to humans or the environment is a critical challenge.
- **Environmental Concerns :** According to studies, around **40%** of the **total energy** that **data centres** consume goes to **cooling IT equipment**. Now, to **reduce energy consumption**, companies are moving their data centres into **cooler climates** such as **Siberia**. The **environmental impact** caused by data centres doesn't stop at **electrical consumption**. Coolants are often made of **hazardous chemicals**, and **battery backups** at data centres – needed for when there are power **shortages** – cause an **environmental impact** both due to **mining for battery components** and the disposal of the **toxic batteries** afterward.
- **Manipulating Human behaviour:** algorithms know us better than we know ourselves. They can nudge our behaviour without our noticing.

Cambridge Analytica in which such **algorithms** and **big data** were used to **alter voting decisions** during **BREXIT- 2016** should serve as a potent warning of the individual and societal concerns resulting from current AI business models.

- **Creates Carbon Footprint :** AI requires massive computational capacity, which means more power-hungry data centres and a big carbon footprint.
- **Digital Exclusion:** Robotics and AI companies are building intelligent machines that perform tasks typically carried out by **low-income workers: self-service kiosks to replace cashiers,** fruit-picking robots to replace field workers, etc. Without clear policies on reskilling workers, the promise of new opportunities will in fact create **serious new inequalities**. Investment is likely to shift to countries where AI-related work is already established, **widening gaps** among and within countries.

Sectoral Applications of AI	
Social	• AI algorithms analyze social media data to detect trends, sentiments, and potential public concerns. **Examples:** Facebook's content recommendation system suggests posts and advertisements based on user behavior.
Political	• AI models analyze data to predict election outcomes, voter behavior, and trends. **Examples:** Cambridge Analytica used AI for political campaign targeting and messaging. • Policy analysis - feedback, monitoring etc
Economic	• AI-powered algorithms make rapid trades based on real-time market data and trends. • **Examples:** Hedge funds use AI to automate trading strategies and achieve higher returns.
Legal	• AI systems analyze legal documents to assist lawyers in research and review tasks. • **Examples:** ROSS, an AI-powered legal research platform, helps lawyers find relevant case law and statutes.
Health	• AI algorithms assist in diagnosing and analyzing medical images. **Examples :** X-rays, MRIs.

Education	• AI algorithms create tailored learning paths and content for students based on their abilities and preferences. **Examples:** Duolingo uses AI to adapt language learning lessons to individual proficiency levels.
Infrastructure	• AI analyzes data from sensors to predict when equipment and infrastructure will require maintenance. **Examples :** Application in various underground gas pipelines and Smart city Projects.
Agriculture	• AI-powered drones and sensors optimize crop management, irrigation, and pest control.
Environmental	• **Climate Modeling :** AI models simulate climate patterns and help predict future environmental changes. • **Wildlife conservation - Ex-** Cheetah of Kuno national park have a Neck Belt to monitor the activity of them.
Technological	• AI enables machines to understand, interpret, and respond in natural language. - **Examples:** Chatbots like Siri, Alexa, and Google Assistant use NLP to interact with users.

Chatbot

- Chatbot is a computer program that **simulates** and **processes human conversation** (either written or spoken), allowing humans to **interact** with **digital devices** as if they were communicating with a real person.
- Chatbots can be as simple as **rudimentary programs** that answer a simple query with a **single-line response**, or as sophisticated as **digital assistants** that learn and evolve to deliver increasing levels of personalization as they gather and process information.
- Though not all chatbots are equipped with artificial intelligence (AI), modern chatbots increasingly use **conversational AI techniques** like **natural language processing** (NLP) to understand the user's questions and automate responses to them.
- Chatbots can make it easy for users to find information by **instantaneously responding** to questions and requests, through **text input**, **audio input**, or both, **without** the need for **human intervention** or **manual research**.

Chatbot technology is now commonplace, found everywhere from **smart speakers** at home to **consumer-facing instances of SMS, WhatsApp** and **Facebook Messenger** to workplace messaging applications like **Slack**.

- The latest evolution of AI chatbots, often referred to as **intelligent virtual assistants** or **virtual agents**, can not only understand free-flowing conversation through use of sophisticated language models, but even automate relevant tasks.
- AI chatbots are chatbots that employ a variety of AI technologies, from machine learning that optimize responses over time to **natural language processing** (NLP) and **natural language understanding** (NLU) that accurately interprets user questions and matches them to specific intents.
- **Deep learning capabilities** allow AI chatbots to become more accurate over time, which in turns allows humans to interact with AI chatbots in a more natural, free-flowing way without being misunderstood.

- **Virtual agents** are a further evolution of AI chatbot software that not only use conversational AI to conduct dialogue and deep learning to self-improve over time, but often pair those AI technologies with **robotic process automation** (RPA) in one interface to act directly upon the user's intent without further human intervention.

Types of Chatbots

- **Task-oriented (declarative) chatbots** : They are **single-purpose programs** that focus on performing one function. Using rules, NLP, and very little ML, they generate **automated** but **conversational responses** to user inquiries. Interactions with these chatbots are highly specific and structured and are most applicable to support and service functions—think robust, interactive FAQs.
- **Data-driven and predictive (conversational) chatbots** : They are often referred to as **virtual assistants** or **digital assistants**, and are much more **sophisticated**, **interactive** and **personalized** than task-oriented chatbots. These chatbots are contextually aware and leverage **natural-language understanding** (NLU), NLP, and ML to learn as they go. They apply **predictive intelligence** and **analytics** to enable personalization based on user profiles and **past user behavior**. Digital assistants can learn a user's preferences over time, provide recommendations, and even anticipate needs. In addition to monitoring data and intent, they can initiate conversations.

Chatbots

- Chatbots are AI-powered virtual assistants that use Natural Language Processing (NLP) to interact with users.
- **ChatGPT (OpenAI)** : Developed by OpenAI using GPT-4o (latest model) Technology.
  - **Features:** Advanced text generation, Contextual understanding, Multimodal capabilities (text, image, code) and Free & paid versions (ChatGPT Plus with GPT-4)
- **Gemini (Google AI, formerly Bard) :** Developed by Google DeepMind using Gemini 1.5 Pro (latest) technology.
  - **Features:** Handles long-context processing, Integrated with Google Search, Supports multiple languages and Available via Google apps (Docs, Gmail, etc.)
- **Claude (Anthropic) :** Developed by Anthropic using Claude 3 technology.
  - **Features:** Focus on safe AI interactions, Ethical & transparent responses, Improved factual accuracy.
- **Grok (xAI – Elon Musk's AI startup) :** Developed by xAI (affiliated with X, formerly Twitter), Based on large language models.
  - **Features:** Integrated into X (Twitter), Access to real-time data from social media, Can generate humorous and controversial responses
- **Meta AI (Facebook/Instagram) :** Developed by Meta Platforms using LLaMA (Large Language Model Meta AI) technology
  - **Features:** Integrated with Facebook, Instagram, and WhatsApp, Image and text-based AI interactions and Standalone app in development
- **PAiGPT (India's First UPSC Chatbot) :** Developed by Project PAi (India) using AI-driven educational model.
  - **Features:** Provides UPSC-related content, Generates MCQs for practice and provides Real-time current affairs updates
- **Watson Assistant (IBM AI Chatbot) :** Developed by IBM using AI-powered cognitive computing technology.
  - **Features:** Used in business and healthcare, Multilingual support and Integrates with customer service platforms.

- **Siri (Apple) & Alexa (Amazon) :** Developed by Apple (Siri) Amazon (Alexa), use AI-powered voice assistants.
    - **Features:** Voice command-based responses, Integrated with smart home devices for Web search and personal assistant functions.

OpenAI

- OpenAI is an artificial intelligence research laboratory (with a non profit ownership structure) established in December 2015 by a group of influential tech visionaries and entrepreneurs such as Elon Musk (Tesla, SpaceX), Sam Altman (OpenAI's current CEO), Reid Hoffman (LinkedIn co-founder), Peter Thiel (PayPal co-founder), and several others dedicated to advancing artificial general intelligence (AGI) in a safe and beneficial manner.
- It actively promotes the development and deployment of AI systems that prioritize safety, fairness, and transparency. The organization conducts cutting-edge research in machine learning, deep learning, reinforcement learning, and related fields, with the goal of pushing the boundaries of AI capabilities while addressing ethical concerns.
- In 2018, OpenAI released the concept of a Generative Pre-trained Transformer (GPT), which is a neural network (a machine learning model) that simulates the human brain and is trained on data sets. In 2021, DALL-E was released, an image version of ChatGPT where humans can prompt the generative AI model to produce images.
- ChatGPT was released in November 2022, and became the most popular chatbot and generative AI tool–for producing anything from chatbot responses to survey questions to resumes.
- OpenAI continuously updates its large language models (LLMs) to improve their performance.
- Microsoft is currently one of the largest stakeholders and backers of the company. However, some investors are still involved, except most notably Elon Musk, who left in 2018 and recently started his own AI company, xAI (which came up with Grok)

Some of the important offerings of Open AI –

- **ChatGPT:** An AI chatbot that generates text and answers to user prompts and questions. It is trained on large data sets and simulates the experience of speaking with and listening to a human.
- **DALL-E 2:** A platform that analyzes descriptions and prompts of images that users want and generates them as described. For example, "paint a cat in Surrealist style."
- **Codex:** Codex is like ChatGPT but for code. It's trained on tons of code in different programming languages to simplify the coding process for developers .
- **Whisper:** An automatic speech recognition tool that's trained on audio data in dozens of languages so that it can transcribe and translate speech.

DeepSeek AI

- DeepSeek is a Chinese AI firm (founded in May 2023 by Liang Wenfeng) disrupting the AI industry with its low-cost, open-source large language models, challenging U.S. tech giants.

> Deepseeks first AI model was launched in November 2023 called Deepseek Coder.

- DeepSeek R1 was officially launched in December 2024, marking a breakthrough in cost-effective AI innovation. In December 2024, the company revealed that training its DeepSeek-V3 model cost less than $6 million using Nvidia H800 chips. DeepSeek's AI Assistant is now the top-rated free app on Apple's U.S. App Store, beating ChatGPT.

- DeepSeek claims to have trained its model for just $6 million, significantly lower than the over $100 million OpenAI spent on GPT-4. The company's founder reportedly stockpiled Nvidia A100 chips—banned from export to China since 2022—pairing them with cheaper chips to develop the AI.
- **Open-Source Accessibility:** DeepSeek-R1 is now live and open source, rivaling OpenAI's Model o1.
- **Multimodal Capabilities:** The model supports both text and image processing, enhancing its versatility.
- **Language Support:** Offers multilingual support, including Chinese and English, catering to a diverse user base.
- **Research and Information Gathering:** DeepSeek can collect data about specific industries, summarize it, and find relevant information efficiently.
- **Coding Assistance:** DeepSeek Coder, the company's first AI model, was designed for coding tasks, trained on 87% code and 13% natural language, offering free open-source access for research and commercial use.
- **Censorship:** Like other Chinese AI models, DeepSeek avoids politically sensitive topics. When asked about the Tiananmen Square massacre, it refused to provide details, highlighting Chinese government-imposed censorship.

Grok AI

- Grok AI is an advanced conversational chatbot developed by Elon Musk's startup, xAI. It is designed to provide meaningful engagement and real-time information access, primarily through the social media platform X (formerly Twitter).
- Grok AI wS the first product from xAI that aims to rival existing chatbots like ChatGPT created in response to Musk's concerns about the perceived biases in AI technologies.
- Grok was released in November 2023 and later released as Grok 2 and on February 17, 2025 as Grok 3 dubbed as smartest AI on the earth. It integrates closely with the social media platform X (formerly Twitter), offering unique features compared to other AI chatbots.
- One of the standout features of Grok 3 is its new DeepSearch tool, an AI-powered search engine designed to go beyond simple answers. Unlike typical chatbots, DeepSearch is built to explain its thought process and how it formulates responses, making it a powerful tool for research, brainstorming, and data analysis that allows for Deeper Reasoning.
- The AI model has been trained on xAI's proprietary Colossus supercomputer cluster that possesses over 100,000 Nvidia Hopper GPUs.
- **Advanced Reasoning:** Grok 3's reasoning capabilities, refined through large-scale reinforcement learning, allow it to think for extended periods, correct errors, explore alternatives, and deliver accurate answers.
- **Real-Time Data Access:** Unlike many other chatbots that rely on static datasets, Grok pulls in live information from X, enabling it to deliver timely responses on various topics ranging from pop culture to technical queries.
- **Image Generation:** The chatbot can create realistic images, including "deepfakes," showcasing its advanced AI capabilities.
- **Conversational Abilities:** Grok can engage users in both serious and light-hearted discussions. It can draft emails, debug code, generate ideas, and even translate languages.
- **Dynamic Interactivity:** The chatbot is capable of understanding nuanced language, including slang and idiomatic expressions, making interactions feel more natural and engaging.
- **Multimodal Capabilities:** The latest version of Grok (Grok-1.5V) enhances its functionality by processing both text and visual data, that allows

it to understand documents, diagrams, create images, interpret audio, and potentially handle videos.

Deepfake

- The word deepfake combines the terms deep learning and fake, and is a form of artificial intelligence.
- A deepfake is an artificial image or video (a series of images) generated by a special kind of machine learning called deep learning (hence the name). Deepfake refers to multimedia that has either been synthetically created or manipulated using some form of machine or deep learning (artificial intelligence) technology.
- Deep learning is a subset of AI, and refers to arrangements of algorithms that can learn and make intelligent decisions on their own.
- Other terms used to describe media that have been synthetically generated and/or manipulated include Shallow/Cheap Fakes, Generative AI, and Computer Generated Imagery (CGI).
- Synthetic media threats include techniques that threaten an organization's brands, impersonate leaders and financial officers, and use fraudulent communications to enable access to an organization's networks, communications, and sensitive information.

Types of Deepfakes

- **Face Swapping:** When the face of one person is superimposed onto anothers using deep learning algorithms.
- **Voice Synthesis:** Generating Synthetic voice recordings, mimicking someone's speech patterns and intonations.
- Gesture and Body Movement Manipulation
- **Text based Deep Fakes:** Imitating the writing style of someone (a high profile author or a celebrity) potentially leading to misleading content creation on wake of credibility of an author.
- **Object Manipulation:** Manipulating Objects within videos leading to deceptive presentations of events or situations.
- **Hybrid Deepfakes:** Combining multiple techniques like face swaps with altered voice and body movements to create more authentic and convincing Deepfakes.

Concerns and Threats

- According to the 2023 State of Deepfakes Report by Home Security Heroes - a US-based web security services company -deepfake videos saw a five-times increase since **2019**.
- At least **500,000 video** and voice deepfakes were shared on social media sites globally in **2023**, estimated DeepMedia, a company developing tools to detect synthetic media.
- Globally, deepfakes have been used to shape narratives around conflicts such as those in Ukraine and Gaza.
- In India, the worrying factor is their potential usage in elections. During the recently concluded Assembly elections, deepfake videos targeted not only individual political leaders but also attempted to influence public narratives.
- In 2018, a video of Barack Obama emerged using some objectionable words for Donald Trump.
- A video of **Ukrainian President Volodymyr Zelenskyy** calling on his soldiers to surrender to **Russia** surfaced in **2022**.
- **Deepfake** images and videos churned out by generative AI tools such as Midjourney, Stable **Diffusion** and **OpenAI's Dall-E** popped up ahead of elections from **New Zealand** to **Turkey** and **Argentina** have raised concerns about their impact on upcoming elections.
- There have been potential threats of Deepfake from a Head of a Nuclear State threatening to

launch Nuclear missiles escalating a world war to a Deepfake video of a celebrity that tarnishes his/ her personal reputation.

- Tech analysts predict disinformation, foreign interference, fraud, and conspiracy will worsen as digital forgeries become indiscernible from reality. They also expect a rise in deepfake cyber-attacks using AI, fake videos, and psychological manipulation to trick people into giving away sensitive information or harming their personal or professional security.

- MeiTY recently collaborated with representatives from academia, industry bodies like NASSCOM and social media companies on the need to ensure effective response to deep fakes coming up with a **4 pillared action** -
  - **Detection:** Deepfake content should be detected before and after such content is posted.
  - **Prevention:** There should be an effective mechanism for preventing propagation of deepfake content.
  - **Reporting:** Effective and expeditious reporting and grievance redressal mechanism should be available.
  - **Awareness:** Mass awareness on the issue of deepfake should be created.

> Indian PM recently addressed the issue of misleading authenticity of deepfake videos created through Generative AI.
>
> These videos, strikingly realistic, demand careful scrutiny before acceptance. India is emphasising a global framework for AI - PM Modi (December, 2023, Smart India Hackathon's grand finale)

Potential Threats of AI

- **Superhuman AI:** The danger of a super intelligent AI converting humans to slaves.

- **Malicious humans with powerful AI:** Even narrow AI tools can cause serious harm when matched with malicious intent. LLMs can generate believable untruths as fake news and create deep mental anguish leading to self-harm. Public opinion can be manipulated to affect democratic elections. AI tools work globally, taking little cognisance of boundaries and barriers. Individual malice can instantly impact the globe.

- **Highly capable and inscrutable AI:** AI systems will continue to improve and will be employed to assist humans. They may end up harming some sections more than others unintentionally, despite the best intentions of their creators. These systems are created using Machine Learning from data from the world and can perpetuate the shortcomings of the data. They may introduce asymmetric behaviours that go against certain groups. Camera-based face recognition systems have been shown to be more accurate on fair-skinned men than on dark-skinned women. Such unintended and unknown bias can be catastrophic in AI systems that steer autonomous cars and diagnose medical conditions. Privacy is a critical concern as algorithmic systems watch the world constantly. Every person can be tracked always, violating the fundamental right to privacy.

Regulations on AI : Towards Responsible AI

- AI holds tremendous potential in different sectors such as public health, agriculture, transportation and governance. As we exploit India's advantages in them, we need more discussions to make AI systems responsible, fair, and just to our society.

- The Association for Computing Machinery released a statement in October 2022 on 'Principles for Responsible Algorithmic Systems', a broader class of systems that include AI systems. Several leading AI experts and thinkers have been part of different cautionary messages about AI, issued by the Future of Life Institute, the Association for the Advancement of Artificial Intelligence and the Centre for AI Safety.

- The European Union is on the verge of enacting an AI Act that proposes regulations based on a stratification of potential risks. India needs a framework for itself, keeping in mind that regulations have been heavy-handed as well as lax in the past.
- The rapid rise in AI has created many opportunities globally, from facilitating healthcare diagnoses to enabling human connections through social media and creating labour efficiencies through automated tasks.
- However, these rapid changes also raise profound ethical concerns arising from the potential AI systems have to embed biases, contribute to climate degradation, threaten human rights and more.
- Such risks associated with AI have already begun to compound on top of existing inequalities, resulting in further harm to already marginalised groups.
- AI technology brings major benefits in many areas, but without the ethical guardrails, it risks reproducing real world biases and discrimination, fueling divisions and threatening fundamental human rights and freedoms.

UNESCO produced the first-ever global standard on AI ethics the Recommendation on the **Ethics of Artificial Intelligence** in **November 2021**, which was adopted by all **193 Member States**. The protection of human rights and dignity is the cornerstone of the Recommendation, based on the advancement of fundamental principles such as **transparency** and **fairness**, recognising the importance of human oversight of AI systems.

- The Recommendation interprets AI broadly as systems with the ability to process data in a way which resembles intelligent behaviour.
- Central to the Recommendations were **4 core** values which lay the foundations for AI systems that work for the good of humanity, individuals, societies and the environment.
    - Human rights and human dignity : Respect, protection and promotion of human rights and fundamental freedoms and human dignity
    - Living in peaceful just, and interconnected societies
    - Ensuring diversity and inclusiveness
    - Environment and ecosystem flourishing
- **10 core principles** laid out a human-rights centred approach to the Ethics of AI.

1. **Proportionality and Do No Harm :** The use of AI systems must not go beyond what is necessary to achieve a legitimate aim. Risk assessment should be used to prevent harms which may result from such uses.
2. **Safety and Security :** Unwanted harms (safety risks) as well as vulnerabilities to attack (security risks) should be avoided and addressed by AI actors.
3. **Right to Privacy and Data Protection :** Privacy must be protected and promoted throughout the AI lifecycle. Adequate data protection frameworks should also be established.
4. **Multi-stakeholder and Adaptive Governance & Collaboration :** International law & national sovereignty must be respected in the use of data. Additionally, participation of diverse stakeholders is necessary for inclusive approaches to AI governance.
5. **Responsibility and Accountability :** AI systems should be auditable and traceable. There should be oversight, impact assessment, audit and due diligence mechanisms in place to avoid conflicts with human rights norms and threats to environmental wellbeing.
6. **Transparency and Explainability :** The ethical deployment of AI systems depends on their transparency & explainability (T&E). The level of T&E should be appropriate to the context, as there may be tensions between T&E and other principles such as privacy, safety and security.

- **Human Oversight and Determination:** Member States should ensure that AI systems do not displace ultimate human responsibility and accountability.
- **Sustainability :** AI technologies should be assessed against their impacts on **sustainability**, understood as a set of constantly evolving goals including those set out in the UN's Sustainable Development Goals.
- **Awareness & Literacy :** Public understanding of AI and data should be promoted through open & accessible education, civic engagement, digital skills & AI ethics training, media & information literacy.
- **Fairness and Non-Discrimination :** AI actors should promote social justice, fairness, and non-discrimination while taking an inclusive approach to ensure AI's benefits are accessible to all.

The 2nd Global Forum on the Ethics of AI (2024): Changing the Landscape of AI Governance was organized by Slovenia, under the patronage of **UNESCO**, on **5 and 6 February 2024**.

NEURALINK

Neuralink is a company founded by **Elon Musk** in **2016** that's developing a **brain-computer** interface called the Link,which is a **surgically embedded neural-chip implant** designed to decode and **stimulate brain activity**, capable of translating thought into action.

Working of Neuralink Brain Chip

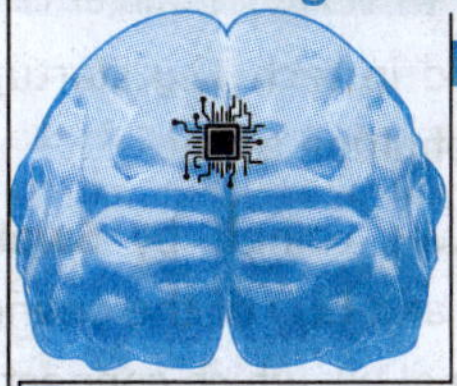

1. Brain consists of special cells called neurons that transmit signals to other cells in the body, like our muscles and nerves.
2. The electrodes of the Neuralink chip are able to read those signals, which are then translated into motor controls.
3. This could control external technologies, like computers or smartphones, or bodily functions like muscle movement.

- Neuralink's technology is capable of **recording and decoding neural signals** and then transmitting information back to the brain using **electrical stimulation.**
- The **coin-sized brain chip** is surgically embedded under the skull, where it receives information from neural threads that fan out into different sections of a subject's brain in control of motor skills.
- Each wire contains **1,024 electrodes**, which are **sensors capable** of recording and emitting electrical currents, and are so fine and flexible that they can't be inserted by the human. That's why Neuralink has built a neurosurgical robot that's designed to become fully automated.
- The device is designed to connect human brains directly to **computers.**
- **Neuralink's** underlying technology works in the same way as **electrophysiology**. The **electrical chemical signals** in our nervous system spark as **neurons** communicate with one another across gaps between nerve cells known as **synapses.**
- This **brain activity** is captured by **electrodes**, or sensors that **detect voltages**, measuring the **change in spikes** of when these voltages fire (or potentially fire).
- Our **brain activity data** is captured not only when we take action, but also if we **think** about taking **action.**
- As these devices **record complex data sets, machine learning algorithms** and other **artificial intelligence agents** are then **employed** to make **sense of the information.**

Applications and Scope of Neuralink

- The company's initial goal is to help those **immobilized** by **paralysis** regain **lost skills** of communication. Down the line, it intends to **pursue restoring motor**, **sensory** and **visual functions** as well as **treatment of neurological disorders.**
- A Neuralink-like device has the **potential** to **enhance human memory, processing speed** and cognitive abilities by creating a direct interface between the human brain and digital devices.

- The venture claims its neural device will allow people with **paraplegia** to regain movement and restore vision to those born blind.

> Someone with **paraplegia** would be able to manipulate a computer or mobile device using speech or **text synthesis** to surf the web and **create digital art.**

- Brain-computer interfaces can be used to control **prosthetics** or **exoskeletons**. This use case would enable people with **paralysis** or amputations to regain a certain level of mobility and independence.
- Neuralink's main focus is to help people who are unable to **speak** or **write communicate** with others by allowing them to control a virtual mouse, keyboard or send messages by thought.
- By **monitoring brain activity, brain-computer interfaces** can also detect changes that may indicate **neurological conditions** such as epilepsy, bipolar disorder, obsessive-compulsive disorder, Alzheimer's or Parkinson's disease.
- They can also be used to monitor mental health symptoms. Electrical stimulation could be delivered to targeted areas in the brain as a treatment for **burnout, fatigue, anxiety** and **depression**, which, unlike motor skills that are localized to one area, are spread throughout the brain.
- The tech can also help people improve their **focus, memory** and **attention** by allowing them to train their brain using real-time biofeedback and other techniques.

Disruptive and Futuristic Technologies

- Disruptive technologies are innovations that significantly alter or revolutionize existing industries, markets, or societal norms by introducing new approaches, products, or services. These technologies often replace established solutions, creating a substantial impact on the status quo.
- Disruptive technologies typically offer improved efficiency, lower costs, or novel features, challenging traditional business models and reshaping entire sectors.
- Futuristic technologies refer to advanced and cutting-edge innovations that are often conceptualized or in development, with the potential to significantly impact various aspects of human life and society in the future.
- Both these terms are also used interchangeably as futuristic technologies are largely held to be disruptive in nature.
  - **Smartphones:** Disrupted traditional mobile phones and various consumer electronics by integrating multiple functions into a single device.
  - **Streaming Services:** Disrupted traditional cable and satellite TV by offering on-demand, subscription-based content delivery over the internet.
  - **Electric Vehicles:** Disrupting the automotive industry by challenging the dominance of internal combustion engines with more sustainable electric alternatives.
  - **3D Printing:** Transforming manufacturing processes by enabling the production of customized, on-demand items with reduced waste.
  - **Blockchain and Cryptocurrencies:** Disrupting traditional financial systems by introducing decentralized and secure methods of digital transactions.

Deep Tech

- Deep tech' is a buzzword in tech and startup circles with no precise definition as yet.
- The term **deep tech** was coined by **Swati Chaturvedi**, the founder and CEO of the online investment platform Propel (x), which connects early stage Deep Tech with investors.
- Deep tech, or deep technology, refers to those startups whose business model is based on high tech innovation in engineering, or significant scientific advances.

- The term deep tech is intended to set it aside from its opposite, "shallow tech". Shallow tech is a relatively simple technological advance moving a business from a non-digital business model to a digital one. Shallow tech advances are easy for competitors to replicate so don't tend to disrupt the market so much.
- Deep tech startups are those that have developed intellectual property that promise an outsize impact but are yet to be realised, and are premised on new scientific breakthroughs. Crucially, businesses and startups based on ideas that are easily replicable do not qualify as deep tech startups.
- Deep-tech startups tackle complex engineering and scientific challenges, typically without any form of existing framework, to develop transformative types of technologies.
- The main areas deep tech startups are working in are artificial intelligence (AI), life sciences, agriculture, aerospace, chemistry, industry, and clean energy.
- India's draft policy document on **Deep tech'** (unveiled in June 2023) cites Startup India's database, which claims that there are 10,298 startups recognised by the Department for Promotion of Industry and Internal Trade which are classified across various sub-sectors within the larger deep tech space as of **May 2023.**

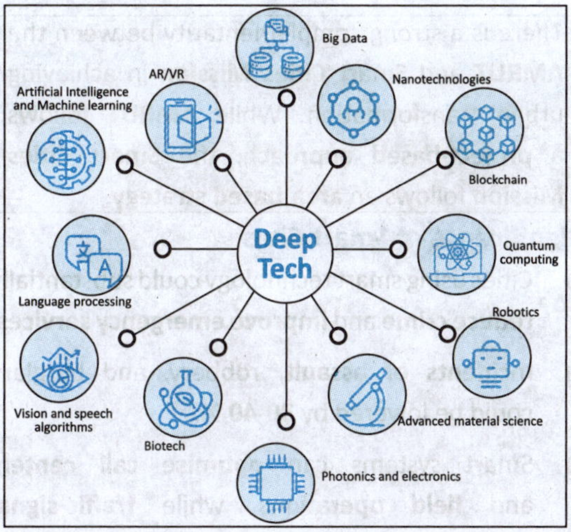

Smart Cities

- Smart Cities Mission launched on **25 June 2015**, is aimed at providing **core infrastructure, clean and sustainable environment** and a **decent quality of life to their citizens** through the **application of smart solutions.**
- It was launched by the **Govt. of India** to improve infrastructure and **drive economic growth** in **100 cities** of the country. The mission also aims to create **replicable models** of these cities that can inspire the country's other cities to become Smart.

Smart City Components	
• Smart Buildings	• Smart Manufacturing
• Mobility/WiFi	• Smart/digital citizens
• Open Data	• Smart transportation
• Smart Health	• Smart farming/ Agriculture
• Smart Government	• Smart Grid/Energy/ Utilities

IoT enabled Smart City	
• Digital Signace	• Pollution
• Parkwide WiFi	• Smart Parking
• CCTV Surveillance	• 3D Map & Interaction
• Weather Sensors	• Analytics
• Public Announcement	• Energy Control
• Operation Control	• Waste Management
• Water Management	• Emergency Systems
• IoT Control	• Inventory/Workflow Monitoring
• People Tracking	
• Smart Metering	

Smart City	
• Smart Building	• Smart Infrastructure
• Smart Education	• Smart Water & Sanitation
• Smart Energy	• Smart Town Planning
• Smart Healthcare	• Smart Transportation Mobility
• Smart Security	
• Smart Governance	

- It is a **transformational mission** aimed to bring about a **paradigm shift** in the practice of **urban development** in the country.

> Of the total proposed projects under **SCM, 6,041** (76%) projects worth **₹1,10,635 crore** have been completed and the remaining **1,894 projects** worth **₹60,095 crore** will be completed by **30 June 2024**.

Features of Smart city

- Society needs well-developed **health care,** education, housing, and infrastructure.
- Deliver enhanced key services to the community reliably and cost-effectively.
- Better housing.
- Improve economic growth of the society.
- Effective management of the resources to reduce depletion.
- Create more job opportunities.
- A well-developed smart plan for data analysis and involvement of the community in broad.
- Boosting the local economy.
- Well-handled urbanization and coping strategies for population growth and climate change.
- Use of smart technology for community needs
- The streamlined transportation system.

- The **Internet of Things**, **public safety**, **smart mobility, increased tourism, social infrastructure,** and **physical infrastructure** make a city's transformation into a smart city smoother.
- The insights drawn from the roadmap of leading Smart cities around the world are summarized into the **4 pillars.**
    - An **IoT-enabled infrastructure** that has a robust network of devices and applications.
    - **Intelligent transport systems,** shared mobility services and more help in achieving effective mobility for smart cities.
    - **Cyber resilience maintains** a balance between efficiency and data privacy.
    - **Participatory Approach:** Involving the community in smart cities initiatives.

Strategy adopted by Smart Cities Mission

- **Pan-city initiative** in which at least one Smart Solution is applied city-wide.
- Develop areas step-by-step.

3 Models of area based developments
- Retrofitting
- Redevelopment
- Greenfield

Core Infrastructure Elements of Smart Cities

- Adequate water supply.
- Assured electricity supply.
- Sanitation, including solid waste management.
- Efficient urban mobility and public transport.
- Affordable housing, especially for the poor.
- Robust IT connectivity and digitalization.
- Good governance, especially e-Governance and citizen participation.
- Sustainable environment.
- Safety and security of citizens, particularly women, children and the elderly.
- Health and education.

- **Comprehensive development** occurs in areas by integrating the **physical**, **institutional**, **social** and **economic infrastructure**. Many of the sectoral schemes of the Government converge in this goal, although the path is different.

> There is a strong complementarity between the **AMRUT** and **Smart Cities Mission** in achieving urban transformation. While **AMRUT** follows a **project-based approach**, the **Smart Cities Mission** follows an **area-based strategy**.

Significance of Smart Cites

- Cities using smart technology could substantially **reduce crime** and **improve emergency services.**
- **Incidents of assault**, robbery, and burglary could be lowered by **30-40 %.**
- Smart systems can **optimise call centers** and **field operations**, while **traffic-signal**

preemption gives **emergency vehicles** a clear driving path. These types of applications could cut emergency response times by **20 to 35 %**.

- Deploying a range of applications to their maximum effect could potentially reduce fatalities (from homicide, road traffic, and fires) by **8 to 10 %**.
- Applications such as **pay-as-you-throw digital tracking** can reduce the volume of solid waste per capita by **10 to 20%**.

PYQ (2013 – 024)

Q. With reference to 'LiFi', recently in the news, which of the following statements is/are correct? 2016

1. It uses light as the medium for high-speed data transmission.
2. It is a wireless technology and is many times faster than 'WiFi.

Select the correct answer using the code given below:

(a) 1 only (b) 2 only
(c) Both 1 and 2 (d) Neither 1 nor 2

Q. With reference to Visible Light Communication (VLC) technology, which of the following statements are correct? 2020

1. VLC uses electromagnetic spectrum wavelengths 375 to 780 nm.
2. VLC is known as long-range optical wireless communication.
3. VLC can transmit large amounts of data faster than Bluetooth
4. VLC has no electromagnetic interference.

Select the correct answer using the code given below:

(a) 1, 2 and 3 only (b) 1, 2 and 4 only
(c) 1, 3 and 4 only (d) 2, 3 and 4 only

Q. Consider the following pairs : 2018

Terms sometimes seen in news	Context /Topic
1. Belle II experiment	-Artificial Intelligence
2. Blockchain technology	-Digital/Cryptocurrency
3. CRISPR — Cas9	- Particle Physics

Which of the pairs given above is/are correctly matched ?

(a) 1 and 3 only (b) 2 only
(c) 2 and 3 only (d) 1, 2 and 3

Q. Consider the following communication technologies:

1. Closed-circuit Television
2. Radio Frequency Identification
3. Wireless Local Area Network

Which of the above are considered of Short-Range devices/technologies?

(a) 1 and 2 only (b) 2 and 3 only
(c) 1 and 3 only (d) 1, 2 and 3

Q. When the alarm of your smartphone rings in the morning, you wake up and tap it to stop the alarm which causes your geyser to be switched on automatically. The smart mirror in your bathroom shows the day's weather and also indicates the level of water in your overhead tank. After you take some groceries from your refrigerator for making breakfast, it recognises the shortage of stock in it and places an order for the supply of fresh grocery items.When you step out of your house and lock the door, all lights, fans, geysers and AC machines get switched off automatically. On your way to the office, your car warns you about traffic congestion ahead and suggests an alternative route, and if you are late for a meeting, it sends a- message to your office accordingly.

In the context of emerging communication technologies, which one of the following terms " best" applies to the above scenario? 2018

(a) Border Gateway Protocol
(b) Internet of Things
(c) Internet Protocol
(d) Virtual Private Network

Q. "3D printing" has applications in which of the following? 2018

1. Preparation of confectionery items
2. Manufacture of bionic ears
3. Automotive industry
4. Reconstructive surgeries
5. Data processing technologies

Select the correct answer using the code given below :

(a) 1, 3 and 4 only (b) 2, 3 and 5 only
(c) 1 and 4 only (d) 1, 2, 3, 4 and 5

Q. With reference to communication technologies, what is/are the difference/ differences between LTE (Long-Term Evolution) and VoLTE (Voice over Long-Term Evolution)? 2019

1. LTE is commonly marketed as 3G and VoLTE is commonly marketed as advanced 3G.
2. LTE is data-only technology and VoLTE is voice-only technology.

Select the correct answer using the code given below.

(a) 1 only (b) 2 only
(c) Both 1 and 2 (d) Neither 1 nor 2

Q. In the context of digital technologies for entertainment, consider the following statements: 2019

1. In Augmented Reality (AR), a simulated environment is created and the physical world is completely shut out.
2. In Virtual Reality (VR), images generated from a computer are projected into real-life objects or surroundings.
3. AR allows individuals to be present in the world and improves the experience using the camera of smart-phone or PC.
4. VR closes the world, and transposes an individual, providing complete immersion experience.

Which of the statements given above is/are correct?

(a) 1 and 2 only (b) 3 and 4
(c) 1, 2 and 3 (d) 4 only

Q. In the context of wearable technology, which of the following tasks is/are accomplished by wearable devices? 2019

1. Location identification of a person
2. Sleep monitoring of a person
3. Assisting the hearing impaired person

Select the correct answer using the code given below:

(a) 1 only (b) 2 and 3 only
(c) 3 only (d) 1, 2 and 3

Q. Consider the following activities: 2020

1. Spraying pesticides on a crop field
2. Inspecting the craters of active volcanoes
3. Collecting breath samples from spouting whales for DNA analysis

At the present level of technology, which of the above activities can be successfully carried out by using drones?

(a) 1 and 2 only (b) 2 and 3 only
(c) 1 and 3 only (d) 1,2 and 3

Q. In India, the term "Public Key Infrastructure" is used in the context of (2020)

(a) Digital security infrastructure
(b) Food security infrastructure
(c) Health care and education infrastructure
(d) Telecommunication and transportation infrastructure

Q. With reference to "Blockchain Technology", consider the following statements: 2020

1. It is a public ledger that everyone can inspect, but which no single user controls.
2. The structure and design of blockchain is such that all the data in it are about cryptocurrency only.
3. Applications that depend on basic features of blockchain can be developed without anybody's permission.

Which of the statements given above is/are correct?

(a) 1 only (b) 1 and 2 only
(c) 2 only (d) 1 and 3 only

Q. 'Project Loon', sometimes seen in the news, is related to (2016)

(a) Waste management technology

(b) Wireless communication technology

(c) Solar power production technology

(d) Water conservation technology

Q. With reference to Web 3.0, consider the following statements: (2022)

1. Web 3.0 technology enables people to control their own data.
2. In Web 3.0 world, there can be blockchain-based social networks.
3. Web 3.0 is operated by users collectively rather than a corporation

Which of the following given above are correct?

(a) 1 and 2 only (b) 2 and 3 only

(c) 1 and 3 only (d) 1, 2 and 3

Q. With reference to "Software as a Service", Consider the following statements. (2022_

1. SaaS buyers can customise the user interface and can change data fields.
2. SaaS users can access their data through their mobile devices.
3. Outlook, Hotmail and Yahoo! Mail are forms of SaaS.

Which of the statements given above are correct?

(a) 1 and 2 only (b) 2 and 3 only

(c) 1 and 3 only (d) 1, 2 and 3

Q. With reference to 'Near Field Communication (NFC) Technology', which of the following statements is/are correct? (2015)

1. It is a contactless communication technology that uses electromagnetic radio fields.
2. NFC is designed for use by devices which can be at a distance of even a metre from each other.
3. NFC can use encryption when sending sensitive information.

Select the correct answer using the code given below.

(a) 1 and 2 only (b) 3 only

(c) 1 and 3 only (d) 1,2 and 3

Q. Which one of the following words/phrases is most appropriately used to denote "an interoperable network of 3D virtual worlds that can be accessed simultaneously by millions of users, who can exert property rights over virtual items"? (2024)

(a) Big data analytics (b) Cryptography

(c) Metaverse (d) Virtual matrix

Q. With the present state of development, Artificial Intelligence an effectively do which of the following? (2020)

1. Bring down electricity consumption in industrial units.
2. Create meaningful short stories and songs.
3. Disease diagnosis.
4. Text-to-Speech Conversion.
5. Wireless transmission of electrical energy.

Select the correct answer using the code given below:

(a) 1, 2, 3 and 5 only (b) 1, 3 and 4 only

(c) 2, 4 and 5 only (d) 1, 2, 3, 4 and 5

Q. In addition to fingerprint scanning, which of the following can be used in the biometric identification of a person? (2014)

1. Iris scanning
2. Retinal scanning
3. Voice recognition

Select the correct answer using the code given below.

(a) 1 only (b) 2 and 3 only

(c) 1 and 3 only (d) 1, 2 and 3

Q. Introduce the concept of Artificial Intelligence (AI). How does AI help clinical diagnosis? Do you perceive any threat to privacy of the individual in the use of AI in healthcare?(2023)

Q. Introduce the concept of Artificial Intelligence (AI). How does AI help clinical diagnosis? Do you perceive any threat to privacy of the individual in the use of AI in healthcare?

(UPSC Mains 2023)

UNIT 7 ROBOTICS

- ***Robotics** is derived from the word **Robot** which was coined by **Karl Joseph Caped,** who used the word is his **1920** play **Rossum's Universal Robots**. How ever in **1940's** Oxford English dictionary credited science fiction author **Issac Asimov** for using the word. Robot is an artificially operated machine which aims to replace **human labour** by **automated devices** with **higher degree of precision** for **extended hours.***
- ***Robotics** deals with design, manufacture and processing of such robots. During the Industrial Revolution and the Age of Enlightenment, an increased focus on engineering, mathematics, and science grew in England, boosting the momentum toward the implementation of robotics in society. In the 1930s, the popularity of computers fueled the development of Numerically Controlled (NC) machines, paving the way for industrial robots. The first known industrial robot dates back to 1937 when Griffith Taylor built a crane-like device capable of automating the stacking of wooden blocks from pre-programmed patterns.In 1954, George Devol known as the Grandfather of Robotics was awarded with first industrial robotics patent. In the 1990s, remote-controlled robots brought synchronisation to the industry.*

Laws of Robotics

They were given by **Issac Asiamov** to provide and **ethical framework** for robotic interaction with Humans.

- A **robot may not injure a human being** or, through **inaction**, allow a **human being** to come to **harm.**
- A robot must **obey the orders** given it by **human beings** except where such orders would conflict with the First Law.
- A robot must **protect** its **own existence** as long as such protection does not conflict with the **First or Second Laws.**

Robotics

- Robot is defined as a **self-controlled device** consisting of **electronic, electrical** or **mechanical** units that can function in place of a living agent.
- Robotics is a **multidisciplinary field** that encompasses the **design, construction, operation** and **use of robots**, which can be **physical machines, software,** or a **combination** of both, designed to perform tasks autonomously or with human guidance.

Components of Robots

- **Actuators:** They are like a robot's muscles, converting energy into motion, powered by electricity, hydraulics, or pneumatics, moving the robot's limbs, wheels, or other parts.
- **Sensors:** Sensors are the robot's eyes and ears, giving information about its surroundings. They come in types like light, proximity, and force sensors.
- **Power supply:** Robots need a power source, like batteries or electricity, to work, depending on the robot type and its tasks.
- **Controller:** The controller is the robot's brain, getting input from sensors and sending commands to actuators. It interprets data, makes decisions, and controls movements.
- **Structure:** It gives physical support and protection to the robot's components. It can be metal, plastic, or composite materials.
- **Programming:** The Brain of the robot includes algorithms, AI, and software for decision-making, movement, and interactions.

- **End effectors:** Tools like grippers, welding arms, or sensors, that allow the robot to interact with its environment.

Types of Robots

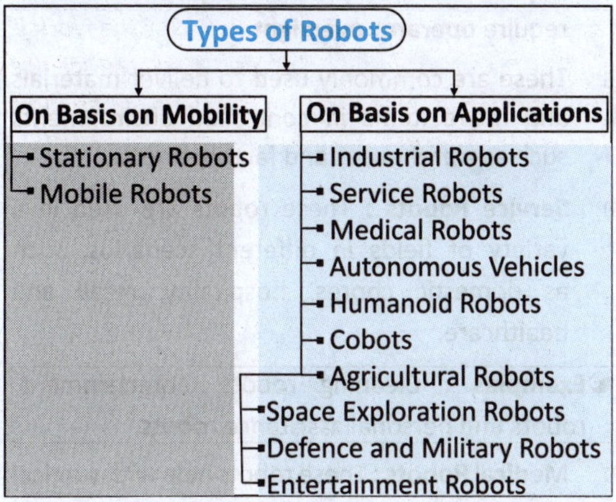

Stationary Robots

- Those which are fixed and lack mobility.

Articulated Robots

- Articulated robots (also known as robotic arms) are meant to **emulate** the **functions of a human arm**.
- Typically, these can feature anywhere from two to **10 rotary joints.**
- Each additional joint or axis allows for a **greater degree** of motion, making these ideal for arc **welding, material handling, machine tending** and **packaging.**

Industrial Robots

- An industrial robot is one that has been developed to automate intensive production tasks such as those required by a constantly moving assembly line.
- As large, heavy robots, they are placed in fixed positions within an industrial plant and all other worker tasks and processes revolve around them.
- They are a **multifunctional, reprogrammable, automatically controlled manipulator,** programmable in three or more axes that can be fixed in one area or mobile for use in industrial automation applications.

Cobots (Collaborative Robots)

- A collaborative robot, also known as a **cobot,** is an **industrial robot** that can safely operate alongside humans in a **shared workspace.**
- In contrast, **autonomous robots** are hard-coded to repeatedly **perform one task,** work **independently** and **remain stationary.**
- These robots are **collaborative** because they can safely work together with people. They can do this because they are equipped with **sensitive sensors** that give the robot feel. If the robot is interrupted in its work, it will shoot into a safety mode.
- **Advances in mobile technology, Artificial Intelligence** (AI), **machine vision, cognitive computing** and **touch technology** are making it possible for small, lower-power robots to be aware of their surroundings and perform multiple types of tasks safely in close proximity to human workers.
- In addition to being programmed to protect the safety of their **human coworkers,** Cobots can quickly learn tasks through **demonstration** and **reinforcement learning.**
- Cobots are equipped with **software-controlled sensors** that enable them to detect objects, people and potential collisions. The software monitors every movement of a cobot and immediately shuts it down if it detects something unexpected.
- The majority of **industrial cobots** are **power and force limitation** (PFL) **cobots,** which means that in the case of an unexpected collision, their **built-in sensors** can identify when abnormal force is applied, causing the cobot to either slow down or cease operating to prevent accidents and injuries. Usually, the edges of these cobots are rounded to mitigate any **potential collisions** with human workers.

> The first cobot was Invented in **1996** by **J. Edward Colgate** and **Michael Peshkin**. They called the cobot **a device and method for direct physical interaction between a person and a computer-controlled manipulator.**

Mobile Robots

- Those that move around their environment.

Autonomous Mobile Robots (AMRs)

- AMRs **move throughout the world** and **make decisions** in **near real-time** as they go.
- Technologies such as **sensors** and **cameras** help them **ingest information** about their **surroundings.**
- **Onboard processing equipment** helps them analyze it and make an informed decision—whether that's moving to avoid an oncoming worker, picking precisely the right parcel, or selecting an appropriate surface to disinfect.

Military Robots

- Military robots are **autonomous robots** or **remote-controlled devices** which designed for **military applications,** They can walk through **minefields, deactivate unexploded bombs** or clear out hostile buildings.
- Robot soldiers are **autonomous robots** or **remote-controlled mobile robots** designed for **military applications,** from transport to search & **rescue** and **attack.**
- Military robots can include different types of weapons and are more efficient than a human controlling these weapons.
- **Military Robots** can be controlled or fully **autonomous, Intelligence, Surveillance** and **Reconnaissance** (ISR) can use **military satellites, UAVs, UGVs, USVs, ROVs, AUVs** and others are extensively used in the ISR application.
- **Rescue Robots** are used in the **military,** and they can play a **crucial role in saving lives,** The majority of casualties happen due to the delay in offering necessary aid to victims, Rescue robots are highly advantageous in war, They can **search, track** and rescue in **nuclear, biological, radiological** and **chemical environments.**
- An AMR might be combined with a **robotic arm** to create a robot for **handling packages** inside of a **warehouse.**

Automated Guided Vehicles (AGVs)

- While AMRs traverse environments freely, AGVs rely on tracks or **predefined paths** and often require **operator oversight.**
- These are commonly used to deliver materials and move items in controlled environments such as warehouses and factory floors.
- **Service Robots :** These robots are used in a variety of fields in different scenarios, such as domestic chores, hospitality, retail and healthcare.

> **Examples :** Cleaning robots, entertainment robots and personal assistance robots.

- **Medical Robots :** These robots help with surgical procedures, rehabilitation and diagnostics in healthcare settings.

> **Examples:** Robotic surgery systems, exoskeletons and artificial limbs.

- **Autonomous Vehicles :** These robots are mainly used for transportation purposes and can include self-driving cars, drones and autonomous delivery robots.

> They navigate and make decisions using advanced sensors and AI algorithms.

- **Agricultural Robots :** These robots are used in farming and agricultural applications. They can plant, harvest, apply pesticides and check crop health.
- **Educational Robots :** These robots are created to instruct and educate kids about robotics, programming and problem-solving. Kits and platforms for hands-on learning in academia are frequent examples of educational robots.
- **Entertainment Robots :** Created for entertainment purposes, these robots come in the form of robotic pets, humanoid companions and interactive toys.

Humanoids

- While many mobile humanoid robots may technically fall under the domain of an AMR, the term is used to identify robots that perform human-centric functions and often take human-like forms.
- They use many of the same technology components as **AMRs** to sense, plan, and act as they carry out tasks such as providing directions or offering concierge services.

> **Sophia** a **Social humanoid robot** developed by a **Hong Kong** based company **Hanson Robotics** and activated on **February 14, 2016** was granted **citizenship** of **Saudi Arabia** in **October citizenship** becoming the first robot to receive personhood. It was named **UNDP's** first **Innovation Champion** becoming the first **non human** to be awarded **UN title.**

Hybrids

- The various types of robots are often combined to create **hybrid solutions** capable of performing more complex tasks.

Nanobots

- Robots that carry out specific precision functions are range **50-100nm in size.**

Other Types of Robots

- **Androids :** Resemble humans and are often mobile.
- **Telechir :** Complex and remotely controlled.
- **Telepresence :** Simulates being physically present.
- **Industrial :** Adaptable, reprogrammable, multipurpose, manipulator.
- **SWARM :** Insect robots working in fleets; supervised by a single controller.
- **Smart :** Built in AI that learns form environment and experiences.
- **Construction robots :** Construction robots can be separated into three types: **traditional robots, robotic arm** and **robotic exoskeleton.**
- **Agricultural robots (AgRobots):** The use of robots in agriculture is closely linked to the concept of **AI-assisted precision agriculture** and **drone usage.**
- **Medical robots** such as da Vinci Surgical System and Hospi.
- **Kitchen automation:** Commercial examples of kitchen automation are **Flippy** (burgers), **Zume Pizza** (pizza), **Cafe X** (coffee), **Makr Shakr** (cocktails), **Frobot** (frozen yogurts) and **Sally** (salads). Home examples are **Rotimatic** (flatbreads baking) and **Boris** (dishwasher loading).
- **Robot combat for Sports:** Hobby or sport event where two or more robots fight in an arena to disable each other. This has developed from a hobby in the 1990s to several TV series worldwide.
- Cleanup of contaminated areas, such as toxic waste or nuclear facilities.

Applications of Robotics

Industrial Applications

- The manufacturing industry has long been at the forefront of using various types of robots to achieve **business results.**
- **AMRs, AGVs, articulated robots** and **cobots** are all deployed on **factory floors** and in **warehouses** to help **expedite processes, drive efficiency,** and **promote safety,** often in conjunction with programmable logic controllers.
- They're used across a variety of applications, including **welding, assembly, materials transportation** and **warehouse security.**

Agricultural Applications

- AMRs are helping farmers **harvest** their crops more quickly and efficientlyand they're using impressive intelligence capabilities to do it.
- Agricultural robots can assess **ripeness, move any branches** or **leaves out** of the way, and pick the crop precisely and delicately to avoid causing any harm to the product.

- **Applications of Robots in agriculture appear to fall into 4 major categories:**
  - **Crop and Soil Monitoring:** Companies are leveraging sensors and various IoT-based technologies to monitor crop and soil health.
  - **Predictive Agricultural Analytics:** Various AI and machine learning tools are being used to predict the optimal time to sow seeds, get alerts on risks from pest attacks, and more.
  - **Supply Chain Efficiencies:** Companies are using real-time data analytics on data-streams coming from multiple sources to build an efficient and smart supply chain.
  - **Agricultural Robots:** Companies are developing and programming autonomous robots to handle essential agricultural tasks such as harvesting crops at a higher volume and faster pace than human labourers.
- **Examples of Agricultural Robots :**
  - **Green seeker sensor:** This smart machine reads a plant's needs and then applies precisely the amount of fertilizer of herbicides needed.

> **Green Seeker** is a machine which uses the sensors to let the plant tell us that what it needs.

  - **Robot drone tractors:** A new generation of robot drones is revolutionizing the way we farm, with manufacturing of different robots, announcing the **first ever robot drone tractor** becomes part of the agricultural mainstream. Robot will decide where to plant, when to harvest and how to choose the best route for crisscrossing the farmland.
  - **Flying Robots To Spread Fertilizer:** A flying robot monitors the growing condition of the crops over farmlands in Ili, a **Kazak autonomous** prefecture in **Northwest China's Xinjiang Uygur autonomous.** With camera equipment and an automatic fertilizing system in the front, the robot can fly autonomously and apply fertilizer independently.
  - **Fruit Picking Robots:** The research is still in full progress, especially as the robots need to be carefully designed so that they do not bruise the fruit while picking. One solution is the use of suction grippers, used on automated fruit picking machines manufactured, for example, by
  - **Robot Cattle Grazing and Automatic Milking:** Is the milking of dairy animals, especially of dairy cattle, without human labour.

> **Automatic milking systems** (AMS), also called **voluntary milking systems** (VMS), were developed in the late 20th century. They are commercially available since the early 1990s.

Logistics

- Robotics help logistics and shipping companies to **deliver goods quickly** and **efficiently.** They use AMRs and AGVs as **warehouse robots** that help them process items, expedite operations, and increase accuracy. They also employ AMRs to take shipments the last mile and ensure safe delivery to customers.
- Robots are used in warehouses for tasks like **picking and packing**, **sorting**, and **inventory management.**

Retail and Hospitality

- Robotics can be used to **enhance the customer** or **guest experience** in a variety of ways.
- **Retail** and **hospitality companies** are using robotics to **automate inventory processes, provide concierge** or **way-finding services,** clean various environments, and assist customers with their luggage or valet parking.

Manufacturing and Assembly

- Robots are extensively used in industries for tasks like welding, painting, assembly, and packaging. They increase efficiency, precision, and consistency in production processes.

Defense and Security

- Robots are employed for tasks such as bomb disposal, surveillance, and reconnaissance in hazardous or high-risk environments, enhancing the safety of human personnel.

Education and Research

- Educational robots are used to teach programming and robotics concepts to students.
- Research robots are employed in various scientific experiments and studies.

Machine Learning

- **Computer vision :** Robots can perceive, identify and navigate their environments with the help of machine vision, which uses ML algorithms and sensors. Computer vision is used in a wide range of settings, including manufacturing procedures, such as material inspection and pattern and signature recognition.
- **Self-supervised learning :** By using large sets of data, robots can be taught to perform tasks without being specifically trained to do so, such as in neural networks. Self-supervised learning can be used to increase the ability of robots to adapt to changing environments.
- **Imitation learning :** This entails educating robots to replicate human behavior by demonstrating desirable actions to them. This can be used to improve the speed and accuracy of automated procedures.
- **Assistive robotics :** Machine learning can be used to create robotic devices that help people with daily tasks such as mobility and household duties. For example, wheelchair-mounted robot arms can offer greater independence to people with limited mobility in their upper extremities.
- **Reinforcement learning :** This entails teaching robots how to carry out challenging tasks through the use of trial-and-error techniques to make robotic systems more effective and efficient.

Autonomous Vehicles

- Self-driving cars, drones, and unmanned aerial vehicles (UAVs) are examples of autonomous vehicles that can transport goods and people without human intervention.

Environmental Monitoring and Cleanup

- Robots are used to monitor and clean up hazardous environments, such as nuclear facilities or polluted areas, where human presence may pose risks.

Mining and Exploration

- Robots are used in mining operations for tasks like drilling, excavation, and transportation of materials in environments that may be dangerous for human workers.

Finance and Banking

- Robots are used in customer service applications, including chatbots and virtual assistants, for tasks like account inquiries and financial advice.

Smart Cities
Robotics help create **smarter** and **safer cities.**
Humanoid robots offer way-finding and information services. AMRs are used to deliver goods and conduct routine security patrols.
Robotics also help **expedite building construction**, **conduct site surveys** and **collect building modeling information.**

Healthcare

- Various types of robots are used in the healthcare industry to **enhance the patient experience.** AMRs are used to **deliver medication, disinfect surfaces,** or provide mobile telepresence functionality.
- Cobots are also used to assist medical professionals during **rehabilitation** or to help nurses better serve their patients.

Significance of Robotics in Pandemics

- **Disinfecting surfaces:** Large and small autonomous or remote-controlled robots could be developed to **locate** and **constantly sterilize** frequently touched surfaces with **ultraviolet light.**
- **Contract Tracing:** The roboticists say combining existing security systems with **facial recognition software** could allow authorities to retrace the steps of patients who tested positive for **COVID-19** and contact others who might be at risk, which is known as contact tracing.

- **Nasal swabs:** Testing for coronavirus involves inserting a swab fairly deep into a **patient's nasal cavity**. There are parts of the process that puts humans at risk of contracting the virus, including collecting the sample, handling the sample, transferring the sample to the test location and the test itself. **Automated** or **robot-assisted nasopharyngeal** and **oropharyngeal swabbing** may speed up the process, reduce the risk of infection, and free up staff for other tasks.
- **Medicine Delivery:** Autonomous drones and ground robots can be used to deliver medicine to patients in isolated wards.

> In the field hospital in **Wuhan, China, CloudMinds robots** were used to deliver food, drink and medicine to patients during CoViD pandemic.

- **Social Robots:** In the time of isolation and quarantine, social robots can help people provide **social stimulation** and **interactions**, in addition to providing reminders to follow treatment regimens (to the elderly).

Robots in Space Exploration

- Robots help NASA explore the solar system and the **Universe**. Spacecraft that explore other worlds, like the Moon or Mars, are all **robotic**.
- These robots include **rovers and landers** on the **surface of other planets**. The **Mars rovers Spirit** and **Opportunity** are examples of this kind of robot.
- Other **robotic spacecraft** fly by or orbit other worlds and study them from space.

> **Cassini**, the spacecraft that studies Saturn and its moons and rings, is this type of robot. The **Voyager** and **Pioneer spacecraft** now traveling outside Earth's solar system are also robots.

Planetary Robot Systems

- **Planetary robot systems** are robots that are **designed to operate** on the **surface of other planets**, such as **Mars** or the **Moon**. These robots are typically much more complex than **microgravity robotics** and must be able to **operate in harsh environments** with **extreme temperatures, radiation** and **dust storms.**
- One of the **primary roles of planetary robot** systems is to **explore the surface of other planets** and **gather scientific data.**

> **Mars rovers, Spirit, Opportunity** and **Curiosity**, have explored the Martian surface and have made numerous scientific discoveries, including **evidence of past water** on **Mars.**

- These robots are equipped with a wide range of scientific instruments, such as **cameras, spectrometers**, and drills, which allow them to **analyse rocks** and **soil samples.**

> The **first robot** ever sent to space was **Sputnik 1**, sent by the **USSR** on **October 4, 1957**, according to **NASA**. Sputnik 1 was the **first artificial Earth satellite** and the **first object** created by **humans to orbit Earth.**

- American space probe **Mariner 2** became the first robotic space probe to complete a successful Venus flyby.

> **Mariner 4**, the first orbiter sent to space, then took the first proximal photos of Mars on **July 14, 1965.**

- While the role of landers is primarily to detect signs of life on planets, the role of orbiters is primarily to take photos for scientists to observe and analyze. Since the roles of these robots are different, orbiters and landers have frequently been sent to explore space in tandem.

> **Robots** exited the solar system in **1977** when **Voyagers 1 and 2** were launched to study the outer solar system.

- According to NASA, the **two robots** were designed to conduct close-up studies of **Jupiter and Saturn, Saturn's rings**, and both **Jupiter** and **Saturn's largest moon.**
- The two robots have continued on this journey for over **40 years** and are presently closer to **Pluto** than to **Earth** or **the sun**. It was not until **August 2012** that **Voyager 1** entered into interstellar space, while **Voyager 2** eventually

followed on **November 5, 2018.** Both robots are still communicating information via the **Deep Space Network** (DSN) currently.

- **Planetary robot systems** play a crucial role in preparing for **human missions** to other **planets.**

> The **Mars rovers** have been used to test technologies that will be used in future human missions, including the production of oxygen from the **Martian atmosphere.**

- By using robots to trial these technologies, scientists can ensure that they are safe and effective before they are used on human missions.
- **Robotic arms on spacecraft** are used to move large objects in space. **Spacecraft** that visit other worlds are robots that can do work by themselves. This type of robot includes the rovers that explore the surface of Mars. **Robotic airplanes** can fly without a pilot aboard.
- NASA is developing new robots that could help people in space. For example, one of these ideas is called **Robonaut.**

> **Robonaut** looks like the **upper body** of a person. It has a chest, head and arms. Robonaut could work outside a spacecraft, performing tasks like an astronaut on a spacewalk. With wheels or another way of moving, Robonaut also could work on the moon, or another world. Robonaut could work alongside astronauts and help them.

- Another robot idea is called **SPHERES.** These are small robots that look a little like **soccer balls.** The **current SPHERES** are being used on the **space station** to test how well they can move in microgravity. Someday, similar robots could fly around inside the station helping astronauts.

Advantages of Robots

- **Safety :** Safety is arguably one of robotics' greatest benefits, as many dangerous or unhealthy environments no longer require the human element. Examples include the nuclear industry, space, defense and maintenance. With robots or robotic systems, workers can avoid exposure to hazardous chemicals and even limit psychosocial and ergonomic health risks.
- **Increased Productivity :** Robots don't readily become tired or worn out as humans do. They can work continuously without breaks while performing repetitive jobs, which boosts productivity.
- **Accuracy :** Robots can perform precise tasks with greater consistency and accuracy than humans can. This eliminates the risk of errors and inconsistencies.
- **Flexibility :** Robots can be programmed to carry out a variety of tasks and are easily adaptable to new use cases.
- **Cost savings :** By automating repetitive tasks, robots can reduce labor costs.

Limitations of Robots

- **Task suitability :** Certain tasks are simply better suited for humans -for example, those jobs that require creativity, adaptability and critical decision-making skills.
- **Economic Challenges:** Since robots can perform most jobs that humans do with more precision, speed and accuracy, there's always a potential risk that they could eventually replace human jobs.
- **Cost :** Most robotic systems have a high initial cost. It can also cost a lot to repair and maintain robots.
- **Increased dependency :** Overreliance on robots can result in a decrease in human talents and problem-solving abilities as well as an increase in technological dependence.
- **Security risks:** There's always a risk of robotic devices getting hacked or hijacked, especially if they're being used for defense and security purposes, especially with the advancement in Artificial intelligence and threats of Cyber Attacks.

- **Power requirements :** Robots consume a lot of energy and constant power to operate. Regular upkeep and maintenance are also required to keep them in good working condition.

Robotics Pros and Cons	
Better than humans	**Shortcomings**
Automate manual, repetitive activities	Restricted by their programming
Work in unpredictable, hazardous environments	Can sense intruders, but not take action
Process, deliver reports for enterprise security	Ease loneliness, empathize
Fill out pharmaceutical prescriptions, prep IVs	Respond to unexpected situations
Deliver necessities during emergencies	Require constant power source, maintenance
Assist during surgeries without getting tired	Open door to cybersecurity issues

National Strategy on Robotics

- Ministry of Electronics and Information Technology is committed to the vision of fostering and promoting cutting-edge technology use cases in the country.
- Advances in AI are expected to have a significant impact in the realm of **Cyber-Physical Systems** (CPS) such as Robotics which relies on AI to enable the interaction of the virtual world with components of physical systems.
- To further maximize the benefits of an AI-integrated society the National Strategy on Robotics has been envisaged as one such key component of IndiaAI.
- The national strategy on robotics policy will present significant opportunities for the manufacturing sector, Industry 4.0 and cyber-physical systems among others, it has the potential to create a lot of impact.
- National Strategy on Robotics aims to capitalize this potential and nurture the development of robotic technology, helping India emerge as a Robotics Hub for the world.
- To drive India's global leadership in Robotics, four sectors of strategic importance have also been identified, namely manufacturing, agriculture, healthcare and national security.
- To enable India's emergence as a global leader in the development and adoption of robotics, a comprehensive, coherent, and efficient deployment of the National Strategy on Robotics is proposed to be undertaken as the National Robotics Mission.
- This will be done through the establishment of the Robotics Innovation Unit (RIU) as an institutional framework under IndiaAI, to facilitate the implementation of the National Strategy on Robotics, adopting a whole ecosystem approach.
- Multiple interventions have been recommended across the key pillars of a robotics innovation cycle which include Research and Development, Demonstration and Testing, Commercialization and Supply Chain Development, and Adoption and Awareness, to ensure the creation of domestic capabilities in robotic technology in India.

ARTPARK

- An AI & Robotics Technologies Park (ARTPARK) was set up in Bengaluru in 2020 to promote technology innovations in AI (Artificial Intelligence) & Robotics leading to societal impact by executing ambitious mission mode R&D projects in healthcare, education, mobility, infrastructure, agriculture, retail and cyber-security focusing on problems unique to India.
- **ARTPARK**, is a unique not-for-profit foundation established by **Indian Institute of Science** (IISc), Bengaluru with support from **AI Foundry** in a public-private model.

- **ARTPARK** will develop AI & Robotics facilities to support technology innovations as well as capacity building through advanced skills training of students and professionals in these areas. Some of these facilities will be key enablers for whole new sets of technologies, products and services.
- It will develop **DataSetu** – that will enable confidentiality and privacy-preserving framework to share data and run analytics spurring the data-sharing ecosystem and create a data marketplace, boosting AI applications and solutions.
- One such service will be **BhashaSetu** – that will enable real-time Indic language translation, both of speech to speech and speech to text, which aims to unlock the economic potential of the country, and enable all Indian citizens to equitably participate in the economic progress, regardless of their language.

RPA

- **Ministry of Electronics and Information Technology** (MeitY) inaugurated **Robotic Process Automation** (RPA) Lab in **NIELIT Gorakhpur** on **16th October 2023** under the Future Skill PRIME Project funded by MeitY with an objective to upskill/reskill manpower in emerging technology of RPA.

This is the **First-of-its-kind** lab in **Uttar Pradesh** under **Future Skill PRIME Project**, which has been established to bridge the gap between **Industry** and **Academia**.

Make-in-India Robots

DAKSHA: An automated mobile platform for multi-purpose payloads. It has stair-climbing capabilities and can be deployed for handling IEDs (Improvised Explosive Devices).

Vyommitra: A spacefaring humanoid robot is being developed by the ISRO to function onboard the Gaganyaan.

MANAV: India's first 3D-printed humanoid robot with inbuilt vision and sound processing capability which allows it to walk, talk and dance just in response to human commands.

Unmanned Aerial Vehicles/Drones

- **Unmanned aerial vehicles** (UAVs), more commonly referred to as **drones**, are **small aircraft** that **fly autonomously**. Originally developed for **military purposes**, they are now a major **focus of research**.
- Apart from unmanned aerial vehicles, drones are also referred to as **Unmanned Aerial Systems** (UAS), **Remotely Piloted Vehicles** (RPV) and **Remotely Piloted Aircraft Systems** (RPAS).

- The term **drone** is commonly known publicly, whereas the other terms, like **UAVs, RPA, RPAS** and **UAS** are official names given to the drone technology depending on the **jurisdiction**.
- Previously, the term drone referred to an **unmanned, radio-controlled military** or **target-towing aircraft**. Nowadays, a drone is defined as an aircraft that flies without a pilot at the controls, but rather with the assistance of a ground operator or through automated flight with no human intervention.

Applications of Drones

- Crime scene surveillance
- Marine fauna detection
- Habitat destruction assessment
- Crop monitoring
- Vegetation mapping
- Construction
- Agriculture
- Mining
- Infrastructure inspection
- Humanitarian relief
- Search and rescue missions
- Disaster management

Drone applications under different Union Ministries		
S.No	**Ministry**	**Illustrative drone applications**
1.	Agriculture & Farmers Welfare	• Crop and soil health monitoring • Irrigation estimation and scheduling • Requirement and efficacy assessment of fertilizer and pesticide spraying • Anti-locust operations • Crop output estimates • River and canal erosion; restoration tracking • Insurance claim surveys
2.	Health & Family Welfare	• Delivery of medicines, equipment and other supplies • Pathology tests - sample collection from remote or epidemic/ pandemic affected areas
3.	Panchayati Raj	• Land records and property rights (SVAMITVA Scheme)
4.	Home Affairs	Surveillance, situational analysis, public announcements and evidence gathering for: • Security of sensitive installations • Raids and counter-terror operations • Crowd management • Crime control • VVIP security • Disaster management; search and rescue; transportation of food, medicines and essentials • Traffic management
5.	Defence	• Surveillance • Combat • Communication in remote areas • Swarm drone solutions • Counter drone solutions
6.	Housing and Urban Affairs	• Urban planning and management • Construction planning and monitoring • Incident reporting • Prevention of encroachment and land-use alteration
7.	Transportation: Road Transport and Highways; Railways; Ports, Shipping and Waterways	• Surveillance • Incident response • Inspection and maintenance • Project monitoring • Disaster management

8.	Mining	• Monitoring and Inspection • Automatic surveying and mapping • Stockpile assessment and management • Haulage road optimisation
9.	Power	• Real-time surveillance of assets and transmission lines • Theft prevention and incident response • Visual inspection and maintenance • Construction planning and management
10.	Petroleum and Natural Gas	• Real-time surveillance of assets and pipelines • Theft prevention and incident response • Visual inspection and maintenance • Construction planning and management
11.	Environment, Forests and Climate Change	• Monitoring of forests and wildlife • Afforestation through seed-balls, irrigation and real-time monitoring • Anti-poaching actions • Pollution assessment and evidence-gathering
12.	Information and Broadcasting	• High quality videography of events and • Difficult-to-reach-places at a fraction of the cost and approvals required • Low altitude shooting without noise and-dust pollution and risk of accidents • Complete replacement of costly helicopter- based videography

Applications of Drones in Agriculture

- Indian Government is promoting the use of drones for the **convenience of the farmers,** reducing the cost and increasing the income.
- Indian Government is promoting **Kisan Drones** for **crop assessment, digitization of land records, spraying of pesticides** and **nutrients** for which provision has also been made in the budget.
- For promoting use of **Kisan Drones**, the government is providing **50%** or **maximum Rs. 5 lakh** subsidy to **SC-ST, small and marginal, women** and **farmers of northeastern states** to buy drones.
- For other farmers, **financial assistance** will be given upto **40%** or **maximum Rs.4 lakh.**
- Pilot studies with different approaches like use of **remote sensing technology** including **satellite data** and **drone based images** especially for **crop cutting experiments** planning, direct yield estimation at **Gram Panchayat level,** risk mapping of district and for dispute/ area discrepancy resolution etc. have been conducted through **Mahalanobis National Crop Forecasting Centre** (MNCFC).
- **Standard Operating Procedures** (SOPs) which provide concise instructions for effective and safe operations of drones for pesticide and nutrient application have been released.
- The awareness among farmers is being created through **demonstration** and **capacity building programmes.**

During the **locust attack**, the government had also promptly used drones and helicopters for the rescue.

Applications of Drones in Healthcare

- Drones are being used to deliver **vital medical supplies** to **hard-to-reach areas.** It performs **emergency surgeries** on patients who are too far from a hospital. It also delivers live **video feeds** of **high-risk birth procedures.**
- Drones enable **doctors** and **nurses** to effectively provide healthcare to populations who were previously **unreachable.** In **remote areas** drones can be used as an **alternative** to **helicopters** for transportation needs.
- Using drones equipped with infrared **cameras, doctors** can **scan patients** for tumors without having to perform invasive procedures or expose the patient to harmful radiation.
- A **biopsy** is performed when doctors want to check out if there are any cancerous cells present inside a tumor or cyst. Usually, a needle is used to extract the tissue and then examined under a microscope for signs of cancerous cells. With **3D biopsies** though, tissue samples can be extracted through **noninvasive methods** such as **ultrasound** and **CT scans** before being analyzed for signs of **cancerous cells.**
- Drones can also be used by **surgeons** during surgery so that they can **trace blood** flow around organs and tumors more easily.
- Doctors use **aerial images** taken from drones during surgery. So that they can see how organs connect with each other and ensure there aren't any areas that could become problematic later during recovery.
- Drones are a powerful tool for **transporting medical supplies** to **remote locations.**
- Using Drones as **Healthcare Drones** have the potential to improve healthcare and save lives.
- Allowing hospitals and doctors to **communicate** with their patients more easily will allow them to provide more **personalized care.**
- They can also be used for **day-to-day tasks** like **checking up on patients** in **rural areas.**
- Drones can be used to **deliver medical supplies cost-effectively** to people residing in remote areas and those affected by **natural** disasters or **emergencies.**
- Drones can be used for the rapid **transportation** of **organs** with **high delicacy.** This can potentially **prevent any damage** to the organs during transportation.
- Drones can also be used **inside hospitals** for **delivering biological samples** or medicines from **floor to floor** or from building to building. However, poor **GPS signals** or radio **frequencies** could be an obstacle to successful indoor drone operations. **Bluetooth technology** may partially overcome this obstacle.
- Drones can also be used for **medical surveillance.** In densely **populated areas** with a high prevalence of **infectious diseases,** drones with **integrated cameras** can take videos or pictures of **on-ground situations** to help healthcare experts identify and restrict the factors responsible for rapid disease spread
- **Small drones with manipulator arms** can be used to provide **older people** with medicines and help them in their day-to-day activities, such as picking up something from the floor or sorting laundry.
- Drones have been used to deliver **automated external defibrillators** (AEDs) and save the lives of outpatients suffering cardiac arrest.

Applications of Drones in Disaster Management

- One of the most significant and promising applications of drones is in disaster management, where they can play a crucial role in **saving lives** and **minimizing damage.**
- In a country like India, which is prone to **natural disasters** such as **floods, earthquakes** and **cyclones,** drones can be an invaluable asset in disaster management efforts.
- By providing high-resolution images and data, drones can help authorities identify vulnerable areas, assess the effectiveness of existing

infrastructure, and plan for future disasters. This information can be used to **develop more effective disaster management strategies**, ultimately **reducing the impact of disasters on communities** and saving lives.

- **Emergency Response :** The severity of the disaster can be analysed through a variety of **instruments** and **procedures** thanks to innovative possibilities and advancements.
    - Drone technology has advanced significantly in disaster management, on a scale of advancement. **Unmanned aerial aircraft** (UAVs) have exhilarating advantages, such as **timely outcomes** and **precise data.**
- **Assessing Situations Remotely :** Helicopter inspections are the conventional approach for examining disaster-affected areas.
    - Drone usage can assist in overcoming such obstacles. Drones can assist in **remotely covering** the **damaged regions** and can be deployed practically immediately without the need to plan for operations or safety.
    - Usage of Drones helped **rescue crews** locate victims of disasters more quickly, so have been deployed in search and rescue missions.
- **Mapping Locations :** Accurate mapping of places is one of drone technology's most prominent features. Drones can now provide a **3D** and **360° perspective** of sites thanks to extensive R&D in the field of drone technology.
    - Drones are also utilized to map out demolished structures, monuments, and residences.
    - The greatest benefit of drone technology is that the **GPS location** and **time stamp** that is displayed in the image and video, which not only provides the visuals of the place but also the location and time information.
- **Delivering Urgent Supplies :** Drones are quite helpful in these situations for the quick delivery of food packages, water bottles and other essential supplies. Drones can assist in providing first assistance to those who require it in addition to delivering food supplies.
- **Extinguishing Fires :** Drones can reduce the impact of **severity of threats** faced by fire extinguishing teams those have been using conventional means.
    - Unmanned aircraft can fly in **poor weather conditions** and **drop fire retardants** more precisely and safely. While many smaller drones may be used to give better situational awareness, larger drones can deliver people and cargo.
    - Drones can be effectively used to extinguish fire in **remote areas**, or **multistoreyed buildings** through with **precision**. They can also be deployed in **rough terrains** line mountains in case of **forest fires.**

Drones in Floods and Earthquake

- Drone observations can be used to determine the **flood's direction.** They can even identify which buildings may be in danger, allowing them to prioritize which locations need to be evacuated.
- **Aerial Mapping and Surveys :** Drones were used during the landslide of Oso, Washington in 2014 to map the region after the incident.
- **Damage assessments :** Damage assessments are a costly but necessary part of disaster management. Usually workers have to walk, drive, hike or even dive into dangerous spots, painstakingly sift through debris, and collect all kinds of information manually to paint an accurate picture of a catastrophe.
    - Drones can also get into the heart of post-disaster chaos with little to no consequences while sending humans into the same situations could result in injuries or even death.
    - Drones streamlines communication between various agencies and individuals.
- **Supply Delivery :** Drones are highly effective at delivering supplies since they don't rely on traditional infrastructure to get from point A to point B.

A US-based company called Matternet did its first field trial of medical delivery using drones to camps set up after the 2010 Haiti earthquake.

- **Communications infrastructure :** Disaster response **crews lose contact** with each other their effectiveness drops dramatically.
  - Drones bypass this problem by carrying **payloads** (like cameras and sensors) that can gather information independently. These tools can be a lifeline during serious disasters.
- **Assessing Structural Damage :** Disaster recovery also involves **rebuilding areas** that were affected whilst also analysing how to mitigate the effects if a similar event were to happen in the future.
  - In the wake of earthquakes, flood or fire, drones can assist in the **safe inspection of infrastructure,** so that repairs can be made more quickly than if they were done using traditional methods.
- **In Disaster Planning :** Drones are increasingly being used to assist emergency services with disaster planning – whether that's assessing the scale and impact of a disaster, **managing traffic flow** after a road **traffic collision** or **monitoring** an ongoing fire **emergency.**
  - **Aerial images** from drones can help build a picture of the **emergency situation,** during or after the event, so that the true scale and impact of can be explored.

Drones in National Security

- **Drone-based surveillance** has become increasingly popular in recent years as a tool for **enhancing national** and **border security**.
- Drones can be equipped with various types of **sensors** and **cameras,** allowing them to gather **real-time information** from the air, which can then be transmitted to **security personnel** on the ground.
- Drones can be used to **monitor** and **protect critical infrastructure** such as **power plants, oil refineries,** and **dams**, which can help prevent **sabotage**, **vandalism**, and other security breaches.
- Drones can be used to monitor **high-crime areas**, providing **real-time images** and **videos** of **suspicious activity**, which can help law **enforcement agencies** prevent crimes before they occur.
- **Effective border security** includes a combination of **physical barriers, surveillance technologies, border patrol agents** and **intelligence gathering** to **detect** and **prevent illegal activities** such as **smuggling, human trafficking, drug trafficking,** and **unauthorized border crossings.**
- Drones can cover **vast stretches of border areas** that are otherwise challenging to monitor effectively. They provide aerial surveillance over remote and **inaccessible terrain,** augmenting the **capabilities of border patrol agents.** With live **video feeds** and **high-resolution imagery,** drones offer real-time monitoring of border activities.
- Drones can be deployed quickly to areas of interest or **potential breaches**, providing a rapid response mechanism.
- Compared to **traditional manned aerial surveillance**, drones offer a **cost-effective solution**. They require fewer resources and operational expenses, making them a more efficient option for continuous monitoring of border areas.

The most interesting use of Drones came during the **1973 Yom Kippur War**, when Israel used **drones** for **electronic surveillance** for the first time and realised the strategic value that an unmanned vehicle can offer.

- These payloads typically consist of **high-resolution cameras, thermal imaging sensors,** and other **optical systems** integrated with **drone platforms**. They offer **real-time video streaming, image capture** and analysis **capabilities from the air.**

Military Applications of Drones
☯ Surveillance and reconnaissance
☯ Border security
☯ Search and rescue missions
☯ Target acquisition
☯ Battlefield monitoring
☯ Mine detection and clearance.

- Over the years, drones have become increasingly prevalent in **conflict zones worldwide**. Their ability to **navigate challenging terrains**, gather real-time intelligence, and perform targeted strikes has made them invaluable assets.

> ☯ In **2020**, the **Indian Army** used drones to deliver **essential medical supplies** to remote areas of Nepal during the **COVID-19 pandemic**. The drones provided a faster and more efficient means of transportation, overcoming the challenges of difficult terrain and limited accessibility.
>
> ☯ In **June 2021**, drones were used to carry out a targeted attack on the **Indian Air Force station in Jammu**, marking a new escalation in the use of unmanned aerial systems in cross-border hostilities. Drones have even been used by Pakistan for cross border drug trade as interupped by **BSF** on several occasions.

- Drones have been utilized by India in border **surveillance** and **monitoring activities** in regions like **Ladakh**, where tensions between **India** and China have escalated in recent years. Drones have helped in **enhancing situational awareness** and **monitoring enemy activities** along the disputed border areas.
- **Indian Navy** has used drones for **maritime surveillance** and **security operations** in the waters surrounding **Sri Lanka**.
- Drones assist in **monitoring maritime activities**, ensuring the **safety of shipping lanes**, and preventing illegal activities such as **smuggling** and **piracy**.

Surveillance and Reconnaissance

- One of the primary applications of drones is **surveillance** and **reconnaissance**. The ability of drones to **survey vast areas, collect visual data** and **relay critical** information in real-time has proven invaluable for **military operations**.
- Drones equipped with high-resolution cameras and thermal imaging technology aid in detecting enemy movements and identifying potential threats.
- **Drones provide Indian Armed Forces** with **unmatched capabilities** to excel in the most challenging conditions. They are capable of helping Defence forces become more flexible and agile to counter the vulnerabilities of traditional systems.
- Our military drones are equipped with **highly advanced sensors** that can collect **accurate data** and provide **decision-makers** with a real-time picture of a situation. They are designed as such that they can fly in some of the most challenging environments – from mountainous terrain, **high-altitude areas** (4500m-6000m), and **extreme temperatures** (-20°C to 55°C) to snow-covered areas, forested regions.
- Drones can help in **creating solutions** that can facilitate **higher adaptability** and **agility** to make Defence personnel cope in a better way with rapidly changing operational environments which helps in the **interoperability** aspect between the different arms of the Defence.
- The utilization of drones in border surveillance not only enhances situational awareness but also helps in preventing infiltrations and minimizing casualties.
- Drones equipped with **advanced sensors** and **cameras** provide an **aerial perspective**, enabling **commanders** to **monitor troop movements, identify enemy positions** and evaluate the **progress of missions**. This enhanced situational awareness contributes significantly to the success of military campaigns.
- In conflict zones plagued by the remnants of war, such as **landmines**, drones are utilized for mine **detection** and **clearance**.
- In India, the utilization of drones has expanded across various domains. Drones offer an **unparalleled advantage, providing real-time intelligence, enhancing situational awareness,** and mitigating risks to human life.

Challenges and Limitations of Drones

- Some challenges may limit the large-scale use of drones in healthcare. **Payload capacity, distance coverage,** and **battery life** are some of these limitations that need to be taken care of.
- Another potential challenge is the **lack of appropriate drone regulations.** Before introducing drones in mainstream healthcare sectors, **effective collaborations** between aviation authorities and **healthcare regulators are needed.**
- One of the primary concerns is the **regulatory framework governing** the use of drones in India. While the government has made significant strides in recent years to develop comprehensive drone regulations, there is still a need for greater clarity and consistency in the rules governing their use, **particularly** in **disaster management scenarios.**
- Policymakers should also **develop appropriate drone regulations** to ensure **patient data security** and **health information privacy.**
- Drones have **limited battery** life that restricts their range from one place to another.
- Security is also a concern as it might be used by malicious people to **infiltrate hospital wards** or **laboratories.**
- In addition, some people may feel **uncomfortable** with seeing **unmanned flying** vehicles whizzing about during their daily activities.
- It can be difficult for hospitals to get insurance **companies** or **Medicare/Medicaid** to cover the cost of drone technology.
- Another challenge is the cost of **deploying drones in disaster management efforts.** While the cost of drone technology has decreased significantly in recent years, it can still be a significant investment for government agencies and disaster management organizations.
- Advancements in technology will only further allow **UAVs to mitigate the devastation** caused by **natural disasters,** as well as becoming an ever more valuable tool available to emergency responders all over the world.

MAINS PYQs

Q. What are the areas of prohibitive labour that can be sustainably managed by robots ? Discuss the initiatives that can propel research in premier research institutes for substantive and gainful innovation. 2015

IQ. What are the areas of prohibitive labour that can be sustainably managed by robots? Discuss the initiatives that can propel research in premier research institutes for substantive and gainful innovation. (2015)

Q. The use of unmanned aerial vehicles (UAVs) by our adversaries across the borders to ferry arms/ammunitions, drugs, etc., is a serious threat to the internal security. Comment on the measures being taken to tackle this threat (2023)

UNIT 8

NANO-TECHNOLOGY

- *Nanoscale science and technology, often referred to as Nanoscience or Nanotechnology, are science and engineering enabled by our relatively new ability to manipulate and characterize matter at the level of single atoms and small groups of atoms. This capability is the result of many developments in the last two decades of the 20th century, including inventions of scientific instruments like the scanning tunneling microscope.*
- *Using such tools, scientists and engineers have begun controlling the structure and properties of materials and systems at the scale of 10^{-9} meters, or 1/100,000 the width of a human hair.*
- *Many of the applications of nanotechnology involve new materials that have very different properties and new effects compared to the same materials made at larger sizes. This is due to the very high surface to volume ratio of nanoparticles compared to larger particles, and to effects that appear at that small scale but are not observed at larger scales.*
- *The applications of nanotechnology can be very beneficial and have the potential to make a significant impact on society. Nanotechnology has already been embraced by industrial sectors, such as the information and communications sectors, but is also used in food technology, energy technology, as well as in some medical products and medicines. Nanomaterials may also offer new opportunities for the reduction of environmental pollution.*

Nano-technology

- Nanotechnology is **science** and **engineering of nanomaterials** at the **scale of atoms and molecules** at nanoscales.
- Nanotechnology involves the understanding and control of matter at the nanometre scale/ nanoscale. Nanoscale deals with dimensions between 1 – 100 nanometres.

1 nanometer = 1nm = 10^{-9} metre

- **Professor Norio Taniguchi** coined the term **Nanotechnology**. The notion of **Nanotechnology** emerged with a talk - **There's Plenty of Room at the Bottom by Richard Feynman at Caltech in 1959.**

- Nanotechnology has gained immense attention in the recent years due to its **wide ranged applications** in several fields like **medicine, medical drugs, energy,** agriculture and electronics.

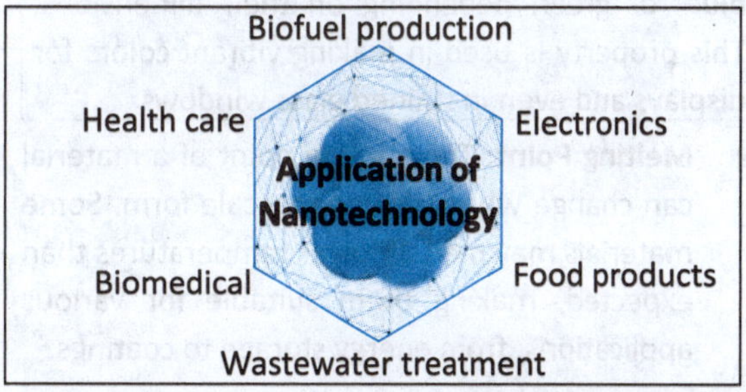

- The discovery of **fullerenes** (1996 Nobel Prize for Chemistry to H.W. Kroto, R.E. Smalley and R.F. Curl) and of **Graphene** (2010 Nobel Prize for Physics to A. Geim and K Novoselov) are important factors in the development of nanotechnology.
- Fullerenes and related materials such as carbon nanotubes have found applications in medicine for the transport of drugs and biological materials to targeted sites

- Nanomaterials can be characterized by a variety of scattering techniques. The simplest, most direct method is x-ray scattering, which can be used to investigate the phase and particle size.
- **Extended x-ray absorption fine-structure spectroscopy** (EXAFS) provides atom-specific structural information.
- **Raman spectroscopy** measures the energy shifts of scattered light due to creating optic mode excitations. In some cases, Raman spectroscopy can be used to determine the particle size and oxidation state of a nanomaterial

Special Properties of Nanomaterials

- **Electrical Conductivity :** At nanoscale, some materials can conduct electricity much better than at larger scales. This property is essential for creating high-performance electronics and energy storage devices.
- **Color Effects :** Nanomaterials can change color based on their size and shape.

Example Gold nanoparticles can appear red, blue, or green depending on their dimensions. This property is used in making vibrant colors for displays and even in stained glass windows.

- **Melting Point:** The melting point of a material can change when it's in nanoscale form. Some materials may melt at lower temperatures than expected, making them suitable for various applications, from energy storage to coatings.
- **Chemical Reactivity:** Nanoscale materials often have a higher surface area, which increases their reactivity. This makes them valuable in catalyzing chemical reactions and creating more efficient chemical processes.
- **Wettability:** Nanoscale textures on a surface can make it super water-repellent or water-attracting, depending on how the tiny structures are arranged. This property is used in creating self-cleaning surfaces and efficient water collection systems.

Significance of Nanoscale

- What makes the nanoscale so special is that it's where the **behavior of matter** starts to shift.
- Materials at the nanoscale can **exhibit properties** that are **different** from those at larger or smaller scales.

Example, gold nanoparticles might show vibrant colors due to their size and shape, while a material's strength and conductivity can dramatically change on the nanoscale. This has opened up a world of possibilities for creating new materials and technologies.

- Nanotechnology is a **captivating field** that explores the properties of matter at an incredibly small scale, ranging from **1 to 100 nanometers.**
- At this size, materials display unique behaviors due to their size-dependent properties and quantum effects.

Types of Nanomaterials (Based on Dimensional)

Types of Nanomaterial
- Dimensional Nanomaterials
- 2-Dimensional Nanomaterials
- 3-Dimensional Nanomaterials

1. Dimensional Nanomaterials

- These nanomaterials have **one dimension** in the **nanoscale range**, while the other two dimensions can be significantly larger.

Examples : Nanowires and Nanotubes.

- **Nanowires** are **elongated structures** with a diameter on the **nanoscale**, while **nanotubes** are **cylindrical structures.**
- They exhibit unique **electrical, thermal** and **mechanical properties** due to their confined dimensions.
- **Nanowires** are used in electronics and sensors, while Nanotubes find applications in **materials reinforcement** and **nanotechnology devices.**

Carbon Nanotubes	
Application	**Description**
Electronics	• Creating transistors and interconnects. • Potential components for quantum computers.
Nanocomposites	• Reinforcing materials for improved mechanical properties. • Enhancing strength and durability in various industries.
Sensors	• High sensitivity for detecting gases and biomolecules. • Applications in healthcare, environment monitoring.
Energy Storage	• Used in supercapacitors for efficient energy storage. • Potential for high-capacity batteries.
Biomedical Applications	• Drug delivery systems for targeted therapy. • Imaging and diagnostics.
Aerospace and Aviation	• Lightweight materials for aircraft parts. • Conductive coatings for deicing and electromagnetic shielding.
Nano-Electro Mechanical Systems (NEMS)	• Construction of nanoscale devices with mechanical and electrical functions.
Environmental Remediation	• Removing pollutants and contaminants from water and air.
Textiles	• Adding electrical conductivity and functionality to fabrics.
Catalysis	• Enhancing chemical reactions for industrial processes.
Structural Applications	• Reinforcement in construction materials.

2-Dimensional Nanomaterials

- These materials have **two dimensions** in the **nanoscale range**, while the third dimension is much larger.
- **Graphene** is a well-known **2D nanomaterial** consisting of a **single layer of carbon atoms** arranged in a **honeycomb lattice**.
- Other examples include **transition metal dichalcogenides** (TMDs) and black phosphorus.
- 2D nanomaterials often possess exceptional **electronic**, **mechanical** and **optical properties**.
- **Graphene**, for instance, is a **highly conductive material** with potential applications in **electronics, energy storage** and **more**.

Graphene : 2D Graphite	
Application	**Description**
Electronics	• High electron mobility for fast electronic devices. • Potential for flexible and transparent electronics. • Quantum dots and nanoribbons for quantum computing
Optoelectronics	• Photodetectors and photovoltaic cells. • Ultrafast lasers and light-emitting devices.
Materials Reinforcement	• Strengthening composite materials. • Improving mechanical properties in various products.
Energy Storage	• Supercapacitors with high energy and power density. • Anodes for high-performance lithium-ion batteries.
Thermal Management	• Efficient heat conduction in electronic devices. • Thermal interface materials for electronics.

Membranes and Filters	• Filtration of liquids and gases. • Desalination and water purification.
Biomedical Applications	• Drug delivery and biosensing applications. • Imaging and cancer therapy.
Sensors	• Gas sensors for environmental monitoring. • Chemical and biological sensors.
Aerospace and Aviation	• Lightweight materials for aircraft components. • Enhanced structural integrity in aerospace.
Coatings	• Corrosion-resistant coatings for metals. • Barrier coatings for preventing gas permeation

3-Dimensional Nanomaterials

- These nanomaterials have all three dimensions in the nanoscale range.

Example: Nanoparticles and Quantum Dots.

- They can be engineered to exhibit specific properties based on their composition, structure, and size.

Nanoparticles are common examples of 3D nanomaterials.

- They include nanoparticles made of **metals, semiconductors** or **polymers**. These materials have diverse applications, such as **drug delivery, catalysis, imaging agents** and more.

Nano Particles

- Nanoparticles are spherical, polymeric particles composed of natural or artificial polymers, ranging in size between 10 and 500 nm.
- Owing to their spherical shape and high surface area to volume ratio, these particles have a wide range of potential applications.

Quantum Dots

- Quantum dots are ultra-fine semiconductor particles, which are only a few nanometers (nm, one billionth of a meter) in size, and their better optical and electrical properties than traditional semiconductor materials allow them to quickly separate electrons and electron holes.

Carbon Nanomaterials

Carbon Nanomaterial
- C-60 Buckminsterfullerene
- Carbon Nanotubes
- Graphene : 2D Graphite

C-60 Buckminsterfullerene	
Applications	**Description**
Medicine	• Drug delivery for targeted therapy. • Photodynamic therapy for cancer treatment.
Optics and Electronics	• Use in organic photovoltaics for efficient solar cells. • Incorporation into OLEDs for brighter displays.
Nanotechnology	• Functionalized C 60-for highly sensitive sensors. • Reinforcing materials in nanocomposites.
Catalysis	• Acting as a catalyst in chemical reactions.
Molecular Electronics	• Utilization in nanoscale electronic devices.
Materials Science	• Building block for designing novel materials.
Nanomedicine	• Imaging and diagnostics applications.

Types of Nanmaterials (Based on Composition)

Types of Nanomaterial (Based on Composition)
- Inorganic based Nanomaterials
- Carbon based Nanomaterials
- Organic based Nanomaterials
- Composite base Nanomaterials

Inorganic-based nanomaterials

- These nanomaterials include metal-based nanoparticles, metal oxide/hydroxide nanoparticles, and **transition metal chalcogenide** (TMC) nanoparticles.
- These nanomaterials can be synthesized into metals like **Ag, Au, Fe** nanoparticles, and metal oxides such as **ZnO**, $\mathbf{TiO_2}$, $\mathbf{Fe_3O_4}$ and $\mathbf{CeO_2}$.
- Inorganic-based nanomaterials include different metal and metal oxide nanomaterials.

Examples of metal-based inorganic nanomaterials are silver (Ag), gold (Au), aluminum (Al), cadmium (Cd), copper (Cu), iron (Fe), zinc (Zn), and lead (Pb) nanomaterials.
Examples of metal oxide-based inorganic nanomaterials are zinc oxide (ZnO), copper oxide (CuO), magnesium aluminum oxide (MgAl2O4), titanium dioxide (TiO2), cerium oxide (CeO2), iron oxide (Fe2O3), silica (SiO2), and iron oxide (Fe3O4), etc.

Carbon-based Nanomaterials

- Due to the unique catenation property, carbon can form covalent bonds with other carbons in different hybridization states such as Sp, Sp2, and Sp3 in order to form a variety of structures of small molecules and longer chains. Carbon-based nanomaterials are found in morphological forms such as ellipsoids, hollow tubes, or spheres.

> Graphene (Gr), carbon nanotubes (CNTs), Fullerenes (C60), carbon nanofibers, carbon onions, and carbon black are the different categories of carbon-based nanomaterials.

Organic-based Nanomaterials

- These nanoscale materials are made mostly from organic matter, aside from inorganic-based or carbon-based nanomaterials.
- The use of noncovalent interactions for self-assembling and molecular designing helps to transform the organic nanomaterials into coveted structures such as micelles, dendrimers, ferritin, micelles, compact polymers, and liposomes nanoparticles.
- These types of nanomaterials are usually biodegradable and nontoxic, and, therefore, considered environmentally friendly materials.

Composite Nanomaterials

- They are any combination of metal-based, metal oxide-based, carbon-based, and/or organic-based nanomaterials, and these nanomaterials have complicated structures like a metal-organic framework.

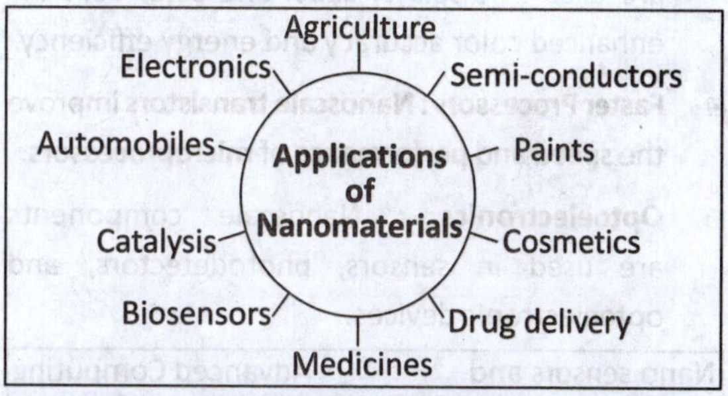

Types of Nano-technology

- **Descending (top-down):** Mechanisms and structures are miniaturised at the **nanometric scale** from **1 to 100 nanometres** in size. This technology gained coide appreciation in electronics.
- **Ascending (bottom-up):** It starts with a nanometric structure a molecule, for example and through a **mounting** or **self-assembly** process creation of a **larger mechanism/structure** than the one started with.
- **Dry nanotechnolgy :** It is used to manufacture structures in **coal, silicon, inorganic materials, metals** and **semiconductors** that do not work with humidity.
- **Wet nanotechnology:** It is based on **biological** systems present in an aqueous environment including genetic material, membranes, enzymes and other cellular components.

Applications of Nano-technology

Electronics and Computing

- **Miniaturization** : Nanotechnology enables the development of smaller, more powerful electronic components and devices.
- **Quantum Dots : Quantum dost** are man made **nano crystals** exhibiting unique **optical** and **electronic properties** , in cluding the ability to **transport electrons** and **emit ligth** of **various colours** on exposure to **UV light**. Quantum dots are used in displays, LEDs, and solar cells for enhanced color accuracy and energy efficiency.
- **Faster Processors : Nanoscale transistors** improve the **speed** and **performance** of **microprocessors**.
- **Optoelectronics** : Nanoscale components are used in sensors, photodetectors, and optoelectronic devices.

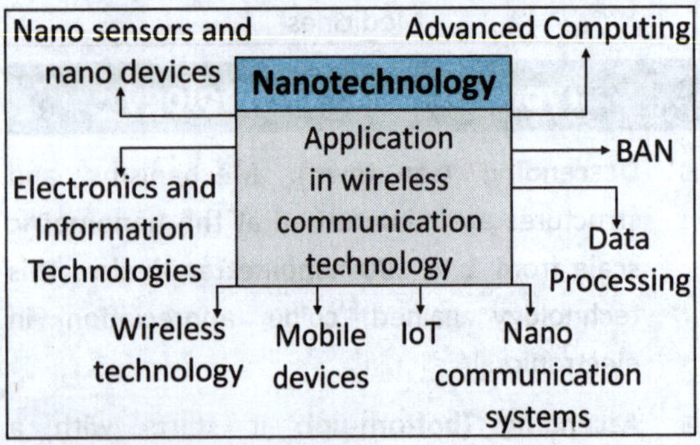

Materials and Coatings

- **Lightweight and Strong Materials:** Nano-composites exhibit improved strength and flexibility, used in aerospace and automotive industries.

Examples : Non flammable furniture- coating, Fabrics and body armour : lightweight

- **Self-Cleaning Surfaces:** Nanocoatings can make surfaces water-repellent and self-cleaning.
- **Anti-Reflective Coatings:** Nanoscale coatings reduce glare and improve optical clarity in eyewear and camera lenses.

Examples : Films on glasses, computers and camera displays.

Energy

- **Solar Cells:** Nanomaterials enhance light absorption and energy conversion in solar cells.
- **Energy Storage:** Nanotechnology improves the performance of batteries and supercapacitors.

Examples : Biofuel production - nanobioengineering of enzymes.

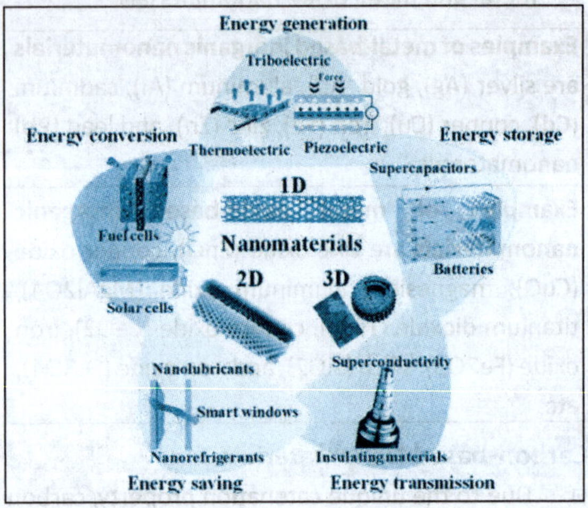

- **Water Purification:** Nanofilters and membranes remove contaminants from water.

Example : Nano membranes- desalinization, Wastewater treatments

Textiles and Fabrics

- **Stain Resistance:** Nanocoatings on textiles repel liquids and stains.
- **UV Protection:** Nanofibers provide improved UV protection in clothing and fabrics.

Nano-Particles	Properties
Silver Nano-Particles	Anti-bacterial finishing
Fe Nano-Particles	Conductive magnetic properties, remote heating.
ZnO and TiO_2	UV protection, fiber protection, oxidative catalysis

TiO_2 and MgO	Chemical and biological protective performance, provide self-sterilizing function.
SiO_2 or Al_2O_3 Nano-particles with PP or PE coating	Super water repellent finishing.
Indium-tin oxide Nano-Particles	EM / IR protective clothing.
Ceramic Nano-Particles	Increasing resistance to abrasion.
Carbon black Nano-Particles	Increasing resistance to abrasion, chemical resistance and impart electrical conductivity, colouration of some textiles.
Clay nano-particles	High electrical, heat and chemical resistance.
Cellulose Nano-whiskers	Wrinkle resistance, stain resistance, and water repellency.

Nanotechnology in Textiles

- Water Repellence
- Anti-Static Properties
- Wrinkle Resistance
- Strength Enhancement
- UV Blocking
- Computing
- Antibacterial/Odor Control
- Sensors
- Optical Displays

Food

- **Food Packaging:** Nanocomposites extend shelf life and provide better barrier properties.

Nanotechnology in the Food Industry	
Food Safety	• **Pathogen Detection :** Against food borne pathogens. • **Allergens Detection :** Used as anti-allergens/pecsticides. • **Toxin Detection :** Reduces chemical toxins and heavy metals. • **Inhibit Biofilms :** Used to inhibit biofilms on food and food contact surfaces.
Food Packaging	• **Improved Packaging :** Improved bio-based, eco-friendly edible packaging. • **Smart Packaging :** nanocoating and nano biosensors for pathogne detection. • **Active Packaging :** Nanoparticles used as antimicrobial agents.
Food Processing	• **Nano additivesa and Nutraceuticals :** Improve quality and nutritional value. • **Nanoencapsulation :** Improves aroma, flavor and other food ingredients. • **Nanoparticles :** Used as gelating and viscosifying agents to enhance food texture. • **Nanoemulsions :** Improve the availability and dispersion of nutrients.

- **Nanopesticides :** Nanotechnology enhances the effectiveness of agricultural pesticides. Ex- Nanoherbicides and Nanopesticides: Precise delivery for improved productivity.
- **Nano Fertilisers :** National Fertilisers Limited (NFL) and Rashtriya Chemicals and Fertilisers Ltd (RCF) signed MoU with IFFCO for transfer of technology of Nano Urea Liquid (NUL) fertiliser
  - NUL contains nano-scale nitrogen particles which have more surface area and number of particles making it more impactful.

India has become the first country globally to start commercial production of Nano Urea Liquid (NUL).

- Nanotechnology-based fertilizers offer a promising solution by reducing the need for traditional urea fertilizers by 50% or more. These innovative fertilizers not only enhance crop yield but also have positive effects on soil health, air quality, and water quality. Moreover, they are **cost-effective** compared to conventional urea, making them a sustainable and economically viable choice for agriculture.

- **Nano-phosphorus Fertilizers:** Benefiting millet and cluster beans.
- **Silver Nanoparticles:** Combatting plant diseases.

- **Carbon Nanoparticles:** Enhancing seed germination.
- **Nickel/Ferrite:** Serving as antifungal agents.
- **Zinc Oxide/Chitosan:** Combating viral diseases.
- **Precision Farming:** Utilizing nanosensors for optimized cultivation.

Environmental Remediation

- Nanoparticles are used to remove pollutants and toxins from soil and water.

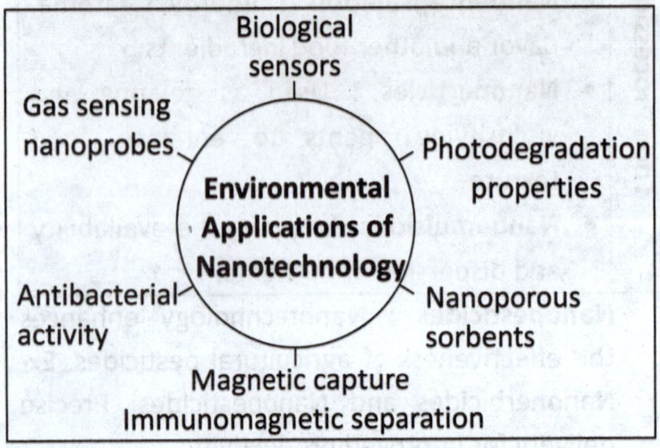

Cosmetics

- Nanoparticles in cosmetics provide better skin penetration and controlled release of active ingredients.

Example: Sunscreens - Titanium dioxide and zinc oxide help block uv radiations.

Space Exploration

- Nanotechnology enhances the durability and performance of materials used in space applications.
- Precision guided missiles.

Agriculture

- These days, sustainable agriculture is needed owing to our commitment to **Sustainable Development – usage of resources** as of today **without exhausting them completely** for the **future generations** to come.
- To meet **human consumption needs**, we have to evolve and develop new technologies like fertilizers and pesticides to ensure food security.

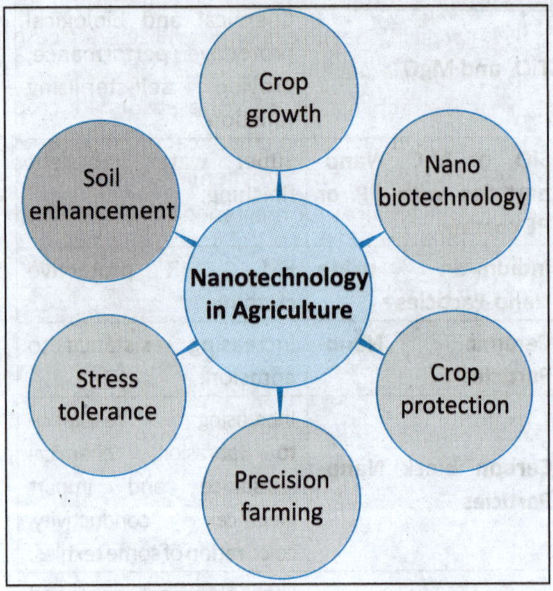

- With the increasing human population, there has been an **increasing demand of food** and **agricultural produce** increasing population has led to an **increased pace** of infrastructure both for **increased demand of habitation** and for **mobility / transport** and **communication** that has led to **massive scale** of deforestation leading to decline of **forest cover**.

Agricultural Revolution 2.0 focusses on **Genetically modified crops** which has raised serious concerns on human health. It's where nanotechnology comes to rescue.

- **Potential Applications of Nanotechnology in Agriculture :**
  - **Increase the productivity** using nanopesticides and nanofertilizers.
  - Improve the **quality of the soil** using nanozeolites and hydrogels
  - **Stimulate plant growth** using nanomaterials (SiO_2, TiO_2, and carbon nanotubes)
  - Provide **smart monitoring** using **nanosensors** by wireless communication devices.
- Application of Nanotechnology in agriculture can increase **agricultural production** as:

- Nanoformulations of agrochemicals for applying pesticides and fertilizers for crop improvement;
- The application of nanosensors in crop protection for the identification of diseases and residues of agrochemicals;
- Nanodevices for the genetic engineering of plants;
- Plant disease diagnostics;
- Animal health, animal breeding, poultry production;
- Postharvest management.

Nano-technology in sustainable agriculture

- Reduced resistance and damage to non target organisms.
- Improve quality of the soil.
- Increased enzymatic activity.
- Increased productivity, stimulated plant growth.
- Targeted and controlled nutrient release.
- Increased nutrient availability and plant uptake efficiency.
- Smart delivery, sensing and monitoring.

Medicine and Healthcare

- **Drug Delivery:** Nanoparticles can be designed to **deliver drugs** to **specific cells** or **tissues,** improving **drug efficacy** and **minimizing side effects.**
- **Imaging:** Nanoparticles enable high-resolution imaging of biological structures and disease detection.
- **Cancer Treatment:** Nanoparticles are used in targeted therapies and hyperthermia treatments for cancer.
- **Diagnostics:** Nanosensors can detect biomarkers for early disease diagnosis.
- **Nanotech detectors** for heart attack.
- **Nanochips** to check plaque in arteries.
- **Nanocarriers** for eye surgery, chemotherapy etc.
- **Diabetic pads** for regulating blood sugar levels.
- Nanoparticles for **drug delivery** to the brain for therapeutic treatment of neurological disorders.
- **Nanosponges** are **polymer nanoparticles** coated with a red blood cell membrane, and can be used for absorbing toxins and removing them from the bloodstream.
- **NanoFlares** are used for detection of cancer cells in the bloodstream.
- **Nanopores** are used in making DNA sequencing more efficient.

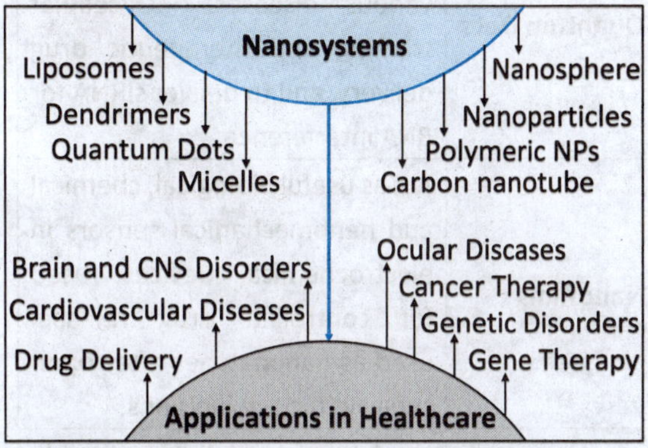

Applications of Nanostructures in Healthcare

Nanostructure	Applications in Health Sector
Nanoparticles	Used as antimicrobials and antifungals; used as sensors, as catalysts, and for imaging in diagnostics.
Carbon Nanotubes	Used for delivering fibrinogen and bovine protein to cells; serve as vectors for gene delivery; and in the treatment of broken bones, osteoporosis, and breast cancer.
Dendrimers	Used for diagnostic applications, for gene delivery, as anti-bacterial agents, as anticancer drugs, to improve vaccine formulations by acting as carriers of antigens, and in treating ocular diseases.

Nano-Diamonds	Used for the treatment of bone disease by targeted drug delivery (bone regeneration); used in imaging and therapy, in the early detection of cancer, and in the treatment of brain and breast cancers.
Quantum Dots	Useful in diagnostics, real time in vivo bio-imaging, in controlling various diseases, intracellular tracking and therapeutic drug delivery, and to deliver siRNA for RNA interference.
Nanofilms	Act as useful biological, chemical and nanomechanical sensors in electrochemical devices, used for controlled drug release, used as nanopatches after open surgery to close incisions.
Liposomes	Used for drug delivery, capable of containing hydrophobic and hydrophilic drugs, protect drugs from chemical and enzymatic degradation, have the ability to encapsulate anti-tumoral drugs, for example, anthracyclines such as epirubicin, daunorubicin, and Dox, etc.

Role of Nanotechnology in Gene Therapy

- **Gene therapy** is a procedure to **replace** a **defective** gene in the **DNA** (which is responsible for causing a disease) with a normal gene.
- The gene is usually inserted into the stem cells using a **vector**.
- **Stem cells** have long life and a self-renewal ability; therefore, they are the most suitable targets for gene therapy.
- The vector used should be **highly specific** and **efficient** in releasing the gene or genes of variable sizes. It should not be recognized as an antigen by the host immune system.
- The vector must have the **ability to express** the inserted gene throughout the life of that organism.
- When the gene is correctly inserted into the cells, it **inhibits** and **corrects** the functions of the mutated gene and induces the normal functioning of cells.

Role of Nano-technology in Targeted Drug Delivery

- **Nanovectors** have great potential in target-specific drug delivery for the treatment of various diseases.
- Targeted drug delivery is important, especially if the solvents of **hydrophobic drugs** are toxic. If these solvents are released somewhere else other than the target cell, they may enter the blood stream or other body fluids and contaminate them.
- Nanostructures allow the **continuous controlled release of drugs in desired amounts.** Specific and localized drug delivery also **reduces drug doses.** The small size of NPs allows them to penetrate deep into the **tumor cells**, and thus they can be useful in **improving cancer treatments.**

Emerging Applications of Nano-Technology

Triboelectric NanoGenerators

- **Centre for Nano and Soft Matter Sciences** (CNSMS) have fabricated a **cost- effective, bio-compatible** (Can be installed in living body as well) **nanogenerator** that can generate **electricity** from **mechanical energy** in the form of vibrations present everywhere.

CNSMS is an **autonomous institute** under the **Department of Science & Technology.**

- The energy harvesting **Triboelectric Nano Generators** works on the principle of creation of electrostatic charges (deficiency or excess of electrons which occurs on ungrounded or insulating surfaces).

Applications of Triboelectric Nanogenerators : optoelectronics, self-powered devices and other biomedical applications.

- Its major application is as **Pacemakers.** (Can regulate heart beat, can be used to give impetus to heart beat- Still research going on.)

In **2014**, a team of researchers from **China** developed a **TENG-powered pacemaker** that was able to successfully regulate the heart rate of a rabbit.

Gold Nano- Particles

- **Gold Nanoparticles** (GNPs) possess exceptional properties, including **biocompatibility, high surface area, stability** and non-toxicity. They have a **lower melting point** than bulk gold, enhancing their versatility in various applications.
- GNPs exhibit **superior solar radiation absorption,** making them invaluable for efficient **photovoltaic cells.**
- Their unique optical characteristics improve resolution in **therapeutic imaging.**
- In the **electronics sector**, GNPs enable advancements like **Nanoparticle Organic Memory Field-Effect Transistors** (NOMFETs), mimicking human synapses for potential AI development.
- These attributes highlight GNPs' wide-ranging potential in **medicine, energy** and **electronics,** propelling innovation across industries.

Nanomicelles

- Nanoparticles are small particles that can be used to **deliver drugs** or other agents to **specific cells or tissues.**
- Nanomicelles are a **type of nanoparticle** that has been shown to have potential for **cancer treatment.**
- Nanomicelles are made up of a **hydrophilic** (water-loving) outer **shell** and a hydrophobic (water-hating) **interior**. This dual property makes them a good carrier for drugs, as the drug can be encapsulated in the hydrophobic interior of the nanomicelle and protected from degradation in the body
- The configuration of the **nanomicelles** aligns well with the structure of **cell membranes,** enabling targeted and effective drug delivery to cancer cells while sparing healthy ones.

Quantum Dots

- Quantum dots are material structures, which are only a few nanometers in size, display a similar behavior to that of molecules or atoms, and their form, size and number of electrons can be modulated systematically.

Applications of Quantum Dots

- Their electrical and optical characteristics can be customized for a number of target areas, such as new display technologies, biomedical applications as well as photovoltaics and photocatalysis.
- Another current line of application-oriented research aims to generate hydrogen directly from water and solar light.
- Hydrogen, a clean and efficient energy source, can be converted into forms of fuel that are used widely, including methanol and gasoline.
- The most promising types of quantum dots previously used in **energy research** contain **cadmium**, which has been banned from many products due to its toxicity.
- The three-nanometer particles consist of a core of **indium phosphide** with a very thin surrounding layer of **zinc sulfide** and **sulfide ligands.**
- Compared to the quantum dots that contain cadmium, the new composites are not only environmentally friendly, but also highly efficient when it comes to producing **hydrogen** from **light** and **water.**
- **Sulfide ligands** on the quantum dot surface were found to facilitate the crucial steps involved in light-driven chemical reactions, namely the

efficient separation of charge carriers and their rapid transfer to the nanoparticle surface.

- **Professor Ji-woong Yang** at the **Department of Energy Science and Engineering, Daegu Gyeongbuk Institute of Science and Technology** has successfully developed the world's highest-performance eco-friendly quantum dot photosensor that does not require any external power source.
- They have developed an **ultra-high-performance** quantum dot photosensor based on the eco-friendly quantum dots of **copper-indium-selenide** (Cu-In-Se), which does not contain heavy metals.
- It had been generally accepted that photosensors based on eco-friendly quantum dots have poor performance.
- Nonetheless, the research team improved the electrical properties of eco-friendly quantum dots by controlling the size and composition of the dots, developed a new organic-inorganic hybrid charge transfer layer, which is suitable for the dots, and created an eco-friendly quantum dot photosensor that surpasses the performance of existing toxic quantum dot photosensors.
- The eco-friendly quantum dot photosensor created by the research team shows high device performance even with a quantum dot absorption layer of about **40 nanometers** (nm). Furthermore, it shows great light-detection performance with no external power source.
- These two properties may serve as a great advantage for wearable **photosensor applications** and **usage**.
- It was confirmed that the eco-friendly quantum dot photonic sensor developed through joint research can stably measure light signals without any external power source, due to the photovoltaic effect.
- Advantages with **perovskite quantum dots include not only good optoelectronic** properties but also mass-producibility with a simple manufacturing process using a solution. This is why many studies have been conducted to apply perovskite quantum dots to next-generation optoelectronic devices.
- To apply perovskite quantum dots to optoelectronic devices, a ligand exchange process is required, which reduces the distance between the quantum dots and thereby improves conductivity.

Researchers at the **University of Zurich** have developed a type of nanoparticle by adding zinc sulfide to the surface of indium-based quantum dots. These quantum dots produce clean hydrogen fuel from water and sunlight, a sustainable source of energy. They introduce new eco-friendly and powerful materials to solar photocatalysis.

Challenges of Nano-technology

Health and Safety Concerns

- **Toxicity:** Nanoparticles can possess different properties than their larger counterparts, potentially causing increased toxicity when interacting with biological systems.
- **Bioaccumulation:** Nanoparticles might accumulate in living organisms over time, leading to potential long-term health effects.
- **Inhalation Risks:** Due to their small size, nanoparticles can be inhaled easily, posing respiratory hazards, particularly in occupational settings.
- **Environmental Impact :** As nanotechnology products become more widespread, there's a risk of nanoparticles being released into ecosystems, potentially causing harm to the environment.

Ecotoxicity: Nanoparticles could impact plants, animals, and ecosystems in unexpected ways, affecting ecological processes and balance.

- **Nano-waste:** The disposal of nanomaterials and products could pose new waste management challenges due to their unique properties and potential environmental persistence.

Ethical and Societal Concerns

- **Privacy:** Advanced nanotechnology applications might lead to increased surveillance capabilities, raising concerns about personal privacy and autonomy.
- **Inequality:** Access to nanotechnology benefits might not be evenly distributed, exacerbating existing social inequalities.
- **Unintended Consequences:** The introduction of nanoscale materials might lead to unexpected societal, economic, or environmental outcomes.

Regulation and Standardization

- **Lack of Regulations:** Regulatory frameworks might struggle to keep up with the rapid advancement of nanotechnology, potentially leaving gaps in safety oversight.
- **Difficulty in Testing:** Traditional testing methods might not effectively evaluate the risks of nanomaterials, making it challenging to establish safety guidelines.

Unpredictable Behavior

- **Quantum Effects:** At the nanoscale, quantum phenomena become significant, resulting in behaviors that can't be predicted using classical physics.

India and Nano-technology

- India has made significant strides in the field of nanotechnology through its **Nano Mission** initiative, launched by **Dr. CNR Rao** in **2007**.
- This initiative, implemented by the **Department of Science and Technology (DST)** under the **Ministry of Science and Technology**, aimed to bolster various aspects of nanotechnology development and application in the country.

> The Government of India launched the **Nano Science and Technology Mission** in **2007** as an **Umbrella Capacity-building Programme.**

- The Nano Mission has established **national dialogues** to **promote R&D in the development of standards** for **nanotechnology** and for laying down a **National Regulatory Framework Road-Map for Nanotechnology** (NRFR-Nanotech).

Mission Objectives
Basic research promotion.
Infrastructure development.
Nano applications & technology development.
Human Resource development.
International collaborations
Today, **India** is amongst the **top 5 nations** in the world in terms of **scientific publications** in **nanoscience and technology.**

Other initiatives by India

- The **Guidelines for Evaluation of Nano-based Agri-input and food products in India (2020)** aim to **assist researchers** in creating **agriculture** and **food products.** They also aid regulators in assessing safety and quality. These guidelines **encourage Indian innovators** and **industries to develop innovative nano-based formulations** and **products.**
- **Nanotechnology initiatives programme (2004)-** focus on nano-electronics aspects of nanotechnology.
- **Nanotechnology regulatory board** established In **February 2010**, to regulate industrial nano-tech products of day to day life.

Previous Year Questions

Q. Consider the following statements: [UPSC 2022]

1. Other than those made by humans, nanoparticles do not exist in nature.
2. Nanoparticles of some metallic oxides are used in the manufacture of some cosmetics.
3. Nanoparticles of some commercial products which enter the environment are unsafe for humans.

Which of the statements given above is/are correct?

(a) 1 only (b) 3 only

(c) 1 and 2 (d) 2 and 3

Q. With reference to carbon nanotubes, consider the following statements

1. They can be used as carriers of drugs and antigens in the human body.
2. They can be made into artificial blood capillaries for an injured part of the human body.
3. They can be used in biochemical sensors.
4. Carbon nanotubes are biodegradable.

Which of the statements given above are correct?

(a) 1 and 2 only (b) 2, 3 and 4 only

(c) 1, 3 and 4 only (d) 1, 2, 3 and 4

Q. With reference to the use of nanotechnology in the health sector, which of the following statements is/are correct?

1. Targeted drug delivery is made possible by nanotechnology.
2. Nanotechnology can largely contribute to gene therapy.

Select the correct answer using the code given below.

(a) 1 only (b) 2 only

(c) Both 1 and 2 (d) Neither 1 nor 2

Q. Graphene is frequently in news recently. What is its importance?

1. It is a two-dimensional material and has good electrical conductivity.
2. It is one of the thinnest but strongest materials tested so far.
3. It is entirely made of silicon and has high optical transparency.
4. It can be used as 'conducting electrodes' required for touch screens, LCDs and organic LEDs.

Which of the statements given above are correct?

(a) 1 and 2 only (b) 3 and 4 only

(c) 1, 2 and 4 only (d) All of the above

Q. Why is nanotechnology one of the key technologies of the 21st century? Describe the salient features of Indian Government's Mission on Nanoscience and Technology and the scope of its application in the development process of the country. (2016)

Q. Why is nanotechnology one of the key technologies of the 21st century? Describe the salient features of Indian Government's Mission on Nanoscience and Technology and the scope of its application in the development process of the country. (2016)

Q. What do you understand by nanotechnology and how is it helping in the health sector? (2020)

UNIT 9 DEFENCE TECHNOLOGY

- *Armed forces, all over the globe, are digitalising and building **network-centric defence ecosystems** to bolster **combat readiness** and **modernise battlefield operation** through initiatives like **autonomous technologies, war clouds** and **defence ICT modernisation.***
- *Indian defence forces have embraced technology with open arms. With a continual focus on building a formidable **defence infrastructure**, India has built a series of expansive and secure defence networks across tri-forces including a robust cyber & space command, with enhancements in the areas of **Jointness, Technology led security solutions** and **ISR** (Intelligence, Surveillance & Reconnaissance), **interoperability** and **cybersecurity** are now imperative.*
- *Warfare is changing and so is the threatscape, especially for India. The warfare paradigm is now multifaceted– **cyber warfare, biowarfare** and **strategic warfare**. India witnesses collusive threats from neighbouring nations, border intrusions across terrestrial borders and the new phenomenon of **multi-front warfare** spanning borders, electronic and cyber domains.*
- ***Technology in Defence aims at –***
  - *Digital defence capabilities powered by technology-enabled military strategy.*
  - *Network-based integration across Tri-forces and Paramilitary forces.*
  - *Sensing and surveillance systems.*
  - *Big data and analytics for augmenting intelligence and ISR.*
  - *AR/VR based troop training.*
  - *Next-gen combat capabilities like IoBT (Internet of Battle Things).*

MISSILE TECHNOLOGY

- A missile is a **guided airborne ranged weapon**, often powered by a **jet engine** or **rocket motor**.

Components of Missile
- Targeting
- Guidance System
- Fight system
- Engine
- Warhead

- Guided missiles can **alter their course** during **flight**, making them **highly accurate**.
- The range of missiles varies depending on their **launch platform**, with **land-based missiles** often having **longer ranges** compared to **air** or **submarine-based versions**.

Classification of Missiles

- **Based on Speed**
  - **SubSonic** (< 1 Mach= 332 m/s) **: Ex-** Nirbhaya
  - **Super Sonic** (1-5 Mach) **: Ex-** Brahmos
  - **Hyper Sonic** (> 5 Mach) **: Ex-** Shaurya
- **Based on Launch Site & Target**
  - **Surface to Surface : Ex-** Prithvi
  - **Surface to Air : Ex-** Akash, Barak
  - **Air to Air : Ex-** Astra
- **Based on Range**
  - **Short Range** (Less than or equal to 500KM): **Ex-** Prthvi

- **Medium Range** (~ 1500 km) : **Ex** - Agni I & II
- **Intermediate** (~ 3000 to 5500 km) : **Ex** - Agni III and IV
- **Long Range** (Above 5500 km) : **Ex**- Intercontinental Ballistic Missiles (Agni V & VI)

▣ **Based on Trajectory followed**

- Ballistic
- Cruise

Ballistic v/s Cruise Missiles

▣ **Ballistic missiles** are known for their ability to target **predetermined objectives.** After an initial rocket-powered phase, they rely on **unpowered** and **unguided flight** for most of their journey. These missiles are often associated with **long-range** applications and operate outside Earth's atmosphere.

Example : ICBMs, a subset of ballistic missiles, follow a suborbital trajectory and are designed for strategic purposes. On the other hand, **Tactical Ballistic Missiles** are employed for shorter-range engagements, typically **within 300 kilometers**, often on the battlefield.

▣ **Cruise missiles** in contrast feature continuous powered flight using jet engine technology. These self-propelled guided missiles remain within the **Earth's atmosphere** and maintain a **relatively constant** speed throughout their flight path. They are primarily used against terrestrial targets, offering precision strikes.

Examples of Cruise Missiles : Brahmos, Harpoon (USA) and Exocet (France).

Ballistic Missile	Cruise Missile
• It is propelled only for a brief duration after the launch. • Similar to a rocket engine. • Long-range missiles leave the earth's atmosphere and reenter it. • Low precision as it is unguided for most of its path and its trajectory depends on gravity, air resistance, and Coriolis Force. • Can have a very long-range (300 km to 12,000 km) as there is no fuel requirement after its initial trajectory. • Heavy payload carrying capacity. • Can carry multiple payloads (Multiple Independently targetable Re-entry Vehicle) • Developed primarily to carry nuclear warheads. • E.g. Prithvi I, Prithvi II, Agni I, Agni II, and Dhanush missiles.	• Self-propelled till the end of its flight. • Similar to a jet engine. • The flight path is within the earth's atmosphere. • Hits targets with high precision as it is constantly propelled. • The range is small (below 500 km) as it needs to be constantly propelled to hit the target with high precision. • Payload capacity is limited. • Usually carries a single payload.. • Developed primarily to carry conventional warheads. • E.g. BrahMos missiles

Intercontinental Ballistic Missiles

▣ ICBMs (Intercontinental Ballistic Missiles) are **long-range missiles** with a **minimum reach** of **5,500 kilometers**, primarily designed for **nuclear warfare.**

▣ **Modern ICBMs** often employ **Multiple Independently Targetable Reentry Vehicles** (MIRVs), allowing a single missile to carry multiple warheads capable of striking different targets.

▣ A MIRV is an **exo-atmospheric ballistic missile** payload containing **several warheads.** Each one of them is capable of being aimed to hit a different target.

▣ This capability enhances the effectiveness of **nuclear deterrence.**

ICBMs are possessed by a **select group of countries**, including **India, Russia, the United States, China, the United Kingdom, France, Israel** and **North Korea.**

Hypersonic Missiles

- **Hypersonic** defines a **speed of about Mach 5.** While, **Ballistic missiles** follow a **fixed trajectory** and travel outside the atmosphere, on the contrary, **hypersonic weapons** travel within the **atmosphere** and can **maneuver midway** which combined with their **high speeds** makes their **detection** and **interception extremely difficult.** This means that **radars** and **air defenses** cannot detect them till they are very close and little time to react.
- **Types of Hypersonic Missiles:**
  - **Hypersonic Cruise Missiles:** powered throughout their entire flight by **rocket** or **jet propulsion systems.**
    - **Maintain** a **sustained hypersonic speed** and can maneuver within the Earth's atmosphere, making them and challenging to intercept.
    - Hypersonic cruise missiles are designed for **precision strikes** and have both **military** and strategic **applications.**
  - **Hypersonic Glide Vehicle (HGV):** Hypersonic Glide Vehicles take a different approach. They are launched into the **atmosphere atop** a **conventional rocket** before being released towards their intended target. Once released, they follow a **glide trajectory**, essentially gliding through the atmosphere at hypersonic speeds.
    - HGVs are **highly maneuverable** and can **perform evasive actions** during their descent. This **maneuverability**, combined with their **high speed**, makes them **difficult to track** and **intercept**. HGVs are often associated with strategic and precision-strike capabilities.

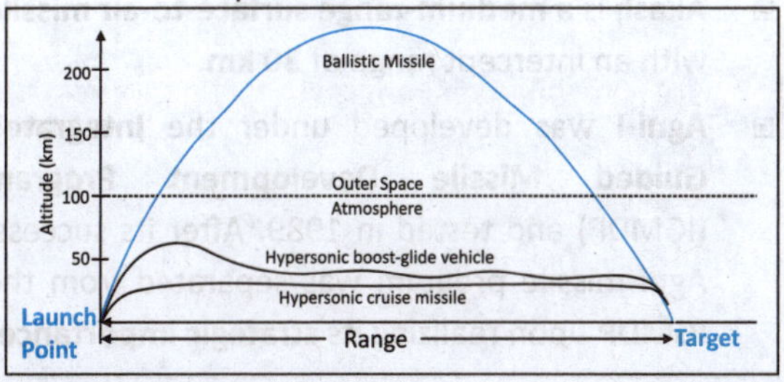

Hypersonic missiles can avoid radar detection for longer than ballistic missiles

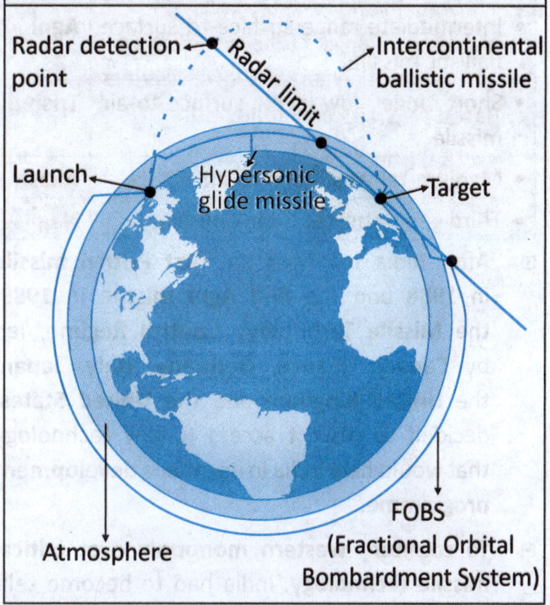

Integrated Missile Development Programme

- **Defence Research and Development Organisation** (DRDO) launched the **Integrated Guided Missile Development Programme** (IGMDP) on **July 26, 1983.**
- The principal aim of **IGMDP** was to develop a family of **strategic** and **tactical guided missiles** based on **local design** and **development** for three **defence services.**
- **Dr. Abdul Kalam**, who had previously been the project director for the **SLV-3 programme** at **ISRO**, was inducted as the **DRDL** (Defence Research & Development Laboratory) Director in **1983** to conceive and lead it. **Dr. Kalam,** headed a **Missile Study Team** to weigh the feasibility of the programme.
- Keeping in mind the requirements of various types of missiles by the defence forces, the team recommended development of **five missile systems-**

• Short-range surface-to-surface ballistic missile	**Prithvi**
• Intermediate-range surface-to-surface ballistic missile	**Agni**
• Short-range low-level surface-to-air missile	**Trishul**
• Medium-range surface-to-air missile	**Akash**
• Third generation anti-tank missile	**Nag**

- After India test-fired the **first Prithvi missile** in **1988** and the **first Agni missile** in **1989**, the **Missile Technology Control Regime**, led by **Canada**, **France**, **Germany**, **Italy**, **Japan**, the **United Kingdom** and the **United States**, decided to restrict access to any technology that would help India in its missile **development programme.**
- To **counter western monopoly** over **critical missile technology**, India had to become self-reliant for which a slew of **public sector firms** with **independent research laboratories** were set up throughout country to develop the **technologies**, the **sub systems**, the **materials**, the **testing facilities.**
- **IGMDP** provided backbone to the **Indian defense system.**

Missile Development in India

> **Prithvi** was the **first missile** to be developed under IGMDP, and the **first ever missile** to be inducted in the **Indian defense services.**

- **Prithvi-I** is an **Indian short-range ballistic missile** with a range of **150 km.** It is the first in a lineage of **indigenous land** and **sea-based missiles** which includes the **Prithvi-II**, the ship-launched **Dhanush**, and the **Prithvi Air Defense interceptor**. The Indian Army has withdrawn **Prithvi-I** from **service** and replaced it with the **Prahaar missile.**
- **Prithvi II class** is also a **single-stage liquid-fueled** missile having a **maximum warhead** mounting capability of **500 kg**, but with an extended range of **250 km** (160 mi). It was developed with the **Indian Air Force** being the **primary** user. It was first test-fired on **27 January 1996** and the development stages were completed in **2004**. This variant has been inducted into the army as well. In a test, the missile was launched with an extended range of **350 km** (220 mi) and had improved navigation due to an inertial navigation system. The missile features measures to deceive anti-ballistic missiles. The range is now increased to **350 km** (220 mi) and the payload capacity now ranges between **500 – 1000 kg.**
- **Prithvi III class** is a **two-stage surface-to-surface missile.** The first stage is solid fueled with a 16 metric ton force (157 kN) thrust motor. The **second stage** is **liquid-fueled.** The missile can carry a **1,000 kg** warhead to a distance of **350 km** (220 mi) and a **500 kg** warhead to a distance of **600 km** (370 mi) and a **250 kg** warhead up to a distance of **750 km.**
- **Dhanush** is a variant of the **surface-to-surface** or **ship-to-ship Prithvi III missile**, which has been developed for the **Indian Navy**. It is capable of carrying both conventional as well as nuclear warheads with **pay-load** capacity of **500 kg-1000 kg** and can strike targets in the range of **350 km.**
- **Trishul** is **short range surface-to-air missile** developed as a part of the **Integrated Guided Missile Development Programme** with a range of **12 km** and is fitted with a **5.5 kg warhead.** Designed to be used against **low-level** (sea skimming) targets at short range, the system has been developed to defend naval vessels against missiles.
- **Akash** is a **medium-range surface-to-air missile** with an intercept range of **30 km.**
- **Agni-I** was developed under the **Integrated Guided Missile Development Program** (IGMDP) and tested in 1989. After its success, Agni missile program was separated from the **IGMDP** upon realizing its **strategic importance.**

Agni Missle Programme

Missile	Project	Type	Warhead	Payload (kg	Range (km)	Fuel/Stages	In service
Agni-I	IGMDP	Strategic	Conventional high explosive-unitary, penetration, cluster munition, incendiary, thermobaric, strategic nuclear weapon	1,000	700–1200	Single stage solid	2009
Agni-II	IGMDP	Strategic	Conventional high explosive-unitary, penetration, sub-munitions, incendiary, thermobaric, strategic nuclear weapon	820–2,000	2,000–3,500	Two and half stage solid	2006
Agni-III	IGMDP	Strategic	Conventional, thermobaric, strategic nuclear weapon	2,500	3,000–5,000	Two stage solid	2011
Agni-IV	Agni-IV	Strategic	Conventional, thermobaric, strategic nuclear weapon	800–1,000	3,500–4,000	Two stage solid	2014
Agni-V	Agni-V	Strategic	Strategic nuclear weapon	1,500	5,000–8,000 (Speculated)	Three Stage solid	2019
Agni-P	Agni-1 Prime	Strategic	Conventional, thermobaric, strategic nuclear weapon	Unknown	1,000–2,000	Two stage solid	In trial
Agni-VI	Agni-VI	Strategic	Strategic nuclear weapon	3,000 (10 MIRV)	11,000-12,000	Four Stage solid	Under development

Indian Missiles

Missile	Type	Stages	Range (Approx.)	Status
Prithvi I	Short-Range Ballistic Missile (SRBM)	India's first indigenous missile, nuclear-capable.	150 km	Not in service
Prithvi II	Short-Range Ballistic Missile (SRBM)	In service.	350 km	In service
Prithvi III	Short-Range Ballistic Missile (SRBM)	In service.	600 km	In service

Dhanush	Naval variant of Prithvi II	Sea-to-Surface missile.	350 km	In service
Astra	A2A Beyond Visual Range	First	80 km	First A2A by DRDO, Mach 4.5 speed, Solid fuel, radar transceiver
Shaurya	Tactical, Hypersonic	N/A	700-1900 km	In service, land-based parallel of submarine-launched K-15
Prahaar	Tactical Ballistic Missile	N/A	150 km	In service, meant to replace Prithvi 1
K4	SLBM, Intermediate Range, Underwater to Surface	N/A	3500 km	In development, named after Dr. Kalam, nuclear triad and second strike capability
Sagarika (K-15)	SLBM, Underwater to Surface	N/A	700 km	SLBM version of Shaurya, to be integrated with INS Arihant
Barak 1	Short Range SAM, Ship Defense	N/A	12 km	Built with Israel, to be integrated with Shivalik Class frigates
Barak 8	SRSAM, Ship Defense	N/A	90 km	Built with Israel, to be integrated with Kolkata class destroyers
Nirbhay	Cruise, Nuclear Capable, Stealth	N/A	1000 km	In service, no MTCR issues

Brahmos

- Brahmos is a **supersonic cruise missile** jointly developed by **India** and **Russia**, named after the **Brahmaputra** and **Moskva rivers.**
- It can be launched from **land-based systems, aircraft**, **submarines** and **ships**, making it a versatile weapon.
- It is known as the **world's fastest anti-ship cruise missile**, traveling at a speed of approximately **2.8 times** the **speed of sound** (Mach 2.8).
- The missile has **two-stage**, with a **solid propellant booster** as the first **stage** and a liquid ramjet as the **second stage.**
- **Range:** Initially, due to restrictions under the **Missile Technology Control Regime** (MTCR), the range was limited to **290 km.** However, after India's entry into the **MTCR** in **2016**, the range was increased to **600 km**. The land-attack version of the missile has a range of **400 km**, which is an extension from the previous **290**

km. This version is designed for **precision strikes** against land targets.

- **Universal Capability**: Capable of being launched from land, sea, and air. It is designed to engage **both surface** and **sea-based targets**.
- The missile operates on a **fire and forget principle**, meaning that once it is launched, it does not require continuous guidance from the launch platform.

> - India has collaborated with **Russia** on the development of **Brahmos II** which is a **Mach 7 hypersonic cruise missile**. It is scheduled to be operational between **2025 and 2028**.
> - **Philippines** became the first Country to sign defence material and equipment purchase agreement of **374 million USD** (in 2022) to purchase **Brahmos missiles** from **India**.
> - UAE, Saudi Arabia, Egypt and Vietnam have shown interest in purchasing Brahmos from India.
> - India is considering $450 million deal with Indonesia to sell Brahmos Supersonic Cruise Missile.

Gandiva Air-to-Air Missile

- The Defence Research and Development Organisation (DRDO) has officially named its latest and most advanced air-to-air missile as 'Gandiva,' after the legendary bow of Arjuna from the Mahabharata. This beyond-visual-range (BVR) missile is designed to be mounted on fighter aircraft, enhancing aerial combat capabilities.

Successful Test of Hypersonic Missile

- India has successfully tested a hypersonic missile, significantly enhancing its military capabilities. The flight test, conducted by the Defence Research and Development Organisation (DRDO) off the Odisha coast, demonstrated a missile capable of carrying payloads over 1,500 km and traveling at speeds exceeding Mach 5. This test places India among a select group of nations with advanced hypersonic technology.

Fractional Orbital Bombardment System (FOBS)

- A **Fractional Orbital Bombardment System** (FOBS) is a type of **space-based ballistic missile** system that uses a **hypersonic weapon**.
- FOBS missiles are unique because they enter low Earth orbit before **descending** on a **trajectory** that allows them to strike targets from unexpected directions.
- The combination of **FOBS technology** with a **hypersonic weapon** makes these systems highly **maneuverable**, **difficult to detect** and capable of delivering devastating strikes with extreme speed and precision, posing significant challenges for defense systems.

> **China** has developed such a system, which poses a direct threat to **USA**.

Missile Defence System

- **Missile defense systems** are a type of weapon system designed to **defend against incoming missiles**. They typically consist of a network of **radars**, **sensors** and **interceptors** that are used to **track** and **destroy incoming missiles**.
- The **United States** has the most **advanced missile defense system** in the world, the **Ground-Based Midcourse Defence** (GMD) system.

> **Russia**, **India**, **France**, **Israel**, **Italy**, **United Kingdom**, **China** and **Iran** also have their own missile defense systems.

India's Ballistic Missile Defence

- India's Ballistic Missile Defence (BMD) Programme is an initiative to develop and deploy a multi-layered ballistic missile defence system to protect India from ballistic missile attacks. The programme was launched in 2000 after the Kargil War, and is being developed by the Defence Research and Development Organisation (DRDO).

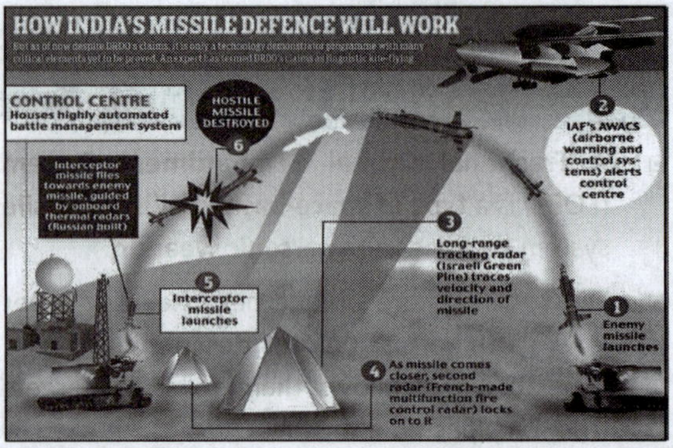

- The **BMD system** is a **two-tiered system** consisting of **two interceptor missiles, namely the Prithvi** (Pradhyumna) **Air Defence** (PAD) and the **Advanced Air Defence** (AAD) missile.

Prithvi / Pradhyumna Air defence

- **PAD** is an **exoatmospheric interceptor** missile that is designed to **intercept incoming ballistic** missiles in their **high-altitude trajectory**.
- The PAD is a **two-stage missile**. The first stage is a **solid-fuelled motor**, while the second stage is a **liquid-fuelled motor**.
- The missile has a maximum interception altitude of **80 km** (50 mi) and a range of up to **3,000 km** (1,900 mi). It is based on the **Prithvi missile**, which is a tactical surface-to-surface short-range ballistic missile.
- The PAD is guided by an **internal navigation system** with **active radar** homing in the **terminal phase**. This means that the missile uses its own navigation system to fly to the target area, and then uses a radar to lock onto the target and guide itself to the interception point.
- The PAD is fast enough to hit **medium-range ballistic missiles** and **intermediate-range ballistic missiles**. It has a speed of **Mach 5**.

Advanced Air Defence

- The AAD is an endo-atmospheric interceptor missile that is designed to intercept incoming ballistic missiles in their lower-altitude trajectory.
- It is designed to **intercept incoming ballistic missiles** in the **endo-atmosphere**, which is the lower part of the atmosphere, at an **altitude** of up to **40 km**.
- The AAD is a **single-stage, solid-fuelled missile**. It is **7.5 meters long** and has a **diameter of 0.6 meters**. The missile weighs **1,000 kg**.
- The AAD is guided by an **inertial navigation system** with active radar homing in the terminal phase. This means that the missile uses its **own navigation system** to fly to the target area, and then uses a radar to lock onto the target and guide itself to the **interception point**.
- The AAD has an **indigenous radio frequency** (RFID) **seeker**. This seeker is designed to track the target missile's **radar signature**.

Detection of Cruise Missiles

- Cruise missiles are **difficult to detect** and **intercept** because they fly at **low altitudes** and use **terrain-following technology** to avoid radar detection. They can also be equipped with **jamming devices** to further complicate their detection.
- The AAD is an **anti-ballistic missile** that can also be used to intercept cruise missiles. It is equipped with an **indigenous radio frequency** (RFID) seeker that is designed to track the **target missile's radar signature.** The RFID seeker is more effective than other types of seekers at tracking targets in the **endo - atmosphere**, where the **radar signature** is **weaker**.

S-400

- India purchased S-400 Triumf air defence system units in 2018 for **5.4 billion USD**, 3 of which have been delivered and **2** expected by **2024**.

> **S-400** is **Russia's fourth-gen long-range surface-to-air missile system.** Its evolved form, the **S-500 Prometheus**, represents a more advanced iteration, enhancing air defense capabilities.

- **Key features of the S-400 system:**
    - **Long range:** The S-400 can engage targets at ranges of up to 400 km.
    - **High altitude:** The S-400 can engage targets at altitudes of up to 30 km.
    - **Multiple target engagement:** The S-400 can engage multiple targets simultaneously.
    - **Mobile:** The S-400 is a mobile system that can be deployed quickly and easily.
    - **Powerful radar:** The S-400 is equipped with a powerful radar system that can track and engage multiple targets simultaneously.

> It has the capability to **engage 80 targets** at one time with a response time of **9-10 seconds.**

- The **anti-ballistic missile** (ABM) **capabilities** o f the **S-400 system** are near the maximum allowed under the Anti-Ballistic Missile Treaty.
- The S-400 air defense system employs a **layered defense strategy** with three types of missiles :
    - The **Long-Range** (40N6) missiles engage targets up to 400 kilometers away.
    - **Medium-Range** (48N6) missiles cover distances of up to 250 kilometers.
    - **Short-Range** (9M96E2) missiles are highly maneuverable and effective against targets at closer ranges, up to 120 kilometers.
    - This **multi-layered approach** ensures comprehensive protection against a wide array of aerial threats.

> S-400 Missile system remained controversial due to the **US imposing sanctions** on countries which bought it.

Warships

- Warships are **naval vessels designed** and **equipped for warfare**. They play a crucial role in protecting a **country's maritime interests, securing sea routes** and **projecting military power**.

Important Warships
Aircraft Carrier
• **Role:** Aircraft carriers are large, powerful ships designed to carry and operate military aircraft. They serve as mobile airbases, allowing for extended air operations in regions without established airfields. • Sea to Air Warship. • **Ex-** IAC-1, Kiev etc
Destroyer
• **Role:** Destroyers are versatile surface combatants equipped with a range of weaponry for anti-air, anti-surface, and anti-submarine warfare. They are heavily armed and often serve as the backbone of a fleet. • Sea to Surface warship. • **Ex-** Rajput
Frigate
• **Role:** Frigates are smaller than destroyers but still versatile. They are used for anti-submarine warfare, anti-surface warfare, and escort duties. They balance firepower, endurance, and maneuverability. • Sea to Surface warship. • **Ex-** Shivalik, Godawari etc
Cruiser
• **Role:** Cruisers are larger warships that combine firepower with endurance. They have historically served as command ships and are equipped with a mix of armament for various types of warfare.
Submarine
• **Role:** Submarines are underwater vessels designed for stealth and surprise attacks. They can be armed with torpedoes, cruise missiles, and ballistic missiles, and play a vital role in naval strategies.
Corvette
• **Role:** Corvettes are small, fast, and maneuverable ships used for coastal defense, anti-submarine warfare, and patrolling littoral zones (nearshore areas).

Aircraft Carriers

- An Aircraft Carrier is a large naval vessel designed to serve as a floating airbase for military aircraft.
- **STOBAR** (Short Take-Off but Arrested Recovery) is a system used for **launching** and **recovering aircraft** from the deck of an aircraft carrier. It combines elements of both **Short Take-Off and Vertical Landing** (STOVL) and **Catapult-Assisted Take-Off But Arrested Recovery** (CATOBAR).
- The **STOBAR** system also uses **arrestor wires** to recover aircraft. The arrestor wires are stretched across the deck of the aircraft carrier and catch the aircraft's tailhook as it lands. This helps to slow down the aircraft and prevent it from crashing.
- **INS Vikramaditya:** INS Vikramaditya is a Kiev-class aircraft carrier that was originally built for the **Soviet Navy**. It was commissioned into the **Indian Navy** in **2013**. The carrier is equipped with a ski-jump and can accommodate up to 30 aircraft, including **MiG-29K fighters, Ka-31 helicopters** and **Sea King helicopters**.
- **INS Vikrant :** Also known as **Indigenous Aircraft Carrier 1** (IAC-1), is an aircraft carrier constructed by **Cochin Shipyard** in **Kochi, Kerala** for the **Indian Navy**. It is the first aircraft carrier to be built in India. It will be equipped with a **CATOBAR** system and can accommodate up to **40 aircraft**, including the **F-35B Lightning II**.
  - **INS Vikrant** was commissioned in **2022**.
  - **76%** indigenous content, showcasing India's advancements in naval technology. project air power over long distances, airborne anti- submarine warfare and airborne early warning etc.

Submarines

- Submarine is a watercraft capable of independent underwater operation.
- A fleet is the group of ships under one autharity.
- Indian Submarine Fleet is based at 2 local **Visakhapatnam** (on east coach) and **Mumbai** (on west coast).

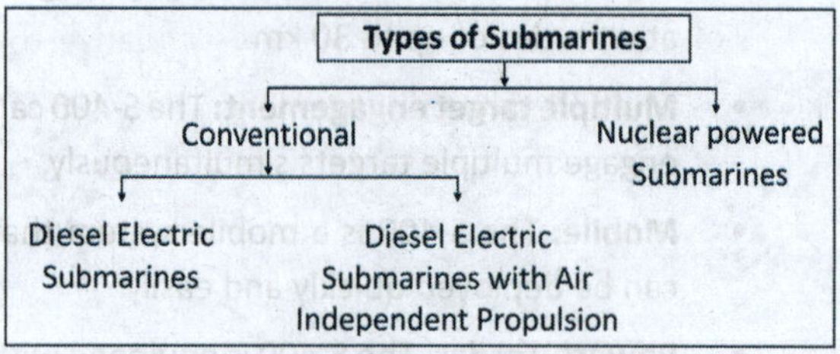

Conventional Submarines

- **Conventional submarines** are **powered by diesel-electric engines** when surfaced and batteries when submerged.
- **Operational Range:** They have a limited underwater endurance and need to surface regularly for air and to recharge batteries.
- **Stealth:** They are quieter than nuclear submarines but are more detectable due to the need for air intake and exhaust when running on diesel.
- **Deployment:** Typically used for littoral (nearshore) operations and coastal defense due to their limited range and endurance.

Indian Navy currently operates 16 diesel powered submarines :	
• INS Sindhughosh (S55)	• INS Shalki (S46)
• INS Sindhudhvaj (S56)	• INS Shankul (S47)
• INS Sindhuraj (S57)	• INS Chakra (S71)
• INS Sindhuratna (S59)	• INS Arihant (S73)
• INS Sindhukesari (S60)	• INS Kalvari (S21)
• INS Sindhukirti (S61)	• INS Khanderi (S22)
• INS Sindhuvijay (S62)	• INS Karanj (S23)
• INS Sindhurashtra (S65)	• INS Vela (S24)
• INS Shishumar (S44)	• INS Vagir (S25)
• INS Shankush (S45)	• INS Arighat (S3)

Project 75- I

- Project 75I is an **Indian Navy project** to build **six advanced conventional submarines.**
- Project-75(I) is a major initiative towards **Make in India**, the Indian government's initiative to **boost domestic manufacturing**. The project envisages the **indigenous construction of six modern conventional submarines** with contemporary equipment, weapons & sensors including **Fuel-Cell** based **AIP** (Air Independent Propulsion Plant) etc.
- AIP technology allows conventional diesel-electric submarines to remain underwater for longer, enhancing its lethality.

Other countries to have an AIP system include **China, Germany, Sweden, France, Spain** and **Russia**. P-75(I) submarine project is the first acquisition India has undertaken through its **Strategic Partnership procurement model.**

Indian Submarines : Diesel Electric Submarines		
Class	**Features**	**Examples**
Shishumar class	Built in Germany in the 1980s, equipped with a variety of weapons, including torpedoes and mines.	INS Shishumar, INS Shaldag
Kalvari class	Attack submarines, jointly developed by France and India, equipped with a variety of weapons, including torpedoes, missiles, and mines, Developed under Project 75 or P 75 of the Indian Navy.	6 submarines under this class: INS Kalvari, Tiger Shark, Khanderi, Karanj, Vela, Vagir, Vagsheer.
Sindhughosh class or kilo class	Russian Attack submarines, Improved version of the Kalvari-class submarines, equipped with a variety of weapons, including torpedoes, missiles and mines.	INS Sindhughosh, INS Sindhudhvaj, INS Sindhuraj, INS Sindhuratna, INS Sindhukesari, INS Sindhukirti, INS Sindhuvijay, INS Sindhurashtra.

Nuclear Submarines

- **Power Source:** Nuclear submarines are powered by a nuclear reactor, allowing them to operate continuously underwater for extended periods.
- **Operational Range:** They have virtually unlimited underwater endurance, capable of staying submerged for months.
- **Stealth:** They are less detectable than conventional submarines due to their continuous operation without the need for air.
- **Deployment:** They are well-suited for long-range missions, deep-sea operations, and strategic deterrence due to their extended endurance and range.

Indian Navy currently operates **2 nuclear** powered submarines: **INS Arihant & INS Arighaat.**

- **INS Arihant:** India's first indigenous nuclear-powered ballistic missile submarine (SSBN), commissioned in August 2016.
- **INS Arighat:** India's second SSBN, commissioned on August 29, 2024.
- **INS Aridhaman:** The third SSBN, set to be commissioned next year.
- **S4* (Codename):** India launched its fourth SSBN at the Ship Building Center (SBC) in Visakhapatnam in October 2024.
- **Nuclear Submarines** can be divided into **three main categories.**

- **Ballistic Missile Submarine** (SSBN- Ship Submersible Ballistic Nuclear Submarine): SSBNs are designed to carry and launch ballistic missiles, providing a strategic nuclear deterrent capability. They are often a key component of a **nation's nuclear triad** (alongside land-based missiles and strategic bombers).

Example: Arihant in India, The **Ohio-class submarines** in the U.S. Navy.

- **Attack Submarine** (SSN- Ship Submersible nuclear): SSNs are **multi-purpose submarines** used for a variety of missions including **anti-submarine warfare, anti-surface warfare, intelligence gathering**, and **special operations.** They are highly versatile and form a critical part of a naval fleet.
    - An attack submarine is specifically designed for **attacking** and **sinking other submarines, surface combatants** and **merchant vessels.**
    - They are also used to protect friendly surface combatants and missile submarines. Many modern attack submarines can launch cruise missiles (and dedicated anti-ship missiles) from their **torpedo tubes,** however the main attack weapon remains the torpedo.

Example: Chakra in India, The Los Angeles-class submarines in the U.S. Navy.

By 2036, India is expected to have its first **indigenous nuclear attack** submarine (at cost of 35,000 crore).

Projecti INS Varsha - a dedicated base for nuclear submarines is set to become operational within the next two year will serve as a hub for **Indian Navy's current** and **Future sub marine.**

The **underground base** is located near coastal village of Rambilli in **Andhra Pradesh.**

- **Cruise Missile Submarine (SSGN):** SSGNs are modified ballistic missile submarines that have been converted to carry a large number of cruise missiles, both conventional and nuclear. They provide a versatile strike capability.

Example: The Ohio-class submarines after being converted from SSBNs to SSGNs in the U.S. Navy.

Advanced Technology Vessel (ATV) Submarine Programme

- India begin the development of its ATV Submarine Programme from 1983.
- ATV is a part of India's sea-based nuclear deterrent, which is one of the three legs of India's triad of airborne, naval, and land-based platforms as a minimum nuclear deterrent (MND).
- In February 2015, Indian government approved the indigenous construction of 6 nuclear-powered attack submarines at the Ship Building Center (SBC) in Visakhapatnam.
- India is indigenously building 6 new Scorpène-class vessels under its Project 75 programme at state-owned Mazagon Dock Ltd. (MDL) in Mumbai in partnership with France's Naval Group.
- The first of these submarines, the Kalvari, was commissioned in late 2017. INS Khanderi (S22) was commissioned on 28 September 2019. The INS Karanj (S23), the INS Vela (S24), and the INS Vagir (S25) were launched and passed sea trials in March of 2021. INS Vagsheer is under construction.
- India's nuclear-powered submarine program is under the **management and operations** (M&O) of the **Defence Research and Development Organisation** (DRDO), the **Department of Atomic Energy** (DAE), and the Indian Navy at Visakhapatnam.
- India took steps to operationalize its nuclear triad by commissioning its first ATV submarine, the INS Arihant, in August 2016.
- India is expected to build four nuclear powered ballistic missile submarines (SSBNs) under its ATV Program.

- The first vessel in this class, INS Arihant, was commissioned in 2016. It is powered by an 83MW pressurized light-water reactor (PWR) fueled with enriched uranium.
- INS Arihant carries 12 Sagarika (K-15) submarine launched ballistic missiles (SLBMs) with a range of around 700 km, as well as versions of the nuclear-capable Nirbhay cruise missile.
- In November 2017, India launched the second nuclear submarine of four planned Arihant-class nuclear submarines, the INS Arighat, which is scheduled to be commissioned by the end of 2023.
- In March 2019, India and Russia signed a deal for the lease of another Akula-class nuclear submarine to India for 10 years. The new vessel, called the Chakra-III, will be delivered to the Indian Navy by 2025.
- India recently constructed two submarine bases. The first is Karwar, located 500 kilometers south of Mumbai. The second is a secret naval base called the INS Varsha which is part of a larger project to increase India's naval nuclear capabilities in response to China's recent upgrades.

> **Nuclear Triad :** The term **nuclear triad** refers to a nation's capability to deliver nuclear weapons using three different delivery platforms: land-based missiles, submarine-launched missiles, and strategic bombers.

The Indian Submarine Program (ISP)

- The **Indian Submarine Program** (ISP) is a long-term plan to build a fleet of **24 (18+6)** submarines for the Indian Navy. The program was launched in **2000** and is expected to be completed by **2030.**
- The ISP aims to build a mix of **conventional** (18) and **nuclear-powered submarines** (6).
- The **18 conventional submarines** under the ISP will be of the **Scorpene class.**
- The **Scorpene class** is a **French-designed submarine** that is also being built for the navies of **Brazil, Chile, Malaysia** and **Peru.** The Scorpene class submarines are equipped with a variety of **weapons, including torpedoes, missiles**, and **mines.** They are also equipped with advanced sonar systems that allows them to **detect** and **track enemy ships** and **submarines.**
- The **6 nuclear-powered submarines** under the ISP will be of the **Arihant class**. The Arihant class is an **Indian-designed submarine** that is also the **first nuclear-powered submarine** to be built in India. The Arihant class submarines are equipped with a **variety of weapons, including nuclear-tipped missiles**. They are also equipped with advanced sonar systems that allow them to detect and track enemy ships and submarines.

AIR DEFENCE

Fighter aircraft

- **MiG-21 :** The **Mikoyan-Gurevich MiG-21** is a **Soviet-designed supersonic jet fighter** and interceptor. **MiG-21** was designed as an interceptor aircraft, which means that it was designed to intercept and destroy enemy aircraft that were attacking from a long distance. It is a small, lightweight aircraft that is capable of flying at high speeds. It is also equipped with a variety of weapons, including air-to-air missiles and cannons.
- **Sukhoi :** The Sukhoi **Su-30MKI** is a twin-engine, multirole, all-weather, long-range fighter aircraft developed by **Russia's Sukhoi** and built by **India's Hindustan Aeronautics Limited** (HAL).
- **HAL Tejas :** The HAL Tejas is an indigenously developed multirole fighter aircraft. It is the first fourth-generation fighter aircraft to be developed in India. The Tejas is currently in service with the Indian Air Force and the Indian Navy.

- Tejas is a lightweight multi-role, single-engine, tailless tactical fighter aircraft with compound delta wing. It is also called a 4.5 generation fighter aircraft because of its advanced features.
- It has Compound delta platform - provide a balance of high maneuverability and stability.
- **Fly-By-Wire Flight Control System:** The Tejas features a sophisticated fly-by-wire flight control system. This electronic system replaces traditional mechanical linkages with computer-controlled systems, allowing for precise control and stability in flight.
- Indigenous Oxygen Generating System for LCA Tejas
- The Defence Bio-Engineering & Electro Medical Laboratory (DEBEL) has successfully conducted high-altitude trials of the Indigenous On-Board Oxygen Generating System (OBOGS)-based Integrated Life Support System (ILSS) for the Light Combat Aircraft (LCA) Tejas. This advancement enhances pilot safety and operational efficiency during high-altitude missions.

- **Rafale :** Rafale is a French twin-engine, multirole, canard delta wing, fighter aircraft. It is known for its agility and versatility, and is capable of carrying a wide range of weapons.

> The Indian Air Force (IAF) ordered **36 Rafales** under the **MMRCA** (Medium Multi-Role Combat Aircraft) programme.

- **Mirage** - The Mirage 2000 is a French-built, single-engine, multirole fighter aircraft. The Mirage 2000 is used by the air forces of over 20 countries, including India, France, and Egypt. It is a highly maneuverable aircraft that is capable of flying at speeds of up to Mach 2.2. It is equipped with a variety of weapons, including air-to-air missiles, air-to-ground missiles, and guided bombs.

> The Mirage 2000 was used by the Indian Air Force in the **Balakot airstrike** in **2019**.

Helicopters

- **Dhruv:** An indigenously developed helicopter that was inducted into the Indian Air Force in the 2000s. It is a versatile helicopter that is capable of a variety of missions, including troop transport, search and rescue, and medical evacuation.
- **Chetak** - A single-engine, light utility helicopter developed by **Hindustan Aeronautics Limited** (HAL) for the Indian Army. It is based on the French Aérospatiale Alouette III helicopter. It has been used by the Indian Army since 1971 and has been exported to a number of countries, including Bangladesh, Nepal, and Sri Lanka.
- **Cheetal** : A larger and more capable version of the Chetak helicopter. It is also developed by HAL and is based on the Aérospatiale SA 315B Lama helicopter. The Cheetal has been used by the Indian Army since 1984 and has also been exported to a number of countries, including Bangladesh, Nepal, and Sri Lanka.

Involvement of Private Sector in Fighter Aircraft Production

A Defence panel has recommended involving India's private sector in manufacturing military aircraft to bolster the Indian Air Force's capabilities. This move aims to address the declining strength of fighter squadrons and delays in aircraft deliveries, potentially reducing the burden on the state-owned Hindustan Aeronautics Ltd.

Development of HAL CATS Warrior Unmanned Combat Aerial Vehicle (UCAV)

The Hindustan Aeronautics Limited (HAL), in collaboration with NewSpace Research and Technologies, is developing the Combat Air Teaming System (CATS) Warrior, an unmanned combat aerial vehicle designed to operate as a "loyal wingman" alongside manned fighter jets. The CATS Warrior features a low-observable design with internal weapon bays and is capable of carrying short-range or beyond-visual-range air-to-air missiles externally, and Smart Anti-Airfield Weapons (SAAW) internally. It employs two modified PTAE-7 engines, each producing 380 kgf of thrust, enabling operations within a combat radius of 350 km for return missions and up to 800 km for one-way missions. A prototype was displayed at Aero India 2025, with further ground testing and a first flight scheduled by the end of 2025.

Enhancement of T-72 Battle Tanks

In March 2025, India signed a $248 million agreement with Russia's Rosoboronexport to procure advanced 1,000 horsepower (HP) engines for its T-72 battle tanks. This upgrade aims to enhance the mobility and offensive capabilities of approximately 2,500 T-72 tanks in the Indian Army, replacing the existing 780 HP engines. The deal also includes technology transfer to the Indian state-owned Armoured Vehicles Nigam Ltd for local production of these engines.

Advancements in Very Short Range Air Defence System (VSHORADS)

The Defence Research and Development Organisation (DRDO) has been developing the Very Short Range Air Defence System (VSHORADS), a man-portable air-defense system designed to neutralize low-altitude aerial threats. The missile incorporates novel technologies, including a miniaturized Reaction Control System (RCS) and integrated avionics.

In February 2025, DRDO conducted three successive flight trials from the Integrated Test Range (ITR), successfully intercepting low-altitude, high-speed targets mimicking adversary UAVs with low thermal signatures. These trials marked the final deployment configuration, demonstrating the missile's capability to engage low-flying drones and other aerial threats.

Generations of Fighter Planes

Generation	Characteristics	Examples
1st Generation	Early jet aviation era. Propeller-driven or early jets, limited avionics, and manual guns for combat. Aircraft relied on basic instrumentation.	Messerschmitt Me 262, F-86 Sabre
2nd Generation	Introduction of afterburners, allowing for supersonic speeds. Infrared homing missiles provided better air-to-air capability. Basic radar systems were implemented.	F-4 Phantom II, MiG-21
3rd Generation	Turbofan engines brought higher efficiency and multirole capabilities. Beyond Visual Range (BVR) missiles extended engagement ranges. Improved radar systems and avionics.	F-16 Fighting Falcon, Mirage 2000
4th Generation	Adoption of fly-by-wire technology for enhanced maneuverability. Compound delta wings and canards improved agility. Advanced avionics and radar systems.	F/A-18 Hornet, Su-27

4.5 Generation	Extensive use of composite materials to reduce radar cross-section. Advanced radars for improved situational awareness. Enhanced avionics and electronic warfare systems.	Rafale, Eurofighter Typhoon
5th Generation	Integration of Command, Control, and Communication (C3) systems. Digital computation for enhanced battlefield awareness. Stealth technology and advanced sensor fusion.	F-35 Lightning II, J-20, Su-57
6th Generation	Under development. Expected to feature advanced technologies like directed energy weapons, advanced AI, and improved stealth capabilities.	Future fighter aircraft designs

Radar Technology

- The word radar comes from the acronym radio detection and ranging. As the name implies, radars use radio waves to determine the distance and velocity of the targets they hit.
- It is a device which uses electromagnetic waves in the microwaves region to detect location (range & direction), **altitude**, **intensity** and **movement of moving and non-moving objects.**
- In **1885**, it was **Scottish physicist James Clerk Maxwell** who came up with the idea that perhaps radio waves could be reflected by metal objects, just like light waves could, which was proved by **German physicist Heinrich Hertz** in **1888.**
- In **1904** a patent was issued to a **German** engineer called **Christian Hulsmeyer** for what was termed an **obstacle detector** and **ship navigation device.**
- **Scottish physicist Sir Robert Watson-Watt,** known as the **father of radar**, took the science that had gone before and created the workable system that formed the basis of **modern radar.**

Components of Radar

- **Transmitter:** The source of the radio pulse.
- **Antenna:** Needed to send the pulse out into the ether and receive it when it is reflected back.
- **Switch:** This tells the antenna when to transmit or receive the pulses.
- **Receiver:** Required to detect and turn the pulses, which come back into a visual format to be read by an operator.
- The process of directing artificial radio waves towards objects is called **illumination**. The radio waves are invisible to the human eye as well as optical cameras, as they are **sent out** at **approximately 300,000,000 metres per second.** Some of the reflected radio waves (echoes) are directed back toward the radar where they are received and amplified, with the data being interpreted by skilled operators with the help of computers.
- Radio waves are cheap to generate, can pass through **snow, mist** and **fog** and are safe, unlike **gamma** and **X rays.**

Applications

- **Detection of objects:** Radar can also be used to detect stationary objects buried underground. In some cases, radar's target detection can identify details like the type of aircraft it has detected.
- **Detect the speed of an object:** Used by law enforcing agencies like Police for speed detection.

- **Mapping :** Space shuttles and orbiting satellites use synthetic aperture radar to create detailed topographic maps of the surface of planets and moons.
- Radar can be used to detect ships, planes and satellites.
- Then there are meteorologists who use Doppler weather radar when tracking weather systems like storms, hurricanes and tornadoes because of radar's ability to work in a range of weather conditions. Doppler radar, for example, can detect precipitation.

Doppler Weather Radars

- Based on Doppler principle, the radar is designed to improve precision in long-range weather forecasting and surveillance using a parabolic dish antenna and a foam sandwich spherical radome. DWR has the equipment to measure rainfall intensity, wind shear and velocity and locate a storm centre and the direction of a tornado or gust front.

X band Radars

- They operate on a wavelength of 2.5-4 cm and a frequency of 8-12 GHz. Because of the smaller wavelength, the X band radar is more sensitive and can detect smaller particles. These radars are used for studies on cloud development because they can detect the tiny water particles and also used to detect light precipitation such as snow.

Stealth technology

- Stealth technology, also known as **stealth**, is a set of techniques and technologies used to make an object, such as an aircraft or a ship, less detectable by radar and other electronic sensors.
- Stealth technology is used to reduce the visibility of an object to radar and other sensors by reducing its radar cross-section (RCS), which is a measure of the amount of radar energy that is reflected back to the radar antenna.

Stealth Technology

- Stealth technology, also known as low **observable technology** or **simply stealth**, is a set of techniques and design principles employed in military and **aerospace engineering** to reduce the detection and **recognition of objects** by **radar**, **infrared**, **sonar** and other **detection methods**.
- The primary objective of stealth technology is to make **military aircraft**, **ships**, **vehicles** and even **individual soldiers** less visible to enemy sensors and detection systems. This enhances their survivability and effectiveness in combat situations.

Ex- Radar Absorbing Materials (RAM): Stealth vehicles are often coated with radar-absorbing materials

- Stealth technology can be used to make an object more difficult to detect by radar, but it does not make the object completely invisible. Instead, it reduces the range at which the object can be detected by radar, making it more difficult for radar operators to detect and track the object.
- Stealth technology can be achieved through a variety of means, including the use of radar-absorbent materials, shaping the object to minimize its RCS, and using techniques such as **low observables** (LOs) to reduce the visibility of the object to radar. Stealth technology is used in a wide range of military and civilian applications, including aircraft, ships, missiles, and ground vehicles.

Applications of Stealth Technology in Defence

- **Stealth Aircraft:** They can be used for a variety of missions, including surveillance, intelligence gathering, and attack.
- **Stealth Ships:** They can be used for a variety of missions, including surveillance, intelligence gathering, and naval warfare.
- **Stealth Missiles:** They can be used for a variety of missions, including precision strikes, intelligence gathering, and air defense.

- **Stealth ground Vehicles:** Stealth ground vehicles, such as tanks and armored personnel carriers, which are designed to be less detectable by radar and other sensors can be used for a variety of missions, including reconnaissance, attack, and defense.

- **Declaration of 2025 as the Year of Defence Reforms :** The Ministry of Defence (MoD) has designated 2025 as the Year of Defence Reforms, emphasizing the modernization of the Armed Forces into a technologically advanced, combat-ready force capable of multi-domain integrated operations.

- **Focus on Cyber Warfare Readiness :** A study analyzing India's cyber warfare readiness highlighted significant shortcomings, particularly in real-time threat detection and response capabilities. The research suggests implementing machine learning-based threat detection systems and developing educational frameworks to train cyber professionals, aiming to bolster national security against cyber threats.

PREVIOUS YEAR QUESTIONS

Q. Which reference to Agni-IV Missile, which of the following statements is/are correct?

1. It is a surface-to-surface missile.
2. It is fuelled by liquid propellant only.
3. It can deliver one-tonne nuclear warheads about 7500 km away.

Select the correct answer using the code given below.

(a) 1 only (b) 2 and 3 only
(c) 1 and 3 only (d) 1, 2 and 3

Q. What is "Terminal High Altitude Area Defense (THAAD)", sometimes seen in the news?

(a) An Israeli radar system
(b) India's indigenous anti-missile programme
(c) An American anti-missile system
(d) A defence collaboration between Japan and SouthKorea

Q. "Orbital Bombardment System" often talked about in media? (2022)

(a) A hypersonic missile is launched into space to counter the asteroid approaching the Earth and explode it in space.
(b) A spacecraft lands on another planet after making several orbital motions.
(c) A missile is put into a stable orbit around the Earth and deorbits over a target on the Earth.
(d) A spacecraft moves along a comet with the same surface. Speed and places a probe on its

Q. Consider the following statements: (2023)

1. Ballistic missiles are jet-propelled at sub-sonic speeds throughout their flights, while cruise missiles are rocket powered only in the initial phase of flight.
2. Agni-V is a medium-range supersonic cruise missile, while BrahMos is a solid-fuelled intercontinental ballistic missile.

Which of the statements given above is/are correct?

(a) 1 only (b) 2 only
(c) Both 1 and 2 (d) Neither 1 nor 2

Q. Consider the following activities: (2024)

1. Identification of narcotics on passengers at airports or in aircraft.
2. Monitoring of precipitation.
3. Tracking the migration of animals.

In how many of the above activities can the radars be used?

(a) Only one (b) Only two
(c) All three (d) None

Q. Consider the following aircraft: (2024)

1. Rafael 2. MiG-29
3. Tejas MK-1

How many of the above are considered fifth generation fighter aircraft?

(a) Only one (b) Only two
(c) All three (d) None

Q. How is the S-400 air defence system technically superior to any other system presently available in the world? (150 words) (2021)

UNIT 10 NUCLEAR SCIENCE

Nuclear Energy

- **Nuclear energy** is the **energy source** found in an **atom's nucleus**, or core. Once extracted, this energy can be used to produce **electricity** in a **reactor** through **two kinds of atomic reactions: nuclear fusion** and **nuclear fission.**

Nuclear Fission

- Nuclear Fission occurs when a neutron slams into a larger atom, forcing it to excite and split into two smaller atoms—also known as fission products. Additional neutrons are also released that can initiate a chain reaction.
- When each atom splits, a tremendous amount of energy is released.
- Uranium and plutonium are most commonly used for fission reactions in nuclear power reactors because they are easy to initiate and control.
- The energy released by fission in these reactors heats water into steam. The steam is used to spin a turbine to produce carbon-free electricity.

Nuclear Fusion

- Nuclear Fusion occurs when two atoms slam together to form a heavier atom, like when two hydrogen atoms fuse to form one helium atom.
- This is the same process that powers the sun and creates huge amounts of energy—several times greater than fission. It also doesn't produce highly radioactive fission products.
- Fusion reactions are being studied by scientists, but are difficult to sustain for long periods of time because of the tremendous amount of pressure and temperature needed to join the nuclei together.

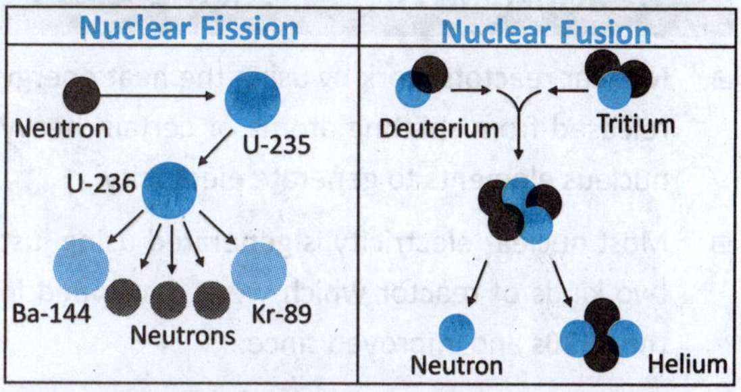

Generation of Atomic Nuclear Power

- **Nuclear power** can be generated through a process called **nuclear fission**, which involves **splitting** the nucleus of an atom into two smaller nuclei.
- During a nuclear fission, **uranium** used as fuel causes atoms to split into two or more **nuclei**. The energy released from **fission generates heat** that brings a **cooling agent**, usually **water**, to **boil**. The **steam** derived from boiling or pressurised water is then **channelled** to **spin turbines** to **generate electricity**. The process is widely used in Nuclear reactors currently across India.
- To generate **nuclear power** under fission **uranium-235** is typically used as the fuel. **Uranium-235** atoms are **bombarded** with **neutrons**, causing them to **split** into **two smaller atoms** releasing more neutrons in the process. These released neutrons can then go on to collide with other **uranium-235 atoms**, causing them to **split** as well in a **chain reaction**.

- The **heat** generated by the **nuclear fission process** is used to **boil water** and **produce steam**, which then **drives turbines** connected to **generators**.
- The **generators** convert the **mechanical energy** from the **turbines** into **electrical energy** that can be used to **power homes** and **industries**.

Nuclear Power Reactors

- Nuclear reactors work by using the heat energy released from splitting atoms of certain heavy nucleus elements to generate electricity.
- Most nuclear electricity is generated using just two kinds of reactor which were developed in the **1950s** and improved since.
- The first generation of these reactors have all been retired, and most of those operating are second-generation.
- In a research reactor the main purpose is to utilise the actual neutrons produced in the core. In most naval reactors, steam drives a turbine directly for propulsion.
- The principles for using nuclear power to produce electricity are the same for most types of reactor.
- The energy released from continuous fission of the atoms of the fuel is harnessed as heat in either a gas or water, and is used to produce steam. The steam is used to drive the turbines which produce electricity (as in most fossil fuel plants).

Components of Nuclear Reactor

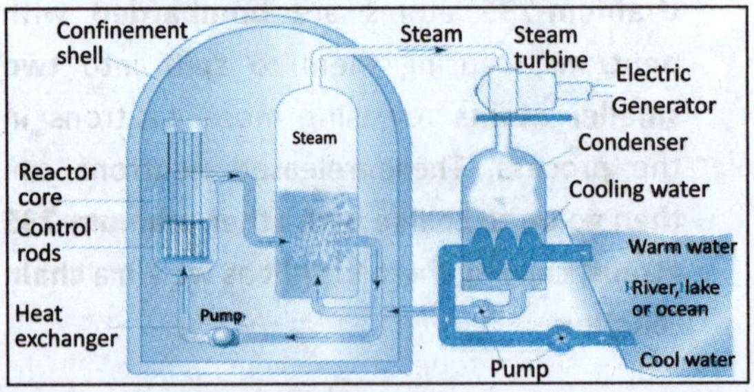

- **Fuel :** Uranium is the basic fuel. Usually pellets of uranium oxide (CO_2) are arranged in tubes to form fuel rods. The rods are arranged into fuel assemblies in the reactor core.
- **Moderator :** It is the material in the core which slows down the neutrons released from fission so that they cause more fission. It is usually water, but heavy water or graphite can also be used.
- **Control rods or blades :** These are made with neutron-absorbing material such as cadmium, hafnium or boron, and are inserted or withdrawn from the core to control the rate of reaction, or to halt it. In some PWR reactors, special control rods are used to enable the core to sustain a low level of power efficiently. (Secondary control systems involve other neutron absorbers, usually boron in the coolant its concentration can be adjusted over time as the fuel burns up.) PWR control rods are inserted from the top, BWR cruciform blades from the bottom of the core.
- **Coolant :** A fluid circulating through the core so as to transfer the heat from it. In light water reactors the water moderator functions also as primary coolant. Except in BWRs, there is secondary coolant circuit where the water becomes steam. A PWR has two to four primary coolant loops with pumps, driven either by steam or electricity.
- **Pressure vessel or pressure tubes :** Usually a robust steel vessel containing the reactor core and moderator/coolant, but it may be a series of tubes holding the fuel and conveying the coolant through the surrounding moderator.
- **Steam Generator :** Part of the cooling system of pressurised water reactors (PWR & PHWR) where the high-pressure primary coolant bringing heat from the reactor is used to make steam for the turbine, in a secondary circuit

- **Containment :** The structure around the reactor and associated steam generators which is designed to protect it from outside intrusion and to protect those outside from the effects of radiation in case of any serious malfunction inside. It is typically a metre-thick concrete and steel structure.

Types of Nuclear Reactors

Pressurised water reactor (PWR)

- The design of PWRs originated as a submarine power plant. PWRs use ordinary water as both coolant and moderator. The design is distinguished by having a primary cooling circuit which flows through the core of the reactor under very high pressure, and a secondary circuit in which steam is generated to drive the turbine.
- Water in the primary circuit is prevented from boiling by pressurising the reactors. Water in the secondary circuit is under less pressure and therefore boils, turning the turbine to generate electricity.

In Russia these are known as **VVER types –** water-moderated and -cooled. They make up almost **70%** of the global reactor fleet.

Boiling water reactor (BWR)

- They are second most common reactor type globally, making up approximately **15%** of the **global fleet**. Unlike PWRs, this design has a single circuit in which water is held at a pressure that allows it to boil. The steam generated in the reactor is fed directly to the turbine.

BWRs are primarily found in the US, Japan, Sweden and Taiwan.

Pressurised heavy water reactor (PHWR)

- The PHWR reactor has been developed since the 1950s in Canada as the CANDU, and from 1980s also in India.
- PHWRs generally use natural uranium (0.7% U-235) oxide as fuel, hence needs a more efficient moderator, in this case heavy water (D2O).
- They are the third most common reactor type, making up 11% of the global fleet. The design uses heavy water, a chemically different form of water, to cool and control the nuclear reactions, making it possible to use naturally-occurring uranium as fuel, rather than the enriched fuel used in PWRs and BWRs.
- The PHWR produces more energy per kilogram of mined uranium than other designs, but also produces a much larger amount of used fuel per unit output.
- Heavy-water reactors are mostly associated with Canada, but they are also used in India, Argentina, Romania, Pakistan and China.

Liquid metal fast reactors (LMFRs)

- It uses different liquid metals (e.g. sodium, lead) to cool the core. Liquid metal reactors can be fuelled with uranium in metallic form (current reactors mostly use uranium in ceramic form), as well as recycled nuclear waste (i.e. plutonium, minor actinides).
- The world's only currently operational fast reactors are the sodium-cooled BN-600 and BN-800 reactors both located at the Beloyarsk Nuclear Power Plant in Russia.

Molten salt reactors (MSRs)

- They use salts as coolant, with either solid fuel rods (similar to current reactors) or with the fuel dissolved in the salt itself. MSRs can use a range of fuels, such as uranium, plutonium, actinides from nuclear waste and thorium, depending on whether they are operating as fast reactors. As MSRs can operate at high temperatures, they can be used to generate hydrogen and heat for different industrial applications.

Advanced gas-cooled reactor (AGR)

- These are the second generation of British gas-cooled reactors, using graphite moderator and carbon dioxide as primary coolant. The fuel is uranium oxide pellets, enriched to 2.5 - 3.5%, in stainless steel tubes.

Light water graphite-moderated reactor (LWGR)

- The main LWGR design is the RBMK, a Soviet design, developed from plutonium production reactors. It employs long (7 metre) vertical pressure tubes running through graphite moderator, and is cooled by water, which is allowed to boil in the core at 290°C and at about 6.9 MPa, much as in a BWR. Fuel is low-enriched uranium oxide made up into fuel assemblies 3.5 metres long.

High-temperature gas-cooled reactors (HTGRs)

- They are cooled by gas (e.g. helium, carbon dioxide) with the uranium fuel being either in the shape of fuel rods (surrounded by graphite blocks) or fuel particles (uranium 'balls' covered with different materials such as silicon carbide). HTGRs operate at very high temperatures (>800°C) and are well suited for the generation of synthetic fuels and district and industrial heat.

Fast neutron reactor (FNR)

- Some reactors do not have a moderator and utilise fast neutrons, generating power from plutonium while making more of it from the U-238 isotope in or around the fuel.

Breeder reactors

- They are a type of nuclear reactor which produce more fissile materials than they consume. They are designed to extend the nuclear fuel supply for the generation of electricity, and have even been mistakenly called a potential renewable energy source.
- There are two categories of breeder reactors, based on the speed of the neutrons. Fast breeder reactors which use uranium-238 as fuel and thermal breeder reactors which use thorium-232 as fuel. Fast breeders do not require moderation since the neutrons need to be moving fast, whereas thermal breeders make us of moderation to achieve slower-moving neutrons.

- In the **1950s**, **early commercial nuclear power stations** started operating, offering to many countries around the world an **alternative** to **oil and gas import dependency** and a far **less polluting energy source** than fossil fuels.
- Following the **1970s energy crisis** and the dramatic increase of **oil prices** that resulted from it, more and more countries decided to embark on nuclear power programmes.
- Indeed, most reactors have been built between **1970** and **1985** worldwide.
- Currently, **nuclear energy** meets around **10% of global energy demand**, with **439** currently **operational nuclear plants** in **32 countries** and about **55 new reactors** under construction.
- In **2020**, **13 countries** produced at **least one-quarter of** their total electricity from nuclear, with the **US**, **China** and **France** dominating the market by far.

Advantages of Nuclear Energy

- **Low-carbon energy sources :** While **traditional fossil fuel generation sources** pump massive amounts of **carbon dioxide** (the primary cause of global climate change) into the **atmosphere**, **nuclear energy plants** do not produce carbon dioxide, or any air pollutant, during operation.
- **Smallest carbon footprints :** Compared to other **common clean energy facilities** (particularly wind and solar power), **nuclear energy plants** take up far less physical space.

> According to the **Department of Energy**, a typical nuclear facility producing **1,000 megawatts** (MW) of electricity takes up about one square mile of space. Comparatively, a wind farm producing the same amount of energy takes **360x** more land area, and a large-scale solar farm uses **75x** more space. That's **431 wind turbines or 3.125 million solar panels.**

- **High Power Output:** Nuclear power plants produce **high levels of energy** compared to **most power sources** (especially renewables), which makes them a great provider of **baseload electricity**.

Baseload electricity simply means the **minimum level of energy demand** on the grid over a span of time, say a week.

- **Reliable and cost-effective : Nuclear energy** is a **reliable renewable energy source** based on it's **constant production** and **accessibility**. Nuclear power plants produce at their **maximum power output** more often (93% of the time) than any other energy source, and because of this **round-the-clock stability**, making theman ideal source for reliable baseload electricity for the grid.

Concerns of Nuclear Energy

- **Uranium is technically non-renewable :** Current nuclear technology relies on **uranium** ore for **fuel**, which exists in **limited amounts** in the earth's crust. The longer we rely on nuclear power (and uranium ore in particular) the more **depleted** the **earth's uranium resources** will become, which will **drive up the cost of extracting** it, as well as the **negative environmental impacts** from **mining** and **processing the uranium**.
- **High upfront costs- Infrastructure installation :** Operating a nuclear energy plant is a relatively **low-cost endeavor**, but **building it in the first place is very expensive.** Nuclear reactors are complex structures that require many levels of safety built around them, which drives up the cost of new nuclear plants.
- **Challenges of Nuclear waste disposal :** Nuclear waste is **radioactive**, making it an **environmental** and **health catastrophe waiting** to happen. These reasons are exactly why governments spend tons of money to safely package up and dispose of used-up nuclear fuel.
- **Malfunctions can be catastrophic :** A nuclear meltdown occurs when the heat created by a nuclear reactor exceeds the amount of heat being transferred out by the cooling systems; this causes the system to exceed its melting point. If this happens, hot radioactive vapors can escape, which can cause nuclear plants to fully melt down and combust, while also releasing harmful radioactive materials into the environment.

Nuclear disasters have been witnessed in **Chernobyl Core Meltdown** (1986). Similarly Nuclear installations under influence of **Earthquakes** or some **natural disaster** may be subjected to a catastrophy like in case of **Fukushima** (2011).

Atomic Energy in India

- Atomic Energy has a key role in reducing the **carbon intensity** of the **overall Power sector** of India.

Thermal power generation from all sources contributes **234,048 MW,** which is **60%** of the **total installed power** while **renewables, hydro** and **nuclear contribute 95,875 MW** (25%), **51,220 MW** (13%) and **6,780 MW** (up to 2%) respectively.

- While renewable sources of energy are **environment friendly**, they are **intermittent sources of power.** Nuclear power, being a non-intermittent and concentrated source of power with **negligible carbon footprint**, is an essential component of the Indian power-mix to meet the International environmental commitments of India.
- India has **limited domestic uranium resources** while we have abundant **Thorium.** To exploit Thorium, our planners envisaged the **Three Stage Nuclear Power Program.**

India's Nuclear programme

- Nuclear energy is the **fifth-largest source** of **electricity** for India which contributes about **3%** of the **total electricity generation** in the country.

India has over **22 nuclear reactors** in **7 power plants** across the country which produces **6780 MW** of nuclear power.

- **Kakrapar Atomic Power Project** (KAPP-3) has also been connected to the grid in **January 2021.**
- **18 reactors** are **Pressurised Heavy Water Reactors** (PHWRs) and **4** are **Light Water Reactors** (LWRs).

- **KAPP-3** is the **India's first 700 MWe unit**, and the biggest indigenously developed variant of the PHWR.

Evolution of India's Nuclear Programme

- Unlike other minerals, **uranium**, the main fuel for **nuclear reactors**, is **not freely traded**. The technology of **building nuclear reactors** is closely guarded by a **voluntary association** of **46 countries** called the **Nuclear Suppliers Group**-NSG (formed in 1974 in wake of India's first nuclear tests in May 1974 Operation Smiling Buddha) which follows certain **guidelines** for supplying **uranium** as well as the **technology** to make **nuclear reactors**.
- Its policies are determined mainly by the **industrialised countries** and many in the **developing world criticise** it for not letting them have access to an **energy source** that can help them meet their growing **energy demand**.
- The **American government** started its **Atom for Peace programme** and enacted the **Atomic Energy Act of 1954**, which provided **American industries** wider access to the **government's nuclear technology**.
- The programme is often seen as an **American attempt** to dominate the **world nuclear market**. Following the Act, there was a **UN conference** on the **peaceful uses of atomic energy** presided over by **Homi Jehangir Bhabha**.
- Under this programme, the **US agreed to sell India heavy water** for a **reactor** that was to be provided by **Canada** with the **stipulation** that it would be only for **peaceful use**.
- In the midst of the **Atom for Peace programme**, when some countries were provided nuclear reactors, many countries including the **UK**, **France** and **China** were testing **atom bombs**.
- Following the **French test** in **1961**, an **Irish resolution** for **international agreement** to refrain from **transfer** or **acquisition** of **nuclear weapons** was unanimously passed by the **United Nations**.
- The negotiations started in **1965** and later a clause was included that only those states that had exploded a **nuclear device** prior to **January 1, 1967** would be recognised as **nuclear weapons** states. This meant **China's inclusion and India's exclusion**. Signing a treaty against nuclear tests without the **complete disarmament** of other nuclear powers was rejected by India and many other countries.

Nuclear Proliferation Treaties and India

- In **1954**, India made the first proposal calling for an agreement to ban nuclear weapons tests.
- In **1958**, the United States, the Soviet Union, and the United Kingdom began a Conference on the Discontinuance of Nuclear Tests in Geneva, aimed at reaching agreement on an effectively controlled test ban. The Conference did not come to fruition because the sides could not reach an agreement on the issue of verification procedures.
- On **5 August 1963**, the **Partial Test Ban Treaty** (PTBT) also known as the **Limited Test Ban Treaty** (LTBT) was signed in Moscow by the United States, the Soviet Union, and the United Kingdom.
- PTBT/ LTBT required Parties to prohibit, prevent, and abstain from carrying out nuclear weapons tests or any other nuclear explosions in the atmosphere, in outer space, under water, or in any other environment if such explosions cause radioactive debris to be present outside the territorial limits of the State that conducts an explosion; to refrain from causing, encouraging, or in any way participating in, the carrying out of any nuclear weapon test explosion, or any other nuclear explosion, anywhere which would take place in any of the above-described environments.

- By **1964** there were **5 nuclear powers** in the world: in addition to the United States, the Soviet Union and the United Kingdom, all of which obtained nuclear capability during or shortly after the **Second World War**, France exploded its first nuclear bomb in **1960**, and the People's Republic of China in **1964** and were collectively regarded Nuclear Weapon States under NPT.

Treaty on the Non-Proliferation of Nuclear Weapons (NPT)

- NPT was adopted on 12 June 1968 at United Nations, New York, USA and entered into force in 1970. Presently, it has 191 member states.
- India alongside Pakistan, Israel, North Korea, and South Sudan haven't yet signed the NPT.
- NPT aims to prevent the spread of nuclear weapons and weapons technology, to foster the peaceful uses of nuclear energy, and to further the goal of disarmament. The Treaty establishes a safeguards system under the responsibility of the IAEA, which also plays a central role under the Treaty in areas of technology transfer for peaceful purposes.
- The 5 NWS agree not to transfer nuclear weapons or other nuclear explosive devices and not in any way to assist, encourage, or induce a non-nuclear weapon state (NNWS) to acquire nuclear weapons.
- India's position on the NPT was probably set in concrete when it became clear that the NPT would recognise NWS only those countries that had exploded a nuclear device prior to January 1, 1967, that included China as a Nuclear State while excluded India, and signing the treaty would bound India not to conduct any nuclear test, despite it's neighbour China (which had a war with India in 1962) being a nuclear state.
- With the signing of the Comprehensive Test Ban Treaty (CTBT) in September 1996, the PTBT became redundant. Comprehensive Nuclear-Test-Ban Treaty (CTBT) bans all nuclear explosions, whether for military or peaceful purposes.
- Treaty on the Prohibition of nuclear weapons (TPNW) entered into force on 22 January 2021 and India is not a member of this treaty.
- After **India's defeat** in the **war** with **China, public opinion** started building for India to conduct its **nuclear test** as a deterrent for **China's future aggression.**
- In **1964**, **China** too joined the **elite club** of **nuclear states** by testing an **atom bomb** and **Homi Bhabha** started **aggressive lobbying** for **Indian nuclear weapons,** giving **radio speeches.** Bhabha died mysteriously in a plane crash in **1966** and the programme was taken forward by **Dr. Ramanna** and **Dr. Sethna.**

> On **May 18, 1974,** India carried out an underground nuclear explosion in **Pokhran** in **Rajasthan** under **Operation Smiling Buddha.**

- A research reactor, **CIRUS**, which was supplied by **Canada**, was used as the **source of plutonium**. This incident became the **trigger** for the formation of the **NSG.**
- This is seen as the first incident when a **weapon** was manufactured by using material diverted from a civilian nuclear programme, but it wasn't the first example of intentional or unintentional help of a nuclear state to a non-nuclear country in making the weapon.
- It is alleged that the **US** aided **UK's weapon programme**, the **Soviets** helped the Chinese and Israel was helped by the **French.**
- India never acknowledged that the **1974 tests** were for a **nuclear bomb** and the peaceful use cause was violated. It was said that the test was done to check the possible use of nuclear explosives in mining and earth moving operations.

- On **May 11, 1998,** India conducted **3 nuclear bomb test explosions** at the **Indian Army's Pokhran Test Range**. Two days later, on **May 13,** two more bombs were tested.
- **Codenamed Operation Shakti** (Strength), these tests displayed India's capability to build fission and thermonuclear weapons with yields up to **200 kilotons**, helping India enter the highly guarded club of countries with capability to **deploy nuclear weapons.**
- After the **1998 tests**, when India acknowledged testing **nuclear bombs** and was followed by **Pakistan**, the **UN Security council** offered both **India** and **Pakistan** the option of becoming state parties to the **NPT** as **non-nuclear weapon states**, which was not accepted.
- **NSG guidelines** contain the so-called **Non-Proliferation Principle**, adopted in **1994,** whereby a supplier, notwithstanding other provisions in the **NSG Guidelines**, authorises a transfer only when satisfied that the transfer would not contribute to the **proliferation of nuclear weapons.**
- The NSG guidelines are consistent with the various **international legally binding instruments** in the nuclear non-proliferation sector.

India's 3-stage Nuclear Programme

- The **3-stage nuclear programme** is developed with the aim of **utilizing** the vast **Thorium reserves** in India (about 25% of the world)
- Besides India has limited availability of Uranium reserves (about 2% of the world's uranium reserves)

First Stage

- **Pressurized Heavy Water Reactors** are based on natural uranium that contains **99.3% U-238** and **0.7% U-235.**
- **U-235** being fissile sets up the **chain reaction** and **U-238** being non-fissile gets converted to **Pu-239** as a byproduct (spent fuel) which is in turn used in the Fast Breeder Reactors in the **2nd Stage.**

Second Stage

- Fast Breeder Reactors are primarily based on **Plutonium.**
- Further the breeder reactors use mix of **Plutonium-239** produced in the **1st stage** and **U-238** that is abundantly found on earth to produce Plutonium inside the reactor.

> **U-238 is not fissile material** and thus cannot set up chain reaction.

- Since the **amount of Plutonium** produced inside the reactor is more than that initially used, it is called **Breeder reactor.**
- In order to increase the **probability of neutron** hitting **U-238,** these reactors **do not use a moderator** to slow down neutrons and thus they are called **Fast Breeder Reactors.**
- Once the **Plutonium-239** is completely used, Thorium is introduced in the reactor to convert it into **U-233** that will be used in **3rd stage.**

Third Stage

- **Thermal Breeder Reactors** uses **U-233** that is produced in the **2nd stage** using **thorium-232.**
- Thorium is also **not radioactive** and thus **not fissile.**
- Since these reactors also produce **U-233** out of **Thorium-232** they are called **breeder reactors.**

> India has **abundant thorium reserves** in the form of monazite sand, and therefore the 3rd stage is critical for **India's nuclear energy basket.**

- Indigenously built **Pressurised Heavy Water Reactors** (PHWRs) form the backbone of the first stage **Indian nuclear power program.** PHWRs use **domestic natural uranium** (UO2) containing **0.7 % fissile 235U** and **99.3% 238U** as fuel and **Heavy water** as **moderator** and **primary coolant.**

- **Reprocessing** of the spent fuel from **PHWRs** and waste management are important components of the three stage nuclear program. These technologies were developed with total indigenous efforts.
- **Uranium** and **Plutonium** are **chemically separated** and **recycled**, while the other **radioactive fission products** were separated and sorted according to their half lives and radioactivity and stored with minimal environmental impact.
- **239Pu** extracted from the **spent fuel** serves as the fuel for the **Fast Breeder Reactors** (FBRs) – part of the **second stage** of the **nuclear program.** FBR fuel is so designed that a blanket of **238U** surrounds **fuel core. 238U** undergoes transmutation to produce fresh **239Pu**. Thus an FBR not only consumes 239Pu but also breeds more 239Pu than it consumes.

> **FBR technology** is very complex and only advanced countries like **USA, UK, France, Japan** and **USSR** have mastered this technology.

- India announced its entry into this exclusive club when the **40 MWth Fast Breeder Test Reactor** (FBTR) went critical in the Indira Gandhi Centre for Atomic Research, Kalpakkam in October 1985.

> A unique feature the FBTR is the **indigenously developed U-Pu carbide fuel rich in Pu.**

- With the operational experience gained from FBTR, India embarked upon the construction of a **500 MWe Prototype Fast Breeder Reactor** (PFBR).
- **232Th**, which is abundant in India, is not a fissile material. However, by a neutron capture reaction, **232Th** transforms into **233U**, which is a fissile material like **235U** and **239Pu**.
- The strategy of the three stage program is to convert **232Th** into **233U** in the fast reactors. **233U** will be the fuel in the futuristic third stage of nuclear program.
- Further, it is proposed to use thorium along with a small feed of plutonium-based fuel in **Advanced Heavy Water Reactors** (AHWRs) which are expected to facilitate large-scale thorium utilization.

India Nuclear/Atomic Power Plant

- India entered the **atomic age**, more correctly the **nuclear age**, on **4th August 1956** when **Apsara, India's first nuclear reactor**, went into operation. This reactor was designed and built by India with the nuclear fuel supplied from the **United Kingdom** under a lease agreement.
- Our **second reactor** for **research purposes, CIRUS**, was built with cooperation with **Canada** and went into operation in the early **1960's**.
- The research reactors were platforms for **conducting research** in **neutron physics,** studies in the **behaviour of materials** under **neutron irradiation** and for **production of radio isotopes**. The latter are very useful for **diagnostics** and treatment of various ailments, especially **cancer**, and useful in industrial applications, especially for the purpose of non-destructive testing.

Nuclear Power Plants in India

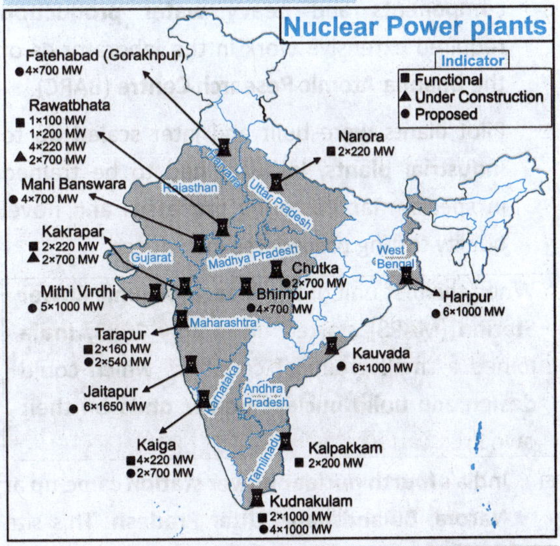

- **Electricity production** using nuclear energy commenced in **October 1969** when the two reactors at **Tarapur** were put into service.

The **Tarapur Atomic Power Station** (TAPS) was built by **General Electric of USA** and is now in its forty-eighth year of service. Tarapur supplies the lowest cost non-hydro electric power in the country.

- **India's second nuclear power station** came up in **Rajasthan**, near **Kota**, the first unit of which went into operation in **August, 1972.**

The first two units at **Rajasthan** were built in collaboration with **Canada**, who pioneered reactors that could use **natural uranium as fuel.** They, however, required heavy water, present in extremely small quantities in ordinary water and can be extracted through complex processes.

- **India's third nuclear power station** came up at **Kalpakkam**, near **Chennai**. This station was designed and built by India, on its own. All the material and equipment were produced within the country.
- This was a huge challenge as Indian industry at that time, had no experience in making complex equipment required for nuclear applications.
- Special materials like **nuclear fuel, zirconium components** and **heavy water production** required extensive work in the laboratories of the **Bhabha Atomic Research Centre** (BARC).
- Pilot plants were built and later scaled up to **industrial plants.** Industry had to be trained in special manufacturing processes and novel quality testing procedures introduced.

When the first unit of the **Madras Atomic Power Station** (MAPS) started up in **July 1983, India** joined a small group of countries which could **design** and **build nuclear power units** on their own.

- India's **fourth nuclear power station** came up at **Narora, Bulandshahr, Uttar Pradesh**. This site has **experienced earthquakes** in the vicinity. So we evolved **designs capable** of withstanding any **foreseeable earthquake** that could visit the site. The design of a **220 MW unit** was also standardized that could be built at a number of sites in the country.

The **first unit** of **Narora** started up in **October 1989**. In the next twenty years, India built and commissioned **eleven 220 MW units** and **two 540 MW units**, all based on its own technology called **Pressurised Heavy Water Reactors.**

- To accomplish this task, **India** also built up a strong **heavy water production capability** and **fuel production, including mining of uranium** in **Jharkhand.**
- Indian industry was mobilized to produce the entire range of equipment and materials to support the **nuclear power programme.**
- Since India was keen to augment the **nuclear capacity** rapidly, it entered into a collaboration with the **former Soviet Union** in **1988** to build **two 1000 MW reactor power units** using **enriched uranium** as fuel. Due to the **disintegration of Soviet Union** in **1990** and the economic difficulties faced by India owing to **BoP crisis** during the period, **Indo-Russian project** was put on the back burner.
- In **1998, India** and **Russia** decided to embark on this project, and work at site commenced in **2003**. When the commissioning activities on the first unit were in progress, the **nuclear accident** in **Fukushima, Japan,** occurred in **March 2011**, which triggered a **strong opposition** to the project amongst people living in the neighborhood. It took **considerable time** and **patience** explaining to inform the public at large about the safety features at **Kudankulam, Tamil Nadu** (where 6 nuclear power units were commissioned with assistance from **Russia**.

The first unit at **Kudankulam** went into operation in **2014** and the second in **2016**.

- India currently has **22 reactor units** in service. The **first unit at Rajasthan** supplied by **Canada** has been out of service due to some equipment deficiencies. The other units with a total capacity of **6700 MW** have been operating reliably. The plant load factor for the five years from **2011** to **2016** has been about **78%**. The nuclear power units have been supplying power at **Rs. 2 to Rs. 3.50 per kwh** (Kilowatt hour).

India signed **cooperation agreements** with the **USA** and **France** in **2008** and they provided for building **nuclear power units** designed in these countries to be set up in India.

- Negotiations have been going on from then on. However, the leading nuclear power plant builder in the **US**, namely **Westinghouse filed** for bankruptcy a few months ago.
- **AREVA of France** lost a lot of money on their nuclear fuel business following the **Fukushima accident**.
- The French government allocated the nuclear reactor business to their national electric utility, **Electricite de France**. There is considerable uncertainty, therefore, with regard to cooperation with USA and France.
- The Government of India decided to build **ten India designed 700 MW Pressurized Heavy Water Reactors** in **June 2017**.
- The **Nuclear Power Corporation** had scaled up the **540 MW size units** to **700 MW** and started work, **two at Kakrapara** (Units 3 and 4) and **two at Rajasthan** (Units 7 and 8).
- This is one of the biggest single commitments in nuclear power, after the **Fukushima accident of 2011**. This programme will provide Indian industry with sustained workload for a period of a decade and establish India firmly as an important player in this field.
- Work has commenced on **Units 3, 4, 5 and 6** at **Kudankulam. Russia** has offered to build **six 1200 MW units** at a second site to be identified by India.
- As a parallel activity, India has designed the Indian Pressurised Water Reactor of 900 MW capacity, using enriched uranium as fuel. Work on two such units may be taken up soon, to be followed thereafter by series building.
- At **Kalpakkam**, the **Prototype Fast Breeder Reactor** of **500 MW** is in the process of commission.
- **Two reactors** of **600 MW** of similar design may follow. The **Bhabha Atomic Research Centre** has completed the design of a **300 MW** reactor called **Advanced Thermal Reactor** which would use thorium. Our long term plans to use thorium depend on fast reactors and thorium based systems.
- The **Department of Atomic Energy** has been actively engaged in supplying **radio isotopes to hospital and industry**, in the use of radiation technologies for preventing spoilage of marine foods, spices and for enhancing the shelf life of onions, mangoes and other food articles, as well as in sterilization of medical products.

India is the only developing nation to have **indigenously developed**, **demonstrated and deployed nuclear reactors** for **electricity generation**, which was made possible through several decades of extensive scientific research and technology development primarily in BARC. In this regard, **Dr. Homi Bhabha** was the architect.

- The country has **nuclear ores** from which a total of about **78,000 tonnes** of **uranium metal** and about **518,000 tonnes** of thorium metal can be extracted.
- If the entire **uranium resources** are first used in **natural uranium–fueled pressurized heavy water reactors** (PHWRs), it is estimated that

about **420 GWe-yrs** of **electricity** can be produced.

- The resulting depleted uranium and separated plutonium from these **PHWRs**, if used in **fast breeder reactors** (FBRs), could generate an additional **54,000 GWe-yrs of electricity.** In these FBRs, production of **uranium-233** (U^{233}) can also be achieved by loading thorium assemblies in their blanket and low-power zones.

- Eventually by transitioning to generations of **Th-U^{233} fueled breeder reactors**, India should be able to produce an additional **358,000 GWe-yrs** of electricity. Thus, even at an installed nuclear power capacity of **500–600 GWe**, the country's nuclear resources will be able to sustain its electricity generation needs far beyond the extinction of its coal deposits.

The **first nuclear power reactors** built in India were **two BWRs** at **Tarapur**, constructed by **GE** as turn key projects through **Indo-US cooperation.**

- As part of setting up of **PHWRs**, subsequent to withdrawal of **Canadian support** in **1974**, **BARC** took the responsibility of components development and testing such as nuclear grade pumps, fueling machine, fuel, clad, etc. and other major R&D support for design and safety of PHWRs from normal operations to design extension conditions.

Subsequent to the accidents at **Three Mile Island** in **USA** in year **1979** (TMI) followed by **Chernobyl** in **1986**, there was **radical change** in philosophy of design of new nuclear reactors. **Passive safety systems** became integral part in **Gen-III** and **III+ reactors.** This philosophy gave birth to the concept of **Advanced Heavy Water Reactor** (AHWR) being designed by **BARC**.

- The **AHWR** retained the **pressure tube concept of PHWRs** but adopted several passive systems in design making the reactor safe enough to deploy close to the population center.

- Apart from this, AHWR targeted to produce significant power (more than 60 %) from **thorium** as a **demonstration reactor** for power from thorium. Of course, the **third stage of nuclear power program** envisages large scale power production from thorium, AHWR will provide enough experience for handling, manufacturing and reprocessing of thorium based fuels before large scale power production from thorium takes place.

World's first thorium-based nuclear plant, Bhavni, using **Uranium-233**, is being set up at **Kalpakkam** in **Tamil Nadu.**

- This plant will be entirely indigenous and will be the first of its kind. The experimental thorium plant **Kamini** already exists in **Kalpakkam.**

- After entering into **International Civil Nuclear Cooperation agreement** in **2008**, (amid Indo US civil Nuclear Cooperation Agreement) India was bestowed with opportunity of setting up **nuclear reactors** with **international cooperation.** This treaty also ensured continuous supply of fuel for Indian NPPs.

- BARC plans to develop PWRs indigenously for **accelerated capacity building.** BARC has achieved forging technology for pressure vessel, reactivity drives, etc to initiate the indigenous PWR programme.

Indian molten salt breeder reactor (IMSBR) is the platform to burn **thorium** as part of **3rd stage of Indian nuclear power programme.**

- The fuel in IMSBR is in the form of a continuously **circulating molten fluoride salt** which flows through heat exchangers for ultimately transferring heat for power production to **Super-critical CO_2 based Brayton cycle** (SCBC) so as to have **larger energy conversion ratio** as compared to **existing power conversion cycle.**

- Because of the **fluid fuel**, online reprocessing is possible, extracting the **233Pa** (formed in conversion chain of **232Th** to **233U**) and allowing it to decay to **233U** outside the core, thus making it possible to breed even in thermal neutron spectrum.

- Hence **IMSBR** can operate in self sustaining **233U-Th fuel cycle**. Additionally, being a thermal reactor, the **233U** requirement is lower (as compared to fast spectrum), thus allowing higher deployment potential.
- These reactors require several new technology development which are being undertaken by **BARC**. These include **7Li enrichment, salt preparation and purification, salt characterisation and chemistry, structural material development and characterisation, nuclear grade graphite development and characterisation, component development**, SCBC and reprocessing for IMSBR.
- In addition, a dedicated facility, **Molten Salt Breeder Reactor Developmental Facility** (MSBRDF) is being designed for full scale demonstration of all major systems for the **5 MWth IMSBR**.
- BARC has also developed **Ni-Mo-Cr-Ti alloy** for the vessel. R&D is being undertaken for **fuel salt optimisation, characterisation, salt preparation, thermal hydraulic** and **corrosion studies of IMSBRs**.
- In addition, BARC is also developing the **Innovative High Temperature Reactor** (IHTR) with an aim to provide **high temperature process heat** for **hydrogen production** by **thermochemical water splitting**.
- This reactor is a molten salt cooled pebble bed type reactor. It uses TRISO type particle fuel made into form of pebbles, cooled with molten fluoride salts.

Currently, a **20 MWth IHTR** is being designed as demonstration reactor.

- Development of high temperature heat pipes, facility for graphite oxidation studies, **TRISO coated particle fuel, fuel pellet fabrication, Niobium alloy** and components of test loop, machining of graphite components for IHTR experimental facility, thermal hydraulic studies on coolants have been completed.

India's Nuclear Energy Generation

- In March 2018, the Indian government stated that nuclear capacity would be about 22.5 GWe by the year 2031, well below earlier targets. This revised target was reaffirmed by Minister of State Jitendra Singh in December 2022, and by the Department of Atomic Energy in February 2025.
- In December 2023, Indian Government launched Viksit Bharat, its strategy to make India a developed nation by 2047.
- In July 2024 the country's 2024-25 budget specified setting up Bharat Small Reactors.
- Bharat Small Reactors, first announced in August 2023 by Minister of State Jitendra Singh are expected to be closely based on the existing 220 MWe PHWR technology India has built since the 1980s.
- In February 2025 Minister of Finance Nirmala Sitharaman announced the Nuclear Energy Mission for Viksit Bharat, and promised federal funds to develop at least five Indian-designed SMRs to be operational by 2033, as well as amendments to Indian legislation to encourage private sector participation, in the budget for 2025-2026. In the same budget she said that the development of at least 100 GW of nuclear energy by 2047 is essential for India's energy transition efforts.
- In February 2025 India and France signed a letter of intent to partner on advanced modular and small modular reactors.
- In February 2025, India and the USA agreed to fully realize the US-India 123 Civil Nuclear

Agreement by moving forward with plans to build US-designed reactors in India.

- India has 22 operating reactors, with an installed capacity of 6780 MWe. Among these eighteen reactors are Pressurised Heavy Water Reactors (PHWRs) and four are Light Water Reactors (LWRs).
- As of January 30, 2025, India's nuclear capacity is 8180 MW.

Tarapur Atomic Power Plant-1 (TAPS-1)	160 MWe
Tarapur Atomic Power Plant-2 (TAPS-2)	160 MWe
Rajasthan Atomic Power Plant-1 (RAPS-1)	100 MWe
Rajasthan Atomic Power Plant-2 (RAPS-2)	200 MWe
Madras Atomic Power Plant-1 (MAPS-1)	220 MWe
Madras Atomic Power Plant-2 (MAPS-2)	220 MWe
Narora Atomic Power Plant-1 (NAPS-1)	220 MWe
Narora Atomic Power Plant-2 (NAPS-2)	220 MWe
Kakrapar Atomic Power Plant-1 (KAPS-1)	220 MWe
Kakrapar Atomic Power Plant-2 (KAPS-2)	220 MWe
Kaiga Generating Station-1 (KGS-1)	220 MWe
Kaiga Generating Station-2 (KGS-2)	220 MWe
Rajasthan Atomic Power Plant-3 (RAPS-3)	220 MWe
Rajasthan Atomic Power Plant-4 (RAPS-4)	220 MWe
Kaiga Generating Station-3 (KGS-3)	220 MWe
Kaiga Generating Station-4 (KGS-4)	220 MWe
Tarapur Atomic Power Plant-3 (TAPS-3)	540 MWe
Tarapur Atomic Power Plant-4 (TAPS-4)	540 MWe
Rajasthan Atomic Power Plant-5 (RAPS-5)	220 MWe
Rajasthan Atomic Power Plant-6 (RAPS-6)	220 MWe
Kudankulam Nuclear Power Station-1 (KKNPS-1)	1000 MWe
Kudankulam Nuclear Power Station-2 (KKNPS-2)	1000 MWe

- Government Initiatives for Enhancing India's Nuclear Capacity
- India is actively enhancing its nuclear power capacity to meet growing energy demands and achieve environmental goals.
- The government has initiated steps to increase nuclear power capacity from the current 8,180 MW to 22,480 MW by 2031-32.
- This expansion includes the construction and commissioning of ten reactors, totalling 8,000 MW, across Gujarat, Rajasthan, Tamil Nadu, Haryana, Karnataka, and Madhya Pradesh. Additionally, pre-project activities for ten more reactors have commenced, with plans for progressive completion by 2031-32.
- Further, the government accorded in-principle approval to set up 6 x 1208 MW nuclear power plant in cooperation with the USA at Kovvada in Srikakulam district in the state of Andhra Pradesh.
- A significant milestone was achieved on September 19, 2024, when the Rajasthan Atomic Power Project's Unit-7 (RAPP-7), one of the country's largest and third indigenous nuclear reactors, reached criticality, marking the beginning of controlled fission chain reaction.
- This event signifies India's growing capability in building and operating indigenous nuclear reactors, contributing to a future powered by homegrown technology.
- Safety remains a cornerstone of India's nuclear energy policy. India's nuclear power plants operate with stringent safety protocols and international oversight. The radiation levels at Indian nuclear facilities are consistently well below global benchmarks, underscoring the country's commitment to secure and sustainable nuclear energy.
- These efforts align with India's broader strategy to provide clean and reliable energy, contributing to long-term energy security and environmental sustainability.

- A significant discovery of new deposit in India's oldest Uranium Mine, the Jaduguda Mines, has been made in and around the existing mine lease area. This will increase the life of an otherwise depleting mine by more than fifty years.
- First two units of the indigenous 700 MWe PHWR at Kakrapar, Gujarat (KAPS - 3 & 4) have started commercial operation in FY 2023-24.
- Closed fuel cycle being the cornerstone of Indian nuclear power program, the country's first Prototype Fast Breeder Reactor (PFBR 500 Mwe) achieved many of the milestones in 2024, viz., Primary Sodium filling in Main Vessel, purification of the filled sodium and commissioning of all the four Sodium pumps (2 Primary Sodium Pumps & 2 Secondary Sodium Pumps). Core loading was commenced with loading of first reactor control rod on 4th March 2024.
- NPCIL and National Thermal Power Corporation (NTPC) have signed a supplementary Joint Venture agreement to develop nuclear power facilities in the country. The JV named ASHVINI will function within the existing legal framework of the Atomic Energy Act 1962 (amended in 2015) and will build, own, and operate nuclear power plants, including the upcoming 4x700 MWe PHWR Mahi-Banswara Rajasthan Atomic Power Project.

Budgetary Provisions (2025-26) for Nuclear Energy Programme

- The Union Budget 2025-26 outlines a significant push towards nuclear energy as part of India's long-term energy transition strategy. The government has set an ambitious target of 100 GW nuclear power capacity by 2047, positioning nuclear energy as a major pillar in India's energy mix. This development aligns with the broader objectives of Viksit Bharat, ensuring energy reliability and reducing dependency on fossil fuels. To achieve this goal, strategic policy interventions and infrastructure investments are being undertaken, with an emphasis on indigenous nuclear technology and public-private collaborations.

Small Modular Reactors (SMRs) and R&D Initiatives

- A key highlight of the Union Budget 2025-26 is the launch of a Nuclear Energy Mission, which is focused on research and development (R&D) of Small Modular Reactors (SMRs).
- The government has allocated ₹20,000 crore for this initiative, aiming to develop at least five indigenously designed and operational SMRs by 2033.

Nuclear Energy Mission for Viksit Bharat

- To facilitate the implementation of the Nuclear Energy Mission, amendments to the Atomic Energy Act and Civil Liability for Nuclear Damage Act will be taken up by the parliament.
- These amendments are expected to encourage private sector investments in nuclear power projects.
- The government will enter into partnerships with the private sector with the motive of:
  - Setting up Bharat Small Reactors
  - Research & development of Bharat Small Modular Reactor
  - Research & development of newer technologies for nuclear energy.

Bharat Small Reactors

- The government is actively expanding its nuclear energy sector by developing Bharat Small Reactors (BSRs) and exploring partnerships with the private sector. BSRs are 220 MW Pressurized Heavy Water Reactors (PHWRs) with a proven safety and performance record. These reactors are being upgraded to reduce land requirements, making them suitable for deployment near industries such as steel, aluminium, and metals, serving as captive power plants to aid in decarbonization efforts.

- The plan involves private entities providing land, cooling water, and capital, while the Nuclear Power Corporation of India Limited (NPCIL) handles design, quality assurance, and operation and maintenance, all within the existing legal framework. This initiative aligns with India's commitment to achieving 500 GW of non-fossil fuel-based energy generation by 2030 and meeting 50% of its energy requirements from renewable energy by 2030, as pledged at the COP26 Summit in Glasgow in 2021.
- In addition to BSRs, the Bhabha Atomic Research Centre (BARC) is developing Small Modular Reactors (SMRs) for repurposing retiring coal-based power plants and meeting power needs in remote locations. The Department of Atomic Energy (DAE) also plans to introduce new nuclear reactors, including high-temperature gas-cooled reactors for hydrogen co-generation and molten salt reactors aimed at utilizing India's abundant thorium resources.
- This strategic move signifies India's dedication to reducing carbon emissions and enhancing its civil nuclear energy program, with private sector participation playing a crucial role within the bounds of Indian laws and regulations

Bharat Small Modular Reactors

- India is actively exploring Small Modular Reactors (SMRs) as a crucial part of its energy transition strategy, aiming to achieve net-zero emissions while ensuring energy security. SMRs, are advanced nuclear reactors with a power generation capacity ranging from less than 30 MWe to 300+ MWe, provide a flexible, scalable, and cost-effective alternative to conventional large nuclear reactors.
- Given India's growing energy demands and the need for reliable, low-carbon power, SMRs can play a transformative role in complementing renewable energy sources and stabilizing the grid.
- Their modular design allows for factory-based manufacturing, reducing construction timelines and costs, making them suitable for both on-grid and off-grid applications, including deployment in remote locations.
- India's expertise in Pressurized Heavy Water Reactors (PHWRs) provides a strong foundation for the development and deployment of indigenous SMR designs.
- By integrating SMRs into its energy mix, India can address land constraints, reduce dependence on fossil fuels, and enhance its ability to meet international climate commitments under the Paris Agreement (2015) which India ratified in October 2016.
- The mission aligns with India's commitment to achieving 100 GW of nuclear energy capacity by 2047, a milestone deemed essential for reducing carbon emissions and meeting future energy demands.

Bhabha Atomic Research Centre

- Atomic Energy Establishment was set up at Trombay, near Mumbai, in 1957 and renamed as Bhabha Atomic Research Centre (BARC) ten years later.
- Plans for building the first Pressurized Heavy Water Reactor (PHWR) were finalized in 1964, and this prototype – Rajasthan 1, which had Canada's Douglas Point reactor as a reference unit, was built as a collaborative venture between Atomic Energy of Canada Ltd (AECL) and NPCIL.
- It started up in 1972 and was duplicated Subsequent indigenous PHWR development has been based on these units, though several stages of evolution can be identified: PHWRs with dousing and single containment at Rajasthan 1-2, PHWRs with suppression pool and partial double containment at Madras, and later standardized PHWRs from Narora onwards

having double containment, suppression pool, and calandria filled with heavy water, housed in a water-filled calandria vault.

- The Indian Atomic Energy Commission (AEC) is the main policy body.
- Nuclear Power Corporation of India Ltd (NPCIL) is responsible for design, construction, commissioning and operation of thermal nuclear power plants.
- NPCIL intends to set up five further Nuclear Energy Parks, each with a capacity for up to eight new-generation reactors of 1,000 MWe, six reactors of 1600 MWe or simply 10,000 MWe at a single location. By 2032, 40-45 GWe would be provided from these five.

BARC has active groups for **Research and Development in Reactor Technologies, Fuel reprocessing and waste management, Isotope Applications, Radiation Technologies and their application to health, agriculture and environment, Accelerator and Laser Technology, Electronics, instrumentation and reactor control** and **Materials Science.**

Research Reactors in BARC

- **APSARA** achieved criticality on **August 4, 1956** and was the **first research reactor** in **Asia** to achieve criticality.
- It was a pool type reactor of **1 MW power** with **highly enriched uranium** as fuel (4.5 kg) in the form of **plates. Light water** was used as both **moderator** and coolant.
- The **maximum neutron flux** was around **1013 neutrons/cm2/s.** It was mainly used for production of **isotopes, basic research, shielding experiments, neutron activation analysis, neutron radiography** and for testing neutron detectors. **Apsara** was permanently shutdown in **June, 2009.**
- **APSARA-U** (Apsara-Upgraded) was successfully commissioned and its **First Approach to Criticality** (FAC) was achieved on **10th September 2018.**
- Indigenously developed **Low Enriched Uranium** (LEU) fuel in **Uranium Silicide** form is used in the reactor.
- **Hot water** layer concept at the top of pool, which is first of a kind in India, is employed to minimize radiation dose.
- By virtue of **higher neutron flux, Apsara-U** will enhance indigenous production of radioisotopes for various societal applications.
- The reactor will also be used extensively for research in **nuclear physics, material science** and **radiation shielding.**
- **CIRUS reactor** (40 MWth) was built in collaboration with **Canada** and was commissioned on **10th July 1960.**
- CIRUS was extensively used for **condensed matter research** using **neutron beams**, material irradiation, fuel testing, neutron activation analysis and production of radioisotopes for applications in medicine, agriculture and industry.
- **CIRUS reactor** proved to be an excellent platform for training of engineers and scientists and in understanding the intricacies of managing **natural uranium, heavy water, reactor systems** which eventually evolved into the **Indian pressurized heavy water reactor programme.** After 50 years of successful operation, it was permanently shut-down in **December 2010.**
- **ZERLINA** was a **100 Watt thermal reactor** based on **natural uranium metallic fuel** and **heavy water** as both **moderator** and **coolant**. It achieved criticality in **January 14, 1961.** It was mainly utilized for reactor lattice studies and was decommissioned in **1983.**
- **DHRUVA** was conceived in the **1970s** out of the need for a **research reactor** with higher **neutron flux** for research in **basic sciences** in

addition to a growing demand of **radioisotopes** and **advanced.**

- Construction of **DHRUVA** was a major milestone in the **development** and **implementation** of **indigenous nuclear technology** in India.
- The reactor incorporates several features not only to satisfy **multidisciplinary** user **community** but also in the production of **radioisotopes** of **high specific activity.**
- **Dhruva** is a **National Facility** for **Neutron Beam Research** to cater to the needs of Indian scientific community where scientists from **BARC**, other units of the **Department of Atomic Energy** (DAE), universities and national laboratories work under collaborative projects.
- **PURNIMA-I** was the **first experimental fast reactor built** in **BARC** with **Plutonium Oxide** as the **fuel.** This 1 Watt reactor was critical on **18th May 1972** and was used for studies of fast reactor physics. It was **decommissioned** in **1973.**
- **PURNIMA-II** was **100 mw** experimental thermal reactor in **BARC** achieved criticality on **May 10, 1984.** This reactor operated on **233U** in the form of **Uranyl Nitrate Solution** as fuel and light water as both moderator and coolant. **PURNIMA-II** had **maximum neutron flux of 107 neutrons/cm²/s.** The purpose of this reactor was **233U fuel evaluation** and **futuristic reactor studies** and was decommissioned in **1986.**
- **PURNIMA-III** was another **233U** based **1 W thermal reactor** built in **BARC** intended for mockup studies for **KAMINI reactor.** It achieved criticality on **November 9, 1990.** Like its predecessor, this reactor too operated on light water as both **moderator** and **coolant. PURNIMA-III** had **maximum neutron flux** of **108 neutrons/cm²/s.** This reactor was decommissioned in **1991.**
- **Critical Facility for Advanced Heavy Water Reactor** (AHWR-CF) attained first criticality on **7th April, 2008.**
- The **Critical facility** is basically a **low power research reactor** with **built-in design features** which allow arrangement of **fuel rods, safety rods** and **experimental assemblies** in the **variable lattice** spacing to simulate different core configurations as per the requirements of various reactor physics experiments for **AHWR** and **500 MWe PHWR.**
- The critical facility has been designed for a nominal power of **100 watts** for the **average flux of 108 n/cm²/sec.**
- Based on requirements, the reactor power can go high up to **400 watts** for short intervals to achieve thermal neutron flux levels of **109 n/cm²/s.**
- Though the critical facility is designed for validating the reactor physics design of AHWR, it is utilized for **neutron activation analysis, nuclear detector testing** and **assessment of negative reactivity** of absorber material.

India's Nuclear Doctrine

- **Building** and **maintaining** a **credible minimum deterrent.**
- A posture of **No First Use nuclear weapons** will only be used in **retaliation** against a nuclear attack on **Indian territory** or on **Indian forces anywhere.**
- **Nuclear retaliation** to a **first strike** will be massive and designed to **inflict unacceptable damage.**
- Nuclear retaliatory attacks can only be authorised by the **civilian political leadership** through the **Nuclear Command Authority.**
- Non-use of nuclear weapons against non-nuclear weapon states;
- However, in the event of a major attack against India, or Indian forces anywhere, by **biological** or **chemical weapons,** India will retain the option of retaliating with nuclear weapons;
- A continuance of **strict controls** on export of nuclear and missile related materials and

technologies, participation in the Fissile Material Cutoff Treaty negotiations, and continued observance of the moratorium on nuclear tests.

- Continued commitment to the goal of a **nuclear weapon free world, through global, verifiable** and **non-discriminatory nuclear disarmament**.

> - The **Nuclear Command Authority** comprises a **Political Council and an Executive Council**. The **Political Council** is chaired by the Prime Minister. It is the sole body which can authorize the use of **nuclear weapons**.
> - The **Executive Council** is chaired by the **National Security Advisor**. It provides inputs for decision making by the Nuclear Command Authority and executes the directives given to it by the Political Council.

Challenges to India's Nuclear Programme

- **Limited Domestic Resources:** India though has a **rich deposit** of **Thorium** in **Monazite sands** of **Kerala**, it has **limited domestic resources of Uranium**, which is the fuel for nuclear reactors. This has forced the country to **import** a significant portion of its **uranium requirements**, making the country's nuclear energy program vulnerable to global market conditions and political tensions.
- **Public Opposition:** The construction of nuclear power plants often faces opposition from local communities due to concerns over the safety of the reactors and the **potential** impact on the **environment**. These oppositions are often fuelled owing to international nuclear disasters like the **Chernobyl** (1986) and **Fukushima** (2011).
- **Technological Challenges:** The development of nuclear power plants involves **complex technical challenges**, including the **design** and **construction** of reactors, the **management of nuclear waste** and the **maintenance of nuclear safety standards**.
- **International Sanctions:** India is not a member of the Nuclear Non-Proliferation Treaty (NPT) and has faced international sanctions in the past for its nuclear weapons program. This has limited its access to advanced nuclear technology and fuel supplies from other countries.
- **Regulatory Barriers:** The regulatory framework for the development of nuclear power in India is complex and has been criticised for being **slow** and **bureaucratic**, leading to delays in the implementation of projects.

Measures to address the challenges

- **Overcoming Public Opposition:** Addressing public concerns and **increasing public awareness** about the safety of nuclear power is critical to overcoming opposition to the construction of new reactors. This can be achieved through **transparent communication** and **consultation** with **local communities**, as well as the implementation of **rigorous safety standards**.
- **Technical Innovation:** To overcome the technical challenges faced by the nuclear energy sector, India needs to focus on **innovation** in **reactor design, waste management** and **safety systems**. This could involve investment in research and development and the **deployment of advanced technologies**.
- **Financial Sustainability:** To overcome the financial challenges faced by the nuclear energy sector, India needs to find ways to make nuclear energy more **cost-competitive** with other forms of energy. This could involve **reducing construction** and **operation costs**, as well as **developing innovative financing models**.
- **International Collaborations:** India needs to **strengthen its international partnerships** to overcome the **limitations posed by international sanctions** and **access to advanced nuclear technology** and **fuel supplies**. This could involve the development of **joint**

ventures with other countries, the participation in international research initiatives, and the negotiation of nuclear trade agreements.

Nuclear Proliferation : Issues and Challenges

- India has a **largely indigenous nuclear power programme**. The Indian government is committed to growing its nuclear power capacity as part of its **massive infrastructure development programme**.
- The government has set ambitious targets to grow **nuclear capacity.**
- Because India is outside the Nuclear Non-Proliferation Treaty due to its weapons programme, it was for **34 years** largely excluded from trade in nuclear plant and materials, which hampered its development of **civil nuclear energy** until **2009.**
- Due to **earlier trade bans** and **lack of indigenous uranium**, India has uniquely been developing a **nuclear fuel cycle** to exploit its reserves of thorium.
- Since **2010**, a **fundamental incompatibility** between **India's civil liability law** and **international conventions** limits foreign technology provision.
- India (along with Pakistan and Israel) was originally a **threshold country** in terms of the **international non-proliferation regime**, possessing, or quickly capable of assembling one or more nuclear weapons: Their nuclear **weapons capability** at the technological level was recognized (all have research reactors at least) along with their military ambitions.
- Then in **1998 India** and **Pakistan's military capability** became more overt. All three remained remained outside the **1970 Nuclear Non-Proliferation Treaty** (NPT), which 186 nations have now signed. This led to their being largely excluded from trade in nuclear plant or materials, except for safety-related devices for a few safeguarded facilities.
- India is opposed to the NPT as it now stands, since it is excluded as a Nuclear Weapons State, and has consistently criticized this aspect of the Treaty since its inception in 1970.

Strategic Concerns for India regarding Nuclear Energy

- **Regional rivalry :** Relations between **India** and **Pakistan** are tense and hostile, and the **risks of nuclear conflict** between them have long been considered quite high.
- In **1974,** India exploded a **peaceful nuclear** device at **Pokhran** and then in **May 1998 India** and **Pakistan** each exploded several nuclear devices underground. This heightened concerns regarding an **nuclear arms race** between them.
- **Kashmir** is a **prime cause** of **bilateral tension** between **India** and **Pakistan,** with the regions sovereignty in dispute since **1948**. There is **persistent low level military conflict** due to Pakistan backing a **religion based rebellion .**
- Both countries engaged in a **conventional arms race** in the **1980s**, including **sophisticated technology** and **equipment** capable of delivering nuclear weapons. In the **1990s** the arms race quickened.
- In **1994** India reversed a **four-year trend** of reduced allocations for defence, and despite its much smaller economy, Pakistan pushed its own expenditures yet higher. Both then lost their patrons: **India**, the former **USSR** and **Pakistan**, the **USA.**
- In **1997** India deployed a **medium-range missile** and is now developing a **long-range missile capable** of reaching targets in **China's industrial heartland.**
- In **1995**, the **USA quietly** intervened to head off a proposed nuclear test. The **1998 tests** were

unambiguously military, including one claimed to be of a sophisticated thermonuclear device. Their declared purpose was to help in the design of nuclear weapons of different yields and different delivery systems.

- It is the **growth** and **modernization** of **China's nuclear arsenal** and its assistance with **Pakistan's** nuclear power program and, reportedly, with missile technology, which now exacerbates Indian concerns. In particular, **China's People's Liberation Army** operates somewhat autonomously within **Pakistan** as an exporter of **military material**.
- It perceives nuclear weapons as a **cost-effective political counter** to **China's nuclear** and conventional weaponry, and the effects of its nuclear weapons policy in provoking Pakistan is, by some accounts, considered incidental.
- India has a **hostile relationship** with **China since** the **1962 Sino India war**, during which **People's Republic of China** occupied a major territory in **Ladakh province** (Aksai Chin). Also Chinese nuclear and missile support for Pakistan is however a major bone of contention.
- **India's weapons material** initially came from the **Canadian-designed 40 MWt CIRUS** research reactor which started up in **1960** (well before the NPT), and the **100 MWt** Dhruva indigenous unit in operation since **1985**, using local uranium. **CIRUS** was supplied with **heavy water** from the **USA** and it was probably only after the **1962** war that it was employed largely to make weapons-grade plutonium.
- **Development of nuclear weapons** apparently began in earnest in **1967**. It is estimated that India may have built up enough weapons-grade plutonium for one hundred nuclear warheads.
- Under **Article III** of the **1956 India-Canada Agreement**, **Government of India** was obliged to ensure that the **reactor** and any **products** resulting from its use will be employed for peaceful purposes only.
- **Clause 9** of the **India-US Heavy Water Agreement** held that he heavy water sold here under shall be for use only in India by the Government in connection with research into and the use atomic energy for peaceful purposes.
- In response to India's **1974** nuclear **test explosion** using plutonium from **CIRUS**, demonstrating that nuclear technology transferred to non-nuclear-weapons states for peaceful purposes could be misused, the Nuclear Suppliers Group was formed and began regulating nuclear trade, particularly with India. This is one reason why the closure of **CIRUS** is a condition of the **NSG** waiver in **2008**.

Indian security policies are driven by:

- Its desire to be recognized as the dominant power in the region.
- Its increasing concern with China's expanding nuclear weapons and missile delivery programs.
- Its enduring concern about Pakistan, with its nuclear weapons capability and now the clear capability to deliver such weapons deep into India.

PYQ (2013 – 2024)

Q. With reference to radioisotope thermoelectric generators (RTGs), consider the following statements:

1. RTGs are miniature fission reactors.
2. RTGs are used for powering the onboard systems of spacecrafts.
3. RTGs can use Plutonium-238, which is a by-product of weapons developments.

Which of the statements given above are correct? (2024)

(a) 1 and 2 only (b) 2 and 3 only
(c) 1 and 3 only (d) 1, 2 and 3

Q. With growing energy needs should India keep on expanding its nuclear energy programme? Discuss the facts and fears associated with nuclear energy (2018)

Q. Give an account of the growth and development of nuclear science and technology in India. What is the advantage of a fast breeder reactor programme in India? (2019)

UNIT 11 SPACE TECHNOLOGY

- *From ancient stargazing to landing on distant celestial bodies and deploying telescopes to the edge of the observable universe, space science has transformed how we perceive the cosmos and our place within it.*
- *The journey began with ancient civilizations like the Babylonians, Greeks, Indians, and Chinese, who meticulously observed the skies, developing calendars and astronomical theories.*
- *Indian astronomer Aryabhata (5th century CE) accurately calculated planetary periods and proposed Earth's rotation on its axis. These early astronomical insights laid the foundation for scientific inquiry into space.*
- *The modern age of space science emerged with the invention of the telescope in the early 17th century. Galileo Galilei, using a refracting telescope, discovered the moons of Jupiter and the phases of Venus, challenging geocentric worldviews. It was followed by Newton's laws of motion and gravity, which provided a mathematical basis for understanding planetary orbits and celestial mechanics.*
- *20th century marked a technological leap with the advent of rocketry. Pioneers like Konstantin Tsiolkovsky in Russia and Hermann Oberth in Germany theorized space travel. During World War II, the German V-2 rocket became the first man-made object to reach the edge of space, that laid the groundwork for post-war space programs in both the United States and the Soviet Union in backdrop of what known as Space Race.*
- *A historic milestone was achieved on October 4, 1957, when the Soviet Union launched Sputnik-1, the first artificial satellite – an event that inaugurated the Space Age and triggered the Cold War-era space race. United States responded with the creation of NASA in 1958. Another monumental moment came in 1961, when Yuri Gagarin became the first human to travel in space. Apollo 11 mission (1969) of NASA saw Neil Armstrong walk on the Moon, a feat unmatched until today.*
- *1970s and 1980s witnessed the expansion of space exploration with space stations like Salyut and Mir, and NASA's Space Shuttle program, which made spaceflight partially reusable. In 1998, the launch of the International Space Station (ISS) marked an era of global collaboration in space research. Space telescopes like the Hubble Space Telescope (1990) and the James Webb Space Telescope (2021) revolutionized space science, providing deep insights into distant galaxies, exoplanets, and cosmic origins.*
- *India's ISRO has emerged as a major space power, launching Aryabhata (1975), achieving feats like Chandrayaan-1, Mangalyaan (2013) – the first Asian Mars mission, and Chandrayaan-3 (2023), which achieved a historic lunar south pole landing.*
- *Recent trends in Space Technology focus on commercial spaceflight, space tourism, and interplanetary colonization. Companies like SpaceX, Blue Origin, and Virgin Galactic are leading innovation in reusable rockets and space access.*
- *The evolution of space science and technology has transitioned from observational astronomy to human spaceflight and robotic interplanetary missions. It represents not only a triumph of human ingenuity but also a beacon for the future of global cooperation, scientific advancement, and exploration.*

Space Science

- Space Science is the study of everything in the universe beyond Earth's atmosphere, including: Celestial bodies (stars, planets, comets, etc.), Space environments, Cosmic events (supernovae, black holes, cosmic microwave background) Md Space technology and exploration
- Space Science is an interdisciplinary field that combines astronomy, astrophysics, planetary science, cosmology, and aerospace engineering.

Significance of Space Science

- **Understanding the Universe:** Helps decode the origin, structure, and evolution of the universe.
- **Technological Innovation:** Leads to advances in communication, navigation (GPS), meteorology, and imaging.
- **National Security and Prestige:** Strategic applications (e.g., satellites), and global leadership in innovation.
- **Earth Monitoring:** Tracks climate change, natural disasters, land use, and pollution.
- **Education:** Promotes scientific curiosity, STEM education, and philosophical inquiry about life beyond Earth.

Major Branches of Space Science

Astronomy	Study of celestial objects and phenomena.
Astrophysics	Physics applied to stars, galaxies, and the universe.
Cosmology	Study of the origin, evolution, and fate of the universe.
Planetary Science	Study of planets, moons, and planetary systems.
Exoplanetology	Study of planets outside the solar system
Astrobiology	Study of the origin and potential existence of life in the universe
Aerospace Engineering	Designing spacecraft, launch vehicles, and related systems
Space Weather	Study of solar wind, cosmic radiation, and magnetic fields in space

Layers of Earth's Atmosphere and the Edge of Space

Layer	Altitude	Features
Troposphere	0-12 km	Weather occurs here
Stratosphere	12-50 km	Ozone layer present
Mesosphere	50-85 km	Meteors burn up
Thermosphere	85-600 km	Aurora, ISS orbits here
Exosphere	600 km+	Gradual transition to space

- Kármán Line (100 km above Earth) is commonly accepted as the boundary of space.

Tools of Space Science

Tool	Purpose
Telescopes	Observe distant objects (optical, radio, infrared, etc.)
Satellites	Remote sensing, communication, navigation, scientific research
Space Probes	Explore deep space and other planets (e.g., Voyager, New Horizons)
Rovers	Mobile robots for planetary exploration (e.g., Perseverance on Mars)
Space Stations	Human habitat for long-term research (e.g., ISS)
Spectrometers	Analyze light to determine composition and properties

Origin of the Universe

- Big Bang Theory proposes that the Universe began as an extremely hot and dense singularity and expanded over time, leading to the current observable universe.

Timeline of Universe

Event	Time After Big Bang	Description
Planck Epoch	10^{-43} seconds	Laws of physics break down; gravity separated.
Grand Unification Epoch	10^{-36} seconds	Strong nuclear force separates.
Inflationary Epoch	10^{-32} to 10^{-30} seconds	Universe expands faster than the speed of light.
Quark Epoch	10^{-12} seconds	Formation of subatomic particles (quarks, electrons).
Hadron Epoch	1 second	Quarks combine to form protons and neutrons.
Nucleosynthesis	3^{-20} minutes	Formation of light elements (H, He, Li).
Photon Epoch	up to 380,000 years	Universe dominated by radiation.
Recombination	380,000 years	Electrons combine with nuclei to form neutral atoms. CMBR emitted.
Formation of Stars & Galaxies	~100 million years	First stars and galaxies formed.

Cosmic Microwave Background Radiation (CMBR):

- Discovered in 1965 by Penzias and Wilson.
- Remnant radiation from the recombination era.
- **Temperature:** ~2.725 K (Kelvin).

Hubble's Law and Redshift:

- Discovered by Edwin Hubble (1929).
- Galaxies moving away → Universe is expanding.
- $V = H_0 \times d$ ($H_0 \approx 70$ km/s/Mpc).

Abundance of Light Elements:

- Big Bang Nucleosynthesis predicted: ~75% Hydrogen, ~24% Helium, trace amounts of Lithium.

Theory	Description
Steady State Theory	Universe is eternal and expanding; new matter continuously created. (Rejected due to CMB evidence)
Oscillating Universe	Universe goes through cycles of expansion and contraction.
Multiverse Theory	Suggests existence of many universes beyond our own (theoretical).

Stellar Formation (Star Formation)

- Star is a massive, luminous sphere of plasma held together by gravity. It produces energy through nuclear fusion, converting hydrogen into helium.

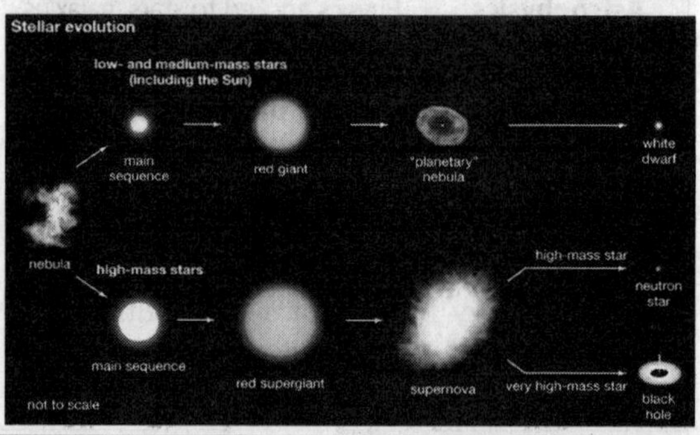

Stages of Stellar Formation:

- **Nebula (Giant Molecular Cloud):** Cold, dense region of dust and gas (mainly hydrogen). Gravity causes clumps to form in the nebula. **Example:** Orion Nebula.
- **Protostar Stage:** As the gas collapses, it heats up due to gravitational compression and forms a protostar at the center surrounded by an accretion disk. No nuclear fusion yet—powered by gravitational energy.
- **Main Sequence Star:** When temperature in the core reaches ~10 million K, hydrogen fusion starts. Star enters the main sequence phase (like our Sun). Balance between gravitational force and radiation pressure.
- **Post-Main Sequence Evolution:** Low-mass stars (like Sun): Expand into Red Giants, then shed outer layers and become White Dwarfs.
  - **High-mass stars:** Become Supergiants, undergo supernova, and leave behind neutron stars or black holes.
  - Nebula → Protostar → Main Sequence → Red Giant/Supernova → End States (White Dwarf, Neutron Star, Black Hole).

Nebula	Birthplace of stars
Protostar	Infant stage of star
Main Sequence	Stable phase of star (e.g., Sun)
Supernova	Explosive death of massive star
CMB	Thermal radiation left from Big Bang
Redshift	Stretching of light wavelength due to expansion

Structure and Composition of the Universe

- **Planets :** Celestial body that orbits a star (like Sun), is massive enough for its own gravity to make it spherical, and has cleared its neighborhood of other objects.
  - **Terrestrial Planets :** Mercury, Venus, Earth and Mars.
  - **Jovian Planets :** Jupitar, Saturn, Uranus and Neptune
  - **Dwarf planets :** Bodies orbiting the sun, yet not a planet, with enough mass to be nearly round. They haven't cleared the area around their orbit and aren't moons. International Astronomical Union (IAU) officially recognizes 5 celestial bodies as dwarf panets in our solar system : Ceres, Pluto, Haumea, Makemake, and Eris.
- **Stars :** A Massive self-luminous celestial body of gas that shines by radiation derived from its internal energy sources as Nuclear Fusion. **Example:** Sun.
- **Solar System :** A Gravitationally bound system of celestial bodies orbiting a star.
- **Star Clusters :** Groups of stars that share an origin, forming at roughly the same time and location, and are tied together by gravity for up to millions or even billions of years
- **Galaxies :** A massive, gravitationally bound system of stars, gas, dust, and dark matter. They are vast cosmic islands, ranging in size from a few thousand stars to trillions, and can be millions or billions of light-years across. **Example:** Milky Way.
- **Galaxy Clusters :** A large-scale structure in the universe consisting of hundreds to thousands of galaxies bound together by gravity. These clusters are the largest gravitationally bound objects in the known universe. They contain not only galaxies but also hot plasma and a significant amount of dark matter.
- **Superclusters :** Group of galaxy clusters typically consisting of 3 to 10 clusters and spanning as many as 200000000 light-years. Example: Laniakea
- **Cosmic Web :** Large-scale structure of the universe, a vast network of interconnected filaments and voids formed by the distribution of matter and energy. It's believed that this web-like structure, primarily composed of dark matter, is the fundamental framework upon which galaxies and galaxy clusters are built.

Components of Universe

- **Ordinary (Baryonic) Matter:** 5%
- **Dark Matter :** ~27%
- **Dark Energy :** ~68% (responsible for accelerating expansion).

Celestial Bodies in Universe

- **Stars:**
  - **Mass:** 0.08–100 solar masses.
  - **Temperature:** 3,000 K (Red Dwarf) to 50,000 K (Blue Giant).
  - **Composition:** ~70% Hydrogen, ~28% Helium, ~2% heavier elements.
- **Spectral Classification:** O, B, A, F, G, K, M (O is hottest, M is coolest).
- **Planets:** Orbit stars; Classified as terrestrial or gas giants. Have no light of their own; reflect starlight.
- **Moons:** Natural satellites of planets. (Largest Moon – Ganymede (Jupiter).
- **Asteroids:** Rock-metallic bodies in the asteroid belt between Mars and Jupiter. (Largest).
- **Asteroid:** Ceres (also a dwarf planet).
- **Comets:** Composed of ice, rock, dust. Develop coma and tail when near the Sun. Example : Halley's Comet (orbital period ~76 years).
- **Meteoroid:** Small object in space.
- **Meteor:** Burns in Earth's atmosphere.
- **Meteorite:** Survives and lands on Earth.

Composition of Solar System

- **Central Star :** Sun (mass: 1.989×10^{30} kg).
- **8 Planets (in order):** Mercury, Venus, Earth, Mars, Jupiter, Saturn, Uranus, Neptune.
- **Dwarf Planets:** Pluto, Ceres, Eris, Makemake, Haumea.

Zonal Divisions of Solar System –

- **Inner Solar System (Terrestrial Planets):** Small, rocky, solid surfaces.
- **Asteroid Belt:** Between Mars and Jupiter.
- **Outer Solar System (Gas/Ice Giants) :** Jupiter and Saturn (gas), Uranus and Neptune (ice).
- **Kuiper Belt :** Region beyond Neptune, includes Pluto.
- **Oort Cloud :** Spherical cloud of icy bodies; theoretical; source of long-period comets.

Stellar Evolution

Star Mass	Evolutionary Path	Final State
< 0.08 solar masses	Never ignites fusion	Brown Dwarf
0.088 solar masses	Nebula → Protostar → Main-sequence → Red Giant → Planetary Nebula → White Dwarf	White Dwarf
> 8 solar masses	Nebula → Protostar → Main-sequence → Supergiant → Supernova	Neutron Star or Black Hole

- **Main-sequence Star:** Stable fusion of H to He (e.g., Sun).
- **Red Giant:** Expands as hydrogen runs out.
- **White Dwarf:** Small, hot remnant; no fusion.
- **Supernova:** Explosive death of massive star.
- **Neutron Star:** Dense core left after supernova.
- **Black Hole:** Infinite gravity, not even light escapes.

Types of Galaxies

Type	Features	Example
Spiral	Central bulge with spiral arms	Milky Way, Andromeda
Elliptical	Spherical/oval, old stars, little gas/dust	Messier 87
Irregular	No defined shape, younger stars	Large Magellanic Cloud

- **Milky Way Galaxy:**
  - **Type:** Barred Spiral.
  - **Diameter:** ~100,000 light-years.
  - Solar System is ~25,000 light-years from galactic center.

Astronomical Distance Units

Unit	Value	Use
Astronomical Unit (AU)	149,597,870.7 km	Average Earth-Sun distance
Light-Year	9.46 x 1012 km	Distance light travels in 1 year
Parsec	3.26 light-years	Used in professional astronomy

Kepler's Laws of Planetary Motion

- Formulated by Johannes Kepler (early 17th century) based on Tycho Brahe's astronomical data.
  - **First Law (Law of Ellipses):** Every planet moves in an elliptical orbit with the Sun at one focus.
  - **Second Law (Law of Equal Areas):** A line joining a planet and the Sun sweeps out equal areas in equal time intervals. Planet moves faster when closer to the Sun (perihelion) and slower when farther (aphelion).
  - **Third Law (Law of Harmonies):** The square of a planet's orbital period (T^2) is proportional to the cube of the semi-major axis (R^3) of its orbit. Mathematically: $T^2 \rightarrow R^3$ Applies to all planets orbiting the same star.

Timeline of Space Exploration

Year	Event	Details
1957	Sputnik-1	First artificial satellite launched by USSR.
1961	Yuri Gagarin	First human in space (Vostok-1, USSR).
1969	Apollo 11	Neil Armstrong became the first human to walk on the Moon (USA).
1971	Salyut-1	First space station (USSR).
1981	STS-1 (Columbia)	First reusable space shuttle launched (USA).
1998	International Space Station (ISS)	Global collaborative project for long-term space research.
2021	James Webb Space Telescope launch	Most advanced space observatory launched by NASA.

World Space Agencies: At a Glance

Space Agency (Country)	Year of Establishment	Headquarters	Important Space Missions
National Aeronautics and Space Administration (NASA) (United States of America)	1958	Washington D.C, USA	Artemis, Discovery, Cassini -Huygens , Spirit, Curiosity, Opportunity and Insights,
SpaceX (First Private Space Agency founded by Elon Musk) (United States of America)	2002	California, USA	Falcon 9, Cargo and Crew Missions to ISS, Starlink Satellites, Starship

Canada Space Agency (CSA) (Canada)	1989	Longueil, Quebec, Canada	Canadarm 2, Artemis Program, RADARSAT Constellation Mission, OSIRIS-Rex, Phoenix Mars Lander, ESA's Herschel Space Observatory, Planck Space Telescope.
European Space Agency (ESA) (Europe)	1975	Paris, France	Rosetta, Cassini-Huygens, ISS, Mars Express, Venus Express, BepiColombo, JUICE (Jupiter Icy Moons Explorer), Euclid, PLATO, ARIEL, EnVision, Copernicus Program, ExoMars, Solar Orbiter, Herschel Space Observatory, Planck, Swarm
China National Space Administration (CNSA) (China)	1993	Haidian, Beijing, China	Chang'e, Tianwen, Tiangong Space Station, Gaofen
Roscosmos – Russia Federal Space Agency (Russia)	1992	Moscow, Russia	Soyuz, Vostok, Salyut & Mir Space Stations, Luna, , Koronas Foton, Spektr R, Spektr RG, Bion-M and Elektro L, Phobos and Venera-D , ExoMars
Japan Aerospace Exploration Agency (JAXA) (Japan)	2003	Tokyo, Japan	BepiColombo Mercury mission, Hayabusa2, SLIM lunar lander mission, MMX (Martian Moons eXploration), Kaguya (SELENE), Kibo, XRISM (X-Ray Imaging and Spectroscopy Mission), Akatsuki (PLANET-C), Ikaros
Indian Space Research Agency (ISRO) (India)	1969	Bengaluru, Karnataka, India	Chandrayaan, Mangalyaan, Aditya L1, Ganganyaan

Important Space Missions of NASA

- **Cassini Huygens :** Joint mission of NASA, ESA and Italian Space Agency to Saturn.
- **Final flyby (2017) :** Firstspacecraft to observe presence of hydrocarbon rains, rivers, lakes and seas on Titan.
- **Discovery :** Mars lander and Rover Mission.
- **Spirit, Curiosity, Opportunity and Insights:** Mars Exploration Rovers.
- **InSights :** Mars' lander mission under Discovery programme, Landed near the equator of Mars to study its interior.
- **Viking Mission :** Flew past Mars.
- **MAVEN:** Mars Atmosphere And Volatile Evolution Mission.
- **Mariner 2:** First flyby of Venus in 1962.
- **Magellan:** Orbiter Mission to Venus.
- **Kepler Mission :** NASA's Mission to search for Earth-like planets around the Milky Way galaxy that might harbour life. Kepler Mission retired recently.
- **Kepler-22b:** First Planet found in the "habitable zone/ Goldilocks zone.
- **TRAPPIST-1 system:** Home to seven Earth-size planets.
- **Transiting Exoplanet Survey Satellite (TESS) :** Successor of Kepler Mission. A 2-year mission in search of exoplanets.
- **Suomi National Polar-orbiting Partnership satellite :** Joint mission of NASA and NOAA to capture the illumination conditions using nighttime data.
- **Moderate Resolution Imaging Spectro-radiometer (MODIS) :** Earth observation satellite of NASA, Monitoring large-scale changes in the biosphere to understand change in global carbon cycle.
- **Dawn Mission :** NASA's first deep space mission to be propelled by an ion engine. First spacecraft to orbit a body in the region between Mars and Jupiter and first mission to visit a dwarf planet. To study two important objects in the asteroid belt, Ceres (dwarf planet) and Vesta (proto planet).
- **Chandra X-Ray Observatory :** Named after the Indian- American astrophysicist Subramanyan Chandrasekhar. An X ray observatory to study X-Ray sources such as starts, galaxies, supernova, blackhole etc (at high temperatures of 10^6 to 10^8 Kelvin, gases emit X-ray photons) and to study hot objects like inside of a star, supernova, centers of galaxies etc X-Ray telescopes are necessary.
- **Solar and Heliospheric Observatory (SOHO) :** Joint project between ESA and NASA to study the Sun, from its deep core to the outer corona, and the solar wind. Objective of SOHO is to study the fundamental scientific questions about the Sun including the structure and dynamics of the solar interior like existence of solar corona, its extreme temperature and generation of solar winds.
- **Large Angle and Spectrometric Coronagraph Experiment (LASCO) :** A telescope on SOHO aircraft designed to block light coming from the solar disk. It studies how the corona is heated and where and how the solar wind is accelerated.
- **New Frontier's Program :** Aimed at exploring the solar system.
- **New Horizons :** Launched in 2006 to investigate distant solar system object including Pluto and its moons and Kuiper Belt.
- **Juno :** Launched in 2016 to study Jupiter
- **OSIRIS-Rex Mission :** To collect samples from an asteroid (Bennu) and carry it to Earth for further study.
- **Dragonfly :** Lander Mission to Saturn's Titan scheduled in 2026 to study its characteristics, Nitrogen-based atmosphere and Clouds and rain of methane.
- **New Horizon :** NASA's space mission to Pluto and also the first mission to explore the solar system's region beyond the giant planets called the Kuiper Belt. Recently discovered Ultima

Thule (a small rocky and icy trans-Neptunian planetesimal in the Kuiper belt) and Arrokoth (a primordial body in Kuiper Belt).

- **Discovery Program :** A series of Solar System exploration missions.
  - **Lucy :** First space mission to study Jupitar's Trojan asteroids.
  - **Psyche :** NASA's first mission to examine an object made not of rock and ice, but metal (between Mars and Jupiter).
  - **Deep Atmosphere Venus Investigation of Noble gases, Chemistry, and Imaging (DAVINCI) :** Proposed atmospheric probe to Venus to study the chemical composition of Venus' atmosphere.
  - **Venus Emissivity, Radio Science, InSAR, Topography, and Spectroscopy Mission (Veritas) :** Proposed mission to map with high resolution the surface of planet Venus.
  - **Lo Volcano Observer :** To study volcano on IO. (one of the Galilean moons of Jupiter).
  - **Trident :** Proposed mission to study Neptune's largest moon Triton.
- **Parker Solar Probe :** First ever Robotic spacecraft to probe outer corona of the Sun.
- **Hubble Space Telescope :** Largest multi-wavelength space telescope, 600 km above the surface of the earth, a Joint project of NASA and ESA. It can observe objects in visible, near-ultraviolet, and near-infrared light.
- **James Web Telescope :** Successor of Hubble Space Telescope to be launched in 2021. 2.5 times bigger than HST and thus 6 times more powerful. JWST will orbit the Sun.
- **Artemis (2007) :** To study effects of solar wind from a lunar orbit. Deployed primarily to observe Moon's interaction with the solar wind.
- **Cosmic Background Explorer (COBE) :** First to confirm CMB radiation.
- **XIPE :** Space-based X-ray telescope – X-ray Imaging Polarimetry Explorer to study X-ray emissions from supernovae, galaxy jets, and black holes.
- **ICEBRIDGE :** Dedicated airborne instruments over Earth's polar ice ever flown. It provides a three-dimensional view of Arctic and Antarctic ice sheets, ice shelves and sea ice.

Orbits

- Orbits are the **paths** followed by objects, like **planets** or **satellites**, as they move around a central body under influence of **gravitational attraction.**
- **Types of orbits:**
  - **Circular Orbit:** Object moves in a **constant circular path** around the central body. Speed is **constant** and **gravitational force** provides the centripetal force.

    Ex- Geostationary orbits
  - **Elliptical Orbit:** Object moves in an elliptical (oval) **path** around the central body. **Speed varies** as it gets closer (perihelion) or farther (aphelion) from the central body.

    Ex- Orbit of planets.

Aspect	Circular Orbit	Elliptical Orbit
Shape	Perfect circle	Oval (ellipse)
Object's Speed	Constant throughout orbit	Varies along the orbit
Gravitational Force	Provides Centripetal force	Provides Centripetal force
Distance	Constant distance from center	Varies distance from center
Examples	Idealized planetary orbits	Many planetary and comet orbits
Special Points	None	Perihelion (closest) and aphelion (farthest) points

Classification of Orbits

On Basis of Revolution

- **Geosynchronous Orbit:** An orbit in which a **satellite orbits the Earth** at the **same rate** as the **Earth's rotation**, resulting in the **satellite remaining fixed** in the same position relative to a specific point on the Earth's surface. Here, the Satellite orbits in the **equatorial plane.**

Geosynchronous Orbit is often used for **communication and navigation satellites.**

- **Geostationary orbit** : A circular orbit around the Earth where a satellite appears fixed above the same spot on the Earth's surface. It is also known as a Geosynchronous Equatorial Orbit (GEO).
- Satellites in a geostationary orbit match the Earth's rotation, so they appear stationary from the ground. The satellite's position is fixed relative to the Earth's surface, so communication antennas can be permanently pointed at it
- The idea for a geostationary orbit was proposed by Arthur C. Clarke in 1945
- First geostationary satellite was the U.S. communications satellite Syncom 3, launched in 1964.
- Geostationary satellites are used for telecommunications, such as relaying television and radio broadcasts. They're also used for remote sensing, such as weather monitoring.

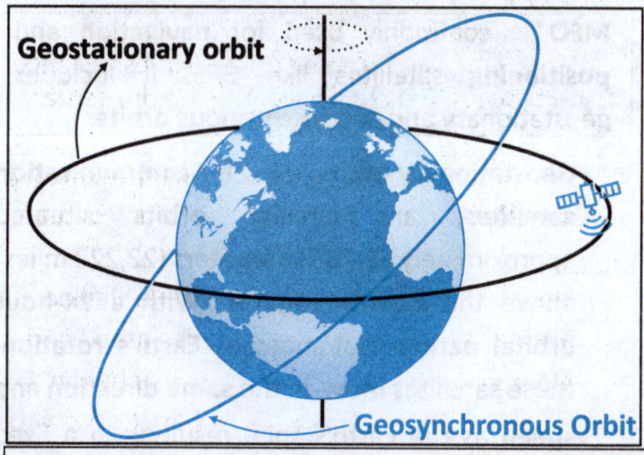

- **Sun-Synchronous Orbit:** Satellites revolution is synchronized on the basis of Earth's Revolution. Satellite Orbits in the Polar plane.

Sun-Synchronous Orbits are commonly used for **Earth observation** and **Remote sensing satellites.**

On basis of Distance from Earth

- **Low Earth Orbit (LEO) :** Orbits located **relatively close** to the **Earth's surface,** typically at altitudes ranging from a **few hundred to about 2,000 kilometers.** LEO is used for many satellites, including **Earth observation, communication** and **scientific missions.**

Space Missions in Low Earth Orbit (LEO)

Hubble Space Telescope

- Launched in **1990** by **NASA.**
- **Orbit:** Hubble operates in LEO, specifically in a near-circular orbit approximately 547 kilometers above the Earth's surface.
- **Observations** : Known for its remarkable observations of **distant galaxies, stars, nebulae** and other **celestial objectsv** and for providing valuable data on cosmic phenomena, helping scientists better understand the universe's origins and evolution.
- In **1993**, astronauts conducted a spacewalk to install corrective optics.

Kepler Space Telescope

- Launched in **2009** by **NASA.**
- **Orbit:** Kepler was also placed in a LEO, **heliocentric orbit** around the Sun.
- **Observations** : Kepler's primary mission was to search for exoplanets by monitoring the brightness of stars and detecting any periodic dimming caused by planets passing in front of them. This technique, known as the transit method, allowed Kepler to discover thousands of exoplanets.

Astrosat

- Launched in **2015** by **Indian Space Research Organisation** (ISRO).
- **Orbit:** Astrosat operates in **LEO** at an altitude of around **650 kilometers.**
- **Observations:** Astrosat is **India's first dedicated multi-wavelength space observatory.** It observes celestial objects in various wavelengths, including X-rays and ultraviolet. It has contributed to study of black holes, neutron stars, and other high-energy phenomena.

International Space Station (ISS)

- **Collaborative project involving NASA** (USA), **Roscosmos** (Russia), **ESA** (European Space Agency), JAXA (Japan Aerospace Exploration Agency) and **CSA** (Canadian Space Agency).
- Operates at an average altitude of approximately **400 kilometers** (about 248 miles) above the Earth's surface.
- First module of **ISS Zarya control module** was launched in **1998** and the station was fully assembled in **2011.**
- **Objective :** A space habitat for scientific research, international collaboration, and technology development in a microgravity environment.

- **Applications of ISS**
  - Microgravity experimentation (test products at zero gravity) Eg. artificial photosynthesis,Metallurgy etc
  - Space observation
  - Space Voyage
  - Space Tourism
  - Servicing workshop

Tiangong Space Station (China)

- **China's space station project,** also known as the **Chinese Space Station** or **Tiangong**, is an independent endeavor by the **China National Space Administration** (CNSA).
- **Orbit:** The core module was launched in **2021,** and China plans to gradually expand the station.
- **Objectives :** Tiangong aims to serve as a **research facility** for **scientific experiments,** technology development, and international collaboration.
- **Concerns:** Potential militarization, weaponization, Spying, Control and Monopoly of space have been raised in the context of China's space activities.

- **Applications of LEO :**
  - Earth observation (Remote sensing)
  - Astronomical observation (Telescope)
  - Capturing data related to radiation - cosmic rays, X-rays, and gamma rays.
  - Space Station
- LEO is a favorable location for **various space-based observatories** and **scientific missions.**

Medium Earth Orbit (MEO)

- Orbits located between **low and high Earth orbits**, generally around **2,000 to 35,786** (~ 36000) **kilometers** above the Earth's surface.

MEO is commonly **used** for **navigation** and **positioning** satellites like GPS. It includes geostationary and **geosynchronous orbits.**

- **Geostationary orbits,** used for **communication satellites**, are **circular orbits** situated approximately **35,786 kilometers** (22,222 miles) above the **Earth's equator**. With a **24-hour orbital period** that matches **Earth's rotation,** these satellites move in the **same direction** and **speed** as the Earth's spin, resulting in a fixed position relative to a specific point on the ground.

- This unique characteristic allows communication satellites to provide constant coverage to a designated region, making them ideal for services like **television broadcasting, telecommunication** and **internet connectivity.**

Satellite Systems in Medium Earth Orbit		
Satellite Mission	**Country**	**Specification**
GPS (Global Positioning System)	USA	Used for global navigation
GLONASS (Global Navigation Satellite System)	Russia	A Russian satellite navigation system that offers **global coverage and positioning services.**
GALILEO	European Union	An EU-based navigation system offering global coverage with enhanced accuracy and reliability. (Highest Accuracy till now.)
BEIDOU-1 (Compass)	China	China's regional navigation system initially deployed for Central Asia, later expanded into a global system (BEIDOU-2) for positioning and timing services.
BEIDOU-2 (Compass)	China	China's second-generation navigation system, providing **global navigation** and positioning services with improved accuracy and coverage.
NAVIC - IRNSS (Navigation with Indian Constellation - Indian Regional Navigation Satellite System)	India	An independent regional navigation system developed by India to provide accurate positioning in the Indian region.
QZSS (Quasi-Zenith Satellite System)	Japan	Japan's regional navigation system with an emphasis on providing enhanced coverage and accuracy over the Japanese archipelago.

GPS : NAVSTAR (Navigation System Using Timing and Ranging)

- **NAVSTAR Orbit Type:** Satellites are in **semi-synchronous orbits**, which are halfway between **Low Earth Orbits** (LEO) and **Geosynchronous orbits.**
- **Number of Satellites:** The GPS constellation consists of **24 satellites.**
- **Orbit Altitude:** The satellites are located approximately **20,200 kilometers** above the Earth's surface.
- **Orbital Period:** Each satellite takes around **12 hours** to complete one orbit around the Earth.
- **Trilateration Concept:** GPS determines the **receiver's location** by **trilateration**, which involves comparing time delays of signals from multiple satellites to calculate precise positions.

Services Provided

- **Location Services:**
  - **Standard Positioning:** Refers to the civilian use of satellite-based navigation systems like GPS for accurate location determination.

- **Restricted Positioning:** Reserved for military applications, offering higher accuracy and additional features.

⊡ **Timing Service:**

- Timing service refers to the **precise synchronization** of **time across devices** and **systems.**
- It's particularly crucial in fields where **accurate timing** is essential, such as **telecommunications, financial transactions, scientific research** and **global network coordination.**

NAVIC (Navigation Indian Constellation)

⊡ NAVIC is **India's independent stand-alone navigation satellite system comprising 7 satellites.**

⊡ **Satellites:** Comprises **4 satellites in geosynchronous orbit** and **3** satellites in **geostationary orbit** at an altitude of **36,000 km.**

⊡ **Coverage:** Covers India and extends up to 1,500 kilometers from its borders. (Not global coverage).

4 Satellites in geosynchronous orbit- in pairs, move in two inclined orbits-appear from ground to travel assist in accurate position determination.
3 satellites in geostationary orbit-appear from ground to be at fixed position in the sky.

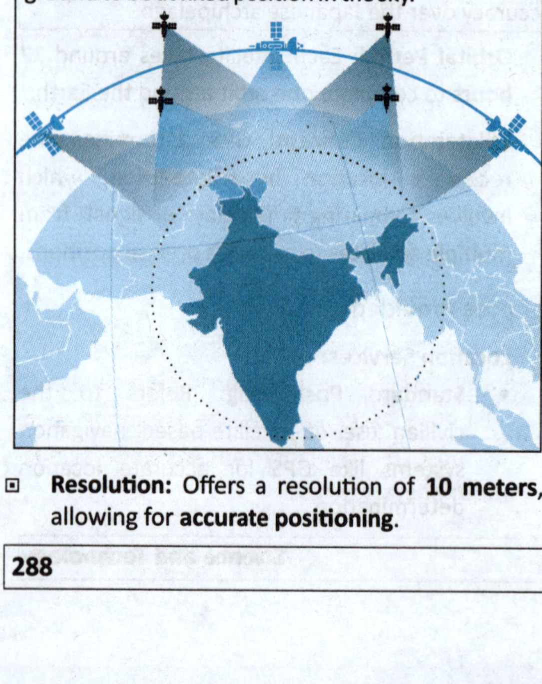

⊡ **Resolution:** Offers a resolution of **10 meters,** allowing for **accurate positioning.**

⊡ **Application:** Utilized for **public vehicle tracking** in India, providing emergency alerts to **fishermen, tracking ships** and aircraft, and **disseminating information** related to **natural disasters.**

⊡ **Smartphone Integration:** Indian authorities are encouraging smartphone manufacturers to enable support for NavIC navigation in new devices.

> The plan is to incorporate **L1 Spectrum band,** commonly used for civilian navigation, into NavIC.

High Earth Orbit (HEO)

⊡ High Earth Orbit is the orbit that is farther away from Earth than geosynchronous orbit.

⊡ It ranges from about **35,786 kilometers** (22,236 miles) to several million kilometers (millions of miles) above the surface.

⊡ HEO is used by some **communications satellites** and **scientific satellites** for research purposes like exploring space.

⊡ One notable application of **HEO** is the utilization of **Lagrange points.**

⊡ **Lagrange points** are **stable points** in space where the **gravitational forces** of two large bodies, such as the Earth and the **Moon** or the **Earth** and the **Sun,** create **equilibrium conditions.**

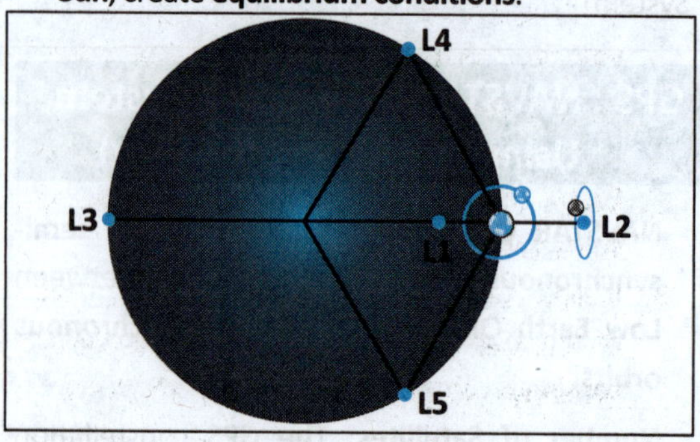

⊡ **Satellites** placed at **Lagrange points** can maintain a **relative position** with respect to these **bodies,** making them valuable for various missions like **space observatories, monitoring solar activity,** or **space weather studies.**

- When a **spacecraft** is positioned at a Lagrange point, particularly **L1**, **L2**, or **L3**, it remains in a type of orbit called a **HALO orbit**. This allows the spacecraft to move in tandem with the Earth as both Earth and the spacecraft orbit the Sun.
- Among the **five Lagrange points**, **L1**, **L2**, and **L3** are points of **unstable equilibrium**. This means that a slight disturbance would cause objects at these points to drift away from their positions.
- On the other hand, **L4** and **L5** are points of **stable equilibrium**. Objects placed at **L4** and L5 will maintain their positions relative to the Earth and the Sun.
- While **L4** and **L5** are in **stable equilibrium**, they are also points where **gravitational forces attract asteroids**. Despite their stability, the presence of asteroids makes these points less suitable for **long-term space missions.** As a result, **L5** is often preferred for certain missions due to its **relative stability** and **lower vulnerability** to **asteroid interference.**

- **India's solar observatory space craft- Aditya L1** was placed at **Halo orbit** (A periodic 3 dimensional orbit) around **L1 point**, involving **Sun**, **Earth** and space craft on **6th January, 2024** to ensure a **mission lifespan** of **5 years.**
- **Advantages of placing Aditya L1 in a Halo Orbit :**
  1. It provides a smooth **Sun spacecraft velocity change** throughout the orbit, appropriate for helioseismology.
  2. It is outside of the **magnetosphere of Earth**, thus suitable for **insitu sampling** of **solar wind** and **particles.**
  3. It allows **unobstructed, continous observation** of the **Sun** and **view of earth** for **enabling continous communication to ground stations.**

Geosynchronous Transfer Orbit (GTO)

- GTO is an **elliptical orbit** used to **transfer** a **satellite** from its **initial launch position** to a **geosynchronous orbit**. It has a **perigee** (closest point to Earth) at a **lower altitude**, typically a few hundred kilometers, and an **apogee** (farthest point) around the altitude of the **intended geosynchronous orbit**, which is about 35,786 kilometers.

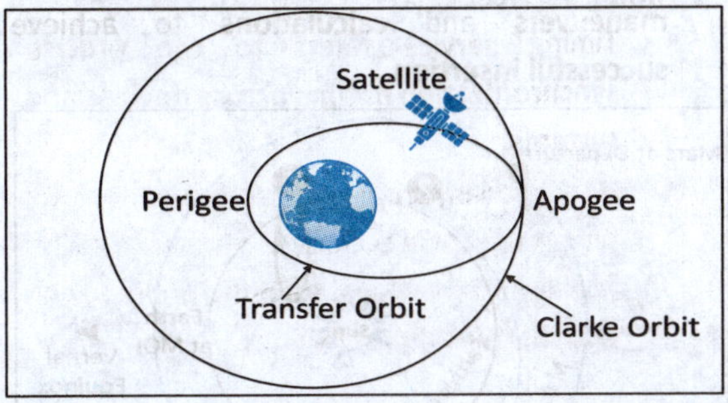

Applications of GTO

- **Launch of Communication Satellites:** GTO is frequently utilized to launch **communication satellites**. After reaching GTO, satellites perform **orbit-raising maneuvers** to achieve their final geostationary orbits.
- **Spacecraft Launch:** GTO serves as an intermediate step for launching various spacecraft, enabling them to reach higher orbits or **specific destinations.**
- **Orbit Maneuvering:** Space agencies use GTO to perform **orbital adjustments**, repositioning, or rendezvous maneuvers for satellites to fulfill their intended missions.

ISRO utilized the **GTO** to launch the **Mangalyaan spacecraft** towards **Mars**. This approach helped reduce costs significantly, with the mission's cost estimated at around **Rs. 7 per kilometer.** Utilizing the GTO for **interplanetary missions** like **Mangalyaan** demonstrated ISRO's ability to **achieve cost savings** by leveraging existing launch capabilities.

Challenges of GTO

- **Heliocentric Orbit Transition:** Moving from Earth's orbit to a heliocentric (Sun-centered) orbit posed a crucial challenge due to the need for **precise trajectory adjustments** during **interplanetary travel.**

- **Risk of Mars Orbit Insertion:** The most critical step in the **Mangalyaan mission** was transitioning from a **heliocentric orbit** to a **stable orbit** around **Mars**, demanding **precise maneuvers** and **calculations** to achieve **successful insertion.**

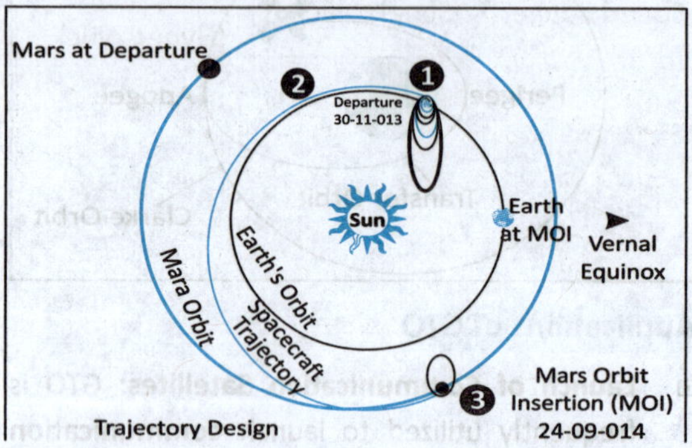

Liquid Apogee Motor -A **Liquid Apogee Motor** (LAM) is a type of **rocket engine** used in **space propulsion systems**. It's designed to provide the necessary thrust for spacecraft to achieve or modify their apogee (farthest point from Earth) in an orbit. LAMs are used to change orbits or make sure spacecraft go where they're supposed to.

LAUNCH VEHICLES

Launch vehicles, also known as **rockets** or **space launch vehicles**, are vehicles designed to **carry payloads** such as **satellites**, **spacecraft**, or **scientific instruments** into space.

Types of Launch Vehicles

- **Expendable launch Vehicle (ELV)** - Used only once for a space mission, **Ex :** PSLV, GSLV
  - Used for Unmanned missions
  - Indian only has ELV, working to develop RLV
  - Create Space debris
- **Reusable launch vehicle (RLV)** - Can be used multiple times. After completing the mission, it returns back to earth.
  - Can be used for both manned and unmanned mission.
  - Reusable, hence economically viable.

Major Components of Launch Vehicles
- Engines
- Fuel
- Satellite/Payload
- Command and Control System

Types of Engines

- **Non-air breathing propulsion system**
  - They use **Oxidisers** to burn fuel.
  - Since oxidisers are kept inside the rocket, these engines are **heavier.**
- **Air-breathing population system**
  - **Air breathing** - They take oxygen directly from air.
  - Since they take oxygen from air to burn fuel, they are lighter. **Ex-** Ramjet/Scramjet

Jet Engines

- A jet engine is a type of reaction engine that **creates thrust** by **expelling a high-speed jet** of gases in one direction. This action generates an equal and **opposite force**, propelling the vehicle forward.
- While this broad definition can include **rocket, water jet** and **hybrid propulsion**, the term jet engine typically refers to an internal combustion airbreathing jet engine such as a **turbojet, turbofan, ramjet**, or **pulse jet**. In general, **jet engines** are **internal combustion engines.**

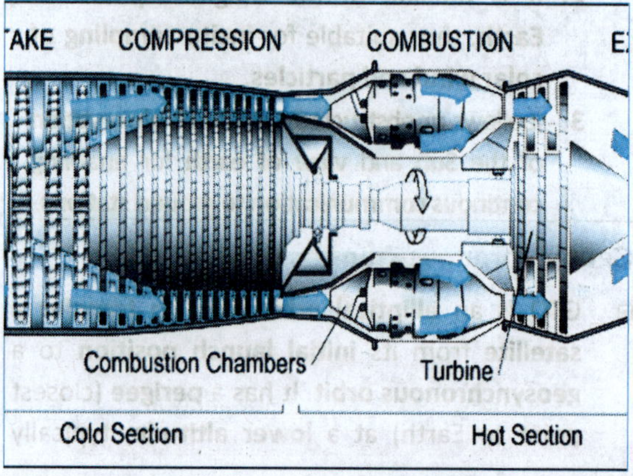

Ramjet Engine

- A ramjet is a type of **airbreathing jet engine** that operates by using the **forward motion** of the engine itself to compress incoming air before combustion. This type of engine is designed to work efficiently at **high speeds**, typically in the **supersonic range**.
- Since it produces no thrust when **stationary** (no ram air) ramjet-powered vehicles require an **assisted take-off**. This assistance can come from **rocket motors** or other propulsion systems that can accelerate the vehicle to a speed at which the ramjet can start working effectively.
- Ramjets work most efficiently at supersonic speeds around **Mach 3 (2,300 mph; 3,700 km/h)** and can operate up to speeds of **Mach 6 (4,600 mph; 7,400 km/h).**

1 Mach = Speed of Sound = 1225.04 kilometers per hour

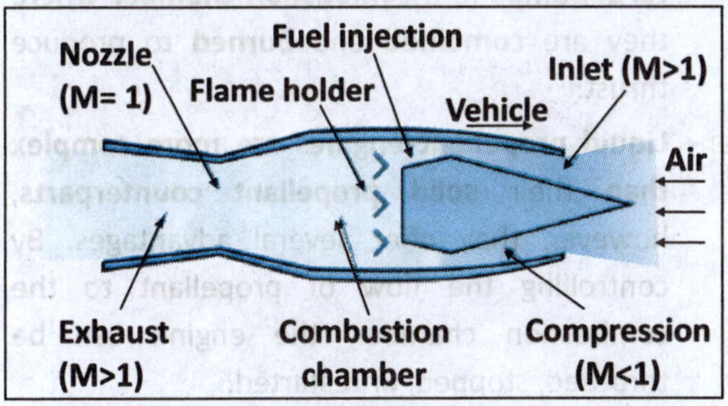

Scramjet Engine (Supersonic Combustion Ramjet)

- A scramjet is an advanced type of **airbreathing jet engine** that operates by **combusting fuel** with **atmospheric** air at **supersonic speeds.**

Scramjet Engine Cross Section

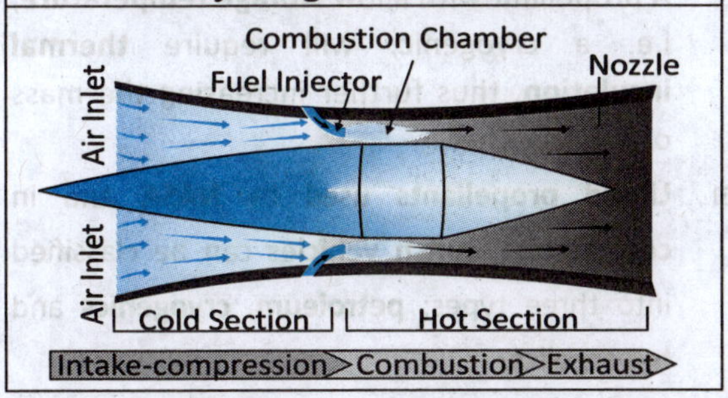

- It is a more **specialized** and **advanced version** of the ramjet, designed to work efficiently in **hypersonic flight regimes.**

Aspect	Ramjet	Scramjet
Operating Speed Range	Mach 2 to 4-5 (Supersonic)	Mach 5 and above (Hypersonic)
Optimal Speed Range	Supersonic	Hypersonic
Combustion Speed	Subsonic	Supersonic
Design Complexity	Relatively simpler	More complex
Take-off Assistance	Rocket assist required	Rocket assist often required
Applications	Missiles, some aircraft	Hypersonic flight, spaceplanes

Dual Mode Ramjet

- It **combines** the capabilities of both a **ramjet** and a **scramjet engine**, allowing the vehicle to operate efficiently over a wide range of speeds, from **subsonic** to **hypersonic.**
- The **DMRJ technology** addresses the limitations of individual ramjet and scramjet engines by providing a **flexible propulsion system** that adapts to changing flight conditions.
- It operate both in **subsonic** and **supersonic combustor modes.**

Cryogenic Engine

- The **indigenous cryogenic engine**, developed by India, stores **fuel** (liquid hydrogen) and **oxidizer** (liquid oxygen) at **extremely low temperatures.**
- **Hydrogen** is stored at **20K** (-253°C) and **oxygen** at **90K** (-183°C). By burning **hydrogen**, this engine produces **high-energy thrust.**

Hydrogen, which is abundant and environmentally friendly, burns to generate **water vapor** (H_2O), making it a cleaner option.

- The cryogenic engine's innovative technology has been pivotal in India's space program, enhancing its launch capabilities and enabling more ambitious missions.

Propellants

- **Propellant** is a **chemical mixture** burned to produre thrust in rockets and consists of a **fuel** and an **oxidizer**.

> - A **Fuel** is a **substance** which **burns** when combined with **oxygen producing gas** for **propulation.**
> - An **oxidizer** is **an agent that releases oxygen** for combination with a fuel.

Solid propellants

- **Solid propellant** motors are the simplest of all rocket designs. They consist of a **casing**, usually **steel**, filled with a mixture of **solid compounds** (fuel and oxidizer) which burn at a **rapid rate**, **expelling hot gases** from a **nozzle** to **produce thrust**.
- When **ignited**, a **solid propellant burns** from the center out towards the sides of the casing. The shape of the center channel determines the rate and pattern of the burn, thus providing a means to control thrust.
- Unlike liquid propellant engines, **solid propellant** motors can not be shut down. Once ignited, they will burn until all the propellant is exhausted.

Soild Propellants

Homogenous | Composite

- Homogeneous propellants are either simple base or double base.
- A **simple base propellant** consists of a single compound, usually **nitrocellulose,** which has both an **oxidation capacity** and a **reduction capacity**.
- **Double base propellants** usually consist of **nitrocellulose** and **nitroglycerine**, to which a plasticiser is added.
- **Modern composite propellants** are **heterogeneous powders** (mixtures) which use a crystallized or finely ground mineral salt as an oxidizer, often ammonium perchlorate, which constitutes between 60% and 90% of the mass of the propellant. The fuel itself is aluminum.
- **Solid propellants**, like **HTPB**, are used in rockets for their **easy storage, high energy density** and **reliability.**

> **Example:** HTPB : Hydroxy terminated poly-butadione (used in PSLV, GSLV)

Liquid propellants

- In a **liquid propellant rocket**, the **fuel** and **oxidizer** are stored in **separate tanks**, and are fed through a system of **pipes, valves** and **turbopumps** to a **combustion chamber** where they are **combined** and **burned** to produce thrust.
- **Liquid propellant engines are more complex** than their **solid propellant counterparts,** however, they offer several advantages. By controlling the flow of propellant to the combustion chamber, the engine can be throttled, stopped, or restarted.
- A good liquid propellant is one with a high specific impulse or, one with a high speed of exhaust gas ejection. This implies a high combustion temperature and exhaust gases with small molecular weights.
- A propellant with a low **storage temperature,** i.e. a cryogenic, will require **thermal insulation**, thus further increasing the mass of the launcher.
- **Liquid propellants** used by **NASA** and in **commercial launch vehicles** can be classified into three types: **petroleum**, **cryogenics** and **hypergolics.**

- **Petroleum fuels** are those refined from **crude oil** and are a **mixture of complex hydrocarbons**, i.e. **organic compounds** containing only **carbon** and **hydrogen**. The petroleum used as rocket fuel is kerosene, or a type of highly refined kerosene called **RP-1** (refined petroleum). It is used in combination with liquid oxygen as the oxidizer.
- **Cryogenic propellants** are liquefied gases stored at very **low temperatures**, namely **liquid hydrogen** (LH2) as the fuel and **liquid oxygen** (LO2) as the oxidizer. **LH2** remains liquid at temperatures of **-423^0 F** (-253^0 C) and **LO2** remains in a liquid state at temperatures of **-298° F** (-183° C).
- Because of the **low temperatures** of **cryogenic propellants,** they are difficult to store over long periods of time. For this reason, they are less desirable for use in **military rockets** which must be kept launch ready for months at a time. Also, liquid hydrogen has a very low density (0.59 pounds per gallon) and, therefore, requires a storage volume many times greater than other fuels. Despite all the drawbacks, these are more energy efficient.
- **Liquid hydrogen** and liquid oxygen are used as the propellant in the **high efficiency** main engines of the **space shuttle**.
- **Hypergolic propellants** are **fuels** and oxidizers which **ignite spontaneously** on contact with each other and require no ignition source. The easy start and restart capability of hypergolics make them ideal for spacecraft maneuvering systems. Also, since hypergolics remain liquid at normal temperatures, they do not pose the storage problems of **cryogenic propellants**. **Hypergolics** are highly toxic and must be handled with extreme care.
- Hypergolic fuels commonly include **hydrazine, monomethyl hydrazine** (MMH) and **unsymmetrical dimethyl hydrazine** (UDMH). The oxidizer is typically nitrog.
- **Liquid propellants,** like **UDMH** (N_2O_4) used in **PSLV** and **GSLV**, offer advantages as **higher efficiency** due to **uniform combustion, demonstrated performance** and **lighter weight** leading to **cost-effective storage.**
- However, challenges include the **flammable** and **corrosive nature** of the propellant, making **storage** and **transport complex.**

Hybrid Propellants

- **Hybrid propellant engines** represent an **intermediate group** between **solid** and **liquid propellant engines**. One of the substances is solid, usually the fuel, while the other, usually the oxidizer, is liquid. The liquid is injected into the solid, whose fuel reservoir also serves as the **combustion chamber**.
- The main advantage of such engines is that they have high performance, similar to that of solid propellants, but the combustion can be moderated, stopped, or even restarted. an **tetroxide** (N_2O_4) or **nitric acid** (HNO_3).

Example : UDMH (N_2O_4) (Unsymmetrical DiMethyl Hydrazine) Used in PSLV and GSLV.

Indian Launch Vehicles

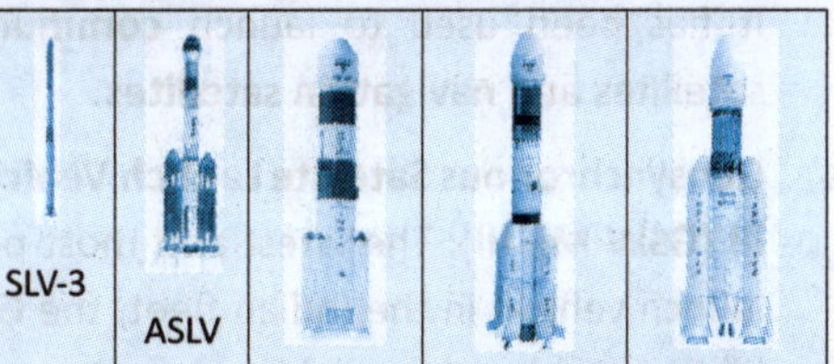

	SLV-3	ASLV	PSLV-XL	GSLV Mk II	GSLV MkIII
Height	22.7	23.5 m	44 m	49 m	43.43 m
Lift-of weight	17 t	39 t	320 t	414 t	640 t
Propulsion	All Solid	All Solid	Solid and Liquid	Solid, Liquid and Cryogenic	Solid, Liquid and Cryogen
Payload mass	40 kg	150 kg	1860 kg	2200 kg	4000 kg
Orbit	Low Earth Orbit	Low Earth Orbit	475 km Sun Synchronours Polar Orbit (1300 kg in Geosynchro-nous Transfer Orbit	Geosynchronous Transfer Orbit	Geosynchronous Transfer Orbit

- **Satellite Launch Vehicle (SLV):** The **first Indian launch vehicle**, was launched in **1979** that successfully placed the **Rohini satellite** in orbit.
- **Augmented Satellite Launch Vehicle (ASLV):** An upgraded version of the SLV, it was launched in **1987** and successfully placed the **IRS-1A** satellite in orbit.
- **Sounding rockets:** These are **small rockets** that are used to conduct experiments in the **upper atmosphere**.
- **Polar Satellite Launch Vehicle (PSLV):** The **workhorse** of the **Indian launch vehicle fleet**, the PSLV is capable of launching satellites into a variety of orbits, including **low Earth orbit**, **geosynchronous transfer orbit** and **geosynchronous orbit**. They have been used to launch a wide variety of satellites, including **weather satellites**, **communication satellites** and **Earth observation satellites**.

> **Chandrayaan 1 & 2, Mangalyaan** and **Aditya L1** were launched using **PSLV**.

- **Geosynchronous Satellite Launch Vehicle (GSLV):** The GSLV is a **heavier launch vehicle** than the PSLV and is capable of launching heavier satellites into **geosynchronous orbit**. It has been used to launch **communication satellites** and **navigation satellites**.
- **Geosynchronous Satellite Launch Vehicle Mark III (GSLV Mk III):** The latest and most powerful launch vehicle in the Indian fleet, the GSLV Mk III is capable of **launching heavier satellites** into geosynchronous orbit and is also being developed to be used for human spaceflight missions.
- **GSLV Mk-III**, also known as **LVM3** (Launch Vehicle Mark-3), is the **heaviest launch vehicle** developed by the **Indian Space Research Organisation** (ISRO). It is designed to carry **heavier payloads** into **Geostationary Transfer Orbit** (GTO) and is crucial for launching larger communication satellites and other payloads.

> **Chandrayaan 3** used **GSLV Mk III** (LVM3) as a launch vehicle.

Features of GSLV

- **Heaviest Indian Launch Vehicle**: The GSLV Mk-III has a liftoff mass of approximately **640 metric tons,** making it the heaviest launch vehicle developed by India.
- **Payload Capacity**: It's capable of launching satellites in the 4,000 to 5,000 kg class into GTO, a much higher payload capacity compared to the earlier GSLV versions.
- **Three-Stage Configuration:** The GSLV Mk-III consists of three stages, each using different types of propulsion.
- **S-200 Boosters:** These are the first-stage boosters, which use solid propellant. They provide the initial thrust required for liftoff.
- **L-110 Stage:** The second stage uses liquid propulsion, specifically the Vikas engine, which uses hypergolic propellants (Unsymmetrical Dimethylhydrazine - UDMH and Nitrogen Tetroxide - N_2O_4).
- **CE-25 Cryogenic Stage:** The third stage is powered by a cryogenic engine (CE-25), which uses liquid oxygen (LOX) and liquid hydrogen (LH2) as propellants. This stage provides the high-energy boost needed to reach GTO.

RLV : Reusable Launch Vehicle

- The central idea behind an RLV is to create a launch vehicle that can return to Earth after deploying its payload into space, much like an aircraft. This reentry vehicle often has wings to facilitate controlled reentry and landing, similar to the way an aircraft glides back to the ground.

> **ISRO** successfully conducted **Reusable Launch Vehicle Autonomous Landing Mission** (RLV LEX) on **April 2, 2023** at Aeronautical Test Range (ATR), **Chitradurga, Karnataka.**

- **Advantages of Reusable Launch Vehicles (RLVs):**
  - **Cost Reduction:** Lower launch costs due to component reuse.
  - **Faster Turnaround:** Shorter time between successive launches.
  - **Increased Accessibility**: Enables a broader range of organizations to access space.
  - **Commercial Viability:** Encourages commercial space ventures and industries.
  - **Space Tourism:** Opens up possibilities for private space travel experiences.
  - **Space Economy Growth:** Stimulates growth in space-related businesses.
  - **Resource Efficiency:** Reduces resource consumption through reuse.
  - **Environmental Impact**: Minimizes space debris and environmental concerns.
  - **Technological Advancement:** Drives innovation in materials and engineering.
- **Challanges :**
  - **Reentry Technology**: Developing effective heat shields and structures for safe reentry.
  - **Safety Concerns:** Ensuring crew and payload safety during all phases of flight.
  - **Technical Complexity:** Balancing reusability with performance and reliability.
  - **High Initial Investment:** Requiring significant funding for research and development.
  - **Infrastructure Requirements:** Establishing suitable launch and landing facilities. ⍰ 10km runway is needed
  - **Operational Logistics:** Managing recovery, refurbishment, and maintenance processes.
  - **Wear and Tear:** Addressing rapid wear of components due to harsh space conditions.
  - **Training and Expertise**: Acquiring and retaining skilled personnel.
  - **Unpredictable Demand:** Navigating fluctuating market demand for launch services.
  - **Regulatory Hurdles:** Adhering to complex spaceflight regulations.
  - **Public Perception:** Addressing safety and environmental concerns.
  - **Environmental Impact:** Balancing launch activities with environmental considerations.
  - **Market Competition:** Competing with established launch providers. Soon, Space X might capture the market. Competition from International space entities. (Falcon-9 Heavy)

Small Satellite Launch Vehicle (SSLV)
• The Small Satellite Launch Vehicle (SSLV) is a compact and **cost-effective launch vehicle** developed by the **Indian Space Research Organisation** (ISRO) to cater specifically to the small satellite market. • SSLV is designed to provide **dedicated launch services** for **small satellites**, including **microsatellites** and **nanosatellites.** • The increasing demand for launching small satellites for various applications, such as **Earth observation, communication, scientific research** and **technology demonstration**, led to the development of SSLV.

ISRO's Launch Vehicles

- Currently, **ISRO** has three active launch vehicles: the **Polar Satellite Launch Vehicle** (PSLV), the **Geosynchronous Satellite Launch Vehicle** (GSLV), and the **Launch Vehicle Mark-III** (LVM3).
- The **PSLV** has **four stages** while the **GSLVs** have **three stages** each. Each stage has a different fuel, and is jettisoned when the fuel is expended as the rocket ascends.
- Primarily, launch vehicles comprise **three or four stages** apart from the payload, which needs to be launched into a polar or a geosynchronous orbit, depending on a mission's requirements.
- In **ISRO's three-stage rockets**, the **first** or **lowermost stage** has a **motor fuelled** by solid

fuel (in the GSLV, this can also be augmented by up to four liquid strap-on boosters); the **second stage** has the **Vikas engine powered** by liquid fuel; and the **third** and **uppermost stage** has a **cryogenic engine**, which uses liquid **oxygen** and **liquid hydrogen**.

- In the **four-stage PSLV**, the first stage has a motor using **solid fuel** (augmentable with up to six solid-fuel strap-on boosters), the **second stage** has a **Vikas engine**, the **third stage** again has a **solid-fuel motor**, and the **fourth stage** has **two liquid engines**.
- The **RLV** (Reusable Launch Vehicle) that ISRO is building has only **two stages** to propel the vehicle into orbit. Once the fuel in the **first stage** has been expended, the vehicle will shed it, and carry on with the **second stage**.
- Once it has been shed, the **first stage** will re-enter the atmosphere and land in an autonomous fashion at a pre-determined location, which be available for re use after some maintenance.

SATELLITES

Space crafts designed to **carry payloads** such as **transponders**, **covers**, **instruments** for various space applications are called satellites.

- There are different types of satellites ranging from **Communication**, **Meteorology**, **Astronomy**, **Remote Sensing**, **Navigation**, **Defence** and **Reconnaissance satellite** based on their application.

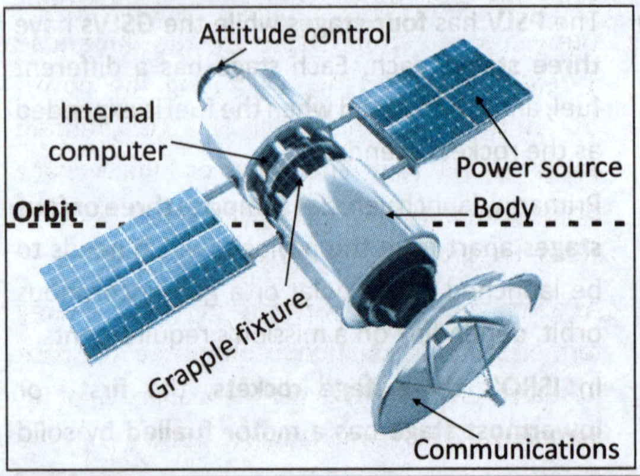

Indian Remote Sensing Satellite

- The **Indian Remote Sensing Satellite** (IRS-1A) was launched in **1988** and was the first in a series of satellites that have been used for a variety of **remote sensing applications**.
- **Applications of IRSS**
    - Survey and management of Natural resources. (Forest, agro, wetlands)
    - **Mineral prospecting :** Locating minerals via Satellite (Resource SAT - 1, 2A, 2B)
    - **Cartography (Contour maps) :** (Cartosat) (gis: geographical information system)
    - **Oceanography :** mapping and study of geography. Eg: OCEANSAT (4-5)
    - **ScatSat-1**: ScatSat-1 was launched in **2016** and is a dedicated scatterometer satellite. It carries a Ku-band scatterometer that is used to measure ocean surface winds. ScatSat-1 has replaced Oceansat-2-A, which was launched in 2008 and decommissioned in 2016.
    - **SARAL: SARAL** is a joint mission between **India** and **France**. It was launched in **2013** and carries a number of sensors, including a **Synthetic Aperture Radar** (SAR) and a **Laser Retroreflector Array** (LRA). The SAR is used to create high-resolution images of the ocean surface, even in cloudy conditions. The LRA is used to track the movement of the satellite and to determine its precise location.
- **Environment :** Pollution management.

Only **3 Countries** have dedicated climate change satellites - **US, China, Japan.**

NISAR- [Nasa ISRO Synthetic Aperture Radar]

- Collaboration between **India** and **NASA** for a dual frequency satellite expected to be launched in **2024**.
- **NISAR** will study **natural processes** on the earth's surface for three years in radar frequency, with a state- of-the-art setup.

ISRO is also expected to launch the **XPoSat satellite**, to study **Xrays streaming** through outer space.

Indian National Satellite System (INSAT) and Geosynchronous Satellite System (GSAT)

Communication Satellite: GSAT-11 (India)

- **GSAT-30:** Launched in **2022** for **high-speed broadband internet access.**

Weather forecasting

- **INSAT-3D:** Launched in **2013** and used for weather forecasting and disaster management.
- **INSAT-3DR:** Enhanced version of INSAT-3D. launched in 2021 and carries a number of new sensors, including a Synthetic Aperture Radar (SAR) and a Lightning Imaging Sensor (LIS).

Tele education

- **EDUSAT:** Launched in **2004** for tele education and distance learning. It carries a number of educational television channels and other educational resources.

Telemedicine

- **GSAT-11:** Launched in **2017** and is used for telemedicine and telehealth services. It carries a number of medical sensors, which can be used to transmit medical data to doctors and other healthcare providers.

Disaster Management

- **GSAT-7A:** Launched in **2022** for disaster management. It carries a number of sensors, which can be used to monitor natural disasters, such as cyclones and floods.

Gagan Satellite

- **GAGAN** is a **GPS-aided geo-augmented navigation satellite system** developed by the **Indian Space Research Organisation** (ISRO) and the **Airports Authority of India** (AAI). It is designed to provide accurate and reliable navigation services to **civil aviation** and air traffic management.
    - Main Purpose is to **prevent airline accidents** and **manage traffic.**
    - GAGAN can provide accuracies of **up to 10 meters**, which is sufficient for most civil aviation applications.

India's Space Programme and ISRO

- **Space research activities** were initiated in India during the early **1960s**, when applications using satellites were in **experimental stages** even in the **United States** and the **USSR** in backdrop of **Space Race.**
- While the two countries focussed on manned missions like **USSR** sending **Yuri Gagarin** to space on **April 12, 1961,** who orbited Earth at a maximum altitude of **187 miles** (301 km) on **Vostok 1 spacecraft. Valentine Tereshkova** was launched on a **solo mission** aboard the spacecraft **Vostok 6** on **16 June 1963**, who spent more than **70 hours** orbiting the **Earth.**
- **USA's space agency NASA** was successful in sending **Apollo 11** as the **first spaceflight** that **first landed humans** on the **Moon**, with **Commander Neil Armstrong** and **Lunar Module Pilot Buzz Aldrin** landing the **Apollo Lunar Module Eagle** on **July 20, 1969.**
- With the live transmission of **Tokyo Olympic Games** across the **Pacific** by the **American Satellite Syncom-3** demonstrating the power of **communication satellites, Dr. Vikram Sarabhai,** the **founding father of Indian space programme**, quickly recognised the benefits of space technologies for India.
- As a first step, the **Department of Atomic Energy** formed the **Indian National Committee for Space Research** (INCOSPAR) under the leadership of **Dr. Sarabhai** and **Dr. Ramanathan** in **1962.**

- Later, the **Indian Space Research Organisation** (ISRO) was formed on **August 15, 1969**, with a prime objective to **develop space technology** and its application to various national needs.
- The **Department of Space** (DOS) and the **Space Commission** were set up in **1972** and **ISRO** was brought under **DOS** on **June 1, 1972**.

India first hit the headlines in space missions when **Rakesh Sharma** alongside two **Soviet cosmonauts**, embarked on his **cosmic journey** aboard **Soyuz T-11** on **April 3, 1984** in a joint collaboration of ISRO and **USSR's Interkosmos** space programme.

- Amid weightlessness, he captured captivating glimpses of space, seamlessly blended yoga into the environment, and conducted experiments that expanded our scientific horizons.
- Since its inception, the **Indian space programme** has been orchestrated well and had **three distinct elements:**
  - Satellites for communication and remote sensing
  - Space transportation system
  - Application programmes.

Two major operational systems have been established – the **Indian National Satellite** (INSAT) for **telecommunication, television broadcasting**, and meteorological services and the **Indian Remote Sensing Satellite** (IRS) for monitoring and management of natural resources and **Disaster Management Support.**

- **India's Space programme** originally focused on **developing space assets** that provided direct **developmental benefits**, for example, **telecommunications** and **remote sensing** satellites that helped both in improving communication facilities and giving direct assistance to **India's farmers.**
- Over the time, India has shifted a part of its focus towards space exploration missions like India's **Mars Orbiting Mission** (MoM) and Moon exploratory missions – **Chandrayaan 1, 2** and **3,** alongside **Aditya L 1** to study **Sun.**

India has been fairly successful in these efforts and its space programme has become a **comprehensive** one that includes not only a **robust launch capacity** and **very large remote sensing satellite systems**, but also a very well-rounded scientific and deep **space exploratory programmes.**

Major Accomplishments of India Space Programmes /Missions

- When India began its space program in the **1960s**, it was a **developing country** with limited resources, and it **focused on using space** to push its **social** and **economic development agenda.**
- Indian space program has expanded over the past decade, with **two important changes**:
  - An ambitious **space exploration program.**
  - An **increased use of space for national security purposes.**
- Intensifying security concerns regarding **China**, including **Beijing's growing counter-space capabilities**, likely will be a major driver of India's space goals in the coming years likely to result in greater attention to national security aspects of India's space program, as well as to **developing new space security partnerships.**
- India has achieved a **multitude of milestones** in the **space sector** ever since the inception of the Indian space programme in **1962.**
- The **Indian Space Research Organisation** (ISRO) has been spearheading the space programme since the agency was established in **1969,** helping the country launch its earliest satellites, **Moon missions** and **spacecraft to Mars.**

Some of the major feats of ISRO	
• Rohini series of satellites	• EDUSAT
• INSAT and GSAT Series	• HAMSAT
• Resourcesat Series	• Bhaskara-1

- Cartosat Series
- Oceansat-1
- Chandrayaan-1
- Chandrayaan-2
- Aditya L1
- Earth Observation Satellite Series
- Indian Regional Navigation Satellite System
- Space Recovery Experiment Satellite
- Mars Orbiter Mission (Mangalyaan)
- Kalpana-1
- SARAL
- AstroSat
- Chandrayaan-3

- In the last few years, there have been reforms in the **commercial space sector** due to the efforts of **ISRO** and the emergence of deep space-tech startups.

In **2022**, **Hyderabad-based space-tech startup Skyroot Aerospace** launched **India's first privately developed launch vehicle**, as part of the firm's maiden mission, **Prarambh.**

- The mission received support from **ISRO** as well as the **Indian National Space Promotion and Authorisation Centre** (INSPACe), an autonomous agency in the **Department of Space** (DoS) that facilitates the participation of **private players** in the space sector.
- India is ushering in a new era in space because of the efforts of **ISRO** and **space-tech startups**, and also because **space firms** are collaborating with **international firms** for satellite launch services.
- **ISRO** has launched the satellites of **London-based communications company OneWeb** on two missions, in collaboration with **New Space India Limited** (NSIL), the commercial arm of **ISRO.**

ISRO Missions : Space Exploration

- **Earth's Moon :** Chandrayaan-1 (2008), Chandrayaan-2 (2019) and Chandrayaan-3 (2023).
- **Mars :** Mangalyaan 1.
- **Astronomical Observation :** AstroSat.
- **Study of Sun :** Aditya L1.

Chandrayaan-1 (2008)

- **Chandrayaan-1**, launched in **2008**, was an **Indian lunar mission featuring an orbiter.** It ended prematurely due to battery problems. It confirmed lunar water presence, later backed by NASA. It discovered remnants of the **Apollo mission's landing site.**

Chandrayaan-2 (2019)

- **Chandrayaan-2**, consisted of an orbiter, a **lander** named **Vikram,** and a **rover** named **Pragyan.** The mission had collaborative assistance from **Russia** and **France.**
- While the orbiter successfully achieved lunar orbit and continues to operate, the lander and rover unfortunately failed to safely land on the **moon's south pole.**
- The Orbiter placed in its intended orbit around the Moon enriches our understanding of the moon's evolution and mapping of the minerals and water molecules in Polar regions, using its **eight state-of-the-art scientific instruments.**
- The **Orbiter camera** was the **highest resolution camera** (0.3 m) in any lunar mission so far and will provide high resolution images immensely useful to the global scientific community.
- **Chandrayaan-2** has already made a number of important discoveries about the Moon, which include:
  - **Presence of water ice** in the Moon's polar regions.
  - **Presence of hydrogen gas in** the Moon's atmosphere.
  - Discovery of **new lunar minerals.**
  - **Terrain** and surface **mapping.**
  - Spectrometry of **Soil of moon** for **Mineral Content.**

LVM3-M4/Chandrayaan-3 (2023)

- Chandrayaan-3 is **India's third lunar exploration mission.**

Successful landing of **Vikram** on **Moon's South Pole** made India the **fourth country** to land on moon after **US**, **Russia** and **China** and the **first country to land on Lunar South Pole.**

- It consisted of **Lander** and **Rover** configuration. It is launched by **LVM3** from **SDSC SHAR, Sriharikota**.
- The propulsion module carries the lander **Vikram** and rover **Pragyan** till **100km lunar orbit**. The propulsion module has **Spectro-polarimetry of Habitable Planet Earth** (SHAPE) payload to study the **spectral** and **Polari metric measurements** of Earth from the lunar orbit.
- The **Rover** (Pragyaan) has the mission life to **14 days** (One Lunar Day).

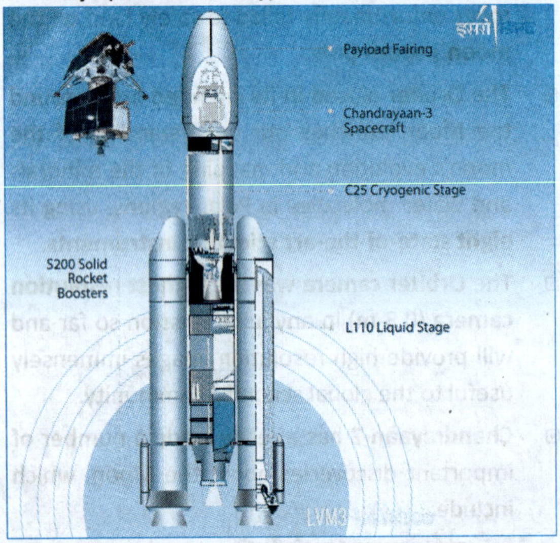

- **Objectives of Chandrayaan-3 mission:**
  - To search for water ice in Moon's south pole.
  - To study the Moon's mineral composition and geology.
  - To search for other resources, such as **Helium-3.**
  - To conduct experiments to study the Moon's environment.
  - To collect data that will help us to better understand the Moon's formation and evolution.

Accomlishments of Chandrayaan-3

- In just **10 days**, the **Chandrayaan-3** covered over **100 metres** of lunar terrain through its Pragyan rover that moves at a speed of **1cm per second.**
- **Chandraayan-3's Vikram lander** studied the **Moon's ionosphere** -successfully measuring **electron densities** ranging from **5 million to 30 million per cubic metres**. These measurements showed fluctuations and would provide insights into developing future communication technology suited for the Moon.
- **Vikram lander** drilled into the lunar surface, revealing temperatures **8 centimetres beneath** the surface. It found that these temperatures showed a difference of **60 degree Celsius** compared to surface temperatures.
- **Vikram lander's seismograph** managed to record a short but significant seismic event, lasting about **4 seconds**. This event could either be a minor moonquake or the result of a small meteorite impact, offering scientists insight into Moon's geological activity.
- Vikram lander conducted the **first-ever measurements** of the near-surface lunar plasma environment of the south polar region; finding relatively sparse.
- **Chandrayaan-3's Pragyan rover** found the **presence of Sulphur** on the lunar surface in the south pole region. In addition, the rover's instruments also detected various elements on the Moon's surface - **aluminum, silicon, calcium,** and **iron.** The discovery of these elements will help scientists develop a better understanding of **lunar geochemistry.**
- Vikram lander performed a **hop experiment"** before it was put to sleep in early **September, 2023**. According to ISRO, Vikram was commanded to fire its engines, it rose up by about **40cm** and landed at a distance of **30-40cm. ISRO** claimed that this means the spacecraft could be used to bring samples back to earth in the future.

Countries with LUNAR missions		
• NASA	:	Apollo
• China	:	Change e-mission
• Russia	:	LUNA Nussion(LUNA 25 Failed recently)
• ESA		
• Japan		

Mangalyaan (MOM) - 1

- India's **Mars Orbiter Mission** (MOM), launched in **2013** aboard **PSLV-C25**, marked India's **first interplanetary endeavor**.
- It successfully made India the first **Asian nation** and the **fourth globally** (after Russia, US, and EU) to **reach Mars**. After 8 years, the spacecraft recently lost communication with ground stations, concluding its remarkable journey in space exploration.

Scientific instruments carried by India's Mars Orbiter Mission (MOM)

1. Mars Color Camera

- **Function:** Captures high-resolution images of Mars' surface, enhancing our understanding of the planet's geology and features.
- **Significance:** Provides visual context to complement other data collected during the mission.

2. Lyman Alpha Photometer

- **Function:** Measures the ratio of deuterium to hydrogen in Mars' upper atmosphere, helping determine the presence and history of water vapor.
- **Significance:** Contributes to understanding the evolution of water on Mars and its potential implications for habitability.

3. Thermal Infrared Imaging Spectrometer

- **Function:** Maps the composition and mineralogy of Mars' surface by measuring thermal emission in the infrared spectrum.
- **Significance:** Provides insights into the geology, composition, and thermal properties of the Martian terrain.

4. MENCA (Mars Exospheric Neutral Composition Analyser)

- **Function:** Analyzes the neutral composition of the Martian exosphere, studying variations in atmospheric elements.
- **Significance:** Contributes to understanding seasonal changes and the interaction between the Martian atmosphere and space environment.

5. Methane Sensor

- **Function:** Scans Mars' entire disc in a short time to measure methane levels, even at very low concentrations.
- **Significance:** Helps determine the presence and sources of methane on Mars, which could indicate geological or possibly biological activity.

Accomplishments of MOM

- **Composition of Martian Exosphere :** MOM's instruments detected and analyzed the **composition of gases in Mars' exosphere**. It made a noteworthy discovery of 'suprathermal' **Argon-40 atoms,** enhancing our understanding of the Martian atmosphere's dynamics and composition.
- **Imaging the Far Side of Deimos :** MOM captured images of the far side of **Deimos,** one of Mars' natural satellites (moons). This marked the first time that this remote area of Deimos was observed, adding to our knowledge of Mars' moon system.
- **Monitoring Martian Polar Ice Caps :** The mission provided valuable data by capturing the time-variation of the Martian polar ice caps, contributing to our understanding of the planet's climate and seasonal changes, particularly the behavior of its ice features.

Other Mars Mission
• Perseverance (NASA, USA)
• Hope Mission (United Arab Emirates)
• Tianwen 1 (China)
• Mars Moons Exploration (MMX) Mission (Japan)

ASTROSAT 2015

- ASTROSAT, launched in **2015**, is **India's first dedicated multi-wavelength space observatory**. It aims to **observe celestial objects** in various wavelengths, including **ultraviolet, visible, and X-rays.**
- **Objectives of ASTROSAT**
  - Observing High energy events of universe.
    - Supernova
    - Collapsing black hole
  - **Binary system study** (2 star system)- quasars and **pulsars**. (just remember the names).
  - **Mapping universe** for **black holes** and study them.

> - Many countries like **Japan, EU**, etc have **Astronomical Observatory Satellites.**
> - **NASA** has **Chandra X-ray** observatory to map for black holes which is named after an Indian Scientist.

- **ASTROSAT's key instruments include:**
  - **UltraViolet Imaging Telescope (UVIT):** Captures images in **ultraviolet wavelengths**, helping study **hot stars, galaxies**, and **interstellar medium.**
  - **Soft X-ray Telescope (SXT):** Observes X-rays from celestial sources, providing insights into high-temperature regions of the universe, like neutron stars and black holes.
  - **Large Area Soft X-ray Proportional Counter (LAXPC):** Detects X-rays in a broader range, aiding research on X-ray binaries and other high-energy phenomena.
  - **Cadmium Zinc Telluride Imager (CZTI):** Focuses on hard X-rays, enabling the study of **gamma-ray** bursts and other **high-energy processes.**
  - **Scanning Sky Monitor (SSM):** Monitors the sky for variations in **X-ray intensity**, helping identify transient events.
- ASTROSAT enhances India's capabilities in **space-based astronomy**, contributing to global research in fields such as **stellar physics, galaxy evolution** and **high-energy astrophysics.**

India's first multiwavelength space observatory ASTROSAT.
The 5 telescopes of the Astrosat
• Large Area X-ray Proportional Counter (LAXPC). • Soft X-ray Telecope (SXT). • Cadmium Zinc Telluride Imager (CZTI). • Scanning Sky Monitor (SSM). • Ultra Violet Imaging Telescope (UVIT).

ADITYA L1

- **Aditya-L1** is **India's first space based observatory** to study the Sun successfully launched by **ISRO** through **PSLV-C57 rocket** on **September 2, 2023.**
- The spacecraft travelled beyond a distance of **9.2 lakh kilometres** from Earth, successfully escaping the sphere of Earth's influence, navigated its path towards the **Sun-Earth Lagrange Point 1 (L1)**, where it was placed in the **Halo Orbit** around the **Lagrange Point L1** on **6th January, 2024.**
- A satellite in a halo orbit around L1 can continuously observe the Sun without any eclipses, offering **real-time observation** of **solar activities** and their impact on space weather.
- ISRO carried out the **Trans-Lagrangian1 Insertion** (TL1I) manoeuvre to send it towards L1 in **September 2023.** The final manoeuvre for pushing Aditya to its new parking spot Lagrange Point 1 was performed on **6th January, 2024,** from where it will have an clear view of the Sun.

> **L1** is about **1.5 million** km from the Earth and the distance of L1 from Earth is approximately 1% of the Earth-Sun distance.

- Aditya-L1 which is dedicated to the comprehensive study of the Sun has **7 payloads.** **5 payloads** were developed by **ISRO** and two by Indian academic institutes in collaboration with the space agency.

Payloads of Aditya L1

Type	Sl.No	Payload	Capability
Remote Sensing Payloads	1	Visible Emission Line Coronagraph (VELC)	Corona/Imaging & Spectroscopy
	2	Solar Ultraviolet Imaging Telescope (SUIT)	Photosphere and Chromosphere Imaging- Narrow & Broadband
	3	Solar Low Energy X-ray Spectrometer (SoLEXS)	Soft X-ray spectrometer: Sun-as-a-star observation
	4	High Energy L1 Orbiting X-ray Spectrometer (HEL1OS)	Hard X-ray spectrometer: Sun-as-a-star observation
In-situ Payloads	5	Aditya Solar wind Particle Experiment (ASPEX)	Solar wind/ Particle Analyzer Protons & Heavier Ions with directions
	6	Plasma Analyser Package For Aditya (PAPA)	Solar wind/ Particle Analyzer Electrons & Heavier Ions with directions
	7	Advanced Tri-axial High Resolution Digital Magnetometers	In-situ magnetic field (Bx, By and Bz)

- **Aditya-L1** has a mission life of **5 years** during which its payloads are expected to provide the most crucial information to understand the problem of coronal heating; coronal mass ejection; pre-flare and flare activities and their characteristics; dynamics of space weather; and propagation of particles and fields.
- **Major Objectives of the Mission:**
  - Study of the Solar upper atmospheric (chromosphere and corona) dynamics.
  - Study of **chromospheric and coronal heating, physics** of the **partially** ionized plasma, initiation of the coronal mass ejections and flares.
  - Observe the in-situ particle and plasma environment, providing data for the study of particle dynamics from the Sun.
  - Physics of the solar corona and its heating mechanism.
  - Diagnostics of the coronal and coronal loops plasma: Temperature, velocity and density.
  - Development, dynamics and origin of coronal mass ejections (CMEs).
  - Identify the sequence of processes that occur at multiple layers (chromosphere, base and extended corona) which eventually leads to solar eruptive events.
  - Magnetic field topology and magnetic field measurements in the solar corona.
  - Drivers for space weather (origin, composition and dynamics of solar wind).

Accomplishments of Aditya L1

- Aditya-L1, made a ground-breaking observation from its scientific payloads- capturing the first-ever image of a solar flare 'kernel' in the lower solar atmosphere, namely the photosphere and the chromosphere, in the images recorded in the Near Ultra-violet (NUV) band.

- On February 22, 2024, the SUIT payload onboard Aditya-L1 observed an X6.3-class solar flare, which is one of the most intense categories of solar eruptions.
- The unique feature of this observation was that SUIT detected brightening in NUV wavelength range (200-400 nm) —a wavelength range never observed before in such greater detail. These observations confirm that the energy released from the flare spread through different layers of the Sun's atmosphere. This provides new insights into the complex physics responsible for these massive solar explosions.
- One of the most exciting revelations in this observation is that thelocalized brightening captured in the lower Solar atmosphere corresponds directly with an increase in the temperature of plasma in the Solar corona at the top of the solar atmosphere. This confirm the linkage between flare energy deposition and associated temperature evolution. This finding also validates long-standing theories while offering new data that will help to reshape our understanding of physics of solar flare.
- During solar flare (as well as before the occurrence of solar flare) that particular region of the Sun generating flare becomes brighter in UV and X-ray.
- Aditya-L1 instruments such as SUIT, SoLEXS and HEL1OS can study these brightening and associated flash of radiation in greater details. This provides a detail picture of various phenomena related to Solar flares.
- It is to be noted that atmosphere of the Earth blocks these harmful radiations from the Sun to reach to the ground. Therefore, such study can be only made from space.
- This observation and associated scientific results marks a major step in understanding the Sun's explosive activity and its impact on Earth.

Solar Space Programmes of Other Countries

- **Helios 2 Solar Probe (1976) :** A collaborative solar probe project between NASA and the space agency of former West Germany. It approached within 43 million km of the Sun's surface.
- **Advanced Composition Explorer (ACE) (1997) :** ACE of NASA is designed to analyze solar wind and cosmic rays, offering insights into the Sun's behaviour and its impact on the interplanetary environment.
- **NASA's Parker Solar Probe (2018):** Its key objective is to track the movement of energy and heat through the Sun's corona and also to investigate the source of acceleration of the solar winds. It is a component of NASA's 'Living with a Star' initiative, that explores various aspects of the Sun-Earth system.
- **Solar Orbiter (2020):** A Joint project between ESA and NASA, Solar Orbiter gathers data to address key concerns in heliophysics as understanding how the Sun generates and manages the ever-changing space environment throughout the solar system. Along with The Solar Dynamics Observatory and Parker Solar Probe, it is a part of the international 'Living with a Star' initiative of NASA.
- Interface Region Imaging Spectrograph (IRIS) (2013) - NASA
  - WIND (1994) - NASA
  - Hinode (2006) - JAEA
- Solar Terrestrial Relations Observatory (STEREO) (2006) - NASA

Gaganyaan

- The Gaganyaan mission, led by **ISRO**, consists of **three flights**, including **two unmanned** and **one manned spaceflight**.
- Gaganyaan project envisages demonstration of **human spaceflight** capability by launching crew of **3 members** to an orbit of **400 km** for a **3 days**

mission and bring them back safely to earth, by landing in Indian sea waters.

- The **Gaganyaan orbital** module has 2 parts the **Crew Module** (CM) and the **Service Module** (SM).
- The **Crew Module** (CM) is a **double walled system** and a **habitat of astronauts**. It has an ablative **thermal protection system** (TPS) to protect it during the intense aerodynamic heating during the flight.
- The **Orbital module** (OM) will be launched by a **human-rated GSLV MK-III** vehicle and will orbit the Earth with a velocity of about **7,800 metre/ second.**

> - The **second phase** of **Gaganyan** will involve **Vyommitra** a **female space faring humanoid robot** equipped with capability to moniter, module parmeters, issue alerts and execute life support operations.
> - The programme will make **India** the **4th country** after **US**, **Russia** and **China** to launch a manned spaceflight.

SpaDeX Mission

- A cost-effective technology demonstrator mission (30 Dec, 2024 -16 Jan 2025) to develop and demonstrate the technology needed for rendezvous, docking, and undocking of two small spacecraft (SDX01- Chaser and SDX02- Target) in a low-Earth circular orbit using PSLV-C60.
- The mission is pivotal for India's future space ambitions, including lunar missions, sample returns, and the development of the Bharatiya Antariksh Station (BAS).
- **Major Objectives of SpaDex Mission :**
  - Develop and demonstrate technology for rendezvous and docking using two small spacecrafts.
  - Showcase controllability in the docked condition.
  - Demonstrate the potential for extending the life of the target spacecraft.
  - Test power transfer between docked spacecraft.
- Space Docking Experiment (SpaDeX) mission's docking operation was successfully completed on 16th January, 2025 marking India's entry into the elite group of nations capable of executing space docking operations.
- India became the fourth country in the world to achieve the capability of space docking.
- ISRO started the mission on 30th December 2024, with the successful launch of the SpaDeX spacecrfts using Polar Satellite Launch Vehicle (PSLV)-C60, from the Satish Dhawan Space Centre, Sriharikota.
- This groundbreaking mission aims to showcase India's technological prowess in spacecraft rendezvous, docking, and undocking — a critical capability for future advancements such as satellite servicing, space station operations, and interplanetary exploration.

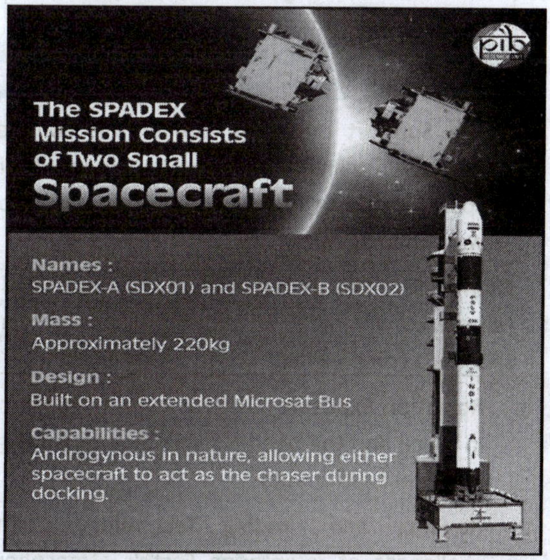

Defence Space Agency (DSA)

- An integrated tri-services agency of the Indian Armed Forces, formed in 2018 headquartered at Bengaluru tasked with operating space warfare and satellite intelligence assets, drawing personnel from all three branches of the armed forces.

Antariksha Abhyas – 2024 : A 3 day (11 - 13 Nov 24) first of its kind exercise to help secure national strategic objectives in space and integrate India's space capability in military operations conducted by Defence Space Agency of Headquarters Integrated Defence Staff.

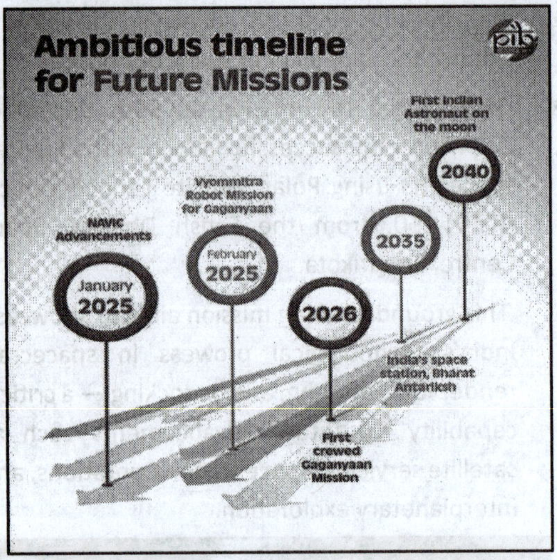

Technology Obstacles in Space Missions

- **Life Support Systems:** Explain the complex systems required to support human life in space, including oxygen, temperature control, waste management, etc.

Examples : The development of a safe and reliable crew module to support human life in space is a complex task.

- **Radiation Exposure :** Higher levels of radiation in space and the need for shielding technology to protect astronauts.
- **Re-Entry and Landing Technology :** The challenges of re-entering Earth's atmosphere and safely landing a spacecraft.

Example: NASA's Space Shuttle program had advanced heat shield technology for re-entry.

- **Launch and Propulsion Systems:** Need for powerful and reliable launch vehicles, as well as propulsion systems for in-space maneuvers.

Example: Reusable launch vehicle used for missions.

- **Astronaut Training :** Adequate astronaut training is a must. Training for space travel involves mastering numerous skills, including piloting spacecraft, handling emergency situations, and coping with long periods in a confined space.

Logistics Obstacles

- **Health of Astronauts :** Discuss the extensive training required for astronauts, both physically and mentally, to handle the challenges of space.
- **Mission Duration and Resources :** Highlight the need for planning and ensuring sufficient resources (food, water, oxygen) for the entire mission duration.

INDIAN SPACE ARCHITECTURE

- The **Space Commission** formulates the policies and **oversees the implementation** of the **Indian space programme** to promote the development and **application of space science** and **technology** for the **socio-economic** benefit of the country. **DOS** implements these programmes through, mainly, **Indian Space Research Organisation** (ISRO) and the **Grant- in-Aid** institutions viz. **Physical Research Laboratory** (PRL), **National Atmospheric Research Laboratory** (NARL), **North Eastern-Space Applications Centre** (NE-SAC), **Semi- Conductor Laboratory** (SCL) and **Indian Institute of Space Science and Technology** (IIST).
- The **Antrix Corporation**, established in 1992 as a government owned company, markets the space products and services. The establishment of space systems and their applications are coordinated by the national level committees,

namely, **INSAT Coordination Committee** (ICC), **Planning Committee on National Natural Resources Management System** (PC-NNRMS) and **Advisory Committee of on Space Sciences** (ADCOS).

- The Secretariat of DOS and ISRO Headquarters are located at Antariksh Bhavan in Bangalore. Programme offices at ISRO Headquarters coordinate the programmes like satellite communication, earth observation, launch vehicle, space science, disaster management support, sponsored research scheme, contracts management, international cooperation, safety, reliability, publications and public relations, budget & economic analysis, civil engineering and human resources development.

Functions and Duties of Department of Space

- **Design**, **development** and **realisation** and launching of Space **Launch Vehicle Systems** and **Sounding Rockets.**
- **Design, development** and **realisation of communication satellites** (carrying transponders) for meeting the **National Demand** towards **telecommunications, television broadcasting, security requirements** and **societal applications.**
- **Design, development** and **realisation of satellites** and/or space based systems for **navigational applications.**
- **Design, development** and **realisation** of **Earth Observation Satellites** for mapping and monitoring of natural resources, **Disastser Management Support** and **Meteorological services.**
- **Design, development** and **realisation** of space systems for carrying out research related to **space sciences** and **planetary exploration.**
- Implementation of **innovative space applications** in the domains of natural resources management, **disaster management support** and several **societal applications.**
- Undertaking **Research and Development activities** towards advanced **launch vehicles, spacecrafts** and ground systems for space missions.
- **Operation and maintenance** of space **assets** and **critical infrastructural facilities.**
- Fostering **international co-operation** in peaceful uses of outer space including adherence to international charters and treaties.
- **Development of Human Resources** and capacity building to carryout the space Research Activities.

Organisational Structure

Indian Space Research Organisation (ISRO)

- It is the **space agency of India.** The organisation is involved in **science, engineering** and **technology** to harvest the benefits of outer space for India and the mankind.
- ISRO is a major constituent of the **Department of Space** (DOS), **Government of India.** The department executes the **Indian Space Programme** primarily through various centres or units within ISRO.
- The prime objective of ISRO/DOS is the **development** and **application** of space technology for various national needs.
- To fulfil this objective, **ISRO** has established major space systems for communication, television broadcasting and meteorological services; resources monitoring and management; space-based navigation services. **ISRO** has developed satellite launch vehicles, **PSLV** and **GSLV**, to place the satellites in the required orbits.
- Alongside its technological advancement, **ISRO** contributes to **science** and **science education** in the country. Various dedicated research centres and autonomous institutions for remote sensing, astronomy and astrophysics,

atmospheric sciences and space sciences in general function under the aegis of Department of Space.

- ISRO's own **Lunar and interplanetary missions** along with other scientific projects encourage and promote science education, apart from providing valuable data to the scientific community which in turn enriches science.
- **ISRO** has its headquarters in **Bengaluru**. Its activities are spread across various centres and units.

> - **Launch Vehicles** are built at **Vikram Sarabhai Space Centre** (VSSC), **Thiruvananthapuram.**
> - **Satellites** are designed and developed at **U R Rao Satellite Centre** (URSC), **Bengalure.**
> - **Integration and launching of satellites** and launch vehicles are carried out from **Satish Dhawan Space Centre** (SDSC), **Sriharikota.**
> - **Development** of **liquid stages** including cryogenic stage is carried out at **Liquid Propulsion Systems Centre** (LPSC), **Valiamala & Bengaluru.**
> - **Sensors for Communication** and **Remote Sensing satellites** and application aspects of the space technology are taken up at **Space Applications Centre** (SAC), **Ahmedabad.**
> - **Remote Sensing satellite data reception processing** and **dissemination** is entrusted to **National Remote Sensing Centre** (NRSC), **Hyderabad.**

Vikram Sarabhai Space Centre (VSSC)

- **VSSC** at **Thiruvananthapuram** is the lead centre for the development of satellite launch vehicles and associated technologies.
- The centre pursues research and development in the fields of **aeronautics**; **avionics**; **composites**; **computer** and **information**; control, guidance and simulation; launch vehicle design; mechanical engineering; mechanisms, vehicle integration and testing; propellants, polymers, chemicals and materials; propulsion, propellants; and systems reliability. Programme planning and evaluation, technology transfer and industrial coordination, human resources development, safety and personnel and general administration groups support the centre.

The Major Programmes at VSSC
▪ **Polar Satellite Launch Vehicle** (PSLV)
▪ **Geosynchronous Satellite Launch Vehicle** (GSLV)
▪ **Geosynchronous Satellite Launch Vehicle Mk III** (GSLV Mk III)
▪ **Sounding Rockets, Space-capsule Recovery Experiment, Reusable Launch Vehicles**
▪ **Air Breathing Propulsion.**

ISRO Satellite Centre (ISAC)

- **ISAC,** located at **Bangalore** is the premier Centre for research and development of **satellite systems. ISAC** is carrying out conceptualisation, design, fabrication, testing and integration and in-orbit commissioning of satellite systems through time bound projects.
- **Cutting edge technologies** meeting various mission requirements are developed in the Centre keeping ISAC in the forefront of spacecraft technology frontiers.

ISAC is functionally organized in 7 major areas:
• Mechanical Systems Area
• Mission Development Area
• Communication and Power Systems Area
• Controls and Digital Area
• Integration and Checkout Area
• Systems Production Area
• Reliability and Quality Control Area

- **Electronic and Mechanical fabrication facilities, Environmental test facilities** support the centre in fabrication and testing activities.
- **Programme Planning and Evaluation Group** is responsible for all planning and acts as the

central coordinating agency and technical secretariat of Director of the Centre.

- **Space Astronomy Group** has been involved in optical, X-ray and Gamma ray astronomy research with strong emphasis on instrumentation.
- **Computer & Information Group** is responsible for establishment and management of centralised IT infrastructure in ISAC.
- **Three Programme Management Offices** coordinate the implementation of the INSAT, IRS & small satellites and satellite navigation programmes.

Satish Dhawan Space Centre (SDSC) SHAR

- SDSC SHAR at Sriharikota, with two launch pads, is the main launch centre of ISRO carries out launch operation. The mandate for the centre is :
  - To produce solid propellant boosters for the launch vehicle programmes of ISRO.
  - To provide the infrastructure for qualifying various subsystems & solid rocket motors and carrying out the necessary tests.
  - To provide launch base infrastructure.
  - For assembly, integration and launching of satellite launch vehicles and satellites.

Space Applications Centre (SAC)

- **SAC** at **Ahmedabad** is one of the major centre of ISRO dealing with wide variety of themes from **payload development** to societal applications, thereby creating a synergy of technology, science and societal applications.
- The Centre is responsible for the **development, realisation** and **qualification of communication, navigation, earth observation** and **meteorological payloads** and related data **processing** and **ground systems.**
- The centre carries out development of ground systems and application activities in the areas of **communications, broadcasting, earth observations** for remote sensing of natural resources, weather and environmental studies, disaster monitoring/mitigation,

ISRO Telemetry, Tracking and Command Network (ISTRAC)

- **ISTRAC** provides mission support to **low-earth orbit satellites** as well as launch **vehicle missions.**
- **ISTRAC** has its headquarters and a **multi-mission Spacecraft Control Centre** at **Bangalore**. It has a network of ground stations at **Bangalore, Lucknow, Sriharikota, Port Blair** and **Thiruvananthapuram** in India besides stations at **Mauritius, Tromso** and **Svalbard** (Norway) & **Troll** (Antartica) and **Biak** (Indonesia).
- **ISTRAC** activities are organised into network operations, network augmentation, mission operation and spacecraft health monitoring, communications and computers and control centre facilities and development projects.

National Remote Sensing Centre (NRSC)

- **NRSC** at **Hyderabad** is responsible for **remote sensing satellite data acquisition** and **processing, data dissemination, aerial remote** sensing and decision support for disaster management.
- **NRSC** has a data reception station at **Shadnagar** near **Hyderabad** for acquiring data from Indian remote sensing satellites as well as others. The Centre is also engaged in executing remote sensing application projects in collaboration with the users.
- The **Aerial Services & Digital Mapping** (ASDM) Area provides **end-to-end Aerial Remote Sensing services** and value-added solutions for various large scale applications like aerial photography and **digital mapping, infrastructure planning, scanner surveys, aeromagnetic surveys, large scale base map,** topographic and cadastral level mapping, etc.

Indian Institute of Remote Sensing (Dehradun)

- Indian Institute of Remote Sensing at Dehradun is a premier institute with the objective of capacity building in Remote Sensing and Geo-informatics and their applications through education and training programmes at postgraduate level.
- The Institute also hosts and provides support to the **Centre for Space Science and Technology Education in Asia and the Pacific** (CSSTE-AP), affiliated to the **United Nations**.

National Atmospheric Research Laboratory (NARL)

- NARL at **Gadanki** near **Tirupati** is an autonomous society supported by DOS.
- It is a centre for atmospheric research with facilities like **mesosphere, stratosphere, troposphere radar, LIDAR, lower atmospheric wind profiler, disdrometer, optical rain gauge** and automatic weather station along with associated facilitie.

North Eastern-Space Applications Centre (NE-SAC)

- **NE-SAC**, located at **Shillong**, is a joint initiative of DOS and North Eastern Council to provide support to the North Eastern region in using space science and technology for development.
- The centre has the mandate to develop high technology infrastructure support to enable NE states to adopt space technology inputs for their development.
- At present, NE-SAC is providing developmental support by undertaking specific projects by utilising space technology inputs– remote sensing, satellite communication and space science.

Indian Institute of Space Science and Technology (IIST)

- IIST, an institute of excellence, has been established at **Thiruvananthapuram** during **2007** with the objective of offering high quality education in space science and technology to meet the demands of Indian Space Programme.

ANTRIX

- **Antrix Corporation Limited** (Antrix) is a wholly owned Government of India Company under the administrative control of the **Department of Space**. It was incorporated on **28 September 1992** (under the Companies Act, 1956), as a marketing arm of **ISRO**.
- Antrix promotes and commercially exploits space products, technical services and applications emanating from ISRO.

New Space India Limited (NSIL)

- **New Space India Limited (NSIL)** is a **Public Sector Undertaking** (PSU) of the Government of India under the **Department of Space**. It was established on March 6, 2019, with the objective of **commercializing space technologies** and services. It will not replace ANTRIX, a private limited company owned by Government of India in 1992 as a Marketing arm of ISRO
- NSIL is responsible for the **production, assembly** and **marketing of satellites** and **launch vehicles**. It also provides **space-based services**, such as earth observation, **satellite communication** and **navigation**.
- It is the sole **nodal agency** responsible for providing end-to-end **Small Satellite Launch Vehicle** (SSLV) services.

Indian National Space Promotion and Authorization Centre (IN-SPACe)

- Government has created Indian National Space Promotion and Authorization Centre (INSPACe) to **boost private sector participation** in the entire range of space activities.
- It is the entity of the **Department of Space** which will have its own chairperson and board.
- It will regulate and promote building of routine

satellites, rockets and commercial launch services through Indian industry and startups.

- It will have its own directorates for technical, legal, safety and security, monitoring and activities promotion.
- It will act as an interface between ISRO and private parties, and assess how best to utilize India's space resources and increase space-based activities.
- It will function autonomously and parallel to ISRO. ISRO will remain the basic body that decides what missions are to be undertaken but **INSPACe** will help fill the gaps.

Indian Space Association

- The **Indian Space Association** (ISpA) is an apex industry body, set up to represent, engage and **enable the Indian space ecosystem.** It was founded in **October 2021,** by a group of leading space companies in India.
- The industry association will act as an independent and a **single window** agency for enabling the opening up of the space sector to start-ups and the private sector.
- ISpA will also work towards building global linkages for the Indian space industry to bring in critical technology and investments into the country to create more high-skill jobs.

Four Pillars of Space Reforms via IsPA

- Government acting as on enabler.
- Preparing the next generation.
- Freedom to innovate in private sector
- Space center used as common resource for progress of humanity.

Emergence of Private Space Sector, India

- India has several **MSMEs** (micro, small and medium enterprises), **small-scale industries** and **new players** emerging in the **space manufacturing** and **production supply-chain.**
- At present, the country has over **140 registered space-tech startups, including Skyroot, SatSure, Dhruva Space** and **Bellatrix**, who are working towards creating technologies that have real-world utilities – from **satellite-based phone signals, broadband, OTT** and **5G** to the operation of solar farms and much more.
- Greater private participation in India's space industry with the approval of the **Indian Space Policy 2023** is likely to provide a bigger boost to the Indian space-tech ecosystem in 2023. Initiatives like the **Indian National Space Promotion and Authorization Centre** (IN-SPACe) have already promoted private participation in space activities.
- The future holds a big chair for the **Indian private space industry** to serve the **global market demand** by **delivering low cost** and **reliable space technology.**
- Space-based services are some of the most interesting opportunities that lie for India in the space sector. This is because the increasing number of **satellite constellations** in **low-Earth orbit** has made space-based services like **remote sensing, communication** and **navigation more serviceable** and **affordable.**
- Since constellations provide **global revisits** daily, it becomes possible to **monitor** and **detect changes daily,** and **communicate** to even remote areas without any **terrestrial network infrastructure.**
- The private space industry in India has a great potential to indigenously develop low-cost technology and infrastructure to provide services from space.
- The number of private satellite launches has increased, paving way for private companies to **develop satellite launch vehicles** for carrying small satellites to orbit, in standalone and rideshare missions.

- The private industry in India has the potential to **develop indigenous launch vehicles** providing very low costs of placing satellites in orbit.

India's first privately developed rocket, Vikram-S was successfully launched on **18 November 2022** in a **sub-orbital mission** from the **Sriharikota spaceport** marking a new era in India's space programme.

- **Vikram S rocket** has been developed by Indian space technology startup **Skyroot Aerospace**. It is named after **Vikram Sarabhai**, the founder of **India's space programme.**
- The mission **Prarambh** marks the beginning of a **private venture** into the promising space launch market. **Prarambh mission** is aimed at carrying **three payloads into space**, including a **2.5-kilogram payload** that has been developed by students from several countries.
- The **Prarambh mission** and the **Vikram-S rocket** were developed by the **Hyderabad-based startup** with extensive support from **Indian Space Research Organisation** (ISRO) and **IN-SPACe** (Indian National Space Promotion and Authorisation Centre).

Need for Private sector in Space

- **Technological Advancements :** Private sector firms often have expertise in cutting-edge technologies that can enhance space capabilities, leading to innovations in satellite technology, launch systems, and more.

Example: Antrix Corporation, the commercial arm of ISRO, collaborates with private firms like Pixxel for advanced satellite imaging technology.

- **Cost-Efficiency and Competitive Pricing :** Competition among private space companies can drive down costs for satellite launches and other space-related services, making space technology more accessible.

Example: New Space India Limited (NSIL) facilitates commercial partnerships with private companies for cost-effective launch services.

- **Innovation and Research & Development :** Private companies often have the flexibility and resources to invest in research and development for cutting-edge space technologies.

Example: Team Indus, a private aerospace company, is working on lunar exploration missions, showcasing their innovative capabilities.

- **Job Creation and Economic Growth :** The involvement of private firms in the space sector leads to the creation of jobs and stimulates economic growth, contributing to the overall development of the country.

Example: Companies like Bellatrix Aerospace, working on satellite propulsion technology, are contributing to job creation in the aerospace industry.

- **Indigenization and Reduced Dependency on Imports :** Private sector firms contribute to the goal of indigenization by manufacturing space equipment and reducing dependency on imports.

Example: Companies like Dhruva Space and Bellatrix Aerospace are developing indigenous propulsion systems for satellites, reducing reliance on foreign technology.

- **Encouraging Entrepreneurship and Start-ups:** The space sector provides opportunities for entrepreneurship and innovation, encouraging the growth of start-ups focused on space technology.

Example: Skyroot Aerospace, founded by former ISRO scientists, is a private start-up working on developing launch vehicles.

- **Strategic Alliances and Global Integration :** Private sector companies can form strategic alliances with global space majors, facilitating technology transfer and integration into the global space industry.

Example: Agnikul Cosmos has partnered with international aerospace companies to develop 3D-printed rocket engines.

- **Diversity of Space Services and Applications :** Private sector participation leads to a diverse range of space services, including satellite-based communication, navigation, Earth observation, and more.

Example: One Web, in collaboration with Bharti Global, aims to provide high-speed internet connectivity through a constellation of satellites.

Opportunities in Space Sector for India

- The entire world has been experiencing a **space fervour** since the beginning of the **21st century**. Over the years, **space missions** have become more complex, and the number of interplanetary or deep space missions has increased.
- **Indian space-tech startups** and **international collaborations** are bringing a revolution in the Indian space sector.
- **Space-based internet**, **space manufacturing** and **production, space education and research, satellite launch services, satellite data-based monitoring** and **international collaborations** are the different opportunities for India in the space sector.

According to a joint report by **Ernst & Young** (EY) and the **Indian Space Association** (ISpA), the apex industry body created to be the collective voice of the Indian space industry, the Indian space economy is projected to grow to **$12.8466 billion** by **2025**.

- In **2022**, the value of the **global space economy** reached **$464 billion**. A large portion of the space economy's revenue is used to fund the **satellite-based service sector.**
- India is actively involved in the service based economy, especially in the **digital domain**, and provides such services through satellites.

Through the **New Space Policy**, India aims to **improve the market presence** of the **country's space sector** to **9%** by **2030.**

- A total of **123 space launches** have been made in **2023** so far. Of these, **90** were launched to **low-Earth orbit**, which presents an area of opportunity as our capabilities align seamlessly with the demands of the LEO segment, unlocking an array of new opportunities.

Two broad categories of opportunities for India in the space sector :

- The upcoming field of space-based Internet beckons.
- India's launch infrastructure is poised to support its development.

- This technology promises **global connectivity** that can **revolutionise communication**, data access, and connectivity, propelling India into a pivotal role.
- The demand for **market-ready satellites**, sub-systems and space hardware has increased of late.
- ISRO's latest mission, **PSLV-C56**, launched **seven Singaporean satellites** into **space**, marking another milestone in international collaborations.
- By **collaborating** with the **space industry** in other countries, India can **learn** and **develop new technologies** and **services.**
- India has great potential in joining hands with the **space industry** in the **overseas countries** and jointly **progressing** towards the development of new technology and services that cater to the growing global demand. The talent and low-cost engineering mindset are a prime driver of India's presence in the global industry.
- **Space parks**, which will serve as manufacturing hubs for **space-related technology**, are likely to give a boost to companies operating across the space value chain, especially manufacturing, and will help attract global startups working in the space sector. Space parks will also help incubate space-tech companies in India, and will provide a ready ecosystem for small to medium-sized businesses and startups focused on satellite manufacturing.

Space Sector Reforms

- On **May 16, 2020**, Union Finance Minister **Nirmala Sitharaman** announced that the **Indian private sector** will be a **co-traveller** in India's **space-sector journey** and a **level-playing field** will be provided for them in **satellites, launches,** and **space-based services.** A **predictable policy** and **regulatory environment** will also be provided to private players.
- The future projects for **planetary exploration,** outer space travel and others are to be opened up for the private sector, adding there will be a liberal geo-spatial data policy for providing remote-sensing data to tech-entrepreneurs subject to various checks.
- On **June 24, 2020** the Union Cabinet decided to set up **IN-SPACe**, making ISRO to focus on **research** and **development** (R&D) of new technologies, exploration missions, and human spaceflight programme/Gaganyaan.
- The **IN-SPACe** would provide a **level playing field for private companies** to use Indian space infrastructure. The government also made it clear to ISRO that the fund tap will not be open and the space agency had to show demand for building any commercial satellites.
- As a part of the **reform** and **rejig measure**, the **New Space India Limited** (NSIL)-the new commercial arm of **Department of Space**-was tasked to re-orient space activities from a **supply driven** model to **demand driven** model, thereby ensuring optimum utilisation of the country's space assets.
- Indian space agency transferred its **operational assets/satellites** to NSIL and the latter also selected a consortium to make **five PSLV-XL rockets**. The private space startups also flew their satellites and rockets in **2022**.
- With the Indian space agency's focus shifting to **research and development** (R&D), a **committee** has been set up to recommend the **methodology** for **rightsizing** and **optimal utilisation** of the existing **science and technology** (S&T) manpower.
- **NSIL** has been tasked with the marketing of India's space sector services, including the rocket launch services for satellite players.
- In order to **enhance** the **diffusion of space technology** and **boost space economy** within the country, DOS desires to encourage the **participation** of **private companies** in space activities. ISRO shall complement DOS in its objective of opening up the space sector to private industries. In this regard, the following reforms are proposed in the **mode of execution of space activities** in the country:
    - In order to **enhance utilization** and **maximize benefits** from the space assets, it is proposed to change the approach from **Supply Based Model** to **Demand Based Model. New Space India Limited** (NSIL) will act as the aggregator of user requirements and obtain commitments.
    - NSIL to take **ownership** from DOS for operational launch vehicles, commercialize launches, satellites and services.
    - **Permit NGPE's** to carry out space activities through an **Indian National Space Promotion and Authorization Center** (IN-SPACe).
    - ISRO to carry out **capacity building** in **Space domain** through development of new technologies and capabilities and enable sharing of facilities by NSIL and NGPE's.
    - Announcement of **Opportunities for NGPE's** offering challenges in new domains of technology.

> ISRO is centrally funded and its annual budget is about **Rs. 15,000 crore,** and most of this is used in **building rockets** and **satellites.** To increase the scale of the sector, it is imperative for private players to enter the market. ISRO is planning to **share knowledge** and **technology**, such as **manufacturing rockets** and **satellites**, to all the private players.

- Indian government realised that space technology can be utilised for **boosting business** and economy by **monetisation of space** knowledge and for **employment generation, arresting brain drain**. The government also realised that ISRO has reached a performance saturation stage and infusing funds and personnel may not bring out a significant outcome. Further, the defence sector too needed space technology to a large extent.

> India's share in the **global space commercial activity** is only **2%. Space reforms** are needed to stimulate the **commercial space sector**.

- Indian Government was particular that there should be more private sector participation and appropriate signals should go to the industry. Towards that, a decision was taken to draw a professional outside of ISRO and the **Department of Space** to head the Indian **National Space Promotion and Authorisation Center** (IN-SPACe)- the regulator for private sector space players.

> Accordingly, the government appointed **Dr. Pawan Goenka**, retired MD and CEO of M&M as **IN-SPACe's Chairman**. The Department of Space and ISRO, then headed by K.Sivan began implementing the reform measures.

- Government's aim is to **boost private industry** with **innovation** but at the same time bereft of **backdoor sabotaging, dumping of old technology** and **manipulation** of nascent space industry by established foreign players.
- Indian government brought out many **financial incentives** and **procedure simplifications** as well as formation of **In-SPACe** for encouraging **startups in space technology**. It is a unique approach by the Indian government to rely on startups to bring out a significant upscaling of the Indian space economy.

Significance of Space Missions

- India's aspirations are reflected in its missions to the **Moon, Mars** and the **Sun**. Two of the most recent space Missions of India **Chandrayaan 3** and **Aditya** within restrains of budget aim at asserting it's position by exploring unaccomplished feats.
- **Chandrayaan 3** was successful in projecting it's **Vikram lander** on the **Lunar South Pole**, becoming the **first country** in the world to do so.
- The **Indian Space Research Organization** is also working on **Gaganyaan**, the country's first human space mission scheduled for **2023**. Though many have questioned these ventures on the grounds that India still faces enormous **developmental challenges**, there are several reasons to continue these ventures.
- **First, space exploration** is the **logical next step as India's space program matures** and **gains sophistication. Indian space capabilities** have grown slowly but steadily, with larger boosters and more complex space operations. Further space exploration to gain greater technological competencies would be the next logical step.
- **Second**, while these missions may not have a direct **developmental** or **social benefit**, they increase the **visibility** and **profile** of the Indian **space program** and make it a more attractive partner for collaboration. These missions also demonstrate New Delhi's ability to undertake **complex projects** despite **tiny budgets.** This enhances the attractiveness of India's space launch facilities, which indirectly benefits the **program's revenue stream** and **soft power value.**
- **Third**, undertaking these missions has resulted in **spin-off technological breakthroughs**. For instance, India's deep space communication capabilities are believed to have benefited because of these missions.

- **India's first Moon mission** as well as the **Mangalyaan mission** for deep space communication functions were assisted by **NASA**. Together, these missions and developments are seen as important credentials for India to gain a louder voice on global governance of outer space.
- India's space missions have garnered **global recognition** for their **ability** to achieve **significant results** with relatively **modest budgets**, with satellite launches costing considerably less than the budgets of most mainstream Hollywood films.
- **Mangalyaan project** was approved in **2011** and implemented in just two years and was launched in **2013** with a budget of **$74 million**. Even **Chandrayaan 1**, India's mission to the Moon that resulted in the discovery of water, was announced in **2003** and successfully launched by **2008**.
- The establishment of the **Integrated Space Cell** in **2010** was a small yet important step in creating greater coordination between the **Department of Space** and the **Indian Armed Forces**, as well as in generating a common understanding of the emerging threats that India faces. The **Defence Space Agency**, set up in **2018**, may be a similar baby step as a forerunner to a full-fledged aerospace command, which the armed forces have demanded for more than two decades.
- **China's anti-satellite** (ASAT) test in **January 2007** was a wake-up call about the potential threats India faces, and it prompted a new debate within India about how it should protect its space assets. From this debate emerged a unanimous view across the political, military, and scientific bureaucracy that India needed to develop an appropriate response in order to deter any attacks on its own space assets.
- **ASAT** was suceesfully tested in **March 2019** as a recognition that India's long-held belief in strengthening **global governance** of outer space was either not going to bear fruit or would be insufficient to protect its interests. It provided credible deterrence against threats to our growing space-based assets from long range missiles.
- India also is building partnerships with other states to **counter China's prowess**. New Delhi has established or strengthened space security partnerships not only with the **Quadrilateral Security Dialogue** (the Quad, which also includes the United States, Japan, Australia), but also with France and others.
- While its **bilateral partnerships** with **Japan**, **France**, and the United States have involved both civil and security developments, the Quad as a group has also **emphasized consultations** on norms of **responsible behavior** and **regulations**, with an eye clearly on China.
- Despite India's reluctance, New Delhi should consider joining the **U.S.-led Artemis Accords**, the bilateral agreements between **Washington** and **participant countries**, based on key principles enshrined in the **Outer Space Treaty** of **1967** for safe, secure, and **transparent exploration** of the Moon.
- India has not endorsed the accords possibly because it is not a multilateral agreement created under a UN umbrella. Nevertheless, it offers an important opportunity to review lunar activities as well as develop norms and standards for lunar activities around themes such as information sharing, interoperability, and lunar governance measures.
- In reality, India has **no realistic alternative** to the **Artemis Accords**; the **International Lunar Research Station** being developed by **China** and **Russia** is simply not a viable option for India, considering the state of India's relations with China.

- With the growing perception of **space security threats from China** and a desire to enhance **India's space capabilities** and **influence in global governance of space**, New Delhi is likely to press ahead with its ambitious space goals in the coming years. This will lead India to focus on **technology development** while also developing and **nurturing space security partnerships** with like-minded countries in the **Indo-Pacific**.
- Compared to ISRO's mission to Mars **NASA's Mars Atmosphere and Volatile Evolution** (MAVEN) spacecraft, which was also launched in 2013 cost the agency **$671 million**.
- Satellite-based systems are **reducing vehicles' carbon dioxide emissions, remote-sensing technology** is making wind turbines more efficient, and information from **weather satellites** is helping **solar cells** to produce more energy.
- Satellites provide more **accurate information** on **weather forecasts** and **assess** (and record) **long-term trends** in the climate and **habitability** of a region.
- Additionally, they can also serve as **real-time monitoring** and **early-warning solutions** against **natural disasters** such as **earthquakes, tsunamis, floods, wildfires, mining** etc.
- Scientists are battling to continue the **Global Ecosystem Dynamics Investigation** (GEDI), slated to be decommissioned in **March 2023**.
- The emergence of **cutting-edge technology** like **Space 2.0 systems** and other developments like **artificial intelligence** (AI), the **IoT, 5G,** and **robotics** adds to the fight against climate change's potential.
- **Better monitoring:** Under the joint mission, NISAR - both ISRO and NASA are working to co-develop and launch a satellite that would **monitor groundwater** supplies and provide early warning indications of volcanic **eruptions**. It will also **monitor ice sheet melting rates** and their **impact on sea-level rise**. The Earth satellite will be the first radar imaging satellite to use dual frequencies and keep track of vegetation distribution changes across countries.
- **Track weather patterns: Ice, Cloud,** and **Land Elevation Satellite-2** (ICESat-2) was launched by NASA in 2018. It depicted **sea ice thinning** and the **disappearance** of ice cover along the coasts of **Greenland** and **Antarctica**. NASA's newest satellite was created to offer additional data on how ice cover fluctuates throughout the year.
- **Assisting farmers:** Sectors including agriculture and industry can benefit from satellite imagery and climate data and the communities they serve. Such data can be utilised to assist farmers in increasing agricultural yields, hence reducing hunger, combating unregulated mining and its consequences, and uncovering new economic growth potential.
- Satellite data helps to **monitor vehicle emissions.**
- A fleet of commercial communication satellites, are operating over India with communication transponders in **C-band, Extended C-band, Ku-band** and **S-band**. These transponders support the services like **television, telecommunication, radio networking, strategic communication** and **societal applications.**
- The prominent users of the **transponders** are **BSNL, Doordarshan, All India Radio, strategic govt. users, public sector units, private VSAT operators, DTH and TV operators, banking** and **financial institutions, etc.**
- Under societal applications, ISRO/DOS has supported programmes like **Telemedicine, Tele-education** and **Disaster Management Support** (DMS) **Programmes** which are solely national development oriented with an aim to address specific requirements at different strata of the society.

Space Tourism

- Space tourism is space travel for **recreational, leisure or business purposes.** There are several different types of space tourism, including **orbital, suborbital and lunar space tourism.**
- To date, orbital space tourism has been performed only by the **Russian Aviation** and **Space Agency- Roscosmos.**
- Several private spaceflight companies are now working towards developing **suborbital space tourism vehicles** to take paying customers to space.
- To send a vehicle to space, it is compulsory for the national and international space law to authorize it according to **Article VI of the Outer Space Treaty.** However, there is **lack of clarity** on **authorization of space travel** with tourists aboard.

No international space law has defined space tourists. Existing space treaties such as **Outer Space Treaty, Rescue Agreement** etc. are only applicable to astronauts, envoys of mankind, or personnel of a spacecraft.

Karman Line and Space Definition

- The Karman line is an internationally accepted boundary that defines where **Earth's atmosphere** ends and **outer space begins.**

According to the **FAI**, the Karman line is located at an altitude of **100 kilometers** (62 miles) above the Earth's surface.

- At this altitude, atmospheric lift is no longer sufficient to support the flight of an object. Beyond this point, an object must reach orbital velocity to remain in space; otherwise, it would start falling back to Earth.

Space Travel and the Karman Line

- Space travel, as defined by the FAI, involves flight operations that take passengers or objects beyond the altitude of 100 km (Karman line) and into space.

	Suborbital tourism	Orbital tourism
Altitude	**About 100 km**	**Over 400 km**
Duration in space	Gives passengers a few minutes in space	Spend days or even more than a week in space.
Velocity	**Sub-Orbital :** • Requires much lower speeds (than orbital) and doesn't have the power to achieve orbit. • Instead, it will fly up to a certain height and then come back down once its engines are shut off.	**Orbital :** Spacecraft must achieve orbital velocity i.e. the speed that on object must maintain to remain in orbit around a planet.

NASA's Space Missions

ARTEMIS I

- **Artemis I** is **first uncrewed mission in NASA's Artemis program**, which aims to return humans to the Moon by **2025**. The mission launched on **November 16, 2022**, atop the **Space Launch System** (SLS) rocket.
- The mission's primary goal was to test the **SLS** and **Orion spacecraft** in a **lunar orbit**. Orion completed one flyby of the Moon on **November 21**, entered a distant retrograde orbit for six days, and completed a second flyby of the Moon on **December 5**. The mission was a success, and it paved the way for Artemis II, which will be the first crewed mission to the Moon in over 50 years.

Objective: To build a long term human presence at the Moon.
With Artemis, NASA is planning to land the first woman on the Moon.

Artemis-1
Space Launch System (SLS) rocket : • The most powerful rocket in the world. • Designed specifically for deep space missions with humons.
The Orion spacecraft : • A designed to carry astronouts to deep space. • Currently the only spacecraft capable of crowed deep space flight and high speed return from the vicinity of the moon.
Ground systems of Kennedy Space Centre, Florida : • To develop and operate the systems and facilities necessary to process, assemble and launch rockets and spacecraft.

Major Objectives of ARTEMIS

- **Demonstrate Orion's heat shield** can withstand the **high speed** only and **high heat conditions** when returning through Earth's atmosphere.
- Study the radiation environment of deep space
- Retrieving orion after splashdown
- Accomplish flight test objectives like certifying Orion's optical navigation system, deploying cube sats.
- Study the Moon to learn more about the origin and history Earth, the Moon, and our solar system.

Retrograde Orbit

- A retrograde orbit is an orbit that goes against the direction of rotation of the body it is orbiting.
- The **Moon** rotates **counterclockwise**, so a **retrograde orbit** would be **clockwise**. After getting closer to the moon, the Orion spacecraft used the gravitational kick to enter a so-called **distant retrograde orbit**.
- The reason why Orion entered a distant retrograde orbit is because it is a stable orbit that requires less fuel to maintain. It is also a good orbit for testing Orion's systems and for collecting data on the Moon's environment.

James Webb Space Telescope

- The **James Webb Space Telescope** (JWST) is NASA's **infrared flagship observatory.** It is an international collaboration between **NASA,** the **European Space Agency** (ESA), and the **Canadian Space Agency** (CSA). It was formerly called the **Next Generation Space Telescope**.
- NASA's James Webb Telescope launched on December 25, 2021 on an Ariane 5 rocket from Europe's Spaceport in French Guiana, on the northern coast of South America.
- James Webb Telescope studies every phase in the history of our Universe, ranging from the first luminous glows after the Big Bang, to the formation of solar systems capable of supporting life on planets like Earth, to the evolution of our own Solar System.
- It does not orbit around the Earth like the Hubble Space Telescope, it orbits the Sun 1.5 million kilometers (1 million miles) away from the Earth at what is called the second Lagrange point or L2.
- Observations from NASA's James Webb Space Telescope have provided a surprising twist in the narrative surrounding what is believed to be the first star observed in the act of swallowing a planet. The new findings suggest that the star actually did not swell to envelop a planet as previously hypothesized. Instead, Webb's observations show the planet's orbit shrank over time, slowly bringing the planet closer to its demise until it was engulfed in full.
- In June 2023, For the first time, James Webb Space Telescope captured bright auroral activity on Neptune.

- Auroras occur when energetic particles, often originating from the Sun, become trapped in a planet's magnetic field and eventually strike the upper atmosphere. The energy released during these collisions creates the signature glow.

- **Four main Instruments of James Webb Telescope**
  - **Near-Infrared Camera** (NIRCam) to image the universe in near-infrared light.
  - **Near-Infrared Spectrograph** (NIRSpec) to study the chemical composition of objects in the universe.
  - **Mid-Infrared Instrument** (MIRI) to image the universe in mid-infrared light.
  - **Fine Guidance Sensor** (FGS) to help JWST to point accurately at its targets.

- **Objectives** :
  - **Search for first galaxies** or **luminous objects** formed after **Big Bang.**
  - Determine how galaxies evolved.
  - Observe stars formation from the first stages to formation of planetary systems
  - **Measure physical** and **chemical properties** of **planetary systems**, including our own **Solar System**, and **investigate potential** for **life** in those systems.

- The **James Webb Space Telescope** (JWST) is destined for a spot called **Sun-Earth Lagrange Point 2** (L2), a stable location in space.

Advantages of point L2

- Spacecraft can communicate with earth.
- Can observe the universe without chances of eclipse : clear view of deep space.
- Solar power from the sun behind it.
- JWST is expected to have a lifespan of about 10 years. However, it is possible that it could last longer, depending on how well it is maintained.

- JWST is being considered as the next-generation successor to the **Hubble Space Telescope** (HST), building upon its legacy of exploring the universe.

How JWST will help in advancing understanding of Universe :

- **Early Universe :** JWST will allow us to see galaxies just 100 million years after Big Bang.
- **Exoplanets :** JWST will scan atmospheres of earth-like exoplants, searching for gases associated with life.
- **Outer Planets :** Will monitor Jupiter, Saturn, Uranus and Nepture to see how their atmosphere change over time.
- **Small Worlds :** From the asteroid belt to Kuiper belt, JWST will determine what makes up some of our solar system's smallest objects.

OBSERVATIONS MADE BY JWST

- New images of Jupiter presented its massive storms, colourful auroras, faint rings and two small moons — Amalthea and Adrastea (Nearer to Jupiter).

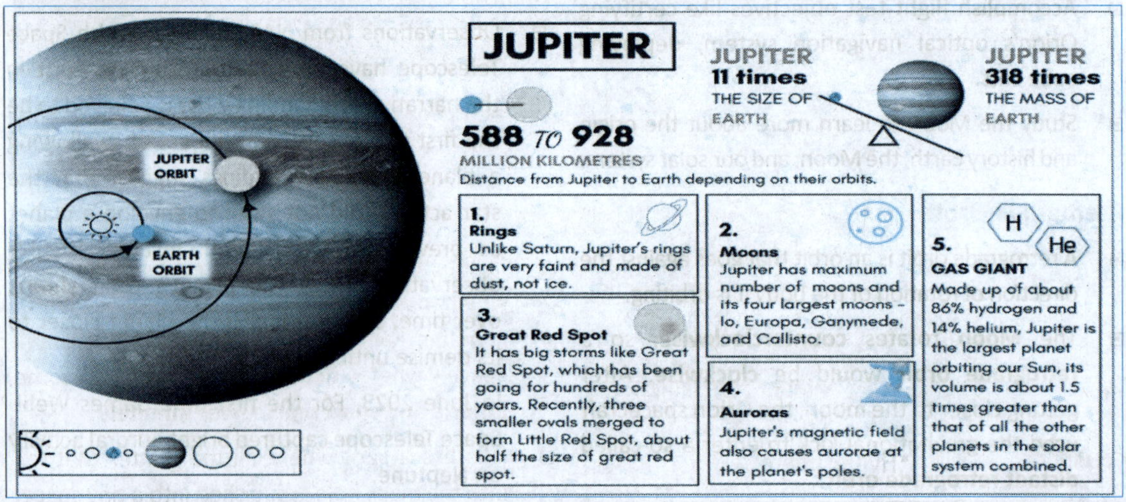

Parker Space Probe

- The **Parker Solar Probe** is a **NASA** spacecraft that is **studying the Sun's atmosphere**, or **corona.**

The Parker Solar Probe was launched on **August 12, 2018**, and is expected to complete its mission in **2025**. During its mission, the probe will make **24 flybys of the Sun**, getting as close as **9.86 solar radii** (4.3 million miles) from the **Sun's surface.**

- It is the **first spacecraft to fly into the corona** and is the **fastest human-made object** ever built.
- The probe is named after **Eugene Parker**, a solar physicist who first theorized the existence of the solar wind. It is part of **NASA's Living with a Star program** to explore aspects of the Sun-Earth system.
- It uses a **carbon-composite shield**, to withstand temperatures nearly **2,500 F** (1,377 C), to protect itself from Sun's heat.
- It became the **first spacecraft** in history to **touch the Sun**. It uses a series of **gravitational encounters** with the planet Venus to gradually lower the orbit of the spacecraft until it enters the outer atmosphere, or corona, of the Sun.

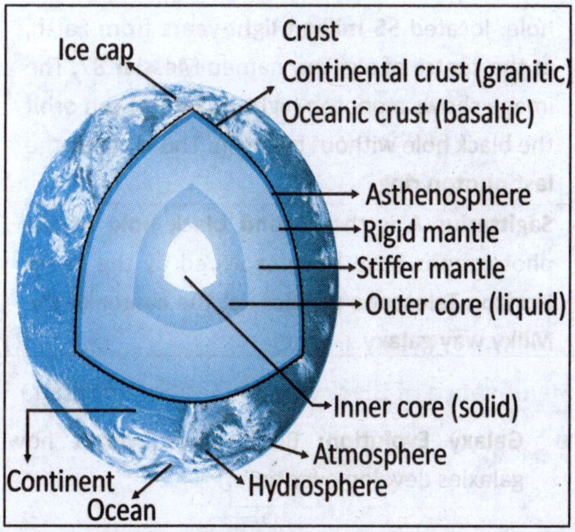

Relevance of PSP

- Deeper insights into sun's evolution.
- Predicting extreme weather events by helping in forecasting solar storms(or Geomagnetic storm).
- Solar storms are the biggest outbursts from the Sun can rattle Earth's magnetic field. In the process:
  - Communications may be disrupted,
  - Satellites can be knocked offline
  - Power grids will be vulnerable to electrical surges.

SPACE SCIENCE RELATED CONCEPTS

Black Hole

- A **black hole** is a **region in space** where the **gravitational pull** is so strong that nothing, not even light, can escape from it. This makes it **invisible** to the **naked eye** and challenging to study directly (Because no light can get out, so they are invisible).

- **Black hole** is a place in space where **gravity pulls** so much that even light cannot get out. The gravity is so strong because matter has been squeezed into a tiny space.
- In the **center of a black hole** is a **gravitational singularity**, a **one dimensional point** which contains a huge mass in an **infinitely small** space, where **density** and **gravity** become **infinite** and **spacetime curves infinitely.**
- It is like a spot where all the matter that fell into the black hole is squished into a tiny space.

This point is so tiny and so heavy that it has an enormously powerful gravitational pull. It's a place of immense curiosity and mystery, as our current understanding of physics can't fully describe what happens there.

Gravity
• Gravity can be understood in two types - **1.** Gravity as a force **2.** Gravity as bending of space time. **Gravity as bending of space time -** • Gravity is what makes things with mass pull toward each other. It's why objects fall when you drop them and why planets orbit stars. Imagine a heavy ball placed on a soft mattress. The mattress bends under the weight of the ball, and if you roll a smaller ball nearby, it will roll towards the bigger ball because of the bending of the mattress. This bending of space caused by mass is what we experience as gravity.

Parts of Black hole

- **Accretion Disc:** Rotating gas and dust spiraling into a black hole, emitting X-rays. **Accretion disc** of superheated gas and dust whirls around black hole at immense speeds, producing electromagnetic radiation (x-rays).
- **Singularity:** Ultra-dense point at a black hole's center where physics changes. The very centre of a black hole where matter has collapsed in a region of infinite density.
- **Event Horizon:** Invisible boundary around a black hole, trapping everything. The radius around a singularity where matter and energy cannot escape the black hole's gravity. The point of no return.
- **Schwarzschild Radius:** The Schwarzschild radius is the distance from the center of a black hole to its event horizon.
- **Ergo Sphere:** Region around a spinning black hole where space drags along with it.
- **Relativistic Jet :** When stars are absorbed by black holes, jets of particles and radiation are blasted out at near light speed.
- **Photon sphere :** Photons emitted from hot plasma near the black their trajectory producing a bright ring.

Categories of Black Hole

- **Stellar :** Formed by the grovitational collapse of a star, Masses ranging from about 5 to several tens of 5 solar masses.
- **Supermassive :** The largest type of black hole, containing a mass of the order of hundreds of thousdands, to billions of times, the mass of the Sun.
- **Intermediate-mass :** Mass in range $10^2 - 10^5$ solar masses, significantly more than stellar black holes but less than 10^5–10^9 solar mass supermassive black holes.
- **Miniture :** Approximately 148 fm, Hypothetical tiny black holes, for which quantum mechanical efforts play an important role, The concept that black holes may exist that are smaller than stellar mass was introduced in 1971 by famous astrophysicist Stephen Howking.

In **2019,** scientists got the **first optical image of a black hole** through **Event Horizon Telescope.** It has captured the just outside region of a black hole, located **55 million light-years** from Earth, at the centre of a galaxy named **Messier 87**. The image shows a photon (light quantum) can orbit the black hole without falling in. This is called the **last photon ring.**
Sagittarius A is the **second black hole** whose photographs have been captured by the **Event Horizon Telescope project :** at the center of the **Milky way galaxy.**

Significance of Black Hole in Space Research

- **Galaxy Evolution:** Black holes impact how galaxies develop over time.

- **Dark Matter Distribution:** Black hole surroundings help us understand the spread of dark matter.
- **Creating Stars:** Gas around black holes triggers the birth of new stars.
- **Einstein's general theory:** test the predictions of Einstein's general theory of relativity.
- **Gravity Waves:** Black holes generate gravitational waves that we can detect.
- **Bending of Light:** Light bending behind black holes shows their strong gravity.

Gravitational Waves

- Gravitational waves are produced by **cataclysmic events** such as **colliding black holes, supernovae** (massive stars exploding at the end of their lifetimes), and colliding neutron stars. They travel at the speed of light, squeezing and stretching anything in their path. Gravitational Waves were detected for the first time in the **LIGO: Laser Interferometer Gravitational Wave Observatory.**

Gravitational waves are created when

- A star explodes asymmetrically (called a supernova).
- Two big stars orbit each other.
- Objects move at very high speeds.
- Two black holes orbit each other and merge.

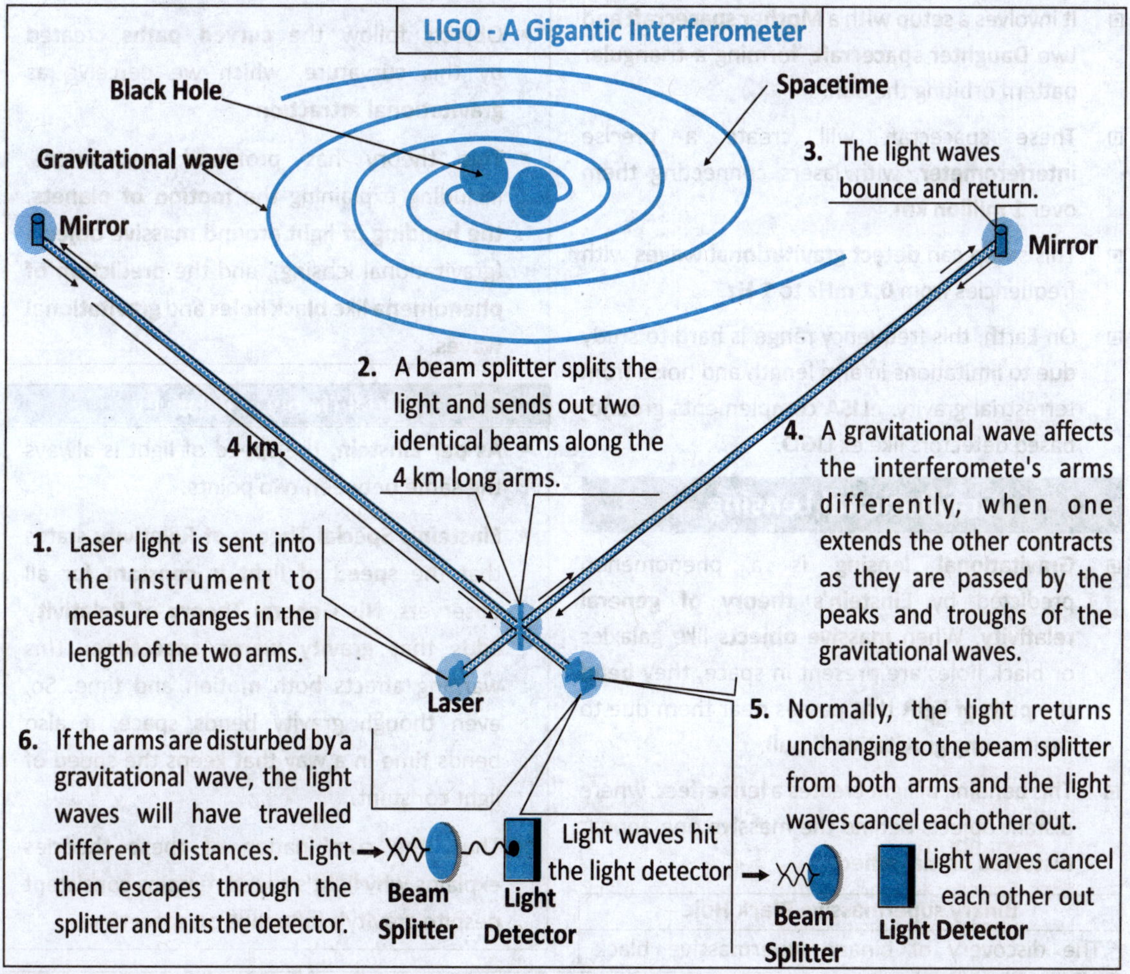

- LIGO (Laser Interferometer Gravitational-Wave Observatory) is a scientific project designed to detect and study gravitational waves. LIGO uses a setup with **two perpendicular arms**, each several kilometers long. When a gravitational wave passes through, it slightly stretches one arm while compressing the other, and vice versa. This minute change is measured with high-precision lasers.

The first direct detection of gravitational waves was made by **LIGO** in **2015**, confirming **Einstein's theory**.

E-Lisa

- The mission of eLISA is to **explore gravitational waves** from space, a **first-time endeavor.**
- It involves a setup with a **Mother spacecraft** and two **Daughter spacecraft**, forming a triangular pattern orbiting the Sun.
- These spacecraft will create a precise **interferometer**, with lasers connecting them over **1 million km.**
- This setup can **detect gravitational waves** with frequencies from **0.1 mHz** to **1 Hz.**
- On Earth, this frequency range is hard to study due to limitations in arm length and noise from terrestrial gravity. **eLISA** complements ground-based detectors like ex **LIGO.**

Gravitational Lensing

- **Gravitational lensing** is a phenomenon predicted by **Einstein's theory of general relativity.** When **massive objects** like galaxies or black holes are present in space, they **bend** the **path of light** that passes near them due to their **strong gravitational pull.**
- This bending of light creates a **lens effect,** where distant objects behind the massive one appear **distorted** or **magnified.**

Binary supermassive Black Hole

The discovery of binary supermassive black hole systems was made possible through the phenomenon of **gravitational lensing of blazars.**

- **Blazars** are incredibly bright and energetic objects, ranking among the most powerful in the cosmos.
- This finding holds significance because it enhances our ability to detect gravitational waves in the future.

General Theory of Relativity

- Albert Einstein's general theory of relativity says that **gravity** is a **result of the curvature** of **spacetime** caused by **mass** and **energy.**
- In this theory, massive objects, such as planets and **stars, warp** the fabric of spacetime around them.
- Objects follow the **curved paths** created by this curvature, which we perceive as **gravitational attraction.**
- This theory has profound implications, including explaining the **motion of planets, the bending of light around massive objects** (gravitational lensing), and the **prediction of phenomena** like **black holes** and **gravitational waves.**

Special Theory of Relativity

- **As per Einstein,** the speed of light is always the same between two points.
- **Einstein's Special Theory of Relativity** states that the **speed of light is constant** for all observers. **His General Theory of Relativity** adds that **gravity warps spacetime.** This warping affects both motion and time. So, even though gravity bends space, it also bends time in a way that keeps the speed of light constant.
- Thus, the combination of these theories explains why light's speed remains consistent despite gravity's influence on spacetime.

Solar Flares

- A solar flare is a **sudden** and **intense burst** of **radiation** from the sun. It is caused by the release of **magnetic energy** in the sun's atmosphere.

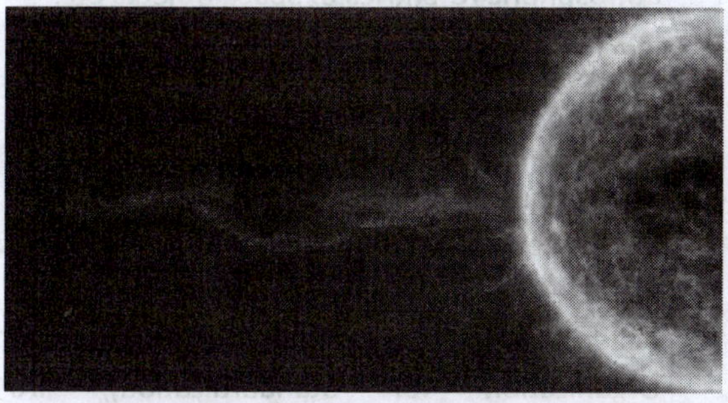

- **Solar magnetic cycle** that works in **deep interior** of Sun creates **regions** that rise to surface and appear like **dark spots**. These are sunspots. They appear dark because they are cooler than other parts of the Sun's surface.
- In a **solar flare**, energy stored in the sun's **magnetic structures** is converted into light and **heat energy.** This causes emission of high **energy x-ray radiation** and highly accelerated charged particles to leave the sun's surface.
- Sometimes solar flares also cause hot plasma to be ejected from the Sun, causing a solar storm, and this is called **Coronal Mass Ejection (CME).**
- The energy, radiation, and high-energy particles released during solar flares can initiate vibrant lights in the sky known as auroras.
- **Auroras** result from the interplay of **energetic electrons** and **protons** from the solar wind with upper atmospheric atoms. This interaction predominantly occurs at high latitudes in both the Northern and Southern Hemispheres.
- In the **Northern Hemisphere**, these auroras are referred to as aurora borealis, aurora polaris, or northern lights. In the Southern Hemisphere, they are known as **aurora australis, or southern lights.**

Solar flare classification	Possible effects of Earth
B	None
C	Possible effects on space missions.
M	Blackout in radio transmissions and possible damages in astronauts outside spacecraft.
X	Damage to satellites, communication systems, power distribution stations and electronic equipment.

Solar Cycle

- The Sun's magnetic field undergoes a complete reversal approximately **every 11 years**.
- Scientists monitor this phenomenon using **sunspots.**
- The start of a new solar cycle is marked by a phase known as **solar minimum,** characterized by fewer sunspots and reduced solar activity.

SPACE DEBRIS

- Space debris encompasses both **natural** (meteoroid) and **artificial** (man-made) particles.
- **Meteoroids** are in orbit about the sun, while most **artificial debris** is in orbit about the Earth which is commonly referred to as orbital debris.

> **Example-** Recently **China rocket debris** fell in **Indian Ocean** near **Maldives.** Even **Chandrayaan-3** lift off was delayed by a minute.

- Much of the debris is in low Earth orbit (LEO), though some debris can be found in geostationary orbit.
- There are about **500,000 pieces of debris** the size of a marble or larger orbiting the Earth, travelling at speeds up to **17,500 mph.**
- **International guidelines** suggest removing space crafts from **LEO** within **25 years** of the end of their mission. However, only 60 percent of missions follow the guidelines.

- Various countries, including Germany, France, the UK, and the USA, track space debris using radar and other technologies to monitor its trajectories and potential collision risks.

India's Space Debris Management / Mitigation Programme

- ISRO System for Safe and sustainable **Space Operations Management** (IS4OM) has been established to focus all efforts related to spaceflight safety and debris mitigation and for dealing with the emerging challenges in operating in a congested space environment.
- **Network for Space object :** Tracking and Analysis (NETRA) has been approved by GOI for SSA capacity building.
- **Project NETRA (Network for Space Object Tracking and Analysis) :** An early warning system in space, launched in December 2019, to detect debris and other hazards to Indian satellites, with a network of observational facilities, including optical telescopes, radars and a command centre at Chandrapur, Assam.
- ISRO adheres to the internationally accepted space debris mitigation guidelines recommended by UN -COPOUS and Inter-Agency Space Debris Coordination Committee (IADC) to the maximum possible extent.
- For all Indian launch vehicles, Collision Avoidance Analysis (COLA) is performed to select collision threat-free lift-off time within the launch window. Continual assessments of any close approach risk to ISRO's operational satellites are carried out and Collision Avoidance Manoeuvres (CAM) are performed as and when needed.
- In case the object posing close approach risk is another active satellite, the required coordination is carried out with the owner/ operator so that only one of the satellites performs the CAM.
- Continual efforts to improve the operational methodologies for close approach assessment are pursued to adapt to the challenges posed by the surging space traffic, apart from modelling on-orbit break-up events and prediction of atmospheric re-entries of space objects etc.
- ISRO contributes substantially to shaping the pertinent guidelines and recommendations for sustainable use of space as an active member of various international agencies dealing with safety and sustainability of outer space activities, such as IADC, IAA (International Academy of Astronautics, ISO (International Organization for Standardization), IAF (International Astronautical Federation), UN Long Term Sustainability Working Group.
- The Indian Space Policy places significant importance in space debris mitigation requirements and SSA capacity building.
- The recently unveiled Debris Free Space Mission (DFSM) initiative is also spearheaded by ISRO with an aim to achieve debris-free space missions by all Indian space actors, both governmental and non-governmental, by 2030. The initiative aligns with global efforts for space sustainability, positioning India as a nation prioritizing safety, security, and sustainability in outer space activities.
- **Avoiding future debris:** by adopting better designs of rockets and other objects. For example, making rockets reusable could vastly cut down waste.
- **UK's TechDemoSat-1** (TDS-1), was designed in such a way that once its mission is over, a system, would drag the satellite to re-enter the atmosphere and burn up.
- **Removal of the debris:**
  - **End-of-Life Services by Astroscale Demonstration (Elsa-D)** is a Japanese-led mission that was launched in 2021. It is the world's first commercial mission to

demonstrate the technologies needed to remove space debris.

- **Remove Debris:** Remove Debris is a European Union project that was launched in 2014. It is the first project to demonstrate a range of technologies for removing space debris from orbit.

▣ **Key technology demonstrations:**

- **Net Capture**: Deploying a net to capture a target satellite or debris.
- **Harpoon Capture:** Using a harpoon to capture and secure debris.
- **Vision-Based Navigation:** Demonstrating computer vision technology for precise navigation.
- **Deorbit Sail:** Deploying a sail to increase atmospheric drag and accelerate deorbit.

SPACE SUSTAINABILITY

▣ **United Nations Office of Outer SPACE Affairs** and the government of **AUSTRIA** organized the **World Space Forum (WSF) 2022** under the theme **Sustainability in Space for sustainability on Earth.**

▣ **World Space Forum** is a platform to promote discussions on the role of space science and technology in global sustainable development. Space sustainability ensures that all humanity can continue to use outer space for peaceful purposes.

Challenges to space sustainability

▣ **Orbital crowding** and Space Debris.

▣ **Militarisation** and **weaponization** of the space: **Antisatellite** (ASAT) weapons by countries like US, Russia, China, and India.

▣ **Rendezvous** and **proximity operations** (RPO): It involves altering the trajectory of one or more space objects to bring them into proximity to each other.

▣ Space weather can impact satellite

Global Initiatives

▣ U.N. Office for Outer Space Affairs (UNOOSA).

▣ Conference on Disarmament (CD): international forum with focus on prevention of an arms race in outer space (PAROS).

▣ Guidelines on space sustainability : by UNCOPOUS

▣ Space Sustainability Rating (SSR)

▣ ASAT test-ban resolution: A non-binding resolution (India abstained) passed by United Nations General Assembly (UNGA) calling for a ban on kinetic ASAT tests.

Indian Initiatives

▣ **Space Situational Awareness** : necessary mitigation measures to safeguard assets. It involves :

- SST : space surveillance and tracking
- Space Weather monitoring
- Near earth objects monitoring

▣ **Project NETRA**

▣ **Digantra :** space sector startup is going to set up India's first commercial SSA observatory.

▣ India-USA bilateral SSA agreement.

▣ **SPADEX :** in orbit servicing platform by ISRO.

COPOUS oversees 5 international treaties underpinning space law :

- **Outer Space Treaty :** It provides the basic framework on international space law such as the peaceful use of space, and the basic responsibility and liability of state for launching space.
- **Rescue Agreement :** It provides that states shall take all possible stemps to rescue and assist astronauts in distress and promptly return them to the launching state.
- **Liability Convention :** It provides for absolute liability on the part of a launching state to pay compensation for damage caused by its space objects.

- **Registration Convention :** It lays down the rules applicable for the registration fo space objects, and the open and free access of these registers.
- **Moon Agreement :** It provides that the Moon and its natural resources are the common heritage of mankind.

Important Termology

- **Transponder :** A transponder, short form of **transmitter-responder** is a key component used in various communication and **navigation systems**, including satellites. It plays a fundamental role in **relaying signals** and **information** between **different points,** often between **ground stations** and **satellites.**
- Big Bang is also called expanding universe hypothesis. It states that all of the current and past matter in the Universe came into existence at the same time, roughly 13.8 billion years ago.
- **Kessler Syndrome :** It explains the process where a single collision could trigger a **chain reaction of debris.**

PYQ (2013 – 2024)

Q. With reference to 'Astrosat', the astronomical observatory launched by India, which of the following statements is/are correct?

1. Other than the USA and Russia, India is the only country to have launched a similar observatory into space.
2. Astrosat is a 2000 kg satellite placed in an orbit at 1650 km above the surface of the Earth.

Select the correct answer using the code given below

(a) 1 only (b) 2 Only

(c) Both 1 and 2 (d) Neither 1 nor 2

Q. Consider the following statements:

The Mangalyaan launched by ISRO -

1. Is also called the Mars Orbiter Mission
2. Made India the second country to have a spacecraft orbit Mars after the USA
3. Made India the only country to be successful in making its spacecraft orbits Mars in its very first attempt.

Which of the statements given above is/are correct?

(a) 1 only (b) 2 and 3 only

(c) 1 and 3 only (d) 1, 2 and 3

Q. What is the purpose of 'evolved Laser Interferometer Space Antenna (eLISA)' project? (2017)

(a) To detect neutrinos

(b) To detect gravitational waves

(c) To detect the effectiveness of missile defence system

(d) To study the effect of solar flares on our communication systems

Q. The terms 'Event Horizon', 'Singularity', `String Theory' and 'Standard Model' are sometimes seen in the news in the context of (2017)

(a) Observation and understanding of the Universe

(b) Study of the solar and the lunar eclipses

(c) Placing satellites in the orbit of the Earth

(d) Origin and evolution of living organisms on the Earth

Q. With reference to the Indian Regional Navigation Satellite System (IRNSS), consider the following statements : (2018)

1. IRNSS has three satellites in geostationary and four satellites in geosynchronous orbits.
2. IRNSS covers entire India and about 5500 sq. km beyond its borders.
3. India will have its own satellite navigation system with full global coverage by the middle of 2019.

Which of the statements given above is/are correct?

(a) 1 only (b) 1 and 2 only

(c) 2 and 3 only (d) None

Q. Consider the following phenomena : (2018)

1. Light is affected by gravity.
2. The Universe is constantly expanding.
3. Matter warps its surrounding space-time.

Which of the above is/are the prediction/ predictions of Albert Einstein's General Theory of Relativity, often discussed in media?

(a) 1 and 2 only (b) 3 only

(c) 1 and 2 (d) 1, 2 and 3

Q. In which of the following areas can GPS technology be used? 2018

1. Mobile phone operations
2. Banking operations
3. Controlling the power grids

Select the correct answer using the code given below:

(a) 1 only (b) 2 and 3 only

(c) 1 and 3 only (d) 1, 2 and 3

Q. With reference to India's satellite launch vehicles, consider the following statements: (2018)

1. PSLVs launch the satellites useful for Earth resources monitoring whereas GSLVs are designed mainly to launch communication satellites.
2. Satellites launched by PSLV appear to remain permanently fixed in the same position in the sky, as viewed from a particular location on Earth.
3. GSLV Mk III is a four-staged launch vehicle with the first and third stages using solid rocket motors; and the second and fourth stages using liquid rocket engines.

Which of the following given above is correct ?

(a) Only 1 (b) 2 and 3

(c) 1 and 2 (d) 3 only

Q. Recently, scientists observed the merger of giant 'blackholes' billions of light-years away from the Earth. What is the significance of this observation? (2019)

(a) 'Higgs boson particles' were detected.

(b) 'Gravitational waves' were detected.

(c) Possibility of intergalactic space travel through 'wormhole' was confirmed.

(d) It enabled the scientists to understand 'singularity'.

Q. "The experiment will employ a trio of spacecraft flying in formation in the shape of an equilateral triangle that has sides one million kilometres long, with lasers shining between the craft". The experiment in question refers to 2020

(a) Voyager (b) New Horizons

(c) LISA Pathfinder (d) Evolved LISA

Q. Which one of the following is a reason why astronomical distances are measured in light-years? (2021)

(a) Distances among stellar bodies do not change.

(b) Gravity of stellar bodies does not change.

(c) Light always travels in a straight line.

(d) Speed of light is always the same.

Q. If a major solar storm (solar flare) reaches the Earth, which of the following are the possible effects on the Earth? (2022)

1. GPS and navigation systems could fail.
2. Tsunamis could occur at equatorial regions.
3. Power grids could be damaged.
4. Intense auroras could occur over much of the Earth.

5. Forest fires could take place over much of the planet.
6. Orbits of the satellites could be disturbed.
7. Shortwave radio communication of the aircraft flying over polar regions could be interrupted.

Select the correct answer using the code given below:

(a) 1, 2, 4 and 5 only

(b) 2, 3, 5, 6 and 7 only

(c) 1, 3, 4, 6 and 7 only

(d) 1, 2, 3, 4, 5, 6 and 7

Q. Consider the following pairs: (2023)

Objects in space		Description
Cepheids	:	Giant clouds of dust and gas in space
Nebulae	:	Stars which brighten and dim periodically
Pulsars :	:	Neutron stars that are formed when massive stars run out of fuel and collapse

How many of the above pairs are correctly matched?

(a) Only one (b) Only two

(c) All three (d) None

Q. Consider the following statements: (2024)

1. **Statement-I:** Giant stars live much longer than dwarf stars.
2. **Statement-II:** Compared to dwarf stars, giant stars have a greater rate of nuclear reactions.

Which one of the following is correct in respect of the above statements?

(a) Both Statement-I and Statement-II are correct and Statement-II explains Statement-I

(b) Both Statement-I and Statement-II are correct, but Statement-II does not explain Statement-I

(c) Statement-I is correct, but Statement-II is incorrect

(d) Statement-I is incorrect, but Statement-II is correct

Q. What do you understand by 'Standard Positioning Systems' and 'Protection Positioning Systems' in the GPS era? Discuss the advantages India perceives from its ambitious IRNSS programme employing just seven satellites. (2015)

Q. Discuss India's achievements in the field of Space Science and Technology. How the application of this technology has helped India in its socio-economic development? (2016)

Q. India has achieved remarkable successes in unmanned space missions including the Chandrayaan and Mars Orbiter Mission, but has not ventured into manned space missions, both in terms of technology and logistics? Explain critically. (2017)

Q. What is India's plan to have its own space station and how will it benefit our space programme? (2019)

Q. Launched on 25th December, 2021, James Webb Space Telescope has been much news since then. What are its unique features which make it superior to its predecessor Space Telescopes? What are the key goals of this mission? What potential benefits does it hold for the human race? (2022)

Q What is the main task of India's third moon mission which could not be achieved in its earlier mission? List the countries that have achieved this task. Introduce the subsystems in the spacecraft launched and explain the role of the 'Virtual Launch Control Centre' at the Vikram Sarabhai Space Centre which contributed to the successful launch from Sriharikota. (2023)

Q. What are asteroids? How real is the threat of them causing extinction of life? What strategies have been developed to prevent such a catastrophe? (2024)

UNIT 12

MINISTRIES AND DEPARTMENTS : INDIAN SCIENCE TECHNOLOGY & INNOVATION

Ministries and Departments related to Indian Science Technology and Innovation

- Department of Science and Technology (DST)
- Department of Biotechnology (DBT).
- Council of Scientific & Industrial Research (CSIR).
- Ministry of Earth Sciences (MoES).
- Department of Atomic Energy (DAE).
- Department of Space (DoS).
- Defence Research and Development Organisation (DRDO).
- Indian Council of Agricultural Research (ICAR).
- Indian Council of Medical Research (ICMR).
- Ministry of Electronics and Information Technology (MeitY).
- Ministry of Environment, Forest and Climate Change (MoEF & CC).
- Ministry of New and Renewable Energy (MNRE).
- Ministry of Education (MoE).
- Technology Development Board (TDB).
- The Science & Engineering Research Board (SERB).

Department of Science and Technology

- **Department of Science & Technology** (DST) was established in **May 1971**, with the objective of promoting new areas of Science & Technology and to play the role of a nodal department for organising, coordinating and promoting science and technological activities in the country.

Functions and Responsibilities of DST

- Formulation of policies relating to Science and Technology (S&T).
- Matters relating to the Scientific Advisory Committee to Cabinet (SAC-C).
- R&D through its research institutions or laboratories for development of indigenous technologies concerning bio-fuel production, processing, standardization and applications, in co-ordination with the concerned Ministry or Department.
- R&D activities to promote utilization of by-products to develop value added chemicals.

Futurology : Coordination and integration of areas of S&T having cross-sectoral linkages in which a number of institutions and departments have interest and capabilities.

- Undertaking or financially sponsoring **scientific** and **technological surveys, research design** and **development**, where necessary.
- Matters commonly affecting **Scientific and technological departments/ organisations/ institutions e.g.** financial, personnel, purchase and import policies and practices.
- **Management Information Systems** for S&T and **coordination** there of. Matters regarding **Inter-Agency/Inter-Departmental coordination** for **evolving S&T missions.**
- Matters concerning **domestic technology** particularly the **promotion of ventures** involving the **commercialization** of such technology other than those under the **Department of Scientific and Industrial Research.**

- Promotion of **S&T** at the **State, District** and **Village levels** for **grass roots development** through **State S&T Councils** and other mechanisms.
- Application of **S&T** for **weaker sections, women** and other **disadvantaged sections** of Society.

Organisational Structure of DST

Secretary
- **Senior Adviser**
  - PCPM
- **Chief Vigilance Officer**
- **Scientific Division**
  - NPNST
  - C3E
  - R&D Infrastructure
  - WISE-KIRAN
  - International S&T Cooperation
  - SEED-SSTP
  - INSPRICE
  - TDT
  - NGP
  - FFT
  - National Supercomputing Mission
  - NCSTC
  - NEB
  - Water Technologies Cell
  - Shri Cell
- **Statutory Bodies**
  - TDB
  - SERB
- **SMP Division (Subordinate Offices)**
  - Survey of India
  - NATMO
- **JS (A)**
  - Admin
- **AS and FA**
  - IFD
- **Autonomous Institutes Divisions**
  - Agharkar Research Institute, Pune
  - Aryabhatta Research Institute of Observational-Sciences, Nanital
  - Bose Institute, Kolkata
  - Birbal Sahni Institute of Palaeobotany, Lucknow
  - Centre for Nano and Soft Matter Sciences, Bangalore
  - Centre for Powder Metallurgy and New Materials, Hydrabad
  - Institute of Nano Science and Technology, Mohali
  - Indian Association for the Cultivation of Science, Kolkata
  - Indian Institute of Astrophysics, Bangalore
  - Indian Institute of Geomagnetism, Mumbai
  - National Innovation Foundation
  - Jawaharlal Nehru Centre for Advanced Scientific Research, Bangalore
  - Raman Research Institute, Bangalore
  - Sree Chitra Tirunal Institute for Medical Sciences and Technology
  - S.N. Bose National Centre for Basic Sciences, Kolkata
  - The Institute of Advanced Study in Science and Technology, Guwahati
  - Technology Information, Forecasting and Assessment Council (TIFAC)
  - Wadia Institute of Himalayan Geology, Dehradun
  - Vigyan Prasar, New Delhi
  - Indian National Science Academy, New Delhi
  - Indian Academy of Sciences, Banglore
  - Indian National Academy of Engineering, New Delhi
  - National Academy of Sciences, Allahabad
  - Indian Science Congress Association, Kolkata

Important Initiatives by DST

Innovation in Science Pursuit for Inspired Research (INSPIRE) Scheme

- It is an innovative programme sponsored and managed by DST for attraction of talent to Science.
- It covers the **entire meritorious youth** who is interested to study science right from **school** to **college** and **university level** and choose **scientific research** as a career. It carries out **enabling activities** of **human capacity building** including **scholarships** and **fellowships, research exposure training of human resources.**

INSPIRE MANAK

- It is a unique initiative to attract talented school students (in the age group of **10-15 years** and studying in Class 6-10) at an **early age** to study **science** and **pursue** research career apart from fostering a culture of innovation among them.

Women in Science and Engineering-KIRAN (WISE-KIRAN)

- It's objective is to **cater women** of all walks of life in order to **enhance their participation** in the field of **Science and Technology** (S&T) with ultimate goal to bring **gender parity**.

WISE Post-Doctoral Fellowship (WISE-PDF)

- It aims to provide opportunity to women to continue research after Ph.D. in Basic and Applied Sciences through independent project grant.

Women's Instinct for Developing and Ushering in Scientific Heights & Innovations (WIDUSHI)

- It aims to **encourage** and **support senior women scientists** (upto the age of 62 years) to conduct research in **interdisciplinary areas** of **Science & Technology**.

WISE-SCOPE

- It encourages **women scientists** and **technologists** to **address societal challenges** through **S&T interventions.**

WISE Internship in Intellectual Property Rights (WISE-IPR)

- It provides **one-year training** to women in the area of Intellectual Property Rights in order to develop a core professional skill in this domain.

Women International Grant Support (WINGS)

- It provides opportunities to Indian Women scientists to undertake research in the International research labs and academic institutions.

Consolidation of University Research for Innovation and Excellence (CURIE)

- It provides support to women institutions for establishing State-of-the art research infrastructure to enhance research facilities and improving R&D activities in order to create excellence in Science & Technology (S&T) domain.
- **The programme has 2 major components:**
  - CURIE Support to Women Universities
  - CURIE Support to Women PG Colleges

Vigyan Jyoti

- It aims to encourage girls to pursue higher education and career in STEM (Science, Technology, Engineering and Mathematics) especially in the areas where women participation is low in order to balance gender ratio across the streams.

Gender Advancement for Transforming Institutions (GATI)

- GATI aims to develop an indigenous charter for Gender Equity in **STEMM** (Science Technology Engineering Mathematics & Medicine), with a focus on bringing about transformational changes at Institutional level.

30 Indian Institutions have participated in GATI pilot.

Mission on Nano Science and Technology

- Government of India launched **Mission on Nano Science and Technology** (Nano Mission) in May 2007.
- Recognizing the success of Nano Mission, the Union Cabinet accorded approval for continuation of the Nano Mission in its **Phase-II** during the **12th Plan period** with an allocation of **Rs. 650 crore**, with **Department of Science and Technology** as the nodal agency.

National Geospatial Programme (erstwhile NRDMS)

- **Natural Resources Data Management System** (NRDMS) was initiated in **1982**, as an interdisciplinary research programme has successfully promoted R&D in emerging areas of Geospatial Science, Technology and providing geospatial solutions to area specific problems.
- Over the years, NRDMS has successfully demonstrated utilities of **Geospatial Technologies** in **decision making** and **developed** capacity for **geospatial data** and information management at **State**, **District** and **local levels** at pilot scale.
- Considering the changing requirements of **Geospatial Science & Technology** in the country, the **NRDMS Division** has now evolved into **National Geospatial Programme** (NGP) to catalyse the **National Geospatial Ecosystem** with the mandate of promoting Geospatial Science and Technology, policy, solution, capacity building, entrepreneurship and international cooperation for sustainable socio-economic development at all levels of governance.

Mission: Promoting Geospatial Science and Technology, Policy, Solution, capacity building, entrepreneurship and International cooperation for sustainable socio-economic development at all levels of Governance.

Objectives of National Geospatial Programme

- Following programmes and sub-programmes are supported under the division–
- **Geospatial Science Programme :** The main aim of the programme is to develop the **fundamental** and **applied scientific knowledge** underpinning the **geospatial sciences** to **strengthen geospatial science research and education** in line with **international standards.**

Submissions
• National Programme on Geodesy • Geospatial Intelligence and Geospatial Analytics • National Programme on Assessment of Regional Hydrological Systems using Space Borne Gravity Observations

- **Geospatial Technology Programme :** The programme aims at **catalysing** the **development of indigenous geospatial/location specific technologies** in the country.

Sub-programmes
• Geospatial Data Capture and Gathering Technologies. • Geospatial Data Management Technologies. • Geospatial Data Processing Technologies. • Development and operationalization of National Data Registry (NDR). • Up-gradation of the existing proof-of-concept (POC) cloud-based Geo-platform. • Development of Decision Support Systems (DSS) and Tools.

Geospatial Solutions Addressing National Priorities and Sustainable Development Goals

- R&D projects and operational scale initiatives for providing **Geospatial solutions** to the **stakeholders** addressing the **National Developmental Priorities and Sustainable Development Goals** viz. **Spatial Disaster Risk Reduction** (SDRR), **Rural Development, Urban Governance; Operationalization and sustenance of NSDI/ State SDI Data Nodes** by coverage of all **States** and **UTs** and **Provision of geospatial data/ products/ services and solutions to potential stakeholders/** beneficiaries of the Ecosystem up to the level of panchayats and wards etc.

National Programme on Spatial Disaster Risk Reduction (SDRR)

- Under this, Landslide hazard mitigation and Coastal hazard risk assessment & reduction are undertaken.

- **Landslide Hazard Mitigation (LHM):** As part of the integrated landslide programme, efforts were made to **develop forewarning system** to monitor the **critical landslides** in different geo-environmental areas.

A set of **07 R&D projects** has been supported for the development of an **early warning system covering areas** (States) like **Sikkim, Nilgiris** (Tamil Nadu), **Manikaran, Kotropi, Mandiand, Darmashala** (Himachal Pradesh) and **Uttarakhand.**

- **Coastal Hazard, Risk Assessment and Reduction (CHRAR):** CHRAR has been initiated to cover the coastal areas of the country with the aim to develop S&T enabled **geospatial techniques** for **coastal disaster studies** encompassing **disaster genetics, propagation, disaster vulnerability mapping, detection of causative factors, mitigation measures** etc. and come out with quantifiable/actionable outputs so that the state governments and the stake holders can readily use them during the disasters for relief, restoration and rehabilitation. R&D projects are being supported in the areas of land subsidence and **sea level rise, tsunamis, cyclones, floods** and **coastal erosion** etc.
- **Geospatial Solutions for Urban Governance:** Under this sub-programme proposals are supported in the areas of city **governance applications** as well as in the **core R&D areas** focusing on **emerging technologies** related to city development using **Geo-ICT.**
- Various R&D projects are being supported focusing on **Smart Parking Management System** using sensors; IoT and GIS technologies; Framework for **flood mapping** and or prepare an **early warning system** in the occurrence of **flood;** City GML based 3D models for smart cities; Industrial Indoor Assets Positioning and Navigation System using Geospatial Analysis; Geomagnetism based Indoor Navigation system etc.

Capacity Building Programmes

- Training on Geospatial Science, Technologies and Disaster Risk Reductions.
- Organising **Geo-Innovation Challenges** for harnessing the new ideas in Geospatial Science/ Technology

Strengthening **Geospatial Training Institutes** and development of **Training modules and kits.**

International Collaborations

- Developing national capacity for Geospatial technology development, acquisition and transfer through international partnerships/ collaborations namely **United Nations Global Geospatial Information Management** (UNGGIM), **Open Geospatial Consortium** (OGC), **Brazil Russia India China South Africa** (BRICS), **Indo-Africa collaborations** etc.

Recent Initiatives

- **First and only National Centre for Geodesy** (NCG) was established by the division at **Indian Institute of Technology, Kanpur** in India in **2019 for 5 years,** to rejuvenate **national-level education** on **Geodesy** and other aligned areas with the primary aim to act as a hub of excellence.

Geodesy is defined as the discipline that deals with the measurement and representation of the earth, its gravity field and geodynamic phenomena in three-dimensional time varying space.

6 Institutions – IIT Bombay, IIST Trivandrum, IRS Anna University, IIT (ISM) Dhanbad, MNNIT Allahabad and **MANIT Bhopal** have been identified and set up in **2022** with same objectives of the NCG.

- **National Networking Programme on Assessment of Regional Hydrological Systems using Space Borne Gravity Observations:** The project was developed involving **03 ministries** and other knowledge institutions to explore the feasibility of monitoring total **water storage variations** from **space.**

Cognitive Science Research Initiative (CSRI)

Cognitive Science is the **study of human mind** and **brain**, focusing on how mind represents and manipulates **knowledge** and how **mental representations** and **processes** are realized in the brain.

- The field is highly **transdisciplinary** in nature, combining ideas, principles and methods of psychology, computer science, linguistics, philosophy, neuroscience etc.
- CSRI was initiated by **DST** in **2008** during **11th Five year plan** to facilitate a platform to scientific community to work for better solution of challenges related with **cognitive disorders** and social issues through various psychological tools & batteries, **early diagnosis** & **better therapies**, **intervention technologies** and **rehabilitation programmes.**

National Science & Technology Entrepreneurship Development Board (NSTEDB)

- It was established in **1982** by the Government of India under the aegis of **Department of Science & Technology** to support various programs on **Science, technology** and **innovation** based **entrepreneurship**, and enables **promotion of knowledge driven** and **technology intensive ventures / startups.**

National Initiative for Developing and Harnessing Innovations (NIDHI)

- It is an **umbrella programme** conceived and developed by the **Innovation and Entrepreneurship Division** (NSTEDB) of **DST, Government of India** in **2016**, for **promoting S&T based entrepreneurship** and **startup ecosystem** across the country.

Technology Mission Programme on Water and Clean Energy

- Development of basket of technically feasible, socially acceptable, environmentally sound and economically viable innovative solutions suited to different spectrum of users in diverse socio-economic contexts.

Water Technology Cell (WTC)

- It started in **2007** with a thrust on **strengthening** the **capability and capacity** of Indian **researchers** and **S&T institutions to encourage research**, design, and development of indigenous low cost technological solutions to ensure safe drinking water for the masses.

In **2009**, based on the directives of **Supreme Court of India**, the WTC initiated and implemented **Winning, Augmentation, and Renovation** (WAR) for Water.

Technology Development Programmes

- The Programme supports activities aimed at developing technologies both in the advanced/ emerging areas and in traditional sectors/areas.
- **Objectives :**
  - Support R&D for development of innovative technologies in identified areas.
  - Promote application of advanced technology for improving the performance and value addition to existing technology.
  - Capacity building in the area of technology development.

Core-Areas for inviting proposals under TDP
• Advanced Manufacturing Technologies (AMT) • Waste Management Technologies (WMT) • Biomedical Device and Technology Development Programme (BDTD) • Device Development Programme (DDP) • Technology Development Programme (TDP) • DHI-DST Technology Platform for Electric Mobility (TPEM) • Science and Heritage Research Initiative (SHRI)

Technical Research Centres

- This programme was launched as a follow-up of the budget announcement made in FY 2014-15.

5 Technical Research Centres (TRCs) a at cost of **467 crores** were established with a mission to provide **techno-legal-commercial** and **financial support to scientists, entrepreneurs,** and **business** fraternity to achieve translation of research into products and processes for greater economic and societal benefits.

Science for Equity Empowerment and Development (SEED) Division

- Recognizing the importance of Equity and Empowerment in the developmental processes, Science and Society Division was renamed as **Science for Equity Empowerment and Development** (SEED) division in **2009**.
- SEED Division **provides opportunities** to **motivated scientists** & **technologists** from national **Research and Development** (R&D) labs, **S&T-driven, Non-Governmental Organizations** (NGOs) and **field-level workers** to take up action-oriented and location-specific projects aiming at **Socio-economic development** of disadvantaged sections of the society through appropriate interventions of **Science, Technology and Innovation** (STI), leading to their improved quality of life and livelihood.
- **Technology Interventions for Disabled and Elderly (TIDE) :** TIDE programme is an initiative of DST to create inclusiveness and universal accessibility for **Divyangjan** and the **Elderly**, through **promotion** and **development** of various assistive **tools**, technologies, techniques, affordable & adaptable to the Indian milieu.
- **Scheme for Young Scientists and Technologists (SYST) :** The scheme encourages **young scientists** and **technologists** (less than 35 years on the last date of submission of the application) to identify **socially relevant challenges** and provide S&T-based solutions using **lab-to-land approach.**
- **National Council for Science & Technology Communication (NCSTC) :** It is mandated to communicate Science and Technology to masses, **stimulate scientific** and **technological temper** and **coordinate** and **orchestrate** such efforts throughout the country.

Important initiatives of SEED Division
• Mission Enlighten. • Mission eco NEXT. • National Children's Science Congress. • National Teacher's Science Congress. • Initiative for Research and Innovation in Science (IRIS). • Health and Nutrition through Community Radio. • Academic/Training courses in S&T communication. • Science and Technology Communication Programmes for Students. • Explaining Science behind Miracles.

Major programmes undertaken by DST

- **National Children's Science Congress :** This is an opportunity for brilliant young scientists (10 -17 years of age group), started since 1993 to popularize the method of science.
- **National Science Day :** Every year on **February 28**, is celebrated as the **National Science Day**. The programme was initiated by Department of Science and Tech to trigger science popularization activities throughout the country and to disseminate scientific education about the current issues of science and technology amongst the citizens of the country.
- **National Teachers' Science Congress (NTSC) :** Initiated by NCSTC, the NTSC provides a forum to teachers of the country to enhance their level of scientific awareness.

The **first national event** was held in **2003**. Presently it has become a **biennial activity of NCSTC.**

- **Interdisciplinary Cyber Physical Systems (ICPS):** Launched by DST to **foster and promote R&D** cyber physical systems.

Cyber Physical System (CPS) is a **mechanism controlled** or **monitored** by **computer-based algorithms**, tightly integrated with **internet** and its users.

- **National Supercomputing Mission (NSM):** NSM has set up to provide the country with supercomputing infrastructure to meet the increasing computational demands of academia, researchers, MSMEs, and startups.

National Super Computing Mission is steered jointly by the **Department of Science and Technology** (DST) and **Ministry of Electronics and IT** (MeitY) and implemented by the **Centre for Development of Advanced Computing** (C-DAC), **Pune** and the **Indian Institute of Science** (IISc), **Bengaluru**.

- With the approval of Technical Advisory Committee and Executive Board, a revised plan based on buy to build-approach was put in place.

The first supercomputer assembled indigenously, called **PARAM Shivay,** was installed in **IIT** (BHU). Similarly, the **14th** machine was dedicated to the nation by the Honorable President of India in **IIT Guwahati**. The installations are all majorly equipped with applications to cater the domains like **Weather and Climate, Computational Fluid Dynamics, Bioinformatics** and **Material science.**

Super Compters installed in India		
Institute Name	**HPC System Name**	**Computing Power**
• IIT (BHU), Varanasi	PARAM Shivay	838TF
• IISER, Pune	PARAM Brahma	1.70PF
• IIT, Kharagpur	PARAM Shakti	1.66PF
• JNCASR, Bangalore	PARAM Yukti	1.8PF
• IIT, Kanpur	PARAM Sanganak	1.66PF
• C-DAC, Pune	PARAM Siddhi-AI	5.2PF/210PF (AI)
• IIT, Hyderabad	PARAM Seva	838TF
• NABI, Mohali	PARAM Smriti	838TF
• IISc, Bangalore	PARAM Pravega	3.3PF
• C-DAC, Bangalore	PARAM Utkarsh	838TF
• IIT, Roorkee	PARAM Ganga	1.66PF
• IIT, Gandhinagar	PARAM Ananta	838TF
• NIT, Trichy	PARAM Porul	838TF
• IIT, Guwahati	PARAM Kamrupa	838TF
• IIT, Mandi	PARAM Himalaya	838TF

III - PARAM Vidya under NSM HRD (For education and training)			
Institute Name	**HPC System Name**	**Computing Power**	**Year of Commissioning**
• C-DAC, Pune	PARAM Vidya1	52.3 TF	2022
• IIT, Kharagpur	PARAM Vidya2	52.3 TF	2022
• IIT, Palakkad	PARAM Vidya3	52.3 TF	2022
• IIT, Chennai	PARAM Vidya4	52.3 TF	2022
• IIT, Goa	PARAM Vidya5	52.3 TF	2022

II - R&D and Application development systems			
Institute Name	**HPC System Name**	**Computing Power**	**Year of Commissioning**
• C-DAC, Pune	SANGAM Testbed	150 TF	2017
• C-DAC, Pune	PARAM Shrestha	100 TF	2018
• C-DAC, Pune	PARAM Embryo	100 TF	2020
• C-DAC, Pune	PARAM Neel	100 TF	2020
• SETS, Chennai	PARAM Spoorthi	100 TF	2020
• C-DAC, Pune	Bioinformatics R&D Facility	230 TF	2021
• C-DAC, Bangalore	System Software lab	82TF	2020
• C-DAC, Pune	PARAM Sampooran	27 TF	2020

National Quantum Mission (NQM)

- National Quantum Mission received cabinet approval on **19th April 2023** at a total cost of **Rs. 6003.65 crore**, from **2023-24** to **2030-31**, aiming to **seed, nurture** and **scale up scientific** and **industrial R&D** and create a **vibrant & innovative ecosystem** in **Quantum Technology** (QT), to **scale up scientific and industrial R&D**, for **accelerating Quantum Technology** led **economic growth** and leverage India into a **leading nation** in the area.
- The new mission targets developing **intermediate scale quantum computers** with **50-1000 physical qubits** in **8 years** in various platforms like superconducting and photonic technology.
- **Satellite based secure quantum communications** between **ground stations** over a range of **2000 kilometres** within India, long **distance secure quantum communications** with other countries, **inter-city quantum key distribution** over **2000 km** as well as **multi-node Quantum network** with quantum memories are also some of the deliverables of the Mission.
- The mission will help develop **magnetometers** with **high sensitivity** in **atomic systems** and **Atomic Clocks** for **precision timing, communications** and **navigation**.
- It will also **support design** and **synthesis of quantum materials** such as **superconductors, novel semiconductor structures** and **topological materials** for fabrication of **quantum devices.**
- **Single photon sources/detectors, entangled photon sources** will also be developed for **quantum communications, sensing** and **metrological applications.**

In September 2024, 4 Thematic Hubs (T-Hubs) were established:

- **Quantum Computing:** Indian Institute of Science (IISc) Bengaluru
- **Quantum Communication:** Indian Institute of Technology Madras (IIT-M) and Centre for Development of Telematics, New Delhi
- **Quantum Sensing & Metrology:** Indian Institute of Technology Bombay (IIT-B)
- **Quantum Materials & Devices:** Indian Institute of Technology Delhi (IIT-D).

- The mission would greatly benefit **communication, health, financial** and **energy sectors** as well as **drug design,** and **space applications.**
- It will provide a huge boost to National priorities like **digital India, Make in India, Skill India and Stand-up India, Start-up India, Self-reliant India** and **Sustainable Development Goals (SDG).**

- In **July, 2023 India** and the **United States** jointly launched a call for proposals on **Critical and**

Emerging Technology: Quantum Technologies and **Artificial Intelligence** for **Transforming Lives, formulated by Indo-U.S. Science and Technology Forum (IUSSTF)** and the Secretariat for **USISTEF.**

- It is a **$2million grant programme** under the **U.S.-India Science and Technology Endowment Fund (USISTEF)** for the joint development and commercialization of **Artificial Intelligence (AI)** and quantum technologies, and encouraged public-private collaborations to develop **high performance computing (HPC)** facilities in India.

Climate Change Programmes

- The Government of India launched **National Action Plan on Climate Change** (NAPCC) on **30th June, 2008** outlining **8 National Missions on climate change.**
- The **Department of Science & Technology, Ministry of Science & Technology** was entrusted with the responsibility of **coordinating two out** of these **8 national missions** on **climate change.**
  1. National Mission for Sustaining Himalayan Ecosystem (NMSHE)
  2. National Mission on Strategic Knowledge for Climate Change (NMSKCC)

1. National Mission on Strategic Knowledge for Climate Change (NMSKCC)

- The consequences of climate change on the social systems are expected to vary in different regions of the world on account of several regional and other local factors. Therefore different **modeling studies, adaptation strategies** and **technology systems** would be required in **differing geographical** and **social contexts.**
- **Accordingly, the following objectives have been identified for the Mission :**
  - **Formation of knowledge networks among the existing knowledge** institutions engaged in research and development relating to climate science and facilitate data sharing and exchange through a suitable policy framework and institutional support.
  - **Establishment of global technology watch groups** with **institutional capacities** to carry out research on **risk minimized technology** selection for developmental choices.
  - **Development of national capacity** for modelling the **regional impact** of climate change on different ecological zones within the country for different seasons and living standards.
  - **Establishing research networks** and **encouraging research** in the areas of **climate change impacts** on important socio-economic sectors like agriculture, health, natural ecosystem, bio-diversity, coastal zones, etc.
  - Providing an improved **understanding and awareness** of the key climate processes and the resultant climate risks and associated consequences.
  - **Building alliances** and **partnerships** through global collaboration in research & technology development on climate change under International and bilateral S&T cooperation arrangements.

Programmes and Initiatives under NMSKCC

- Centres of Excellence (CoE)
- State Climate Change Centres (SCCC)
- National Network Programmes (NNPs)
- Major R&D Programmes (MRDP)
- Human Capacity Building Programmes (HCB)
- Global Technology Watch Groups (GTWGs)
- Vulnerability assessments at State and District Level
- **International Collaboration–** Indo-US Fulbright-Kalam Fellowships in Climate Change; Indo-German Research Collaboration

2. National Mission for Sustaining the Himalayan Ecosystem (NMSHE)

- The **Himalayan eco-system** possesses nearly **51 million people** who practice hill **agriculture.** Most of the India's river systems in the North originate from **glaciers** in the **Himalayan region.**

- Glacial melt may impact their **long-term lean-season flows**, with **adverse impacts** on the **economy** in terms of **water availability** and **hydropower generation**. For centuries, Himalayan ecosystem has remained delicately balanced, and has been responsible for the tremendous biodiversity of the region.
- The ecosystem has become **increasingly vulnerable** to the **impacts of changes** due to **natural causes**, **anthropogenic emission related causes** and also due to **developmental paradigms** of the **modern society**.
- **National Mission for Sustaining the Himalayan Ecosystem** has been launched with the goal of addressing all such issues **holistically** and in **coordinated manner** by involving all possible stakeholders by developing a sustainable National capacity to continuously assess the **health status** of the **Himalayan Ecosystem** and enable policy bodies in their **policy-formulation functions** and assist States in the Indian Himalayan Region with their implementation of actions selected for sustainable development.
- **Objectives identified under National Mission for Sustaining Himalayan Ecosystem**
    - Building human and institutional capacities in the different existing / new Institutions in the Himalayan region.
    - Identification of national knowledge institutions and development of a self sustaining knowledge network.
    - Development and adoption of new methods for assessing the health of the Himalayan eco system including those of glaciers and create a data base of the same.
    - Assessment and quantification of the changes in the Himalayan eco system attributable to the climate change as a result of global emissions and human activities in the region and model for future projections.
    - Exploration of linking of traditional and formal knowledge systems through strategic mechanism of formalization for mutual benefit and value for the sustainability of the Himalayan ecosystem.
    - Identification of most-desirable Adaptation Policies to improve Regional Sustainability.

Programmes and Initiatives under NMSHE

- Thematic Task Forces.
- State CC Centres in Himalayan States/UTs.
- Centres of Excellence.
- State Network Programmes in IHR states.
- Major R&D Programmes.
- Inter-University Consortium.
- Indo-Swiss Capacity Building Programme in glaciology and related areas.

Department of Biotechnology (DBT)

- The Department of Biotechnology (DBT), set up in **1986** is at the forefront of **promoting biotechnological innovation missions** and **entrepreneurship** leveraging the strength of **strategic partnerships** and **building capacities** across the country.
- Department of Biotechnology is the **nodal agency** supporting **research** and its applications in the **Life Sciences and promotes** & **accelerates** the pace of **development** and **large scale use of biotechnology** in the country. The department has made significant achievements in the **growth** and application of biotechnology in the broad areas of agriculture, health care, animal sciences, environment, and industry.
- Through strong foresight and vision, efforts have been made by DBT to create and nurture a vibrant biotech research and innovation ecosystem across the country in alignment with national missions of our Government such as AatmaNirbhar Bharat, Swasth Bharat, Swachh Bharat, Startup India and Make-in-India.

- DBT has emphasis on promotion of excellence and innovation driven discovery research in biotechnology and modern biology. The focus is also on promoting public-private partnership, nurturing innovation & entrepreneurship, bio-incubators, building capacity in cutting edge areas of research, scaling-up of existing infrastructure, creating right kind of new infrastructure, establishing national and international partnerships.

Mandates of DBT

- Promoting large scale use of Biotechnology.
- Supporting R&D and manufacturing in Biology.
- Responsibility for Autonomous Institutions.
- Promoting University and Industry Interaction.
- Identifying and Set up Centres of Excellence for R&D.
- Integrated Programme for Human Resource Development.
- Serving as Nodal Point for specific International Collaborations.
- Establishment of Infrastructure Facilities to support R&D and production.
- Evolving Bio Safety Guidelines, manufacture and application of cell based vaccines.
- Serving as nodal point for the collection and dissemination of information relating to biotech.
- The **Biotechnology Industry Research Assistance Council (BIRAC)**, instituted in 2012 under the Department of Biotechnology, aims to facilitate collaboration between innovators and funders. This platform serves as a catalyst for turning innovative ideas into tangible realities, fostering advancements in biotechnology.
- Under the **Make in India initiative**, the biotechnology sector has been identified as a champion sector.
- The **National Biotechnology Development Strategy** sets forth an ambitious vision for India, aspiring to achieve global competitiveness in biotechnology research, innovation, translation, entrepreneurship, and industrial growth. The aim is to establish a robust bioeconomy, reaching a valuation of USD 150 billion by 2025.
- **National Biopharma mission:** Through the "Innovate in India" initiative (I3), the mission seeks to drive innovation in the biopharma sector, fostering a dynamic ecosystem for the advancement of biopharmaceuticals in India.

Achievements of DBT

- Vaccines for **Swasth Bharat**.
- **Quadrivalent Human Papilloma Virus vaccine against cervical cancer:** India's 1st indigenously developed quadrivalent Human Papilloma Virus (qHPV) vaccine, CERVAVAC, against cervical cancer, supported by DBT and BIRAC received market authorization in July, 2022.
- **World's first and India's indigenously Developed COVID-19 DNA** vaccine supported by **DBT-BIRAC** under **Mission COVID Suraksha**, received **Emergency Use Authorization** (EUA) for use in 12 years and above. This vaccine also received EUA as a heterologous booster (3mg single dose) in **April, 2023**.
- India's **1st Intranasal Vaccine** for CoViD-19 received EUA for use in primary series (18 years & above) and for use as homologous & heterologous booster, in **November, 2022**.
- India's **1st Omicron Booster Vaccine** based on mRNA Platform, has been developed under Mission CoViD Suraksha and was released in **June, 2023**.
- **DBT-BIRAC** supported 15-valent Pneumococcal Polysaccharide conjugate vaccine received market authorisation for manufacturing in **December, 2022**.
- **Vaccines for Dengue, Influenza and Chikungunya:** Inactivated vaccine for chikungunya is undergoing Phase II/III clinical

trials. Live attenuated tetravalent Dengue Vaccine developed based on in-licensed technology from **National Institute of Health, USA**, is undergoing Phase I clinical trials.

- Recombinant tetravalent protein subunit vaccine for Influenza is in advanced preclinical development.
- DBT launched Data Driven Research to Eradicate TB with Dare2eraD TB as an umbrella program on TB.
- **Pan India Genome India project:** Whole genome sequencing of **6,425 individuals** have been completed.
- Unique Methods of Management of Inherited Disorders (UMMID) Initiative

Indian TB Genomic Consortium is a joint initiative of MoS&T and MoH&FW led by the DBT, aimed at performing Whole Genome Sequencing of 32,500 TB strains and applying AI based methods for prediction of drug resistance, strain lineage, etc. It is aligned with **TB Mukt Bharat** initiative of Govt. of India.

- Under **National Biopharma Mission, Vaccine candidates** (15) for **Cholera, Influenza, Dengue, Chikungunya, Pneumococcal disease, CoViD-19** (early development) and related technologies (4); Biosimilar products and related technologies (21) for **Diabetes**, **Rheumatological** and **ophthalmic diseases**, **Cancer**; **Medical Devices** & **Diagnostics** (29) have been supported so far.
- **Control Programme for Sickle Cell Anemia and Thalassemia:** DBT has implemented this program in **6 districts** (Balasore, Bargarh, Cuttack, Jharsuguda, Koraput, Sambalpur) of Odisha, including an **Aspirational** District **Koraput.** Several training workshops were conducted at different levels (State / Regional levels) for doctors/other healthcare workers to train them on different aspects of management and prevention of **sickle cell disease** and **thalassemia** in the State.
- DALI, a package containing **screening tools** for **school teachers** and assessment tools for **psychologists** in Indian languages to identify dyslexia was developed by **National Brain Research Centre, Manesar.**
- **Indigenous technology** has been developed on iron, **vitamin B12, folate fortified rice premix** from **broken rice kernels** for addressal of **anaemia in women** and **children.**
- **Biodesign program,** twinning of **engineering** and **medical skills** for unmet clinical needs has ignited the nascent med-tech ecosystem in the country through 4 different centers across the country partnering **clinical, research** and **technical institutions.**
- **International Cancer Genome Consortium:** India is one of the **7 founding members** of **ICGC**. Now, **40 countries** are participating in this consortium. **ICGC-India Project** has established a **dedicated bio-repository** with best international practices at **ACTREC, Mumbai** and **State-of-the-art** high throughput **Genome** sequencing center at **NIBMG, Kalyani.**
- **Agriculture Biotechnology, Animal Biotechnology, Aquaculture and Marine Biology:**
  - Transfer of technologies to companies has been facilitated for mustard and cotton.
  - White rust resistance varieties Varuna, Pusa bold, Pusa Jai Kisan and Rohini were transferred to eight seed companies. Two transgenic events of Cotton (Tg2E-13 and TM2) containing Cry1Ac gene are being transferred through BIRAC.
  - **DBT-NGGF National Genotyping and Genomics Facility** (NGGF) a single-window service system for advanced genomics technology services was established and has become operational under PPP mode.
  - **Genomic selection and Speed Breeding Facility** was supported under a Network project at IRRI, Varanasi, to facilitate faster genetic gains through speed breeding for generation advancement.

- Speed breeding facility is targeted to undertake haplotype-based backcross breeding to transfer the superior haplotypes from landraces into elite backgrounds, and training and capacity development of 40 young plant breeders from India on breeding innovations.

- **Biotech-KISAN Hubs:** DBT connected the science with the farmers and established **Biotech-KISAN Hubs** at pilot-scale level in all **15 agro-climatic zones**. The programme has now been scaled up and expanded its activities covering **112 Aspirational Districts** in the country. In addition, **15 Biotech KISAN Hubs** have been setup in the NER to cover **40 backward blocks** and villages of the region. The programme leads to link the farmers with the **latest scientific innovations** to **enhance agricultural production.**

Council of Scientific & Industrial Research (CSIR)

- **CSIR**, was established by the **Government of India** in **September 1942** as an autonomous body on initiatives of **Arcot Ramaswamy Mudaliar and Shanti Swaroop Bhatnagar.** It comes under the **Ministry of Science and Technology.**

- **CSIR** has a dynamic network of **37 national laboratories, 39 outreach centres, 1 Innovation Complexes** and **3 units** with a pan-India presence.

- CSIR covers a **wide spectrum of science and technology from oceanography, geophysics, chemicals, drugs, genomics, biotechnology and nanotechnology to mining, aeronautics, instrumentation, environmental engineering and information technology.**

- It provides significant **technological intervention** in many areas concerning societal efforts, which include **environment, health, drinking water, food, housing, energy, farm** and **non-farm sectors**. Further, CSIR's role in S&T human resource development is noteworthy.

- Pioneer of India's intellectual property movement, CSIR today is strengthening its patent portfolio to carve out **global niches** for the country in select technology domains. CSIR filed about **229 Indian patents** and **202 foreign patents** during **2021-22.**

- CSIR envisages a vision of **CSIR@2030** as to Enhance quality of life of the citizens of India through innovative Science and Technology, globally competitive R&D, by developing sustainable solutions and capacity building to fulfil dream of **Atmanirbhar Bharat.** This vision of CSIR is aligned to the Government of India's vision for the next 25 years **Amrit Kal** when independent India becomes **100 years old.**

Ministry of Earth Sciences (MoES)

- MoES formerly the Department of **Ocean Development** (DOD), was created in **July 1981** as a part of the **Cabinet Secretariat directly** under the charge of the **Prime Minister of India.** It came into existence as a separate department in **March 1982.**

- Erstwhile DOD functioned as a nodal institution for organizing, coordinating and promoting ocean development activities in the country.

The Government of India notified DOD as the **Ministry of Ocean Development** in **February 2006.**

- In **July 2006**, the **Ministry of Ocean Development** was reorganized by the Government of India Vide Presidential notification into the new

MoES. This brought the **Indian Meteorological Department** (IMD), **Delhi**, the **Indian Institute of Tropical Meteorology** (IITM), **Pune**, and **National Centre for Medium Range Weather Forecasting** (NCMRWF), Noida under the purview of MoES administration.

- The Government also approved the setting up of Earth Commission on the pattern of **Space Commission** (government department responsible for administration of the Indian space program) and **Atomic Energy Commission** (governing body of the Department of Atomic Energy).
- It is mandated to provide services for weather, climate, ocean and coastal state, hydrology, seismology, and natural hazards; to explore and harness marine living and non-living resources in a sustainable manner for the country and to explore the **three poles of the Earth** (Arctic, Antarctic and Himalayas).

Department of Atomic Energy (DAE)

- It was set up under the direct charge of the Prime Minister through a Presidential Order on **August 3, 1954**.
- All businesses of the Government of India, related to Atomic Energy and to the functions of the Central Government under the **Atomic Energy Act, 1948** (XXIX of 1948) were directed to be transacted in the department.

Atomic Energy Commission was first setup in **August 1948** in the **Department of Scientific Research**, which was created a few months earlier in **June 1948**.

- The **Department of Atomic Energy** was setup on **August 3, 1954** under the direct charge of the Prime Minister through a Presidential Order.

Subsequently, in accordance with a Government Resolution dated **March 1, 1958**, the **Atomic Energy Commission** (AEC) was established in the **Department of Atomic Energy**.

- According to the Resolution constituting the AEC, the Secretary to the Government of India in the **Department of Atomic Energy** is **ex-officio Chairman** of the Commission.

Department of Space (DoS)

- With the setting up of **Indian National Committee for Space Research** (INCOSPAR) in **1962**, the space activities in the country were initiated. **Indian Space Research Organisation** (ISRO) was established in **August 1969**.

Government of India constituted the Space Commission and established the **Department of Space** (DoS) in **June 1972** and brought **ISRO** under **DoS** in **September 1972**.

- **Department of Space** (DoS) has the primary objective of promoting development and application of space science and technology to assist in all-round development of the nation.
- DOS has evolved the following programmes under this:
  - **Launch Vehicle programme** having indigenous capability for launching spacecrafts.
  - **INSAT Programme for telecommunications, broadcasting, meteorology, development of education** etc.
  - **Remote Sensing Programme** for **application of satellite imagery** for various developmental purposes.
  - **Research and Development in Space Sciences and Technology** for serving the end of applying them for national development.
- Space Commission formulates the policies and oversees the implementation of the Indian space programme to promote the development and application of space science and technology for the socio-economic benefit of the country.

- DOS implements these programmes through, mainly, **Indian Space Research Organisation** (ISRO), **Physical Research Laboratory** (PRL), **National Atmospheric Research Laboratory** (NARL), **North Eastern-Space Applications Centre** (NE-SAC) and **Semi-Conductor Laboratory** (SCL).

The Antrix Corporation, established in 1992 as a government owned company, markets the space products and services.
Secretariat of DOS and ISRO headquarters are located at **Antariksh Bhavan** in **Bangalore.**

- Programme offices at ISRO Headquarters coordinate the programmes like **satellite communication, earth observation, launch vehicle, space science, disaster management support, sponsored research scheme, contracts management, international cooperation, safety, reliability, publications and public relations, budget & economic analysis, civil engineering** and **human resources development.**

Defence Research and Development Organisation (DRDO)

- **DRDO** was formed in **1958** from the amalgamation of the then already functioning **Technical Development Establishment** (TDEs) of the **Indian Army** and the **Directorate of Technical Development & Production** (DTDP) with the **Defence Science Organisation** (DSO).
- DRDO is the R&D wing of Ministry of Defence, Govt of India, with a vision to empower India with cutting-edge defence technologies and a mission to achieve self-reliance in critical defence technologies and systems, while equipping our armed forces with state-of-the-art weapon systems and equipment in accordance with requirements laid down by the three Services.
- DRDO is a network of around **41 laboratories** and **05 DRDO Young Scientist Laboratories** (DYSLs) which are deeply engaged in developing defence technologies covering various disciplines, like **aeronautics, armaments, electronics, combat vehicles, engineering systems, instrumentation, missiles, advanced computing and simulation, special materials, naval systems, life sciences, training, information systems** and **agriculture.**
- DRDO's pursuit of self-reliance and successful indigenous development and production of strategic systems and platforms such as **Agni** and **Prithvi** series of missiles; **light combat aircraft** (Tejas), **multi-barrel rocket launcher** (Pinaka), **air defence system** (Akash) a wide range of radars and electronic warfare systems; etc., have given quantum jump to India's military might, generating effective deterrence and providing crucial leverage.

Indian Council of Agricultural Research (ICAR)

- Formerly known as **Imperial Council of Agricultural Research** (ICAR) was established on **16 July 1929** as a registered society under the **Societies Registration Act, 1860** in pursuance of the report of the **Royal Commission on Agriculture.**

Indian Council of Agricultural Research

- It an autonomous organisation under the **Department of Agricultural Research and Education** (DARE), **Ministry of Agriculture and Farmers Welfare, Government of India.**

ICAR has its headquarters at **New Delhi.**

- The Council is the apex body for co-ordinating, guiding and managing research and education in agriculture including **horticulture, fisheries** and **animal sciences** in the entire country.

- With **113 ICAR institutes** and **74 agricultural universities** spread across the country this is one of the largest national agricultural systems in the world.
- ICAR has played a pioneering role in ushering **Green Revolution** and subsequent developments in agriculture in India through its research and technology development that has enabled the country to increase the **production of foodgrains** by **6.21 times, horticultural crops** by **11.53 times, fish** by **21.61 times, milk** by **13.01 times** and **eggs** by **70.74 times** since **1950-51** to **2021-22,** thus making a visible impact on the national food and nutritional security. It has played a major role in promoting excellence in higher education in agriculture.

Indian Council of Medical Research (ICMR)

- First meeting of the Governing Body of the **Indian Research Fund Association** (IRFA) was held on **November 15, 1911** (at the Plague Laboratory, Bombay, under the Chairmanship of Sir Harcourt Butler). **Indian Journal of Medical Research** was started in **1913-14.**
- IRFA was registered as a local body not administered by the Government on **March 22, 1938.** In the same year, **Malaria Survey of India** was redesignated as the **Malaria Institute of India.**

Dr. C.G. Pandit was appointed as the first full time secretary of **IRFA** in **July 1948**. IRFA was redesignated as the **Indian Council of Medical Research** (with Dr. C.G. Pandit as its first Director) in **1949.**

- **Indian Council of Medical Research** (ICMR), **New Delhi,** the apex body in India for the formulation, coordination and promotion of biomedical research.

ICMR has its headquarters at **New Delhi**

- ICMR is funded by the Government of India through the **Department of Health Research, Ministry of Health & Family Welfare.**

Institutes of Indian Council of Medical Research (ICMR)

Institutes	Places
• ICMR National Institute of Cancer Prevention and Research (NICPR)	**Noida**
• ICMR Bhopal Memorial Hospital & Research Center (BMHRC)	**Bhopal**
• ICMR National Institute for Research in Environmental Health (NIREH)	**Bhopal**
• ICMR Centre for Ageing & Mental Health (CAMH)	**Kolkata**
• ICMR National Animal Resource Facility for Biomedical Research (NARFBR)	**Hyderabad**
• ICMR National Centre for Disease Informatics and Research (NCDIR)	**Bengaluru**
• ICMR National Institute of Research in Tribal Health (NIRTH)	**Jabalpur**
• ICMR National Institute for Implementation Research on Non-Communicable Diseases	**Jodhpur**
• ICMR National AIDS Research Institute (NARI)	**Pune**
• ICMR National Institute of Immunohaematology (NIIH)	**Mumbai**
• ICMR National Institute for Research in Reproductive and Child Health (NIRRCH)	**Mumbai**
• ICMR National Institute for Research in Tuberculosis (NIRT)	**Chennai**
• ICMR National Institute of Epidemiology (NIE)	**Chennai**

Ministry of Electronics and Information Technology (MeitY)

- Ministry of Electronics and Information Technology was formed after the bifurcation of **Department of Electronics and Information Technology** from **Ministry of Communications and Information Technology in 2016.**
- **Mission Objective of MeitY** is to **promote e-Governance** for **empowering citizens,** promoting the **inclusive** and **sustainable growth of the Electronics, IT & ITeS industries,** enhancing India's role in Internet Governance, adopting a multipronged approach that includes development of human resources, promoting R&D and innovation, enhancing efficiency through digital services and ensuring a secure cyber space.

Objectives of MeitY

- **e-Government:** Providing e-infrastructure for delivery of e-services.
- **e-Industry:** Promotion of electronics hardware manufacturing and IT-ITeS industry.
- **e-Innovation/R&D:** Implementation of R&D Framework - Enabling creation of Innovation/ R&D Infrastructure in emerging areas of ICT&E/Establishment of mechanism for R&D translation.
- **e-Learning:** Providing support for development of e-Skills and Knowledge network.
- **e-Security:** Securing India's cyber space.
- **e-Inclusion:** Promoting the use of ICT for more inclusive growth.
- **Internet Governance:** Enhancing India's role in Global Platforms of Internet Governance.

The Ministry of Environment, Forest and Climate Change (MoEFCC)

- It is the nodal agency in the administrative structure of the Central Government for the planning, promotion, co-ordination and overseeing the implementation of India's environmental and forestry policies and programmes.
- **Department of Environment** was created in **1980** in backdrop of constitutional amendments under **Article 48-A,** which turned into the **Ministry of Environment and Forests** in **1985.**
- In **May 2014** the ministry was renamed to the current title of **Ministry of Environment, Forest and Climate Change.**

Ministry of New and Renewable Energy (MNRE)

- It is the nodal Ministry of the Government of India for all matters relating to new and renewable energy.
- The broad aim of the Ministry is to develop and deploy new and renewable energy to supplement the energy requirements of the country.
- The role of new and renewable energy has been assuming increasing significance in recent times with the growing concern for the country's energy security.
- The sudden increase in the price of oil, uncertainties associated with its supply and the adverse impact on the balance of payments position led to the establishment of the **Commission for Additional Sources of Energy** in the **Department of Science & Technology** in **March 1981.**
- The Commission was charged with the responsibility of formulating policies and their implementation, programmes for development of new and renewable energy apart from coordinating and intensifying R&D in the sector. In **September 1982**, a new department, i.e., **Department of Non-conventional Energy Sources** (DNES), that incorporated CASE, was created in the then **Ministry of Energy.**

- In **1992**, DNES became the **Ministry of Non-conventional Energy Sources.**

In **October 2006**, the Ministry was renamed as the **Ministry of New and Renewable Energy**.

Ministry of Education (MoE)

- **Ministry of Education** (MoE) was created on **September 26, 1985**, through the **174th amendment** to the **Government of India** (Allocation of Business) **Rules, 1961**. Currently, the MoE works through **two departments:**
  - Department of School Education & Literacy
  - Department of Higher Education

Technology Development Board (TDB)

- Government of India constituted the **Technology Development Board** (TDB) in **September 1996**, under the **Technology Development Board Act, 1995**, as a **statutory body**, to promote development and commercialization of indigenous technology and adaptation of imported technology for wider application. The board consists of **11 Board members.**
- TDB is the first organization of its kind within the government framework with the sole objective of commercializing indigenous research.
- The Board plays a pro-active role by encouraging enterprises to take up technology oriented products.
- Provides **equity capital** or **loans** to **industrial concerns** and **financial assistance** to **research** and **development institutions**. The loan carries a **simple interest rate** of **5% per annum.** With its pro-active stance the Board:
  - Facilitates interaction between industry, scientists, technocrats and specialists.
  - Fosters and innovation culture through contract and cooperative research between industry and institutions.
  - Provides an interface with financial institutions and commercial banks for leveraging funds.
  - Facilitates the creation of new generation of entrepreneurs.
  - Assists partnerships with other, similar technology financing bodies.
  - Provides vistas for venturing into hi-tech areas.
  - Creates new job opportunities.

Science and Engineering Research Board (SERB)

- It is a statutory body established through an **Act of Parliament.**
- Science and **Engineering Research Board** was established through an Act of Parliament, viz. the **Science and Engineering Research Board Act, 2008** for promoting basic research in Science and Engineering and to provide financial assistance to persons engaged in such research, academic institutions, research and development laboratories, industrial concerns and other agencies for such research and for matters connected therewith or incidental thereto are the primary and distinctive mandate of the Board.
- SERB aims to build up best management systems which would match the best global practices in the area of promotion and funding of basic research.

◈◈◈◈◈

UNIT 13 MISCELLANEOUS

Intellectual Property Rights (IPR)

- **Intellectual Property Rights** (IPR) refer to the **legal protections** granted to the **creators** and owners of intellectual property. These rights are designed to **safeguard** and **incentivize innovation** and **creativity** by providing **exclusive control** over the **use** and **distribution** of **intellectual assets.**
- **Intellectual property** encompasses various forms of creations generated by the **human mind, including inventions, literary** and **artistic works** and **commercial symbols.**
- Intellectual Property is classified into **2 main categories: industrial property,** which includes patents, trademarks, industrial designs and and **copyright,** which covers literary, artistic, and musical works, films, and architectural designs. Rights related to copyright also extend to performers, phonogram producers, and broadcasters.
- **Copyright:** Copyright protection is granted to original **literary, artistic** and **musical works.** It gives the creator the **exclusive right** to reproduce, distribute, and display their work.
- **Trademark:** Trademarks protect **distinctive signs, symbols, names** and **logos** used to identify goods and services. They help consumers distinguish between products or services from different sources.
- **Patent:** Patents grant inventors exclusive rights to their inventions for a specified period, typically 20 years. This includes the right to make, use, and sell the invention, preventing others from doing so without permission.
- **Trade Secret:** Trade secrets encompass confidential and proprietary information, such as manufacturing processes, formulas, or business strategies. Companies can protect trade secrets through confidentiality agreements and security measures.
- **Geographical Indication:** Geographical indications protect products associated with a specific geographical region and their unique characteristics, such as Champagne or Swiss watches.
- **Industrial Design Rights:** These protect the visual design of products, such as the shape, color, and ornamentation, preventing unauthorized copying.
- **Plant Breeders' Rights:** These protect new plant varieties developed through breeding and provide exclusive rights to produce, sell, and distribute them.
- **Database Rights:** These rights protect collections of data, preventing unauthorized extraction or use of substantial parts of a database.

The Indian Patent Act, 1970

- The **Indian Patent Act, 1970** is the primary legislation governing patents in India. It was enacted to **promote technological innovation** and to protect the rights of inventors. The Act defines a patent as an **exclusive right** granted to an inventor for a period of **20 years** to prevent others from making, using, offering for sale, selling, or **importing** the invention without the consent of the inventor.
- To be eligible for a **patent**, an invention must meet the following criteria:

- **It must be new:** The invention must not have been known or used by others in India or anywhere else in the world before the date of the application for the patent.
- **It must be inventive:** The invention must involve an inventive step. This means that it must not be obvious to a person skilled in the art.
- **It must be capable of industrial application:** The invention must be capable of being used in a practical way.

▣ The Indian Patent Act also lists a number of inventions that are not eligible for patent protection, such as:

- Discoveries of scientific principles or abstract theories.
- Mental acts, schemes, or methods of operation.
- Traditional Knowledge - Ayurveda.
- Aesthetic creations.
- Mathematical methods.
- Plant and animal varieties.
- Processes for medical, surgical, or diagnostic treatment.
- Inventions that are contrary to public policy or morality.

Important Terminologies associated with IPR

▣ **Compulsory licensing** is a legal mechanism that allows a government or relevant authority to grant a license for the use, manufacture, or sale of a patented invention to a third party without the consent of the patent holder. This is typically done in the interest of public health, safety, or other significant public policy objectives. Compulsory licensing aims to balance the rights of patent holders with the broader societal interest in access to essential goods and services.

- CL is permitted under the **WTO's TRIPS** (IPR) Agreement provided conditions such as **'national emergencies**, other circumstances of **extreme urgency** and anti-competitive practices' are fulfilled.

▣ **Parallel import,** also known as Parallel trade or **Grey Market Trade**, refers to the importation and sale of genuine branded products into a country's market without the authorization of the **trademark** or copyright holder. These products are typically purchased in one country, often at a lower price, and then resold in another country where the same product is sold at a higher price.

Parallel importation can encompass a wide range of goods, including **electronics, pharmaceuticals, cosmetics** and more.

▣ **Evergreening of Patent:** It is a corporate, legal, business, and technological strategy for extending / elongating the term of a granted patent in a jurisdiction that is about to expire, in order to retain royalties from them, by taking out new patents. **Section 3(d)** of the **Indian Patent Act 1970** (amended in 2005) does not allow patents to be granted to inventions involving new forms of a known substance unless it differs significantly in properties with regard to efficacy.

- This means that the **Indian Patent** Act does not allow evergreening of patents.

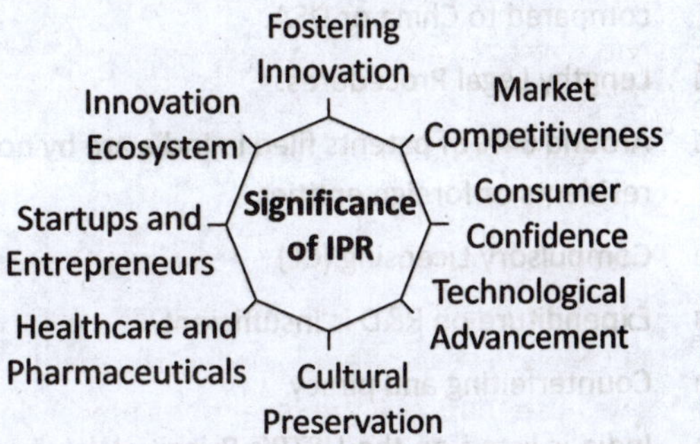

National IPR Policy

- **National Intellectual Property Rights (IPR) Policy 2016** was adopted in **May 2016** as a guiding vision for the development of IPRs in India.
- The policy's focus is on fostering a **Creative India; Innovative India** through a comprehensive approach that integrates all forms of intellectual property and relevant statutes.

> The **Department for Promotion of Industry and Internal Trade** (DPIIT) under the **Ministry of Commerce** is responsible for **coordinating** and **overseeing IPR implementation** and **development.**

Objectives

- IPR Awareness, Outreach & Promotion
- Generation of IPRs
- Establish robust and balanced IPR laws that protect rights owners and public interests.
- Modernize and strengthen service-oriented IPR administration.
- Commercialization of IPRs
- Strengthen mechanisms to combat IPR infringements.
- Enhance teaching, training, research, and skill-building in IPRs by expanding resources and institutions.

Issues Related to IPR in India

- Weak enforcement of IPR laws.
- Low number of granted patents in India compared to China or USA.
- Lengthy Legal Procedures.
- Around 64% of patents filed in India are by non-residents or foreign entities.
- Compulsory Licensing (CL)
- Expenditure on R&D is insufficient.
- Counterfeiting and piracy.
- India is listed on the USTR's Priority Watch List for alleged violations of intellectual property rights.
- Vacancies in the Patent Office.
- Limited awareness of IPR laws, leading to inadvertent infringement.

Way Forward

- **Enhanced Enforcement and Deterrence Measures:**
  - Strengthen law enforcement agencies.
  - Increase penalties for infringement.
  - Improve coordination among authorities.
- **Promotion of IPR Awareness and Education:**
  - Conduct educational programs and campaigns.
  - Target various sectors and stakeholders.
  - Foster a culture of IPR respect.
- **Streamlined Legal Processes and Policy Clarity:**
  - Simplify patent and trademark procedures.
  - Provide clear guidelines on complex IPR issues.
  - Reduce ambiguity to encourage innovation.

Traditional Knowledge Digital Library

- **Traditional Knowledge Digital Library** (TKDL) is a **pioneering initiative** of India to protect **Indian traditional medicinal knowledge** and prevent its misappropriation at International Patent Offices.
- **Traditional Knowledge** (TK) is a valuable yet vulnerable asset to indigenous and local communities who depend on TK for their **livelihood.**
- The healthcare needs of more than 70% population and livelihood of millions of people in India is dependent on traditional medicine. Globally too there has been renewed attention and interest in the use of traditional medicine increasing its vulnerability to exploitation.

> The **Traditional Knowledge Digital Library** (TKDL) is a **database** of **traditional knowledge**

(TK) from India. It was established in **2001** by the **Council of Scientific and Industrial Research** (CSIR) in collaboration with the **Department of AYUSH**, Ministry of Health and Family Welfare, Government of India.

- The TKDL contains information on TK from various sources, including **ancient texts, oral traditions** and **folk practices**. The TKDL is a valuable resource for **researchers, scientists,** and **policymakers**. It can be used to identify TK that is relevant to new **products** and **technologies.** It can also be used to protect **TK** from **misappropriation** and **abuse.**
- The TKDL is accessible to the **public** through a **website.** The website provides **access** to the database, as well as **information on** TK and its **protection.**
- There have been instances in the past where patents have been mistakenly granted for inventions based on **traditional knowledge** that **lack novelty** and **inventive steps.** This has specifically occurred with products like **Turmeric, Neem, Basmati** and others.
- These cases highlight the need for a **robust examination process to identify** and consider relevant prior art, including traditional knowledge, to prevent the granting of patents for inventions that are already known or derived from traditional knowledge.
- TKDL translates and presents traditional knowledge in **English, French, Spanish, German** and **Japanese**, using a patent application format that is easily comprehensible to patent examiners. This ensures that the valuable traditional knowledge is accessible and can be effectively considered during the patent examination process
- TKDL is documenting over **1500 yoga postures** to prevent foreign parties from patenting them. It has successfully stopped patent applications in countries such as the **USA, Japan, UK, Italy, Germany** and more. **Yoga**, practiced by over 300 million people globally, faces misappropriation of traditional Indian knowledge. TKDL's efforts aim to protect Indian systems of medicine.

TKDL – Goals and Objectives

- Seeks to **prevent** the **granting of patents** for products developed utilizing TK where there has been little, if any, inventive step.
- Intends to act as a **bridge** between **information recorded** in ancient **Sanskrit** and **patent examiners** (with its database containing information in a language and format understandable to patent examiners)
- **Facilitates access to information** not easily available to patent examiners, thereby minimizing the possibility that patents could be granted for "inventions" involving only minor or insignificant modifications.
- Indian traditional knowledge (TK) offers immense potential to serve national and global needs, therewith providing societal benefits as well as economic growth.

For example, the traditional systems of medicine and wellness from our country, namely **Ayurveda, Siddha, Unani, Sowa Rigpa** and **Yoga** are serving the needs of people from India and abroad even today.

- The recent CoViD- 19 pandemic has also been witnessing extensive use of Indian traditional medicines whose benefits range from immune-boosting to symptoms-relief to anti-viral activity.

In **April, 2023** the **World Health Organization** (WHO) established its first off-shore **Global Centre for Traditional Medicines** (GCTM) in India. These demonstrate the continued relevance of traditional knowledge in address the current and emerging needs of the world.

- The approval of the Cabinet to widen the access of the **database beyond patent offices** lays emphasis on **integrating** and **co-opting** traditional knowledge with current practices towards enhancing innovation and trade.

- The current contents of TKDL shall facilitate wider adoption of **Indian traditional medicines**, while also propelling new manufacturers and innovators to gainfully build enterprises based on our valuable knowledge heritage.
- TKDL can cater to a vast user base that would include businesses/companies {**herbal healthcare** (AYUSH, pharmaceuticals, phytopharmaceuticals, and nutraceuticals), **personal care** and **other FMCG**}, research institutions: public and private; educational institutions: educators & students; and others: ISM practitioners, knowledge holders, patentees and their legal representatives, and government, among several others. The access to the TKDL database would be through a paid subscription model with a phase-wise opening to national and international users.
- In future, more information on Indian traditional knowledge from other domains will be added to the TKDL database from the perspectives of the **"3P – Preservation. Protection and Promotion"**. While catering to its primary mandate of preventing grant of wrong patents on Indian traditional knowledge, the **TKDL database** will also push creative minds to innovate for better, safer and more effective solutions for a healthier and technology endowed population. India's rich heritage shall lay a strong foundation for newer socio-economic developments.
- Making the Traditional Knowledge Digital Library (TKDL) publicly available under open-source licensing has both advantages and disadvantages:

Pros

- **Accessibility:** Open-source licensing would enhance the accessibility of TKDL to a broader audience, including researchers, practitioners, and traditional knowledge holders worldwide.
- **Promotes Collaboration:** It encourages collaboration and contributions from experts globally, potentially enriching the database with diverse perspectives and additional information.
- **Preserves Traditional Knowledge:** Sharing TKDL openly can help preserve traditional knowledge by providing a centralized, easily accessible repository for future generations.
- **Educational Resource:** It becomes a valuable educational resource, benefiting students, scholars, and institutions interested in traditional medicine and practices.
- **Innovation:** Open access fosters innovation as developers can build applications and tools based on TKDL, potentially leading to new discoveries and applications.
- **Transparency:** Open-source licensing promotes transparency, allowing users to verify the accuracy and credibility of the information.

Cons

- **Misuse of Knowledge:** There's a risk of misuse, where unscrupulous individuals or entities could use the knowledge for commercial gain without proper attribution or consent.
- **Cultural Appropriation:** Open access may lead to cultural appropriation, as traditional knowledge may be used without respecting its cultural and historical context.
- **Privacy Concerns:** Traditional knowledge holders may have concerns about their knowledge being made freely available, potentially leading to a loss of control over their heritage.
- **Legal and Ethical Issues:** Open access could raise legal and ethical dilemmas, such as conflicting with existing intellectual property rights or ethical guidelines for handling traditional knowledge.
- **Sustainability:** Ensuring the sustainability of the database and its continuous updating may become a challenge without a clear funding model.

Digital India

Digital India programme was launched on **1st July, 2015** to enable **digital delivery of services** to citizens with the vision of transforming India into a digitally empowered society and a **knowledge-based economy**, by ensuring **digital access, digital inclusion, digital empowerment** and **bridging the digital divide.**

- The programme is centred on **three key vision** areas, namely digital infrastructure as a core utility to every citizen, governance and services on demand, and digital empowerment of citizens.
- The overall goal is to ensure that digital technologies improve the life of every citizen, expand **India's digital economy**, and creating investment and employment opportunities and create digital technological capabilities in India.
- Digital India has considerably reduced the distance between **Government** and **citizens.** It has also helped in **delivery** of **substantial** services directly to the beneficiary in a transparent and corruption free manner. In the process, India has emerged as one of the pre-eminent nations of the world to use technology to transform the lives of its citizens.
- Digital India is an umbrella programme that covers multiple projects of various Central Ministries/Departments and States and Union Territories (UTs).
- The Government had launched the **India BPO Promotion Scheme** (IBPS) and the **North East BPO Promotion Scheme** (NEBPS) under the **Digital India programme**, with the aim of creating employment opportunities and dispersal of the Information Technology and **Information Technology Enabled Services** (ITES) industry in small cities and towns by incentivising the setting up of **Business Process Outsourcing** (BPO) and ITES operations by providing financial support of up to ₹ 1 lakh per seat in the form of viability gap funding towards capital and operational expenditures.

Key Initiatives undertaken by MeitY under Digital India

- **Aadhaar:** Aadhaar provides **12 digit biometric and demographic based identity** that is unique, lifelong, online and authenticable. Further to give statutory backing to Aadhaar 'The Aadhaar (Targeted Delivery of Financial and Other Subsidies, Benefits and Services) Act, 2016' was notified on **26th March 2016**. Over 135.5 crore residents have been enrolled.
- **Common Services Centres :** CSCs are offering **government** and **business services** in digital mode in rural areas through **Village Level Entrepreneurs** (VLEs). Over 400 digital services are being offered by these CSCs.
- **DigiLocker:** Digital Locker provides an ecosystem with collection of repositories and gateways for issuers to upload the documents in the digital repositories.
- **Unified Mobile Application for New-age Governance (UMANG) :** For providing government services to citizen through mobile. More than 1668 e-Services and over 20,197 bill payment services are made available at UMANG.
- **e-Sign:** e-Sign service facilitates instant signing of forms/documents online by citizens in a legally acceptable form. The services are being leveraged by various applications using OTP based authentication services of UIDAI.
- **MyGov:** It is a citizen engagement platform developed to facilitate participatory governance. Presently, over 2.76+ crore users are registered with MyGov, participating in various activities hosted on MyGov platform.
- **MeriPehchaan**: National Single Sign-on (NSSO) platform called MeriPehchaan has been launched in **July 2022** to facilitate / provide citizens ease of access to government portals.

- **Digital Village:** MeitY has also initiated the **Digital Village Pilot Project** in **October, 2018. 700 Gram Panchayats** (GPs)/Village with atleast one Gram Panchayat/Village per District per State/UT are being covered under the project. The digital services being offered are **Digital Health Services, Education Service, Financial Services, Skill Development, Solar panel** powered street lights including **Government to Citizens Services** (G2C), **Business to Citizen (B2C) Services.**
- **National Rollout of eDistrict MMP:** e-District is a Mission Mode Project (MMP) that aims at electronic delivery of identified high volume citizen centric services at the district or sub-district level. Presently 4,671 e-services have been launched in 709 districts across India.
- **Open Government Data Platform:** To facilitate data sharing and promote innovation over non-personal data, Open Government Data platform has been developed. More than 5.93 lakh datasets across 12,940+ catalogues are published. The platform has facilitated 94.8 lakh downloads.
- **eHospital/ Online Registration System** (ORS): e-Hospital application is the Hospital Management Information System for internal workflows and processes of hospitals. Currently, 753 Hospitals have been on-boarded on e-Hospital and ORS has been adopted by 557 hospitals across the country with over 68 lakh appointments booked from ORS.
- **CO-WIN:** It is an open platform for management of registration, appointment scheduling & managing vaccination certificates for Covid-19. It has registered 110 crore persons and has facilitated administration of 220 crore doses of vaccinations.
- **Jeevan Pramaan:** Jeevan Pramaan envisages to digitize the whole process of securing the life certificate for Pensioner. With this initiative, the pensioner is no more required to physically present himself or herself in front of disbursing agency or the certification authority. Over 685.42lakh Digital Life certificates have been processed since 2014.
- **NCOG-GIS Applications:** National Centre of Geo-informatics (NCoG) project, is a GIS platform developed for sharing, collaboration, location based analytics and decision support system for Departments. So far, 659 applications across various domains are operational.
- **National Knowledge Network:** A high speed data communication network has been established to interconnect Institution of higher learning, and research. So far, 1752 links to Institutions have been commissioned and made operational. 522 NKN links have been connected to NIC district centers across India.
- **Pradhan Mantri Gramin Digital Saksharta Abhiyaan** (PMGDISHA): The Government has approved a new scheme titled "Pradhan Mantri Gramin Digital Saksharta Abhiyan (PMGDISHA)" to usher in digital literacy in rural India by covering 6 Crore rural households (one person per household). It has 6.63 crore registered candidates and out of this, 5.69 crore candidates have been trained and 4.22 crore have been certified.
- To further mitigate the language barrier, Bhashini, an **AI enabled national language translation platform** has been launched by ensuring the access to internet for citizens who do not know English. As on date, **1000+ pre-trained AI models** for language translation in 10 Indian languages have been made available on the Bhashini platform
- **Unified Payment Interface** (UPI) is the leading digital payment platform. It has onboarded 376 banks and has facilitated **730 crore transactions** (by volume) worth **Rs 11.9 lakh crore.**

- **FutureSkills Prime:** MeitY in collaboration with **NASSCOM** has initiated a programme titled **FutureSkills PRIME**. The programme is aimed at re-skilling/ up-skilling of IT professionals in 10 new/emerging technologies which include **Augmented/Virtual Reality, Internet of Things, Big Data Analytics, Artificial Intelligence, Robotic Process Automation, Additive Manufacturing/ 3D Printing, Cloud Computing,** Social & Mobile, Cyber Security and Blockchain.
- **Cyber Security:** The Government has taken necessary measures to tackle challenges with regard to data privacy and data security through administering the Information Technology (IT) Act, 2000 which has necessary provisions for data privacy and data security.

Global Cybersecurity Index (GCI) 2024

GCI, launched in 2015, published by the International Telecommunication Union (ITU) measures the comprehensive development and commitment to cybersecurity at a global level, utilising a multi-stakeholder approach and leverages the capacity and expertise of different organisations.

Countries are categorised into five tiers based on their cybersecurity efforts, with Tier 1 representing the highest level.

- Tier 1- Role-modelling (score of 95–100)
- Tier 2- Advancing (score of 85–95)
- Tier 3- Establishing (score of 55–85)
- Tier 4- Evolving (score of 20–55)
- Tier 5- Building (score of 0–20).

The 4th edition of the GCI report was published in 2020.

India has achieved a major milestone in cybersecurity by securing Tier 1 status in the 5th edition of Global Cybersecurity Index (GCI) 2024. India scored 98.49/100, an improvement from 97.5 in the 2020 edition due to its robust legal framework like the Information Technology Act (2000), the Digital Personal Data Protection Act (2023).

- **Modified Special Incentive Package (M-SIPS):** As on date, 315 applications with proposed investment of approximately Rs. 85,632 crore have been approved.
- **Electronic Manufacturing Clusters (EMC):** Under EMC scheme, 19 Greenfield EMCs and3 Common Facility Centres (CFCs) measuring an area of 3,464 acres with project cost ofRs. 3,732 crore including Government Grant-in-aid of Rs. 1,529 crore have been approved in 15 states across the country. Based on closure of receipt of applications under EMC scheme, MeitY notified Modified Electronics Manufacturing Clusters (EMC 2.0) Scheme on 1st April, 2020 for further strengthening the infrastructure base for electronics industry in the country and deepening the electronics value chain.
- To support Aatmanirbhar Bharat, the ecosystem for Supercomputers is being created under National Super Computing Mission. The indigenous components, such as, Rudra Server Board, Trinetra Network card, Software stack, AUM HPC processor have been developed. Till date,18 Super Computers have been deployed across the country with a total computing capacity of 24 Peta Flops.
- Due to highly disruptive nature of Technology, it is essential to continuously upgrade through skilling and re-skilling. FutureSkills PRIME programme is providing a platform for IT professionals to upgrade their skills in emerging technologies like AI, Big Data, AR/VR, Blockchain etc.

- **Major Educational initiatives under Digital India –**
  - **DIKSHA** the **nation's digital infrastructure** for providing **quality e-content** for school education in **States/UTs** and QR coded Energized Textbooks for all grades (one nation, one digital platform). Till date (25.07.2023) DIKSHA has clocked more than **524 crores learning sessions**, more than **6,125 crore learning minutes** with more than **2.2 crore average daily page hits.** A total of **3,17,496 pieces of e-contents** are live on DIKSHA as on date.
  - **12 DTH Channels** in school education and **22 SWAYAM PRABHA channels** in higher education are already functional. As per budget announcement for Financial Year 2022-23, the 12 DTH Channels would be expanded to 200 (Two hundred) **PM e-Vidya DTH TV Channels.**
  - **SWAYAM** (Study Webs of Active-Learning for Young Aspiring Minds) is the national MOOC platform with provision of credit transfer to Universities, for Higher Education Courses. NIOS and NCERT are National Coordinator for school sector courses under SWAYAM, delivering school courses from 9th to 12th. On SWAYAM Portal a total of 10,451 Courses are available out of these courses, 257 courses of NCERT and 431 courses of NIOS are available. For **NCERT courses 4.1 lakh students** are registered and for NIOS courses more than **34 lakh students** are registered.
- To realize the vision of **Digital India,** all efforts related to digital/online/on-air education to enable **multi-mode access** to **education** are organized under PM e-Vidya banner as part of Atma Nirbhar Bharat Abhiyaan.
- **Ministry of Electronics and IT** through the **Digital India Programme** has given a special focus on supporting start-up industries in the country; for attracting investment in semiconductors and strengthening the semiconductor ecosystem in the country, Quantum computing, Digital Public Infrastructure, etc.
- **Initiatives and measures to promote technology led startup-innovation ecosystem in the country:**
  - **Technological Incubation and Development of Entrepreneurs (TIDE 2.0)** is handholding and nurturing more than 2000 technology startups as well as augmenting capacities of selected 51 technology incubation centres to spur innovation and create economic wealth. Under the scheme, 920+ startups have been onboarded across 51 Incubation Centres.
  - **SAMRIDH Scheme** to support existing and upcoming accelerators to select and accelerate potential product-based start-ups to scale. So far, 22 accelerators across 14 states and 12 cities have been supported under the SAMRIDH Scheme.
  - A total of **42 Centres of Excellence** (CoEs) in diverse areas of national interest have been initiated for driving self-sufficiency and creating capabilities to capture new and emerging technology areas.
  - In addition, a nodal entity to interconnect tech startup infrastructure pan India a **MeitY Start-up Hub** (MSH) has been set up under MeitY as an Independent Business Division (IBD) with a consolidation of over 3365 startups, 482 incubators, 424 mentors which has successfully conducted 143 challenges in different technology areas encouraging development of innovative products / services to address current and pressing challenges.
  - Recently, Government has approved an umbrella program **Gen-Next Support for Innovative Startups** (GENESIS)' with a budget of 490 Cr for 5 years to discover, support, grow and make successful startups in Tier-II and Tier-III cities.

Deep Technology

- Deep Technology / Deep Tech refers to advanced and disruptive technologies that rely on significant scientific and engineering breakthroughs. These innovations often require long-term research and development and have the potential to create transformative changes across industries such as healthcare, defense, artificial intelligence, and biotechnology.
- Deep Technology refers to innovations founded on advanced scientific and technological breakthroughs. Due to their disruptive nature, they have the potential to solve India's most pressing societal issues.
- **According to NASSCOM's report "India's DeepTech Dawn:** Forging Ahead", the country had over 3,600 DeepTech startups, with 480 launched in 2023—double the number from 2022. While India ranks as the 3rd largest startup ecosystem globally, its DeepTech sector stands at the 6th position.

Examples of Deep Tech

- **Artificial Intelligence (AI) & Machine Learning:** Self-learning algorithms, autonomous systems.
- **Quantum Computing :** High-speed computation beyond classical computing limits.
- **Biotechnology & Genetic Engineering :** CRISPR gene editing, personalized medicine.
- **Semiconductors & Advanced Materials :** Nanotechnology, graphene-based materials.
- **Aerospace & Defense Technologies :** Hypersonic vehicles, advanced missile systems.
- Renewable Energy & Battery Technologies : Solid-state batteries, hydrogen fuel cells

Features of Deep Tech -

- **High Research & Development Intensity :** Requires deep scientific knowledge and long-term investment.
- **Disruptive Innovation :** Capable of significantly transforming industries.
- **High-Risk, High-Reward :** Uncertain in early stages but can yield substantial economic and strategic benefits.
- **Interdisciplinary Approach :** Combines multiple fields such as AI, biotech, and quantum physics.

Government Initiatives on Deep Tech

- **Draft National DeepTech Start-up Policy :** Aimed at fostering innovation.
- **₹1 Lakh Crore Corpus (Interim Budget 2024) :** To boost research and development.
- **₹1,000 Crore Venture Capital Fund for the Space Sector :** Supporting space-tech startups.
- **National Quantum Mission (2023) :** Investment in quantum computing and communications.
- **India AI Mission :** Strengthening AI research, innovation, and startups.
- Initiatives like the Atal Innovation Mission, NITI Aayog's programs, and Start-up India providing support through accelerators and incubators.
- **Union Budget 2025-26 and Deep Tech :** ₹20,000 crore to be allocated to implement private sector driven Research, Development and Innovation initiative announced in the July 2024-25 Budget.
- **Deep Tech Fund of Funds :** Deep Tech Fund of Funds to be explored to catalyze the next generation startups.
- **Key initiatives for Tech Sector :** Enhanced India AI mission funding, an AI Centre of Excellence for Education etc.

Draft National Deep Tech Startup Policy (NDTSP)

- National Deep Tech Startup Policy (NDTSP) aims to address the challenges confronting deep tech startups through definitive policy interventions to create a conducive ecosystem. Acknowledging the key significance of deep technology in propelling innovation, economic growth, and societal development, the NDTSP lays the foundation for India's emerging Deep Tech Startup ecosystem.
- National Deep Tech Startup Policy (NDTSP) strives to drive innovation, economic growth,

and societal development through the utilization of advanced research-based deep tech inventions. NDTSP will support deep tech startups and secure India's financial future, progress towards a knowledge-driven economy, and bolster productivity. NDTSP also aims to unleash the power of technological growth in all sectors, catalyse multiplier effects and create new industries for enhancing India's capability and global competitiveness.

- NDTSP is strategically formulated to stimulate innovation, spur economic growth, and promote societal development through the effective utilization of deep tech research-driven innovations.
- The initiative centralizes on bolstering deep tech startups, thereby solidifying India's financial stability and stimulating the transition towards a knowledge-centric economy, consequently augmenting India's overall productivity.
- NDTSP aims to harness the transformative potential of technological advancement across diverse sectors, serving as a catalyst to stimulate ripple effects throughout the economy and laying the groundwork for new industry creation. This policy aims to significantly strengthen India's capabilities and enhance global competitiveness

PYQ (2013 – 2024)

Q. Bringing out the circumstances in 2005 which forced an amendment to the section 3(d) in Indian Patent Law, 1970, discuss how it has been utilized by the Supreme Court in its judgement in rejecting Novartis' patent application for 'Glivec'. Discuss briefly the pros and cons of the decision. (2013)

Q. How does 3D printing technology work? List out the advantages and disadvantages of the technology. (2013)

Q. Scientific research in Indian universities is declining, because a career in science is not as attractive as our business operations, engineering or administration, and the universities are becoming consumer-oriented. Critically comment. (2014)

Q. In a globalised world, intellectual property rights assume significance and are a source of litigation. Broadly distinguish between the terms – copyrights, patents and trade secrets. (2014)

Q. India's Traditional Knowledge Digital Library (TKDL) which has a database containing formatted information on more than 2 million medicinal formulations is proving a powerful weapon in the country's fight against erroneous patents. Discuss the pros and cons of making this database publicly available under open-source licensing. (2015)

Q. How can the 'Digital India' programme help farmers to improve farm productivity and income? What steps has the Government taken in this regards? (2015)

Q. What is allelopathy? Discuss its role in major cropping systems of irrigated agriculture. (2016)

Q. Discuss the work of 'Bose-Einstein Statistics' done by Prof. Satyendra Nath Bose and show how it revolutionized the field of Physics. (2018)

Q. How is science interwoven deeply with our lives? What are the striking changes in agriculture triggered off by science-based technologies? (2020)

Q. COVID-19 pandemic has caused unprecedented devastation worldwide. However, technological advancements are being availed readily to win over the crisis. Give an account of how technology was sought to aid the management of the pandemic. (2020)

Q. Describe the context and salient features of Digital Personal Data Protection Act 2023. (2024)

Q. What is the present world scenario of intellectual property rights with respect to life materials? Although India is second in the world to file patents, still only a few have been commericialized. Explain the reasons behind this less commercialization. (2024)

NOTES

NOTES